ScottForesman

EXPLORING MATHEMATICS

AUTHORS

L. Carey Bolster
Coordinator of Mathematics
Baltimore County Public Schools
Towson, Maryland

Clem Boyer
Coordinator of Mathematics, K-12
District School Board of Seminole County
Sanford, Florida

Thomas Butts
Associate Professor,
Mathematics Education
University of Texas at Dallas
Richardson, Texas

Mary Cavanagh
Math/Science Coordinator
Solana Beach School District
Solana Beach, California

Marea W. Channel
Mathematics Resource Teacher
Los Angeles Unified School District
Los Angeles, California

Warren D. Crown
Associate Professor of
Mathematics Education, Rutgers,
The State University of New Jersey
New Brunswick, New Jersey

Jan Fair
Mathematics Department
Allan Hancock College
Santa Maria, California

Robert Y. Hamada
District Mathematics Specialist, K-12
Los Angeles Unified School District
Los Angeles, California

Margaret G. (Peggy) Kelly
Associate Professor
California State University, San Marcos
San Marcos, California

Miriam Leiva
Professor of Mathematics
University of North Carolina at Charlotte
Charlotte, North Carolina

Mary Montgomery Lindquist
Callaway Professor of Mathematics Education
Columbus College
Columbus, Georgia

William B. Nibbelink
Professor, Division of Early Childhood and
Elementary Education, University of Iowa
Iowa City, Iowa

Linda Proudfit
University Professor of Mathematics
and Computer Education, Governors State
University, University Park, Illinois

Cathy Rahlfs
Mathematics Coordinator
Humble Independent School District
Humble, Texas

Rosie Ramirez
Assistant Principal
Highland Elementary School
Silver Spring, Maryland

Jeanne F. Ramos
Assistant Principal
Nobel Middle School
Northridge, California

Gail Robinette
Vice-Principal
Fresno Unified School District
Fresno, California

David Robitaille
Head, Department of Mathematics
and Science Education
University of British Columbia
Vancouver, British Columbia,
Canada

James E. Schultz
Project LITMUS
University of Georgia
Athens, Georgia

Richard Shepardson
Professor, Division of Early Childhood
and Elementary Education
University of Iowa
Iowa City, Iowa

Jane Swafford
Professor of Mathematics
Illinois State University, Normal, Illinois

Benny Tucker
Dean, School of Education and Human Studies
Union University
Jackson, Tennessee

John Van de Walle
Professor of Education
Virginia Commonwealth University
Richmond, Virginia

David E. Williams
Former Director of Mathematics Education
School District of Philadelphia
Philadelphia, Pennsylvania

Robert J. Wisner
Professor of Mathematics
New Mexico State University
Las Cruces, New Mexico

Multicultural Reviewers

Cherry McGee Banks
University of Washington
Seattle, Washington

Armando Ayala
Director of Bilingual Education
Placer County, California

Diane Deckert Jost
Field Museum of Natural History, Chicago, Illinois

Patricia Locke
(Ta Wacin Waste Win)
Lakota, Chippewa Educator
Wakpala, South Dakota

Vicky Owyang Chan
Multicultural Educator
Fremont, California

Seree Weroha
Kansas State University, Manhattan, Kansas

Efrain Melendez
Dakota School, Los Angles, California

Linda Skinner
Choctaw Educator, Edmond, Oklahoma

ScottForesman
A Division of HarperCollins*Publishers*

Editorial Offices: Glenview, Illinois Regional Offices: Sunnyvale, California • Tucker, Georgia • Glenview, Illinois • Oakland, New Jersey • Dallas, Texas

Contents

Exploring Mathematics Book Two © Scott, Foresman and Company

Chapter 3 Place Value Through 99, Money, and Patterns

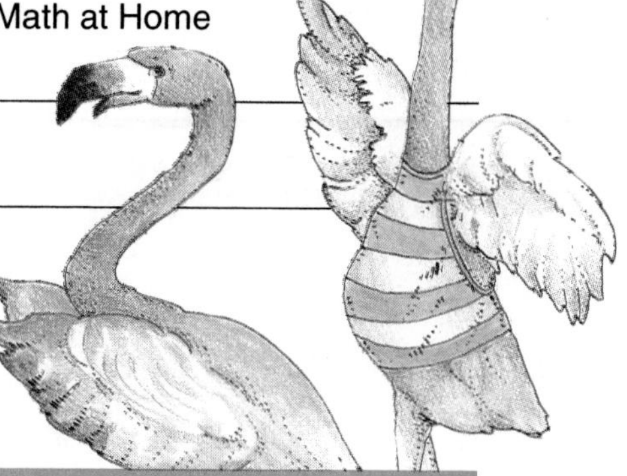

Chapter 4 Subtraction Through 18

Chapter 5 Time and Measurement

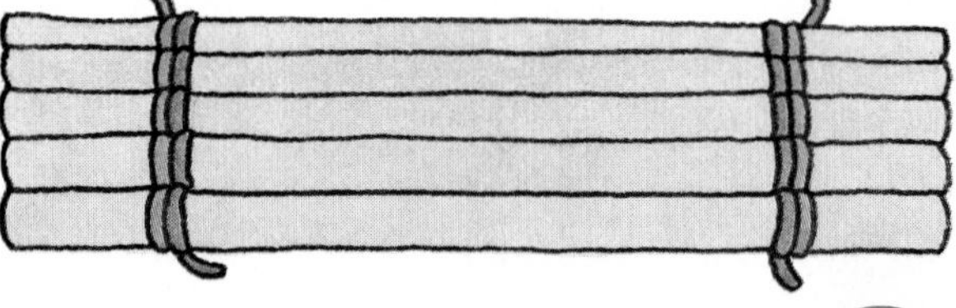

Chapter 6 Readiness for Two-Digit Computation

Exploring Mathematics Book Two © Scott, Foresman and Company

Chapter 7 Two-Digit Addition

Chapter 8 Two-Digit Subtraction

Chapter 9  Place Value Through 999 and Patterns

Chapter 10 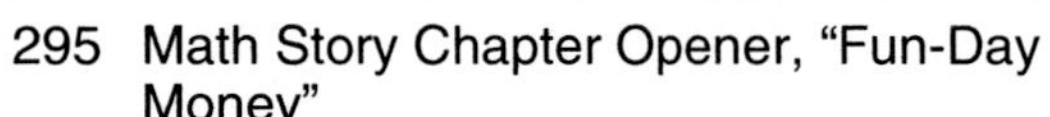 Money

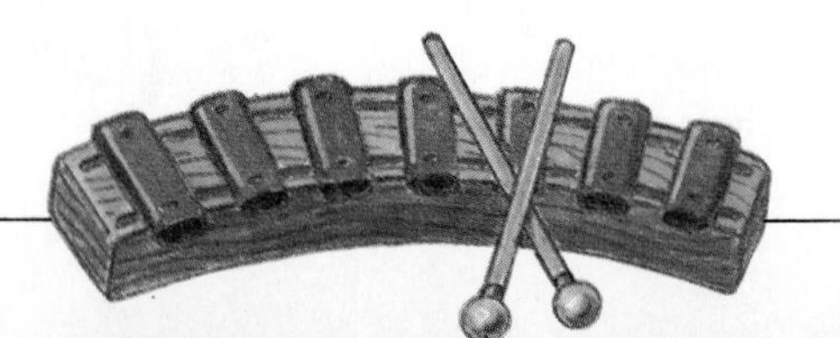

Exploring Mathematics Book Two © Scott, Foresman and Company

Chapter 11 Fractions and Probability

Chapter 12 Geometry and Measurement

Chapter 13 Three-Digit Addition and Subtraction

Chapter 14 Exploring Multiplication and Division

Exploring Mathematics Book Two © Scott, Foresman and Company

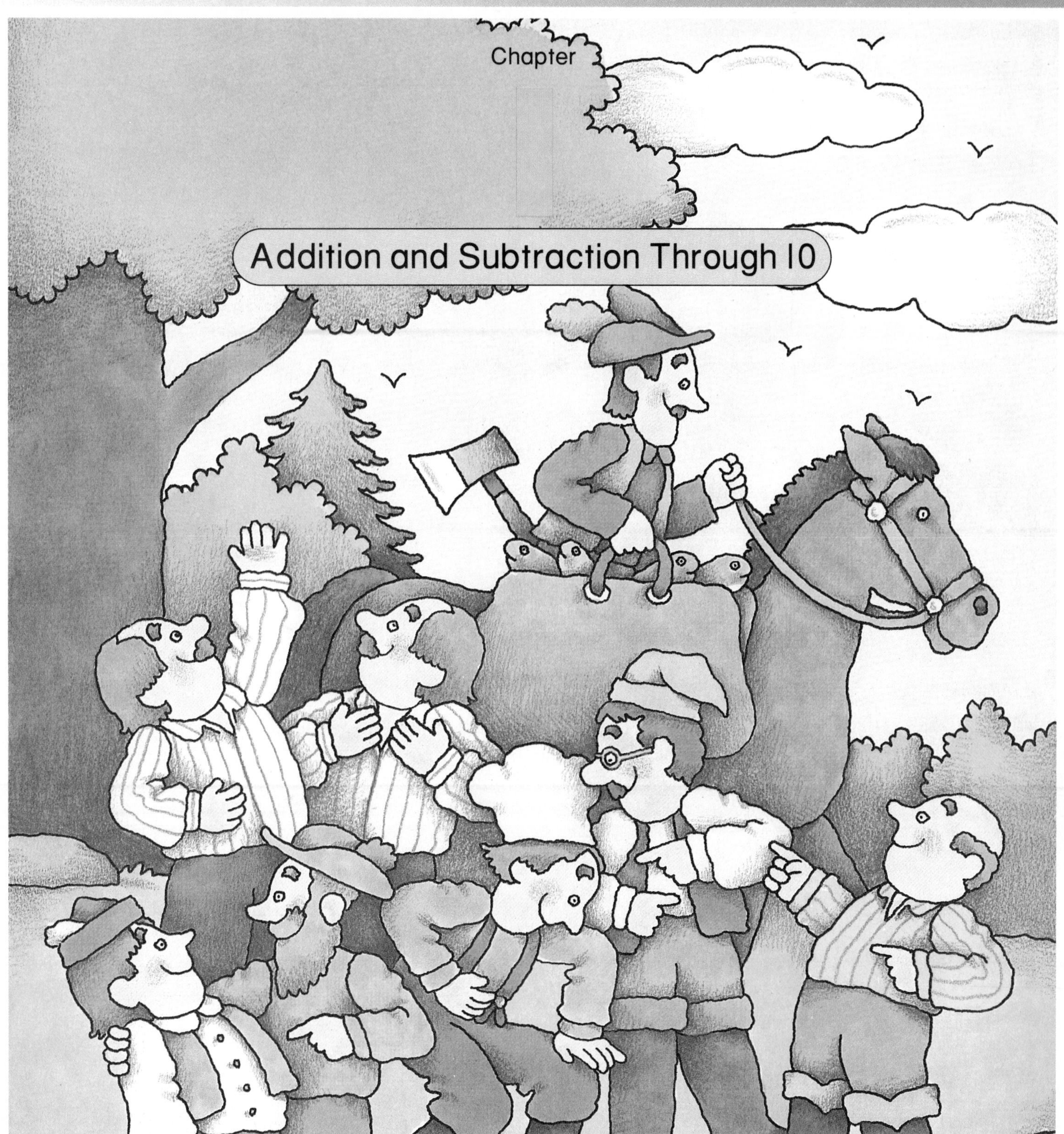

Listen to the math story, "The Wise Woodsman."
The baker counted 6 fishermen.
Which man did he forget to count?

Notes for Home Children listen to a math story introducing chapter concepts and skills, and then they answer a question about the story.

Name

Numbers Through 10

Write the number.
Trace the word.

1.

	0	zero
1 ladybug		one
2 ladybugs		two
3 ladybugs		three
4 ladybugs		four
5 ladybugs		five
6 ladybugs		six
7 ladybugs		seven
8 ladybugs		eight
9 ladybugs		nine
10 ladybugs		ten

Write the number.

2.

 ____

 ____

 ____

Notes for Home Children identify number of objects through 10. Then they write the numbers and number words.

Exploring Mathematics Book Two © Scott, Foresman and Company

Name

ACTIVITY Finding Sums Through 10

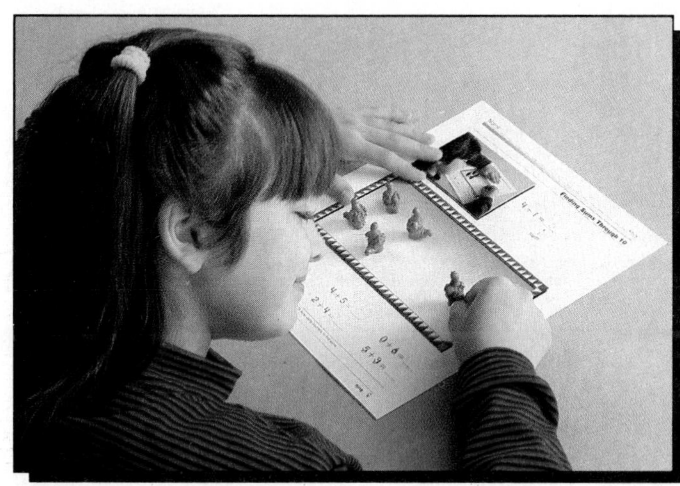

$4 + 1 = \underline{5}$

↑ sum

Use counters.
Add.

1. $3 + 2 =$ ___ $4 + 5 =$ ___ $0 + 6 =$ ___

2. $1 + 8 =$ ___ $2 + 4 =$ ___ $5 + 3 =$ ___

Notes for Home Children explore at the CONCRETE level using counters to find sums.

Use counters.
Add.

3.

4	1	2	5	0	4	5
+ 4	+ 5	+ 7	+ 5	+ 8	+ 2	+ 4
8						

4.

1	2	4	8	0	5	7
+ 7	+ 3	+ 6	+ 1	+ 0	+ 2	+ 0

5.

0	7	3	2	5	0	3
+ 5	+ 2	+ 1	+ 4	+ 1	+ 4	+ 6

Exploring Mathematics Book Two © Scott, Foresman and Company

Notes for Home Children explore at the CONCRETE level using counters to find sums.

Name

Adding 1, 2, or 3

How many oranges are in the crate?
How many are next to the crate?
How can you find how many in all?

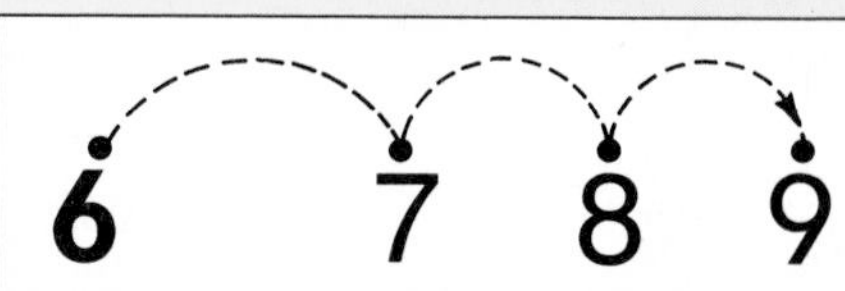

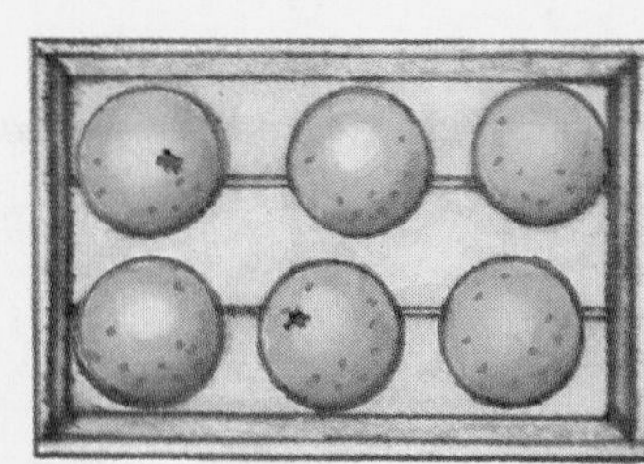

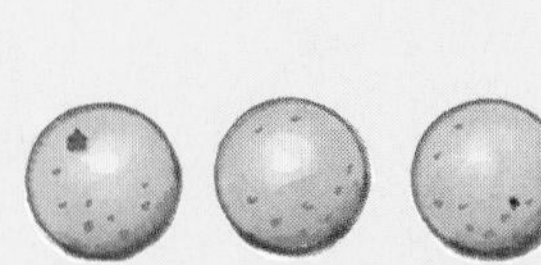

$6 + 3 =$ 9

Add by counting on.

1.

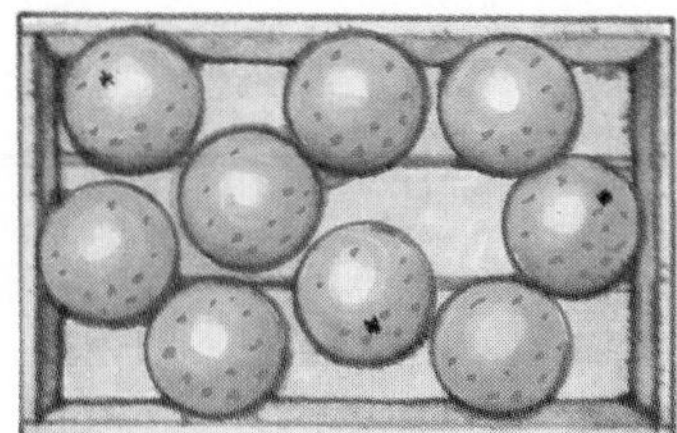

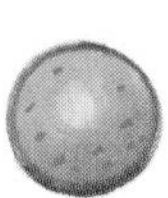

$9 + 1 =$ ____

2.

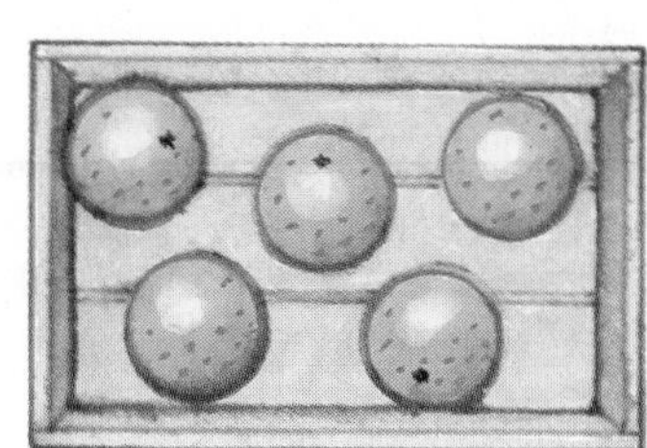

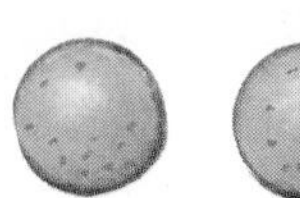

$5 + 2 =$ ____

3.

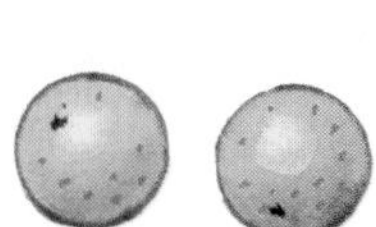

$8 + 2 =$ ____

4.

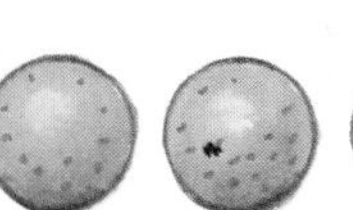

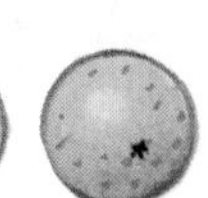

$4 + 3 =$ ____

Notes for Home Children learn to find sums by counting on 1, 2, or 3.

Add by counting on.

5.

2	3	6	7
+ 1	+ 2	+ 1	+ 2
3			

6.

7	3	2	8
+ 1	+ 1	+ 2	+ 1

7.

4	6	5	7	3	8	3
+ 2	+ 2	+ 3	+ 3	+ 3	+ 2	+ 2

8.

6	5	5	9	4	6	7
+ 1	+ 2	+ 1	+ 1	+ 1	+ 3	+ 2

Problem Solving

Solve.

9. Bobby has 7 big 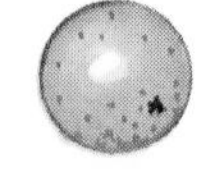 and 2 small. How many does he have in all?

_____ oranges

10. Jan has 3 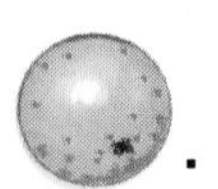.

Bobby gives her 4 more. How many does Jan have in all?

_____ oranges

Exploring Mathematics Book Two © Scott, Foresman and Company

Notes for Home Children practice finding sums by counting on 1, 2, or 3. Then they solve problems involving addition.

Name

Adding in Any Order

Add by counting on.

1.

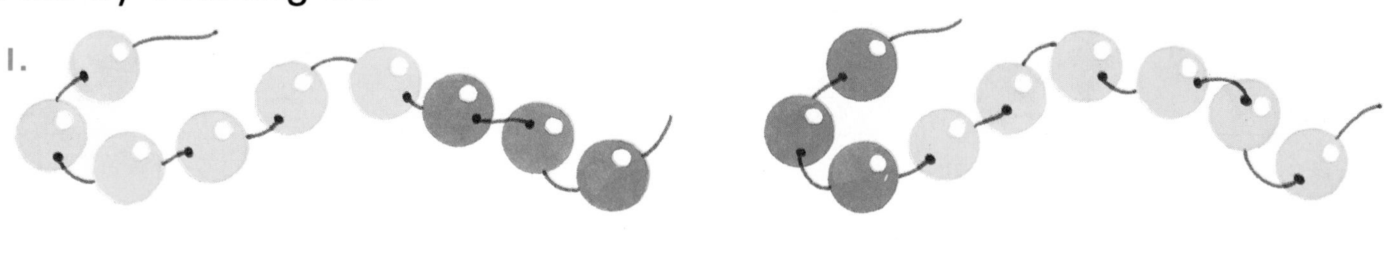

6 + 3 = ____   3 + 6 = ____

2.

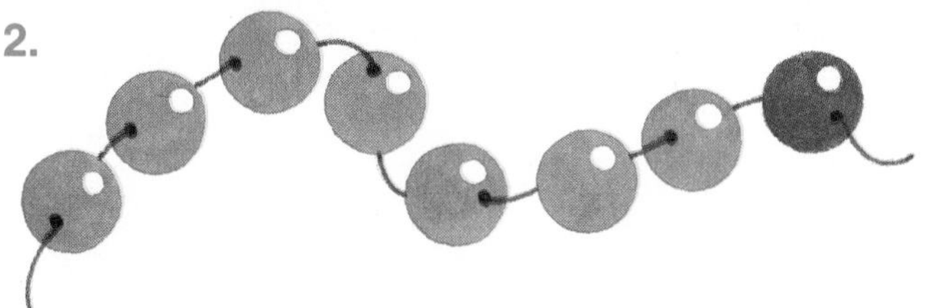

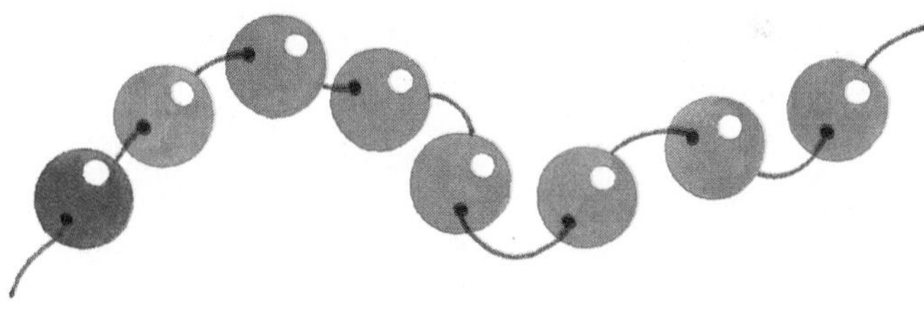

7 + 1 = ____   1 + 7 = ____

3.

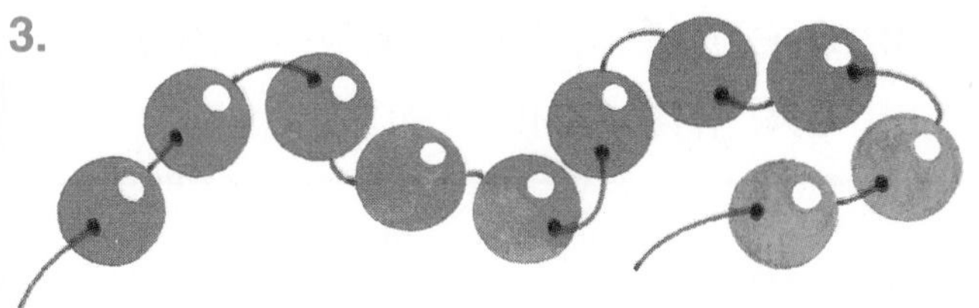

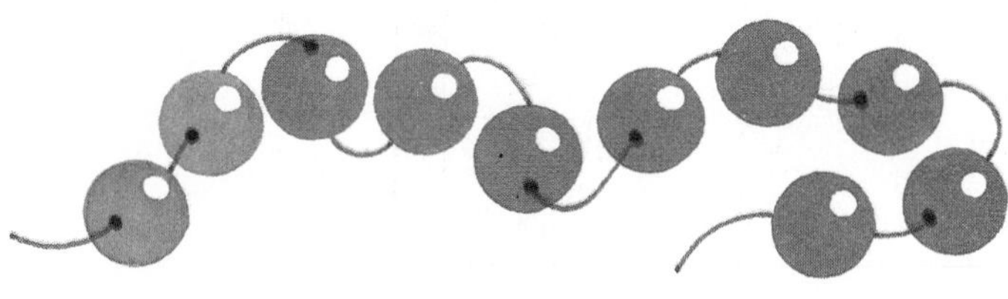

8 + 2 = ____   2 + 8 = ____

Notes for Home Children identify the greater of two numbers. They add by counting on to find the sums.

Think of the greater number.
Then add by counting on.

4. $\begin{array}{r} 6 \\ +2 \\ \hline 8 \end{array}$ $\begin{array}{r} 2 \\ +6 \\ \hline \end{array}$

5. $\begin{array}{r} 7 \\ +2 \\ \hline \end{array}$ $\begin{array}{r} 2 \\ +7 \\ \hline \end{array}$

6. $\begin{array}{r} 8 \\ +2 \\ \hline \end{array}$ $\begin{array}{r} 2 \\ +8 \\ \hline \end{array}$

7. $\begin{array}{r} 4 \\ +1 \\ \hline \end{array}$ $\begin{array}{r} 1 \\ +4 \\ \hline \end{array}$

8. $\begin{array}{r} 5 \\ +3 \\ \hline \end{array}$ $\begin{array}{r} 3 \\ +5 \\ \hline \end{array}$

9. $\begin{array}{r} 3 \\ +1 \\ \hline \end{array}$ $\begin{array}{r} 1 \\ +3 \\ \hline \end{array}$

10. $\begin{array}{r} 3 \\ +7 \\ \hline \end{array}$ $\begin{array}{r} 1 \\ +2 \\ \hline \end{array}$ $\begin{array}{r} 3 \\ +2 \\ \hline \end{array}$ $\begin{array}{r} 4 \\ +3 \\ \hline \end{array}$ $\begin{array}{r} 5 \\ +2 \\ \hline \end{array}$ $\begin{array}{r} 1 \\ +9 \\ \hline \end{array}$ $\begin{array}{r} 2 \\ +3 \\ \hline \end{array}$

11. $\begin{array}{r} 4 \\ +2 \\ \hline \end{array}$ $\begin{array}{r} 2 \\ +5 \\ \hline \end{array}$ $\begin{array}{r} 1 \\ +8 \\ \hline \end{array}$ $\begin{array}{r} 2 \\ +4 \\ \hline \end{array}$ $\begin{array}{r} 8 \\ +1 \\ \hline \end{array}$ $\begin{array}{r} 1 \\ +6 \\ \hline \end{array}$ $\begin{array}{r} 1 \\ +5 \\ \hline \end{array}$

Talk About Math

How are these facts the same?
How are they different?

$4 + 3 = 7$ $3 + 4 = 7$

Exploring Mathematics Book Two © Scott, Foresman and Company

Notes for Home Children practice finding sums by counting on from the greater number.

Name

Using Doubles to Add

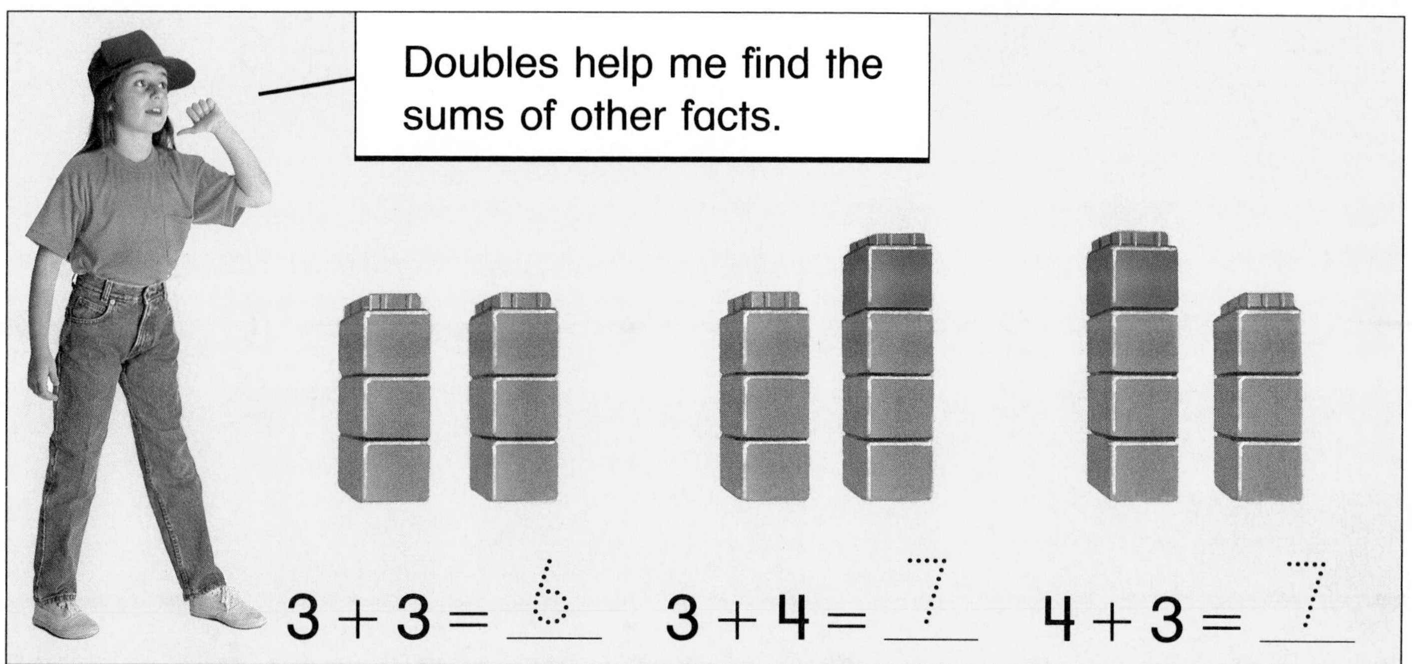

$3 + 3 =$ 6 $3 + 4 =$ 7 $4 + 3 =$ 7

Write the sum.

1.

$4 + 4 =$ ___

$4 + 5 =$ ___

$5 + 4 =$ ___

2.

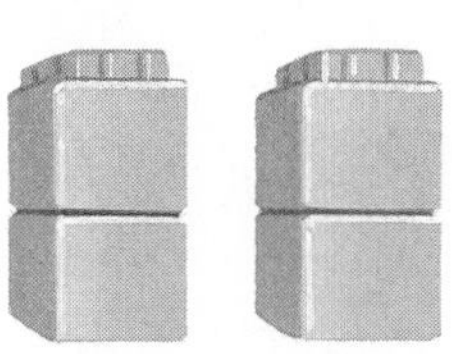

$2 + 2 =$ ___

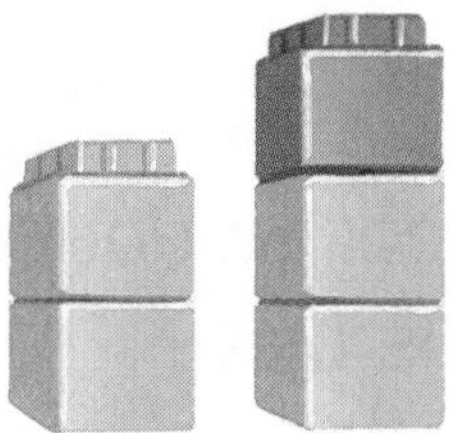

$2 + 3 =$ ___

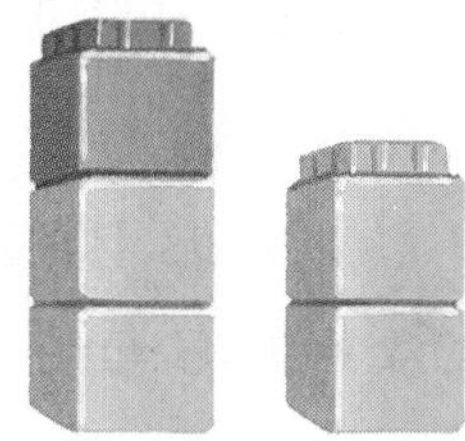

$3 + 2 =$ ___

Notes for Home Children use doubles facts to find sums of doubles and 1 more.

Write the sum.

3. $\begin{array}{r} 3 \\ +\,3 \\ \hline 6 \end{array}$ $\begin{array}{r} 3 \\ +\,4 \\ \hline \end{array}$ $\begin{array}{r} 4 \\ +\,3 \\ \hline \end{array}$

4. $\begin{array}{r} 4 \\ +\,4 \\ \hline \end{array}$ $\begin{array}{r} 4 \\ +\,5 \\ \hline \end{array}$ $\begin{array}{r} 5 \\ +\,4 \\ \hline \end{array}$

5. $\begin{array}{r} 2 \\ +\,2 \\ \hline \end{array}$ $\begin{array}{r} 2 \\ +\,3 \\ \hline \end{array}$ $\begin{array}{r} 3 \\ +\,2 \\ \hline \end{array}$

6. $\begin{array}{r} 1 \\ +\,1 \\ \hline \end{array}$ $\begin{array}{r} 1 \\ +\,2 \\ \hline \end{array}$ $\begin{array}{r} 2 \\ +\,1 \\ \hline \end{array}$

7. $\begin{array}{r} 8 \\ +\,2 \\ \hline \end{array}$ $\begin{array}{r} 2 \\ +\,4 \\ \hline \end{array}$ $\begin{array}{r} 3 \\ +\,6 \\ \hline \end{array}$ $\begin{array}{r} 5 \\ +\,5 \\ \hline \end{array}$ $\begin{array}{r} 2 \\ +\,7 \\ \hline \end{array}$ $\begin{array}{r} 3 \\ +\,7 \\ \hline \end{array}$ $\begin{array}{r} 4 \\ +\,4 \\ \hline \end{array}$

8. $\begin{array}{r} 5 \\ +\,3 \\ \hline \end{array}$ $\begin{array}{r} 3 \\ +\,3 \\ \hline \end{array}$ $\begin{array}{r} 6 \\ +\,3 \\ \hline \end{array}$ $\begin{array}{r} 2 \\ +\,8 \\ \hline \end{array}$ $\begin{array}{r} 2 \\ +\,5 \\ \hline \end{array}$ $\begin{array}{r} 7 \\ +\,2 \\ \hline \end{array}$ $\begin{array}{r} 4 \\ +\,3 \\ \hline \end{array}$

Talk About Math

Which facts are doubles?
Why do you think they are called doubles?
Which facts are doubles plus one?

Exploring Mathematics Book Two © Scott, Foresman and Company

Notes for Home Children practice finding sums through 10. Then they discuss doubles and doubles plus one.

Name

Addition Facts for 10

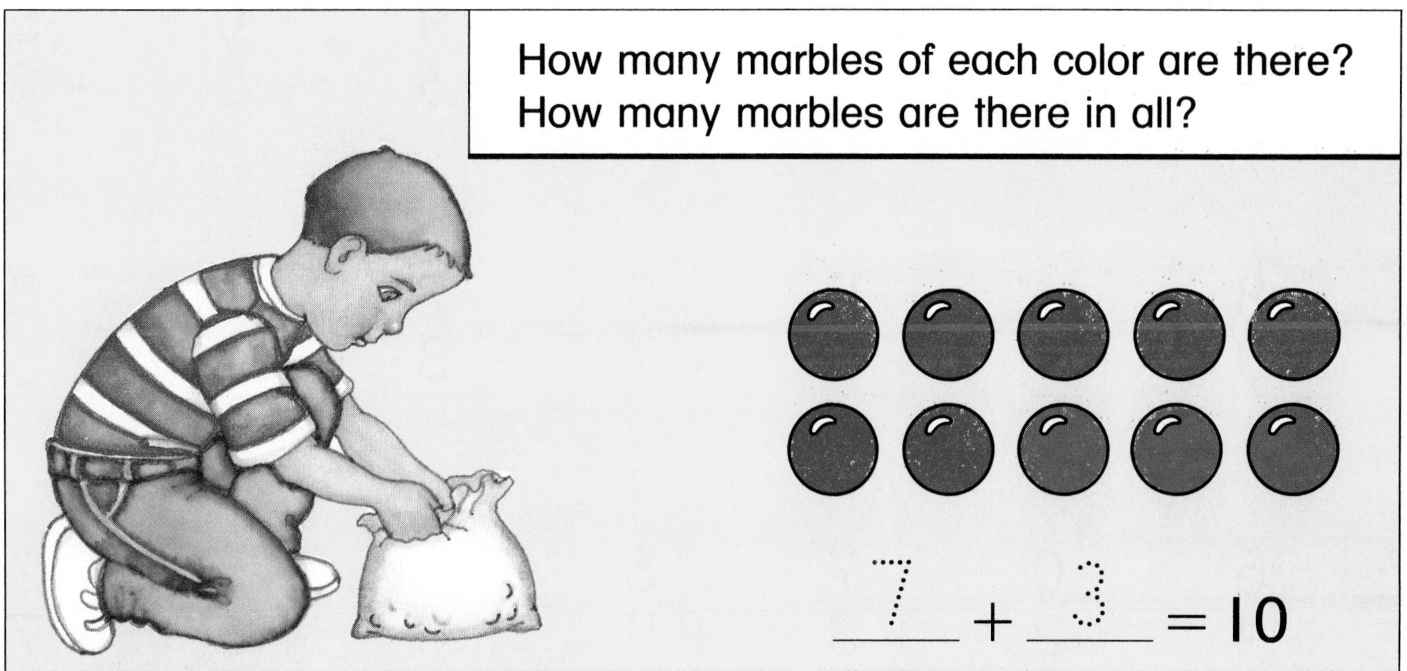

Find different ways to make 10.
Color some marbles red and some blue.
Complete the number sentence.

1. ____ + ____ = 10

2. ____ + ____ = 10

3. ____ + ____ = 10

4. ____ + ____ = 10

Notes for Home Children find pairs of numbers that equal 10 by coloring some objects red and some blue. They complete number sentences.

Add. Ring the sums of 10.

5. $\begin{array}{r}5\\+5\\\hline 10\end{array}$ $\quad\begin{array}{r}6\\+4\\\hline\end{array}$ $\quad\begin{array}{r}0\\+7\\\hline\end{array}$ $\quad\begin{array}{r}8\\+2\\\hline\end{array}$ $\quad\begin{array}{r}4\\+6\\\hline\end{array}$ $\quad\begin{array}{r}0\\+3\\\hline\end{array}$ $\quad\begin{array}{r}5\\+2\\\hline\end{array}$

6. $\begin{array}{r}8\\+0\\\hline\end{array}$ $\quad\begin{array}{r}1\\+9\\\hline\end{array}$ $\quad\begin{array}{r}4\\+5\\\hline\end{array}$ $\quad\begin{array}{r}3\\+7\\\hline\end{array}$ $\quad\begin{array}{r}2\\+8\\\hline\end{array}$ $\quad\begin{array}{r}6\\+2\\\hline\end{array}$ $\quad\begin{array}{r}3\\+5\\\hline\end{array}$

7. $\begin{array}{r}5\\+4\\\hline\end{array}$ $\quad\begin{array}{r}0\\+2\\\hline\end{array}$ $\quad\begin{array}{r}7\\+3\\\hline\end{array}$ $\quad\begin{array}{r}6\\+4\\\hline\end{array}$ $\quad\begin{array}{r}3\\+0\\\hline\end{array}$ $\quad\begin{array}{r}5\\+5\\\hline\end{array}$ $\quad\begin{array}{r}2\\+7\\\hline\end{array}$

8. $\begin{array}{r}2\\+5\\\hline\end{array}$ $\quad\begin{array}{r}4\\+0\\\hline\end{array}$ $\quad\begin{array}{r}9\\+0\\\hline\end{array}$ $\quad\begin{array}{r}9\\+1\\\hline\end{array}$ $\quad\begin{array}{r}3\\+4\\\hline\end{array}$ $\quad\begin{array}{r}6\\+0\\\hline\end{array}$ $\quad\begin{array}{r}3\\+6\\\hline\end{array}$

Problem Solving

Solve.

9. Mark has 6 green .

Susie has 4 blue .

How many  do they have in all?

______ marbles

Exploring Mathematics Book Two © Scott, Foresman and Company

Notes for Home Children practice finding sums through 10 and identifying sums of 10. Then they solve a problem involving addition.

See More Practice Set A on page 41.

Name ____________________ Algebra Readiness

PROBLEM-SOLVING GUIDE
Understand
Plan and Solve
Look Back

Write a Number Sentence

2 turtles are in one box.
3 turtles are in another box.
How many turtles in all?

2 + 3 = 5 turtles

How many?
Write a number sentence to solve.

1. 4 kittens are resting in a basket.
5 kittens are resting in another basket.
How many kittens altogether?

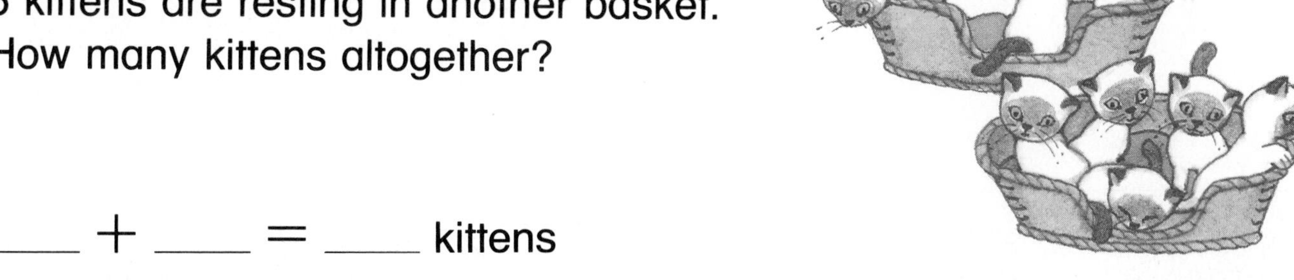

____ + ____ = ____ kittens

2. 3 ladybugs are in a jar.
5 ladybugs are in another jar.
How many ladybugs in all?

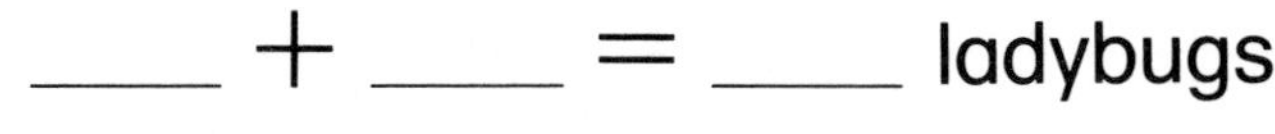

____ + ____ = ____ ladybugs

3. 6 goldfish are in a bowl.
2 angelfish are in another bowl.
How many fish are in both bowls?

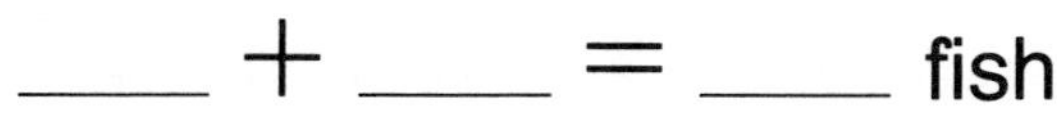

____ + ____ = ____ fish

Notes for Home Children solve problems by writing addition number sentences.

How many?
Write a number sentence to solve.

4. 3 squirrels are climbing.
6 squirrels are on the grass.
How many squirrels altogether?

3 + 6 = 9 squirrels

5. 4 dogs are sleeping.
3 dogs are eating.
How many dogs in all?

____ + ____ = ____ dogs

6. 4 birds are standing.
4 birds are flying.
How many birds in all?

____ + ____ = ____ birds

7. 5 ducks are swimming in the water.
2 ducks are standing near the water.
How many ducks altogether?

____ + ____ = ____ ducks

Exploring Mathematics Book Two © Scott, Foresman and Company

Notes for Home Children solve problems by writing addition number sentences.

Number Sense

Find different groups of tennis shoes to make a sum of 10.

Let's do some more!

Draw a picture showing different groups of 10.
Write a story about your picture.

Notes for Home Children develop number understanding by describing different combinations of tennis shoes that make a total of 10.

SKILLS REVIEW

Skills Review

Fill in the correct ⬭.
Add.

1. $\begin{array}{r} 5 \\ +2 \\ \hline \end{array}$ Ⓐ 7 Ⓑ 8 Ⓒ 9

2. $\begin{array}{r} 7 \\ +3 \\ \hline \end{array}$ Ⓐ 6 Ⓑ 8 Ⓒ 10

3. $\begin{array}{r} 8 \\ +1 \\ \hline \end{array}$ Ⓐ 8 Ⓑ 9 Ⓒ 10

4. $\begin{array}{r} 6 \\ +3 \\ \hline \end{array}$ Ⓐ 6 Ⓑ 8 Ⓒ 9

5. $\begin{array}{r} 5 \\ +5 \\ \hline \end{array}$ Ⓐ 6 Ⓑ 8 Ⓒ 10

6. $\begin{array}{r} 2 \\ +8 \\ \hline \end{array}$ Ⓐ 2 Ⓑ 8 Ⓒ 10

Vocabulary

Match.

one •

four •

six •

eight •

ten •

Exploring Mathematics Book Two © Scott, Foresman and Company

Notes for Home Children review finding sums through 10. Then they review number words.

Name

Finding Differences Through 10

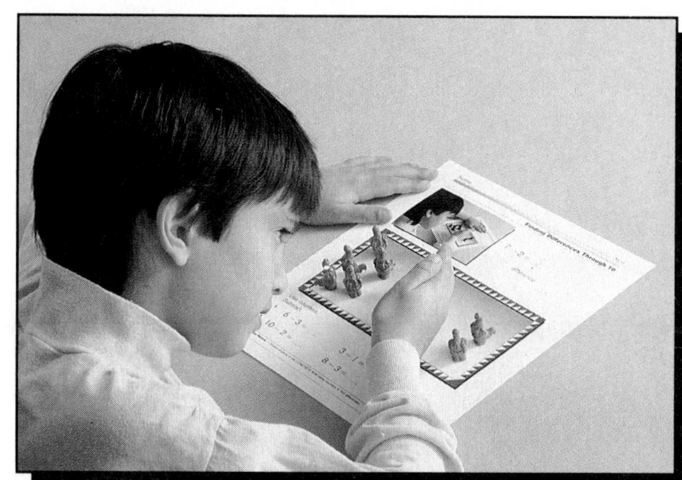

$7 - 2 = 5$

difference

Use counters.
Subtract.

1. $6 - 3 =$ ___ $3 - 1 =$ ___ $5 - 2 =$ ___

2. $10 - 2 =$ ___ $8 - 3 =$ ___ $4 - 0 =$ ___

Notes for Home Children explore at the CONCRETE level using counters to find differences.

Use counters.
Subtract.

3.

6	7	5	9	8	5	6
− 1	− 2	− 5	− 1	− 0	− 4	− 3
5						

4.

6	7	2	4	3	10	7
− 2	− 0	− 2	− 1	− 2	− 9	− 3

5.

6	0	7	5	10	1	4
− 4	− 0	− 1	− 0	− 6	− 1	− 3

Exploring Mathematics Book Two © Scott, Foresman and Company

Notes for Home Children explore at the CONCRETE level using counters to find differences.

Name

6 puppies live in the doghouse.
2 come out to play.
How can you find how many are left in the doghouse?

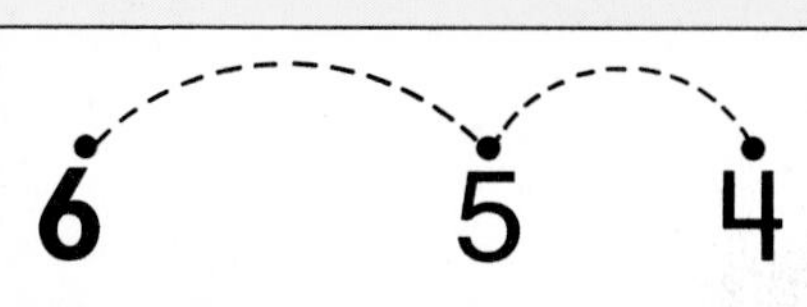

6 − 2 = 4

Subtract by counting back.

1.

7 − 1 = ___

2.

10 − 3 = ___

3.

8 − 2 = ___

4.

5 − 2 = ___

Notes for Home Children learn to find differences by counting back 1, 2, or 3.

Subtract by counting back.

5.	8	5	9	10	4	8	4
	− 1	− 2	− 1	− 3	− 1	− 3	− 2
	7						
6.	10	9	2	5	3	4	7
	− 1	− 2	− 1	− 3	− 2	− 2	− 3
7.	8	5	7	4	3	6	8
	− 2	− 1	− 1	− 3	− 1	− 2	− 1
8.	6	6	7	8	10	7	9
	− 3	− 1	− 2	− 1	− 2	− 3	− 3

Problem Solving

Solve.

9. Tim has 9 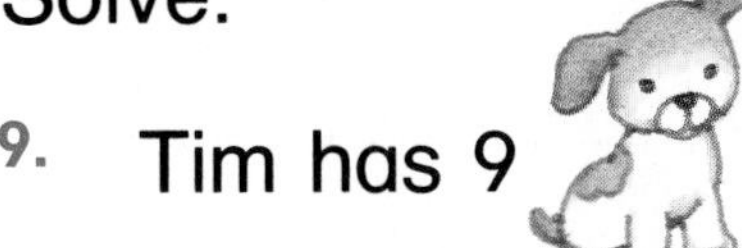 .

He gives 1 to Sam.
How many does Tim have left?

_____ puppies

10. Kim has 5  .

She gives Carole 2  .
How many does Kim have left?

_____ puppies

Exploring Mathematics Book Two © Scott, Foresman and Company

Notes for Home Children practice finding differences by counting back 1, 2, or 3. Then they solve problems involving subtraction.

Name

Related Subtraction Facts

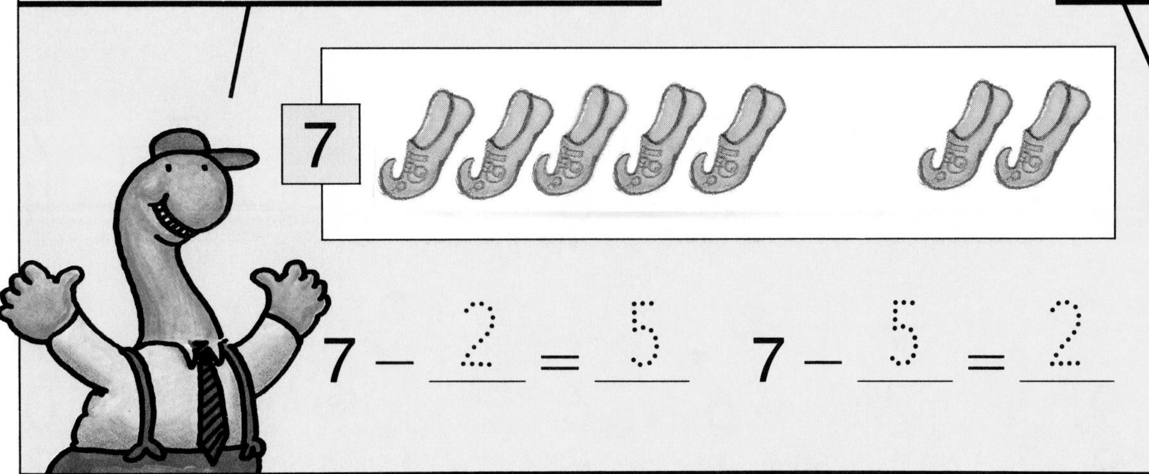

7 − 2 = 5   7 − 5 = 2

Write the difference.

1.

8 − ___ = ___

8 − ___ = ___

2.

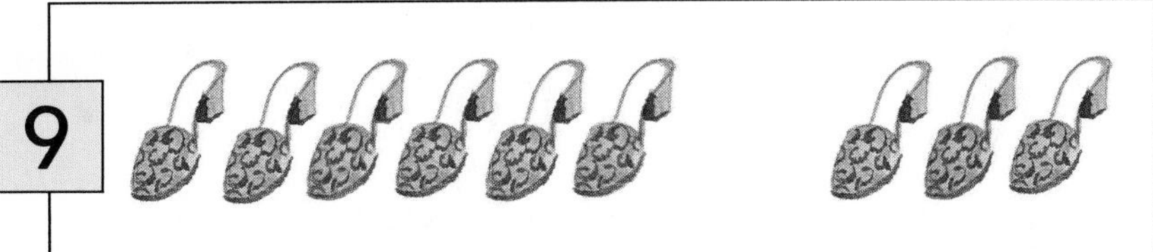

9 − ___ = ___

9 − ___ = ___

3.

6 − ___ = ___

6 − ___ = ___

4.

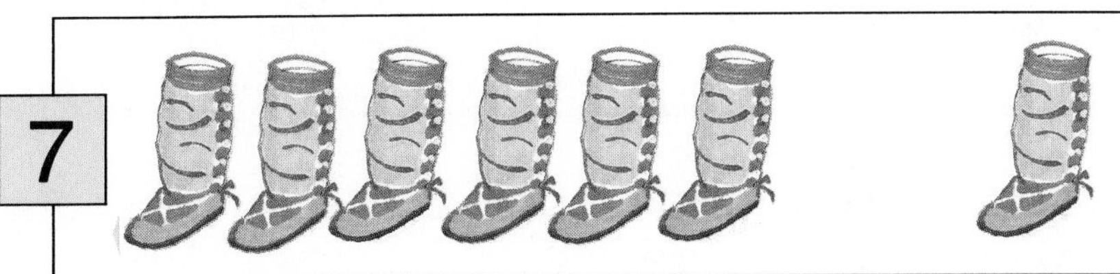

7 − ___ = ___

7 − ___ = ___

Notes for Home Children learn to use a known subtraction fact to solve a related subtraction fact.

Write the difference.

5. $\begin{array}{r}10\\-1\\\hline 9\end{array}$ $\begin{array}{r}10\\-9\\\hline\end{array}$

6. $\begin{array}{r}8\\-1\\\hline\end{array}$ $\begin{array}{r}8\\-7\\\hline\end{array}$

7. $\begin{array}{r}9\\-2\\\hline\end{array}$ $\begin{array}{r}9\\-7\\\hline\end{array}$

8. $\begin{array}{r}8\\-2\\\hline\end{array}$ $\begin{array}{r}8\\-6\\\hline\end{array}$

9. $\begin{array}{r}10\\-2\\\hline\end{array}$ $\begin{array}{r}10\\-8\\\hline\end{array}$

10. $\begin{array}{r}7\\-3\\\hline\end{array}$ $\begin{array}{r}7\\-4\\\hline\end{array}$

11. $\begin{array}{r}9\\-1\\\hline\end{array}$ $\begin{array}{r}9\\-8\\\hline\end{array}$

12. $\begin{array}{r}6\\-1\\\hline\end{array}$ $\begin{array}{r}6\\-5\\\hline\end{array}$

13. $\begin{array}{r}10\\-3\\\hline\end{array}$ $\begin{array}{r}10\\-7\\\hline\end{array}$

14. $\begin{array}{r}9\\-7\\\hline\end{array}$ $\begin{array}{r}8\\-5\\\hline\end{array}$ $\begin{array}{r}5\\-4\\\hline\end{array}$ $\begin{array}{r}2\\-1\\\hline\end{array}$ $\begin{array}{r}10\\-7\\\hline\end{array}$ $\begin{array}{r}6\\-4\\\hline\end{array}$ $\begin{array}{r}9\\-8\\\hline\end{array}$

15. $\begin{array}{r}7\\-2\\\hline\end{array}$ $\begin{array}{r}8\\-6\\\hline\end{array}$ $\begin{array}{r}10\\-8\\\hline\end{array}$ $\begin{array}{r}5\\-1\\\hline\end{array}$ $\begin{array}{r}10\\-9\\\hline\end{array}$ $\begin{array}{r}7\\-5\\\hline\end{array}$ $\begin{array}{r}7\\-1\\\hline\end{array}$

16. $\begin{array}{r}4\\-3\\\hline\end{array}$ $\begin{array}{r}9\\-6\\\hline\end{array}$ $\begin{array}{r}7\\-4\\\hline\end{array}$

Critical Thinking How does knowing that 2 and 3 are parts of 5 help you find 5 − 2 and 5 − 3?

Notes for Home Children practice subtraction facts through 10. Then they discuss how knowing the parts of a number helps find the difference of 2 numbers.

Exploring Mathematics Book Two © Scott, Foresman and Company

Name

Subtracting with Doubles

Add or subtract.

1.

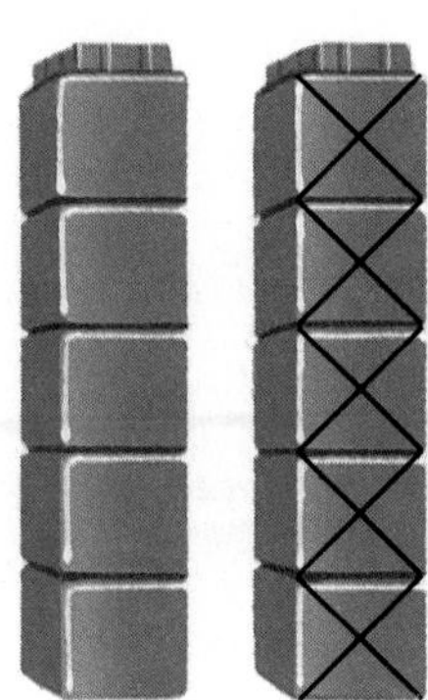

$5 + 5 =$ _____ $10 - 5 =$ _____

2.

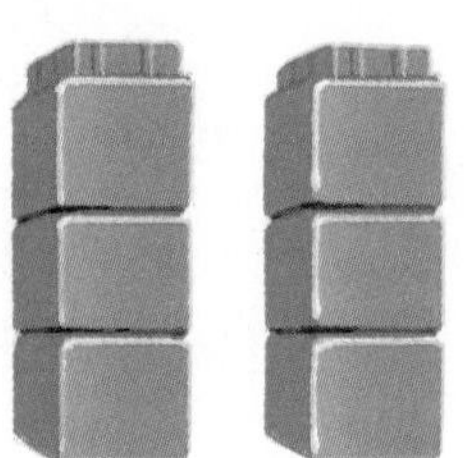

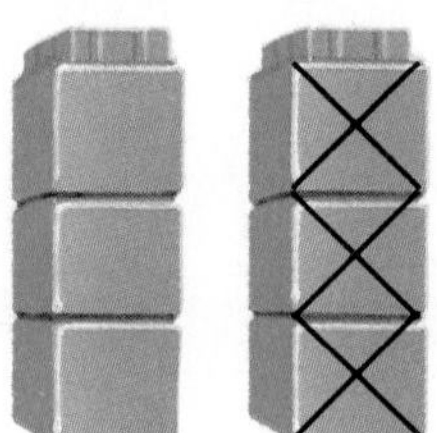

$3 + 3 =$ _____ $6 - 3 =$ _____

Notes for Home Children learn to use an addition doubles fact to solve a related subtraction fact.

Add or subtract.

3. $1 + 1 = 2$ $2 - 1 =$

4. $4 + 4 =$ $8 - 4 =$

5. $3 + 3 =$ $6 - 3 =$

6. $5 + 5 =$ $10 - 5 =$

7. $2 + 2 =$ $4 - 2 =$

8. $4 + 4 =$ $8 - 4 =$

9. $9 - 7 =$ $4 - 3 =$ $9 - 8 =$ $10 - 9 =$ $5 - 3 =$ $10 - 7 =$ $9 - 3 =$

10. $4 - 3 =$ $10 - 5 =$ $8 - 7 =$ $6 - 1 =$ $6 - 3 =$ $7 - 6 =$ $8 - 4 =$

11. $4 - 2 =$ $6 - 5 =$ $8 - 2 =$ $6 - 2 =$ $6 - 4 =$

Critical Thinking How can you use the double $5 + 5 = 10$ to find a related subtraction fact?

Exploring Mathematics Book Two © Scott, Foresman and Company

Notes for Home Children learn to use an addition doubles fact to solve a related subtraction fact. Then they discuss related subtraction facts for doubles.

Name

Subtracting from 10

Show different ways to subtract from 10.
Put an X on some apples.
Complete the number sentence.

1. 

10 – ____ = ____

2. 

10 – ____ = ____

3. 

10 – ____ = ____

4. 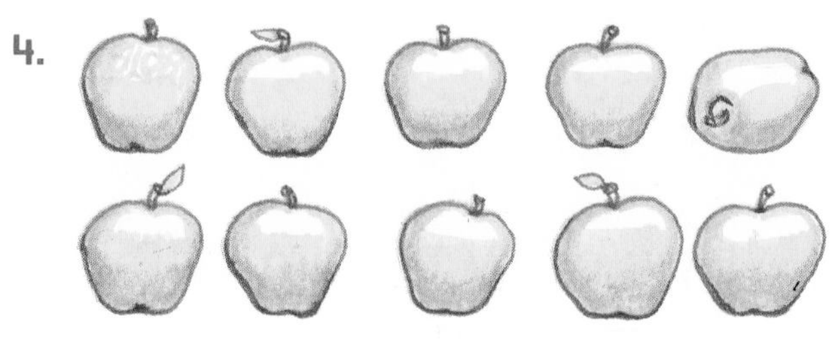

10 – ____ = ____

Notes for Home Children learn facts of 10 by showing different ways to subtract from 10. They complete number sentences.

Subtract.

5.	$\begin{array}{r}10\\-6\\\hline 4\end{array}$	$\begin{array}{r}10\\-3\\\hline\end{array}$	$\begin{array}{r}10\\-8\\\hline\end{array}$	$\begin{array}{r}10\\-4\\\hline\end{array}$	$\begin{array}{r}10\\-7\\\hline\end{array}$	$\begin{array}{r}10\\-1\\\hline\end{array}$	$\begin{array}{r}10\\-5\\\hline\end{array}$
6.	$\begin{array}{r}10\\-2\\\hline\end{array}$	$\begin{array}{r}10\\-9\\\hline\end{array}$	$\begin{array}{r}10\\-5\\\hline\end{array}$	$\begin{array}{r}10\\-8\\\hline\end{array}$	$\begin{array}{r}10\\-6\\\hline\end{array}$	$\begin{array}{r}10\\-4\\\hline\end{array}$	$\begin{array}{r}10\\-8\\\hline\end{array}$
7.	$\begin{array}{r}8\\-5\\\hline\end{array}$	$\begin{array}{r}6\\-4\\\hline\end{array}$	$\begin{array}{r}8\\-7\\\hline\end{array}$	$\begin{array}{r}9\\-8\\\hline\end{array}$	$\begin{array}{r}10\\-7\\\hline\end{array}$	$\begin{array}{r}7\\-5\\\hline\end{array}$	$\begin{array}{r}6\\-2\\\hline\end{array}$
8.	$\begin{array}{r}9\\-2\\\hline\end{array}$	$\begin{array}{r}10\\-3\\\hline\end{array}$	$\begin{array}{r}9\\-6\\\hline\end{array}$	$\begin{array}{r}10\\-2\\\hline\end{array}$	$\begin{array}{r}8\\-6\\\hline\end{array}$	$\begin{array}{r}7\\-3\\\hline\end{array}$	$\begin{array}{r}9\\-3\\\hline\end{array}$

Problem Solving

Solve.

9. 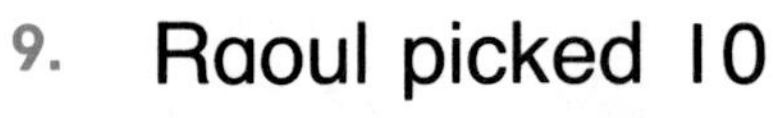

Raoul picked 10 .

He used 6  to make a pie.

How many  are left?

_____ apples

10. Ellen used 5 big  and

4 little  to make a pie.

How many did she use in all?

_____ apples

Exploring Mathematics Book Two © Scott, Foresman and Company

Notes for Home Children practice subtraction facts through 10.

Name

ACTIVITY

Finding Families of Facts

$4 + 6 = 10$

$6 + 4 = 10$

$10 - 6 = 4$

$10 - 4 = 6$

Use counters. Add or subtract.

1. $3 + 7 =$ 10
   $7 + 3 =$ ____
   $10 - 7 =$ ____
   $10 - 3 =$ ____

2. $3 + 6 =$ ____
   $6 + 3 =$ ____
   $9 - 6 =$ ____
   $9 - 3 =$ ____

3. $3 + 5 =$ ____
   $5 + 3 =$ ____
   $8 - 5 =$ ____
   $8 - 3 =$ ____

Notes for Home Children explore at the CONCRETE level using counters to find answers to families of facts.

Add or subtract.

4. $3 + 4 =$ 7	5. $4 + 5 =$ ____	6. $4 + 6 =$ ____
$4 + 3 =$ ____	$5 + 4 =$ ____	$6 + 4 =$ ____
$7 - 4 =$ ____	$9 - 5 =$ ____	$10 - 6 =$ ____
$7 - 3 =$ ____	$9 - 4 =$ ____	$10 - 4 =$ ____
7. $3 + 6 =$ ____	8. $2 + 6 =$ ____	9. $3 + 7 =$ ____
$6 + 3 =$ ____	$6 + 2 =$ ____	$7 + 3 =$ ____
$9 - 6 =$ ____	$8 - 6 =$ ____	$10 - 7 =$ ____
$9 - 3 =$ ____	$8 - 2 =$ ____	$10 - 3 =$ ____

Talk About Math

What fact is missing from this family?
Why does it belong with the family?

$4 + 5 = 9$ $5 + 4 = 9$ $9 - 4 = 5$

Exploring Mathematics Book Two © Scott, Foresman and Company

Notes for Home Children practice finding sums and differences for families of facts. Then they talk about families of facts.

Name

Addition and Subtraction Through 10

The plus sign tells me to add.

The minus sign tells me to subtract.

$$\begin{array}{r} 3 \\ +5 \\ \hline 8 \end{array} \qquad \begin{array}{r} 9 \\ -4 \\ \hline 5 \end{array}$$

Add or subtract.

1. $\begin{array}{r} 1 \\ +5 \\ \hline \end{array}$ $\begin{array}{r} 6 \\ +1 \\ \hline \end{array}$ $\begin{array}{r} 0 \\ +9 \\ \hline \end{array}$ $\begin{array}{r} 8 \\ -7 \\ \hline \end{array}$ $\begin{array}{r} 5 \\ -4 \\ \hline \end{array}$ $\begin{array}{r} 8 \\ -2 \\ \hline \end{array}$ $\begin{array}{r} 10 \\ -7 \\ \hline \end{array}$

2. $\begin{array}{r} 8 \\ -8 \\ \hline \end{array}$ $\begin{array}{r} 4 \\ +2 \\ \hline \end{array}$ $\begin{array}{r} 6 \\ -6 \\ \hline \end{array}$ $\begin{array}{r} 9 \\ -4 \\ \hline \end{array}$ $\begin{array}{r} 0 \\ +3 \\ \hline \end{array}$ $\begin{array}{r} 6 \\ +2 \\ \hline \end{array}$ $\begin{array}{r} 2 \\ +7 \\ \hline \end{array}$

3. $\begin{array}{r} 0 \\ +1 \\ \hline \end{array}$ $\begin{array}{r} 6 \\ -5 \\ \hline \end{array}$ $\begin{array}{r} 2 \\ +6 \\ \hline \end{array}$ $\begin{array}{r} 1 \\ +0 \\ \hline \end{array}$ $\begin{array}{r} 5 \\ -4 \\ \hline \end{array}$ $\begin{array}{r} 9 \\ -9 \\ \hline \end{array}$ $\begin{array}{r} 4 \\ +5 \\ \hline \end{array}$

4. $\begin{array}{r} 3 \\ -1 \\ \hline \end{array}$ $\begin{array}{r} 9 \\ -5 \\ \hline \end{array}$ $\begin{array}{r} 3 \\ +5 \\ \hline \end{array}$ $\begin{array}{r} 5 \\ -2 \\ \hline \end{array}$ $\begin{array}{r} 3 \\ -3 \\ \hline \end{array}$ $\begin{array}{r} 5 \\ +4 \\ \hline \end{array}$ $\begin{array}{r} 10 \\ -4 \\ \hline \end{array}$

Notes for Home Children practice addition and subtraction facts through 10.

Ring the facts for each number.

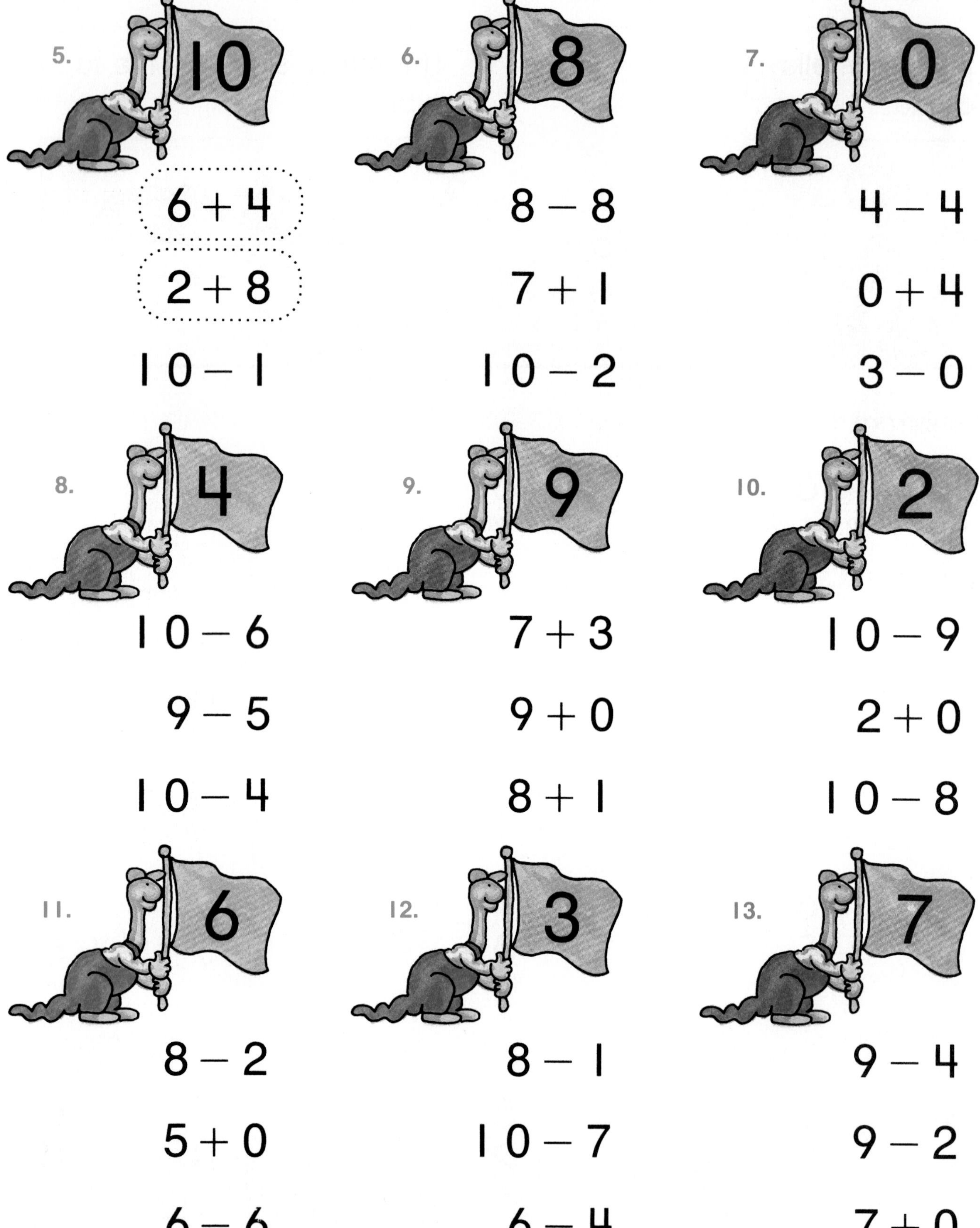

5. 10

6 + 4

2 + 8

10 − 1

6. 8

8 − 8

7 + 1

10 − 2

7. 0

4 − 4

0 + 4

3 − 0

8. 4

10 − 6

9 − 5

10 − 4

9. 9

7 + 3

9 + 0

8 + 1

10. 2

10 − 9

2 + 0

10 − 8

11. 6

8 − 2

5 + 0

6 − 6

12. 3

8 − 1

10 − 7

6 − 4

13. 7

9 − 4

9 − 2

7 + 0

Exploring Mathematics Book Two © Scott, Foresman and Company

Notes for Home Children practice addition and subtraction facts through 10 by identifying facts for a given number.

See More Practice Set B on page 41.

Name

Choose an Operation

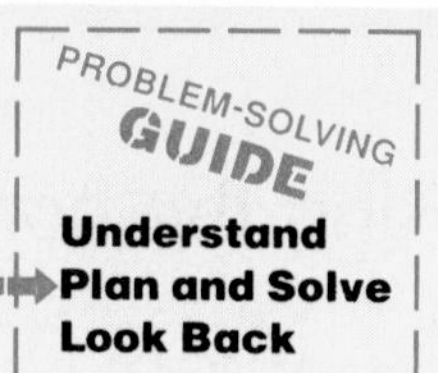

Ann has more money now.
Add to find how much.

Ann had 5¢.
She found 2¢ more.
How much does she have now?

$5¢ + 2¢ = 7¢$

Ring the correct number sentence.

1. Darrel had 6¢.
He spent 4¢.
How much does he have left?

$6¢ + 4¢ = 10¢$ $6¢ - 4¢ = 2¢$

2. Dora had 5¢.
She spent 3¢.
How much does she have left?

$5¢ + 3¢ = 8¢$ $5¢ - 3¢ = 2¢$

3. Carol had 8¢.
She earned 2¢.
How much does she have now?

$8¢ + 2¢ = 10¢$ $8¢ - 2¢ = 6¢$

Notes for Home Children solve money problems by choosing an addition or a subtraction number sentence.

Ring the correct number sentence.

4. Maria had 7¢.
She spent 3¢.
How much does she have left?

7¢ + 3¢ = 10 ¢   7¢ − 3¢ = 4 ¢

5. Jason had 6¢.
He spent 3¢.
How much does he have now?

6¢ + 3¢ = 9 ¢   6¢ − 3¢ = 3 ¢

6. Keith earned 5¢.
Then he earned 4¢.
How much did he earn in all?

5¢ + 4¢ = 9 ¢   5¢ − 4¢ = 1 ¢

7. Chelsea spent 8¢.
Then she spent 2¢.
How much did she spend in all?

8¢ + 2¢ = 10 ¢   8¢ − 2¢ = 6 ¢

Exploring Mathematics Book Two © Scott, Foresman and Company

Notes for Home Children solve money problems by choosing an addition or a subtraction number sentence.

Name

Problem-Solving Workshop

Explore as a Team

Work with a partner.
Make these number circles.
1 2 3 4 5 6 7 8 9

Use them on the path to solve.

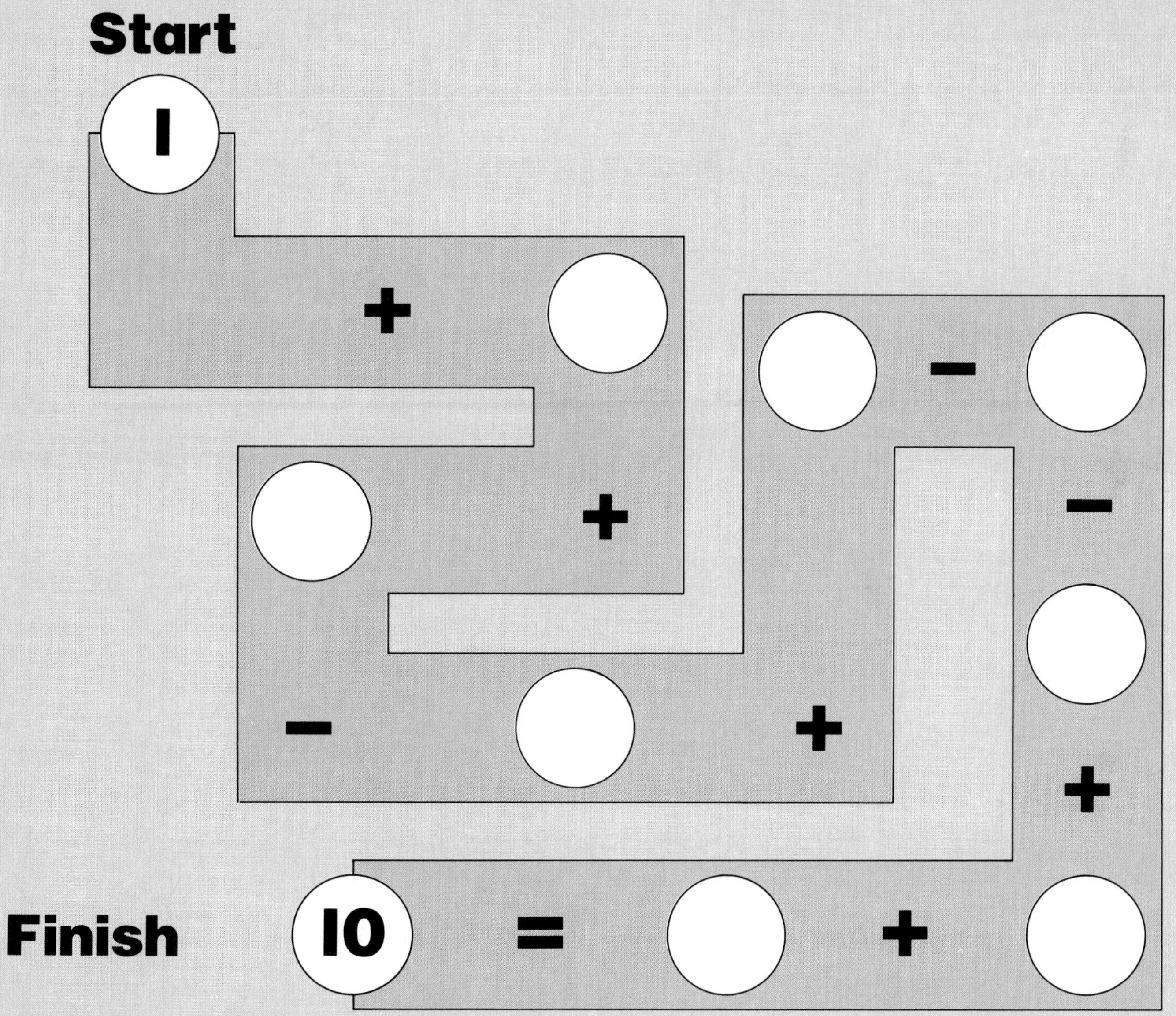

Start

1 + ◯ + ◯ − ◯ + ◯ − ◯ − ◯ + ◯ + ◯ = 10

Finish

Notes for Home Children explore with a partner to solve a problem involving addition and subtraction.

Problem-Solving Workshop

Explore with a Computer

Money and Time Project

1. Choose a price for the toy.

49¢

75¢

97¢

2. At the computer, type a price for the toy.
Put the coins you need in the sack.

3. Check your work. Have the computer count the coins.
Then buy the toy.

Exploring Mathematics Book Two © Scott, Foresman and Company

Notes for Home Children identify the coins needed to buy an item of given value. At the computer, they put the coins into the sack on the computer screen and have the computer count the coins to check their work.

Name

More Practice

Set A Use after page 18.

Add.

Ring the sums of 10.

1.

9	7	3	4	0	9
+ 0	+ 3	+ 4	+ 6	+ 2	+ 1
9					

2.

2	5	0	8	5	2
+ 8	+ 4	+ 3	+ 2	+ 5	+ 5

Set B Use after page 36

Add or subtract.

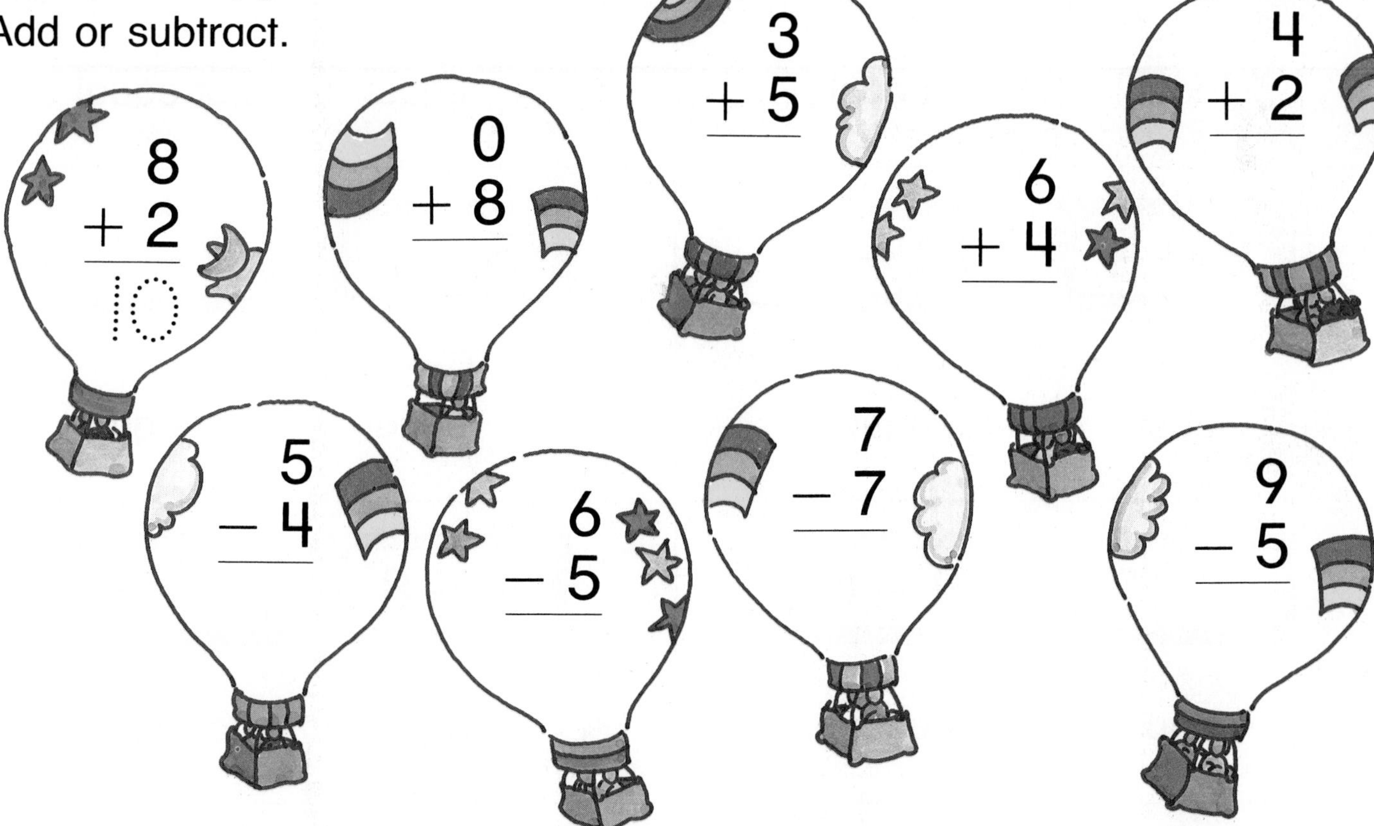

Notes for Home Set A: Children practice sums through 10.
Set B: Children practice addition and subtraction facts through 10.

Enrichment

2 + 7 is a name for 9.
5 + 4 is a name for 9.
2 + 7 equals 5 + 4.

3 + 5 is a name for 8.
1 + 6 is not a name for 8.
3 + 5 does not equal 1 + 6.

Ring equal or not equal.

1. 4 + 4 | 3 + 5
   equal   not equal

2. 5 + 5 | 1 + 7
   equal   not equal

3. 3 + 2 | 1 + 0
   equal   not equal

4. 2 + 4 | 4 + 2
   equal   not equal

5. 8 − 4 | 10 − 6
   equal   not equal

6. 5 − 1 | 9 − 3
   equal   not equal

7. 9 − 7 | 9 − 0
   equal   not equal

8. 9 − 8 | 1 − 0
   equal   not equal

Exploring Mathematics Book Two © Scott, Foresman and Company

Notes for Home Children are challenged to compare two number facts and determine if they are equal or not equal.

Name ______________________________

1. Add.

$2 + 3 = \_\_\_$

2. Subtract.

$6 - 3 = \_\_\_$

3. Add.

$\begin{array}{r} 4 \\ +5 \\ \hline \end{array}$ $\begin{array}{r} 8 \\ +2 \\ \hline \end{array}$ $\begin{array}{r} 3 \\ +0 \\ \hline \end{array}$

4. Subtract.

$\begin{array}{r} 10 \\ -8 \\ \hline \end{array}$ $\begin{array}{r} 8 \\ -4 \\ \hline \end{array}$ $\begin{array}{r} 6 \\ -0 \\ \hline \end{array}$

5. Add or subtract.

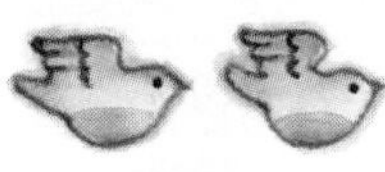 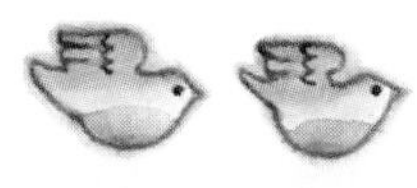 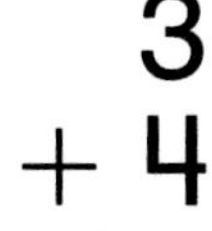

$\begin{array}{r} 3 \\ +4 \\ \hline \end{array}$ $\begin{array}{r} 4 \\ +3 \\ \hline \end{array}$ $\begin{array}{r} 7 \\ -4 \\ \hline \end{array}$ $\begin{array}{r} 7 \\ -3 \\ \hline \end{array}$

6. Write a number sentence.

2 books are on one side.
4 books are on the other side. How many books in all?

___ + ___ = ___ books

7. Ring the correct number sentence.

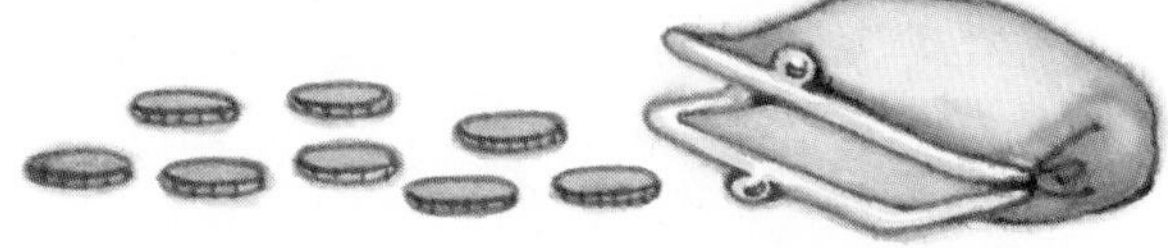

Joy had 8¢. She gave 3¢ to Jim. How much does she have left?

$8¢ + 3¢ = 11¢$

$8¢ - 3¢ = 5¢$

Notes for Home Children are assessed on Chapter 1 concepts, skills, and problem solving.

Exploring Math at Home

Dear Family,

In this chapter I have learned addition and subtraction facts through 10. Please help me practice these skills by helping me with the activities below.

Love, ______________________________

1.

Make a set of addition flash cards for facts through 10. Use them daily for a few minutes.

2.

Make a set of subtraction flash cards for facts through 10. Use them daily for a few minutes.

Coming Attractions

In the next chapter I will learn addition facts through 18.
I will also learn to solve problems using a graph.

Exploring Mathematics Book Two © Scott, Foresman and Company

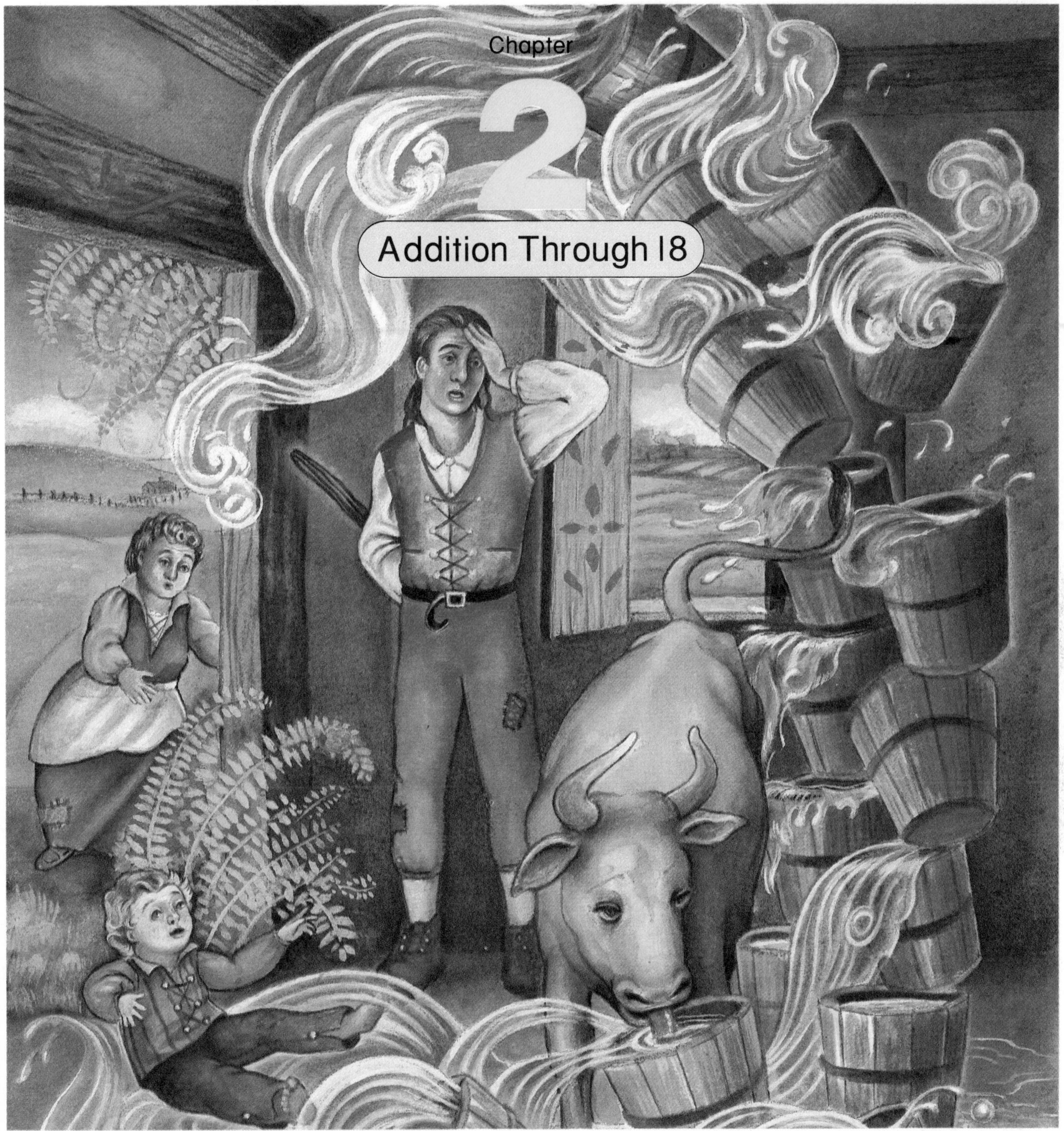

Listen to the math story, "Double Trouble."
Johan had 8 pails of water.
What did he do to get more pails of water?

Notes for Home Children listen to a math story introducing chapter concepts and skills. Then they answer a question about the story.

Name

Numbers Through 19

1. Write the number.

eleven 11

twelve ____

thirteen ____

fourteen ____

fifteen ____

sixteen ____

seventeen ____

eighteen ____

nineteen ____

2. Ring how many.

12

18

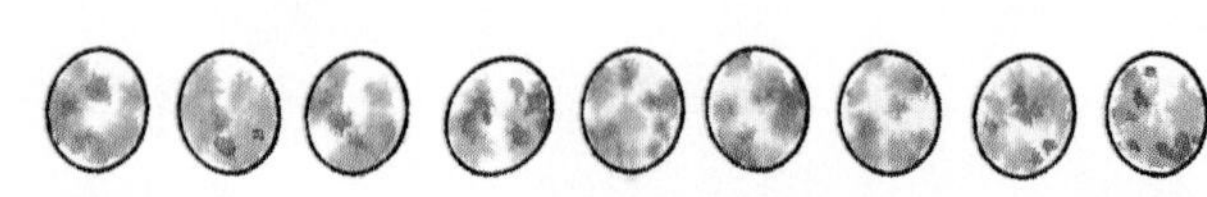

15

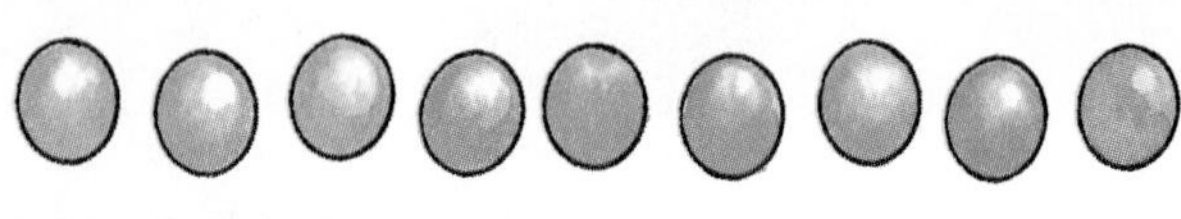

19

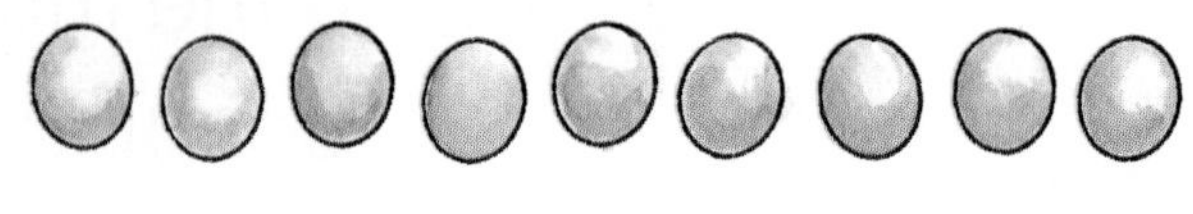

14

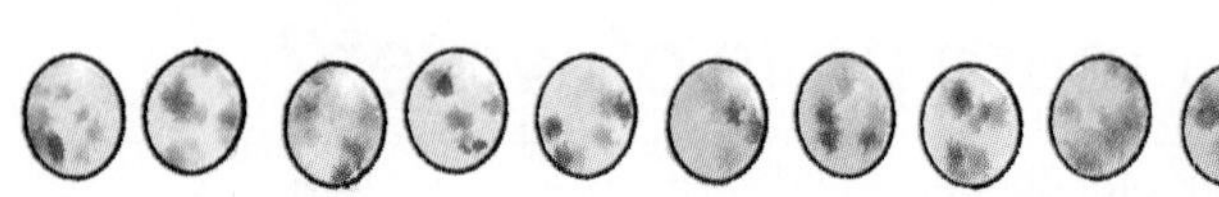

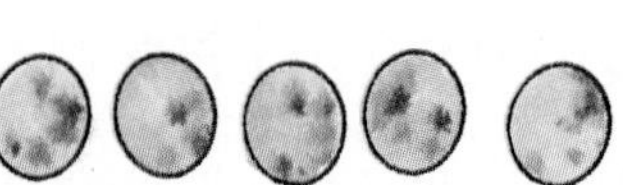

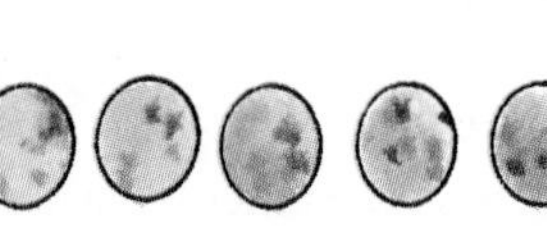

Notes for Home Children identify groups of objects and number words through 19.

Exploring Mathematics Book Two © Scott, Foresman and Company

Name

Adding 2 or 3

How many stamps are on each page?
How can you find how many stamps in all?

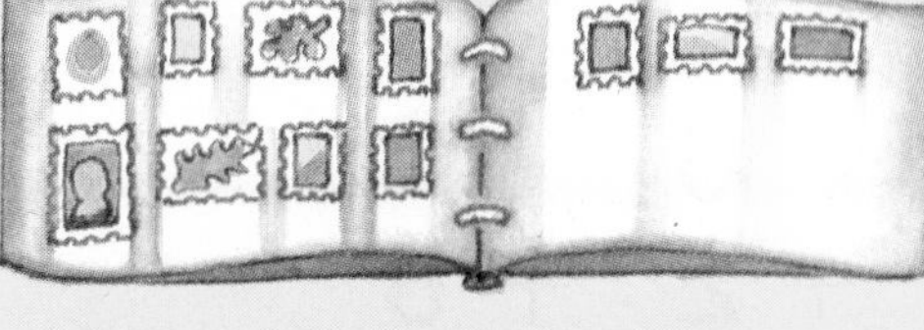

$8 + 3 =$ 11

$3 + 8 =$ 11

Think of the greater number.
Then add by counting on.

1.

$9 + 2 =$ ____

$2 + 9 =$ ____

2.

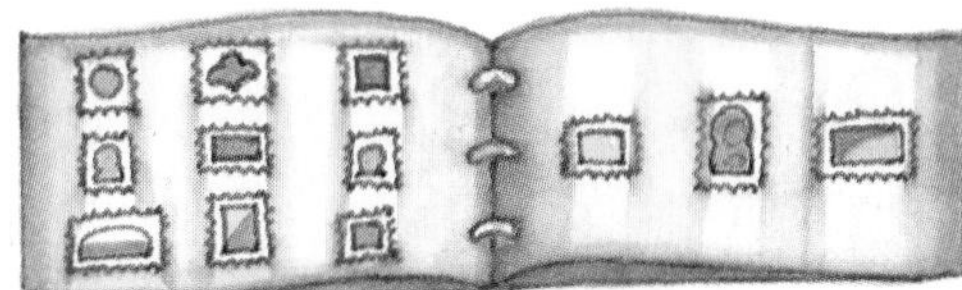

$9 + 3 =$ ____

$3 + 9 =$ ____

3.

$8 + 3 =$ ____

$3 + 8 =$ ____

4.

$8 + 2 =$ ____

$2 + 8 =$ ____

Notes for Home Children learn sums by counting on 2 or 3.

Think of the greater number.
Then add by counting on.

5. $\begin{array}{r} 2 \\ +9 \\ \hline \end{array}$ $\begin{array}{r} 9 \\ +2 \\ \hline \end{array}$ 6. $\begin{array}{r} 8 \\ +3 \\ \hline \end{array}$ $\begin{array}{r} 3 \\ +8 \\ \hline \end{array}$ 7. $\begin{array}{r} 9 \\ +3 \\ \hline \end{array}$ $\begin{array}{r} 3 \\ +9 \\ \hline \end{array}$

8. $\begin{array}{r} 8 \\ +2 \\ \hline \end{array}$ $\begin{array}{r} 2 \\ +8 \\ \hline \end{array}$ 9. $\begin{array}{r} 6 \\ +3 \\ \hline \end{array}$ $\begin{array}{r} 3 \\ +6 \\ \hline \end{array}$ 10. $\begin{array}{r} 3 \\ +5 \\ \hline \end{array}$ $\begin{array}{r} 5 \\ +3 \\ \hline \end{array}$

11. $\begin{array}{r} 3 \\ +2 \\ \hline \end{array}$ $\begin{array}{r} 2 \\ +7 \\ \hline \end{array}$ $\begin{array}{r} 2 \\ +5 \\ \hline \end{array}$ $\begin{array}{r} 7 \\ +2 \\ \hline \end{array}$ $\begin{array}{r} 2 \\ +6 \\ \hline \end{array}$ $\begin{array}{r} 7 \\ +3 \\ \hline \end{array}$ $\begin{array}{r} 4 \\ +2 \\ \hline \end{array}$

12. $\begin{array}{r} 2 \\ +4 \\ \hline \end{array}$ $\begin{array}{r} 4 \\ +3 \\ \hline \end{array}$ $\begin{array}{r} 3 \\ +7 \\ \hline \end{array}$ $\begin{array}{r} 6 \\ +2 \\ \hline \end{array}$ $\begin{array}{r} 2 \\ +3 \\ \hline \end{array}$

13. $\begin{array}{r} 3 \\ +4 \\ \hline \end{array}$ $\begin{array}{r} 5 \\ +2 \\ \hline \end{array}$ $\begin{array}{r} 9 \\ +2 \\ \hline \end{array}$ $\begin{array}{r} 3 \\ +8 \\ \hline \end{array}$ $\begin{array}{r} 3 \\ +5 \\ \hline \end{array}$

14. $\begin{array}{r} 2 \\ +8 \\ \hline \end{array}$ $\begin{array}{r} 7 \\ +3 \\ \hline \end{array}$ $\begin{array}{r} 3 \\ +9 \\ \hline \end{array}$ $\begin{array}{r} 5 \\ +3 \\ \hline \end{array}$ $\begin{array}{r} 2 \\ +7 \\ \hline \end{array}$

Exploring Mathematics Book Two © Scott, Foresman and Company

Notes for Home Children practice finding sums by identifying the greater number and counting on.

Name

Adding with Doubles

How many points did Anna score in each game?
How can she find her total points?

Anna	Points
Game 1	8
Game 2	8

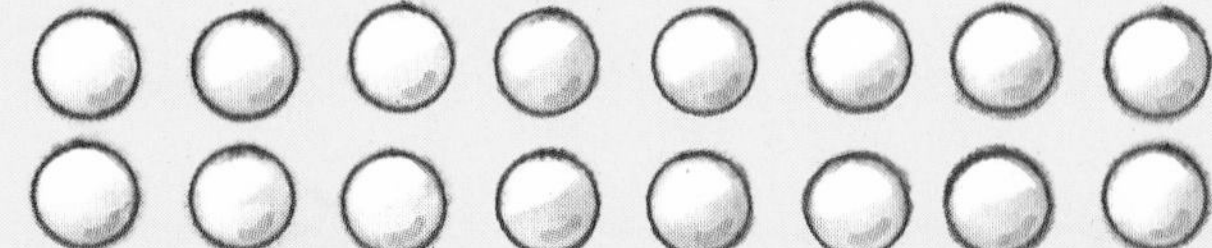

8 + 8 = 16

Add.

1.

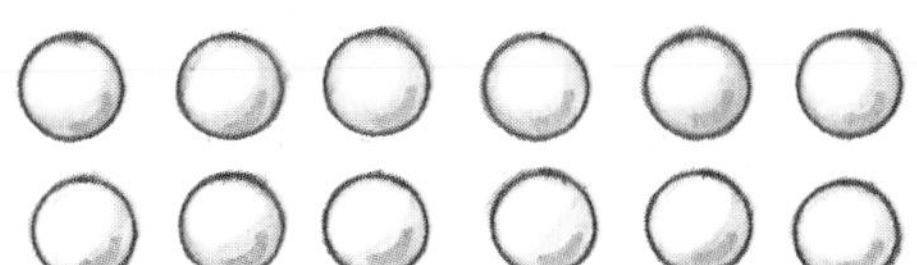

6 + 6 = ____

2.

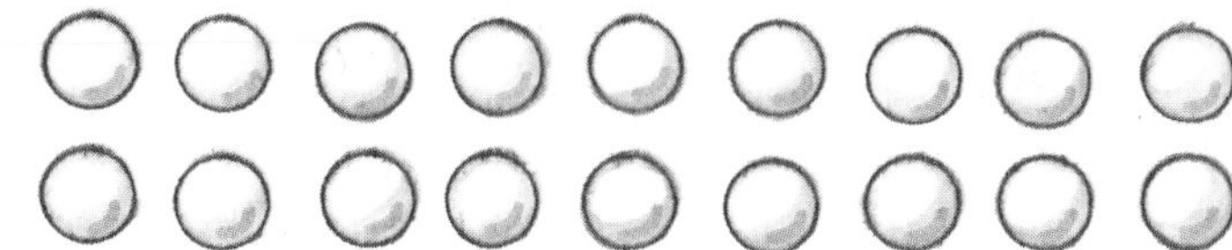

9 + 9 = ____

3.

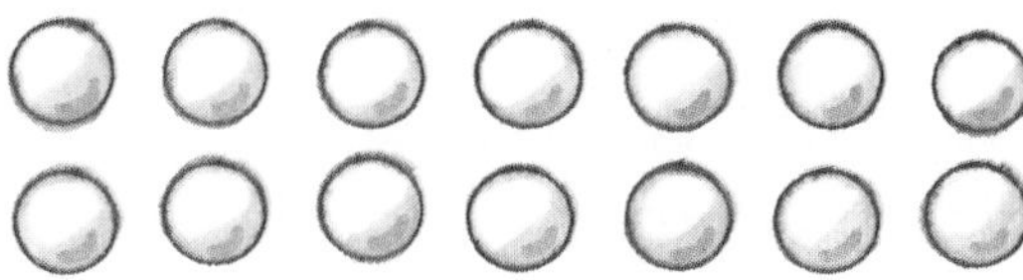

7 + 7 = ____

4.

5 + 5 = ____

Notes for Home Children learn to use doubles facts to find sums through 18.

Add.

5.

$\begin{array}{r} 6 \\ +\ 6 \\ \hline 12 \end{array}$	$\begin{array}{r} 8 \\ +\ 8 \\ \hline \end{array}$	$\begin{array}{r} 9 \\ +\ 9 \\ \hline \end{array}$	$\begin{array}{r} 7 \\ +\ 7 \\ \hline \end{array}$

6.

$\begin{array}{r} 2 \\ +\ 2 \\ \hline \end{array}$	$\begin{array}{r} 5 \\ +\ 5 \\ \hline \end{array}$	$\begin{array}{r} 3 \\ +\ 3 \\ \hline \end{array}$	$\begin{array}{r} 4 \\ +\ 4 \\ \hline \end{array}$

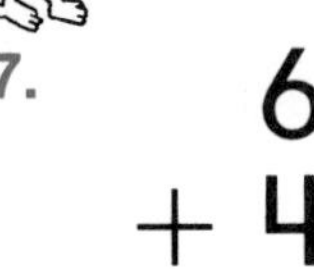

7.

$\begin{array}{r} 6 \\ +\ 4 \\ \hline \end{array}$	$\begin{array}{r} 9 \\ +\ 9 \\ \hline \end{array}$	$\begin{array}{r} 3 \\ +\ 8 \\ \hline \end{array}$	$\begin{array}{r} 2 \\ +\ 7 \\ \hline \end{array}$	$\begin{array}{r} 8 \\ +\ 8 \\ \hline \end{array}$	$\begin{array}{r} 2 \\ +\ 9 \\ \hline \end{array}$	$\begin{array}{r} 8 \\ +\ 2 \\ \hline \end{array}$

8.

$\begin{array}{r} 5 \\ +\ 2 \\ \hline \end{array}$	$\begin{array}{r} 4 \\ +\ 5 \\ \hline \end{array}$	$\begin{array}{r} 2 \\ +\ 8 \\ \hline \end{array}$	$\begin{array}{r} 9 \\ +\ 3 \\ \hline \end{array}$	$\begin{array}{r} 0 \\ +\ 0 \\ \hline \end{array}$	$\begin{array}{r} 1 \\ +\ 1 \\ \hline \end{array}$	$\begin{array}{r} 3 \\ +\ 3 \\ \hline \end{array}$

Problem Solving

Solve.

9. There are 6 boys and 6 girls on the team. How many children are on the team in all?

______ children

10. Steve scored 9 points. Gail scored 3 points. How many points did they score together?

______ points

Exploring Mathematics Book Two © Scott, Foresman and Company

Notes for Home Children practice finding sums through 18. Then they solve problems involving addition.

Name

Adding with Doubles and 1 More

Knowing $7 + 7$ helps me know $7 + 8 = 15$.
$7 + 8$ is 1 more than $7 + 7$.

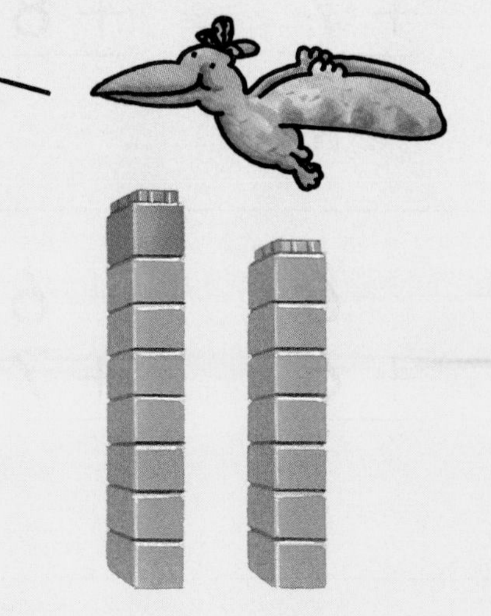

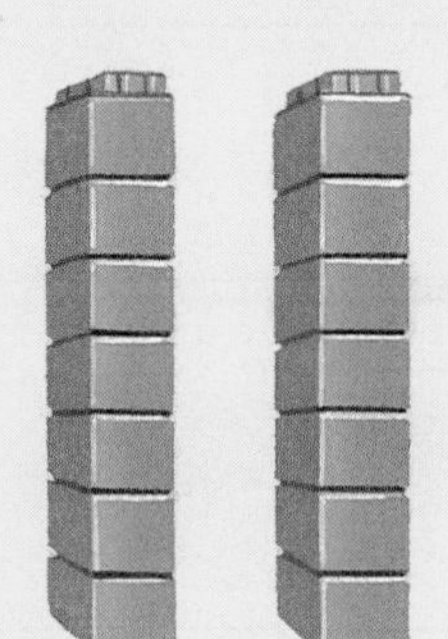

$7 + 7 =$ 14

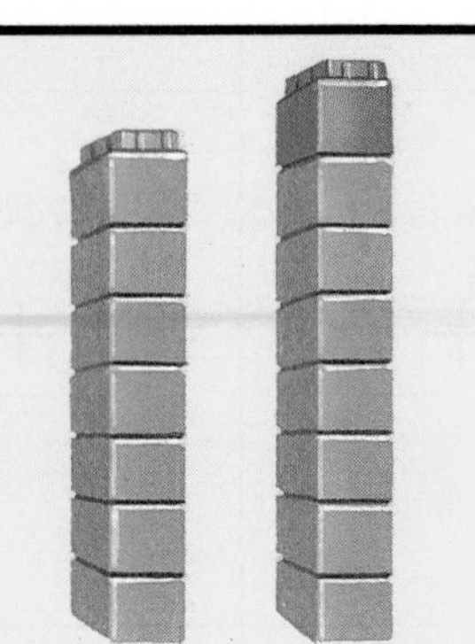

$7 + 8 =$ 15

$8 + 7 =$ 15

Write the sum.

1.

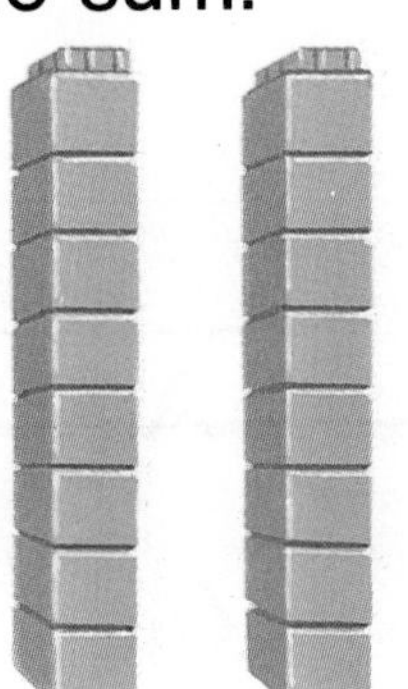

$8 + 8 =$ ____

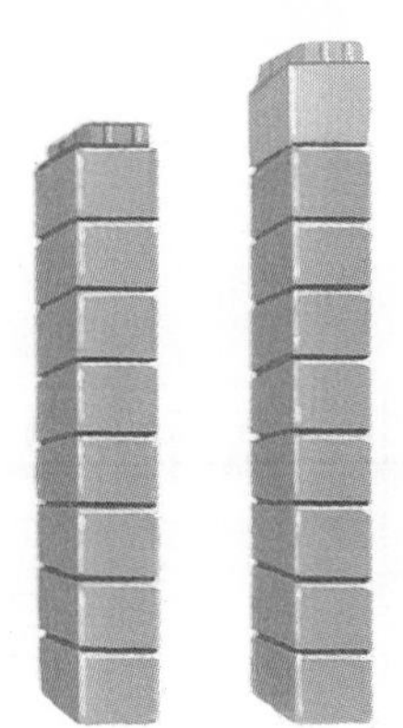

$8 + 9 =$ ____

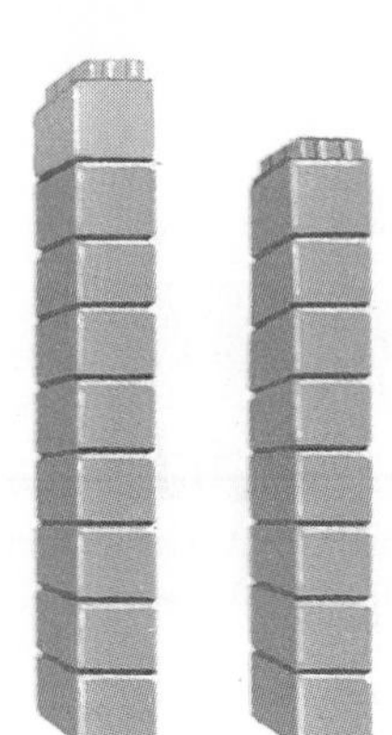

$9 + 8 =$ ____

2.

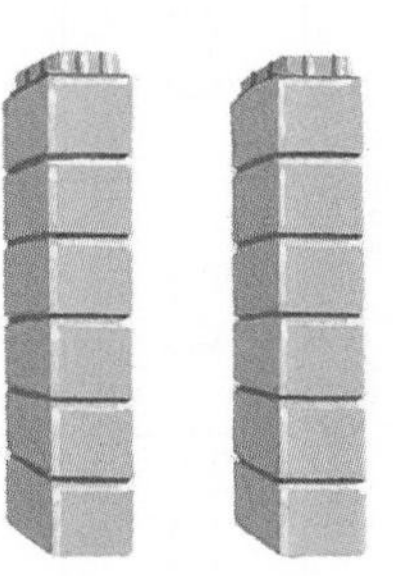

$6 + 6 =$ ____

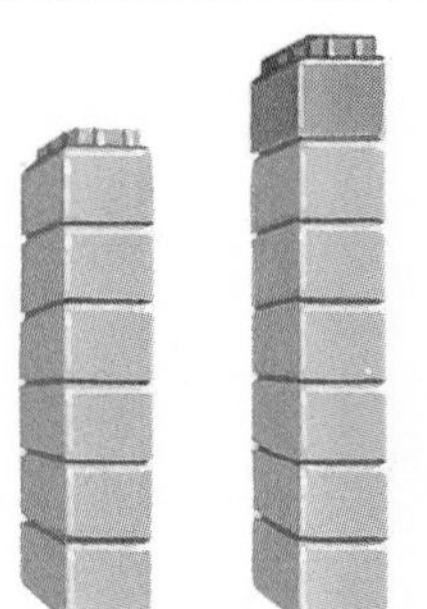

$6 + 7 =$ ____

$7 + 6 =$ ____

Notes for Home Children learn to use doubles and 1 more to find sums.

Write the sum.

3. $\begin{array}{r} 7 \\ +7 \\ \hline 14 \end{array}$ $\begin{array}{r} 7 \\ +8 \\ \hline \end{array}$ $\begin{array}{r} 8 \\ +7 \\ \hline \end{array}$

4. $\begin{array}{r} 8 \\ +8 \\ \hline \end{array}$ $\begin{array}{r} 8 \\ +9 \\ \hline \end{array}$ $\begin{array}{r} 9 \\ +8 \\ \hline \end{array}$

5. $\begin{array}{r} 6 \\ +6 \\ \hline \end{array}$ $\begin{array}{r} 6 \\ +7 \\ \hline \end{array}$ $\begin{array}{r} 7 \\ +6 \\ \hline \end{array}$

6. $\begin{array}{r} 5 \\ +5 \\ \hline \end{array}$ $\begin{array}{r} 5 \\ +6 \\ \hline \end{array}$ $\begin{array}{r} 6 \\ +5 \\ \hline \end{array}$

7. $\begin{array}{r} 3 \\ +3 \\ \hline \end{array}$ $\begin{array}{r} 3 \\ +4 \\ \hline \end{array}$ $\begin{array}{r} 4 \\ +3 \\ \hline \end{array}$

8. $\begin{array}{r} 4 \\ +4 \\ \hline \end{array}$ $\begin{array}{r} 4 \\ +5 \\ \hline \end{array}$ $\begin{array}{r} 5 \\ +4 \\ \hline \end{array}$

9.

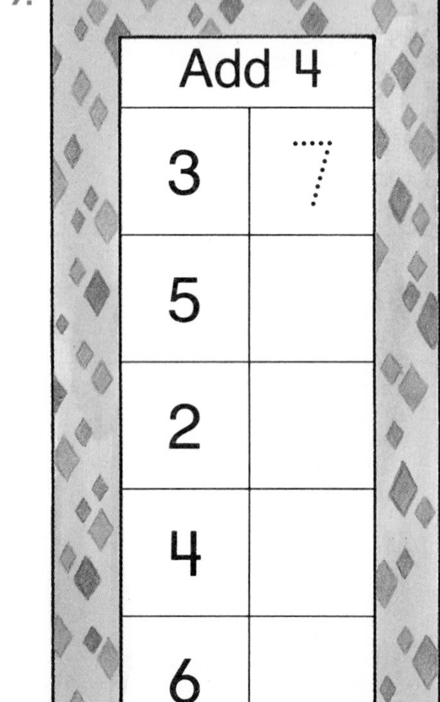

Add 4	
3	7
5	
2	
4	
6	

10.

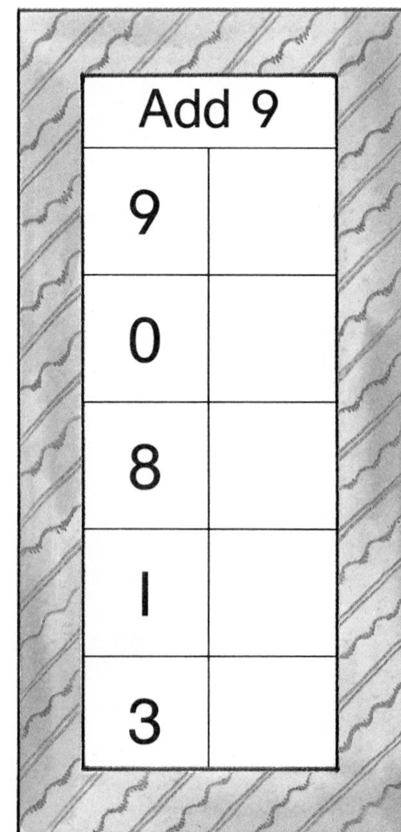

Add 9	
9	
0	
8	
1	
3	

11.

Add 5	
6	
3	
5	
2	
4	

Exploring Mathematics Book Two © Scott, Foresman and Company

Notes for Home Children practice finding sums through 18.

Name

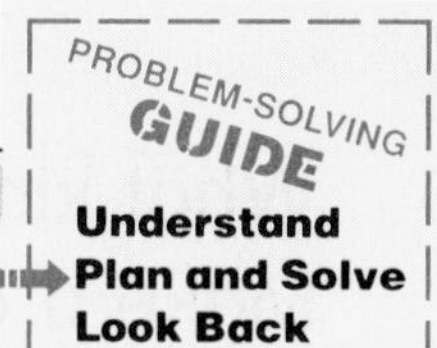

Make a Graph

How many of each kind are there?

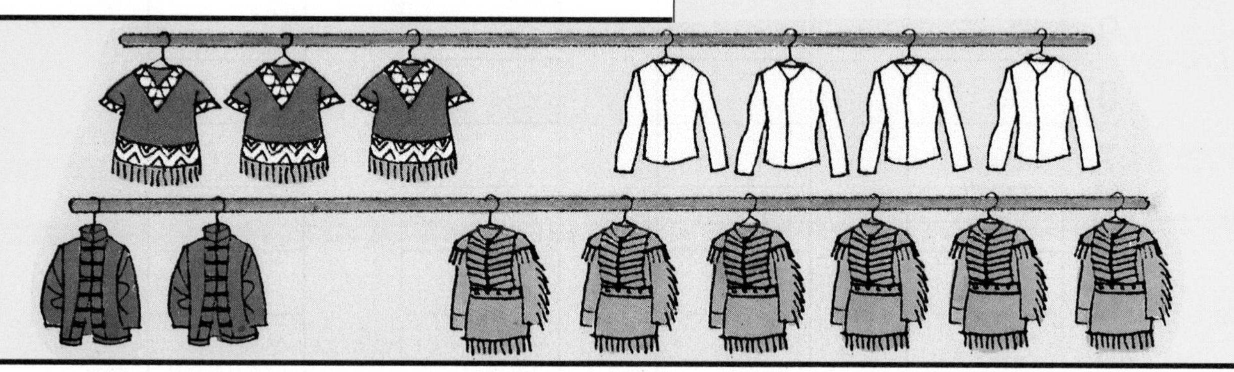

1. Make a graph. Color one ▭ for each.

Clothing Supply

7
6
5
4
3
2
1

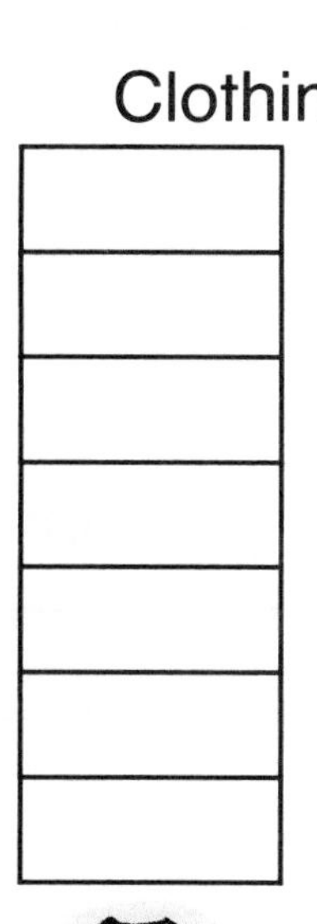
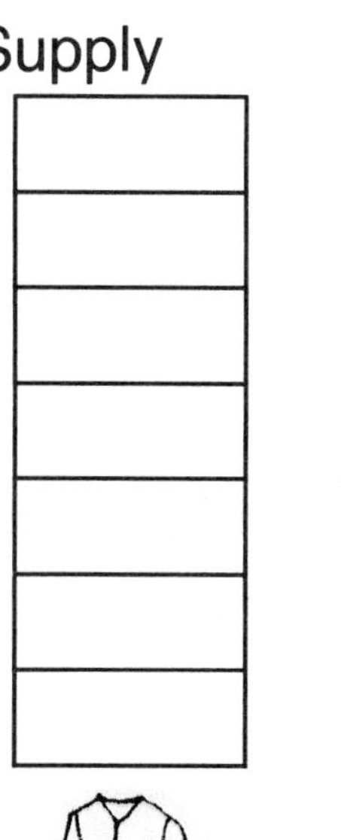
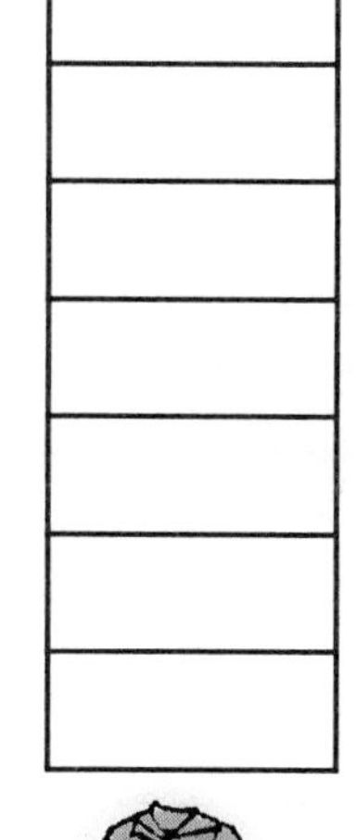

Solve.

2. How many and are there? ____

3. How many more than are there? ____

4. How many more than are there? ____

Notes for Home Children solve problems by making a bar graph.

5. What kind of hat is the favorite in your class?
Make a graph.

9
8
7
6
5
4
3
2
1

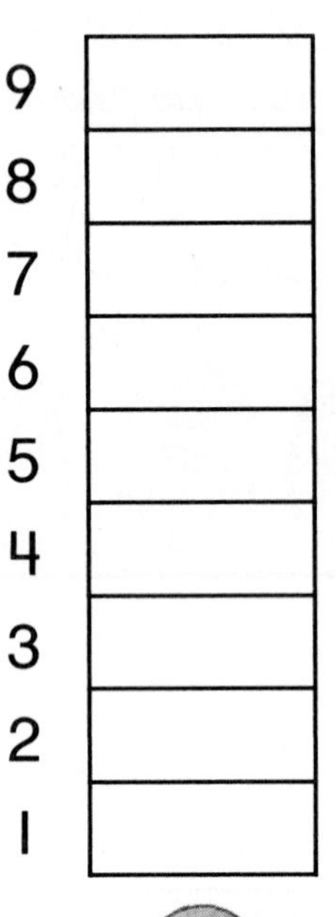
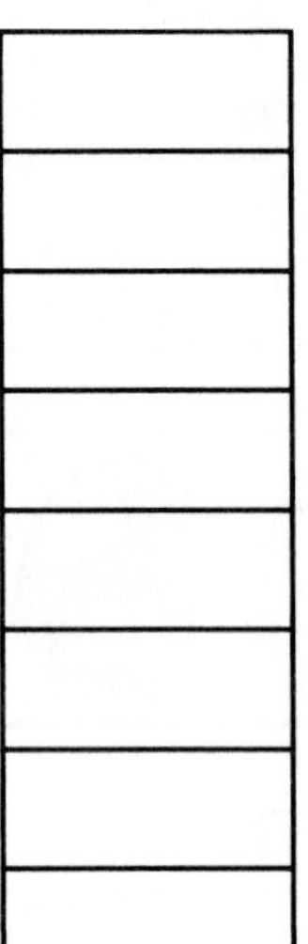
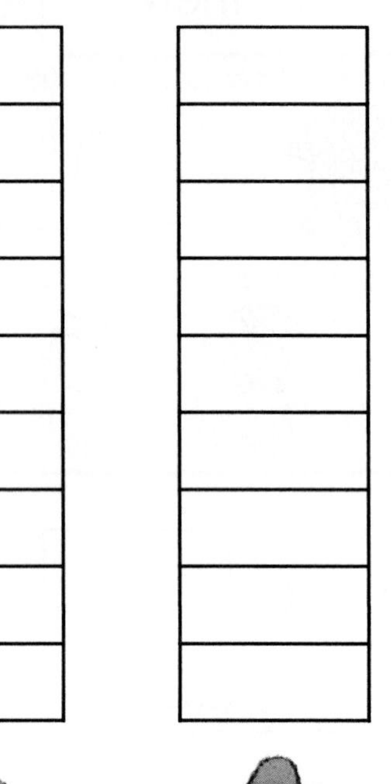
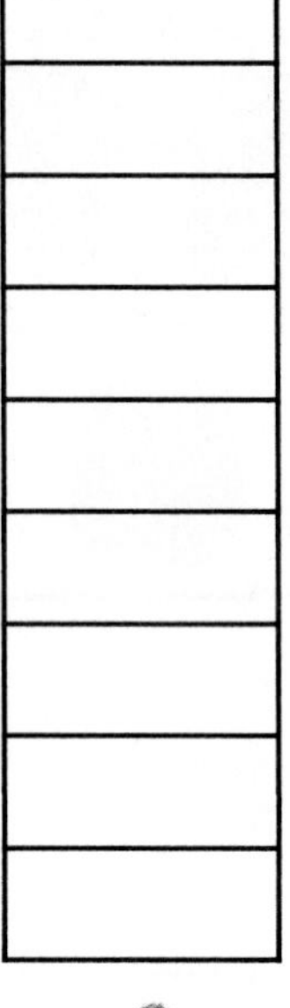

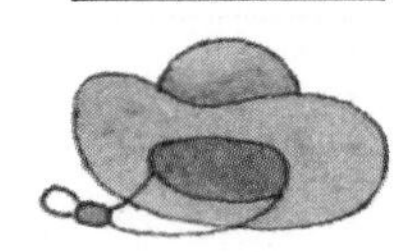

6. Write a sentence that tells something about your graph.

7. Write a sentence about your favorite hat.

Exploring Mathematics Book Two © Scott, Foresman and Company

Notes for Home Children solve a problem by taking a survey and then making a bar graph.

Name

Number Sense

Find all the doubles in the picture.

Let's do some more!

Look for doubles in your classroom.
Draw some.

Notes for Home Children develop number understanding by finding doubles.

Skills Review

Fill in the correct ◯.
Add or subtract.

1. $\begin{array}{r} 9 \\ +\ 1 \\ \hline \end{array}$ Ⓐ 6 Ⓑ 8 Ⓒ 10

2. $10 - 7 =$ Ⓐ 3 Ⓑ 4 Ⓒ 5

3. $\begin{array}{r} 7 \\ +\ 3 \\ \hline \end{array}$ Ⓐ 10 Ⓑ 9 Ⓒ 8

4. $9 - 5 =$ Ⓐ 3 Ⓑ 4 Ⓒ 5

5. $\begin{array}{r} 6 \\ +\ 4 \\ \hline \end{array}$ Ⓐ 8 Ⓑ 9 Ⓒ 10

6. $10 - 6 =$ Ⓐ 2 Ⓑ 3 Ⓒ 4

Vocabulary

Draw a ▭ around the plus signs.

Draw a □ around the sums.

Draw a △ around the minus signs.

Draw a ◯ around the differences.

7. $\begin{array}{r} 4 \\ +\ 3 \\ \hline 7 \end{array}$

8. $\begin{array}{r} 10 \\ -\ 2 \\ \hline 8 \end{array}$

9. $\begin{array}{r} 9 \\ -\ 6 \\ \hline 3 \end{array}$

10. $\begin{array}{r} 7 \\ +\ 3 \\ \hline 10 \end{array}$

Exploring Mathematics Book Two © Scott, Foresman and Company

Notes for Home Children review addition and subtraction facts through 10. Then they review addition and subtraction terms.

Name

Adding Three Numbers

I add the two greater numbers first.
Then I add the last number.

$$\begin{array}{r} 4 \\ 3 \\ +\ 2 \\ \hline 9 \end{array}$$

4 + 3 = 7

7 + 2 = 9

Add.

1.
$$\begin{array}{r} 4 \\ 5 \\ +\ 3 \\ \hline \end{array}$$

2.
$$\begin{array}{r} 2 \\ 5 \\ +\ 3 \\ \hline \end{array}$$

3.
$$\begin{array}{r} 6 \\ 2 \\ +\ 3 \\ \hline \end{array}$$

4.
$$\begin{array}{r} 5 \\ 2 \\ +\ 1 \\ \hline \end{array}$$

Notes for Home Children learn to add three numbers by first adding the two greater numbers and then adding the third.

Add.

5.

4	2	8	3
4	4	0	2
+ 1	+ 3	+ 3	+ 3
9			

6.

4	0	3	6
3	0	4	0
+ 6	+ 0	+ 5	+ 5

7.

4	2	2	4	3	2	2
4	4	6	5	4	5	1
+ 3	+ 2	+ 2	+ 1	+ 3	+ 2	+ 4

8.

2	3	7	2	4	0	3
3	6	6	7	2	9	1
+ 3	+ 1	+ 0	+ 2	+ 1	+ 2	+ 5

Talk About Math

How are these the same?
How are they different?

2	3
5	2
+ 3	+ 5
10	10

Exploring Mathematics Book Two © Scott, Foresman and Company

Notes for Home Children practice finding sums with three numbers. Then they talk about how the order of the addends does not affect the sum.

See More Practice Set A on page 69.

Name

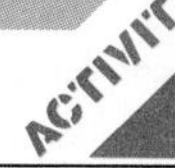

Using 10 When Adding 7 or 8

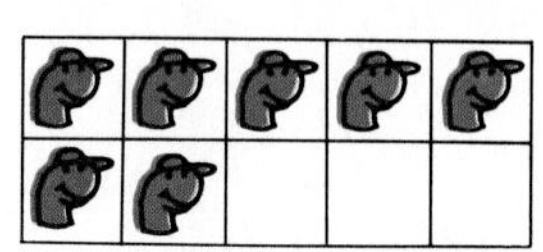

1. To add 7 + 5, you can first show 7.

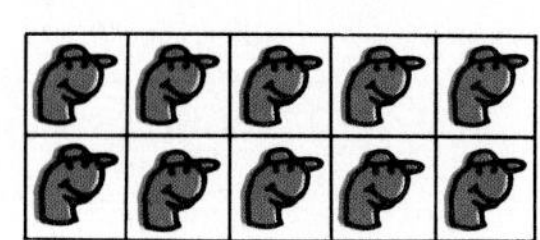

2. Then add to make 10.

3. Then add to find the sum.

7 + 5 = 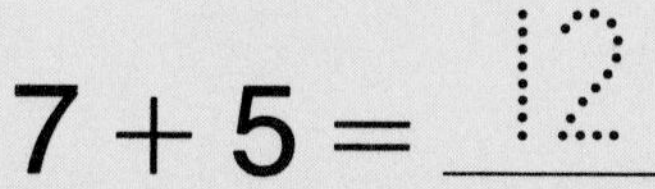

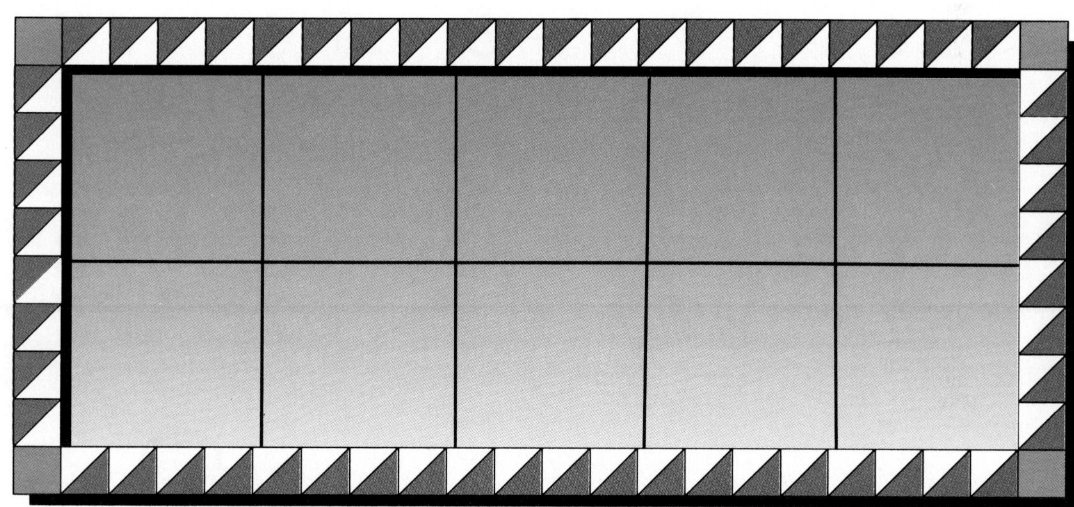

Use counters.
First add to 10.
Then find how many in all.

1. 8 + 4 = ____

   4 + 8 = ____

2. 8 + 5 = ____

   5 + 8 = ____

3. 8 + 6 = ____

   6 + 8 = ____

Notes for Home Children explore at the CONCRETE level using counters to find sums when one of the addends is 7 or 8. They add to 10, then count on to find the sum.

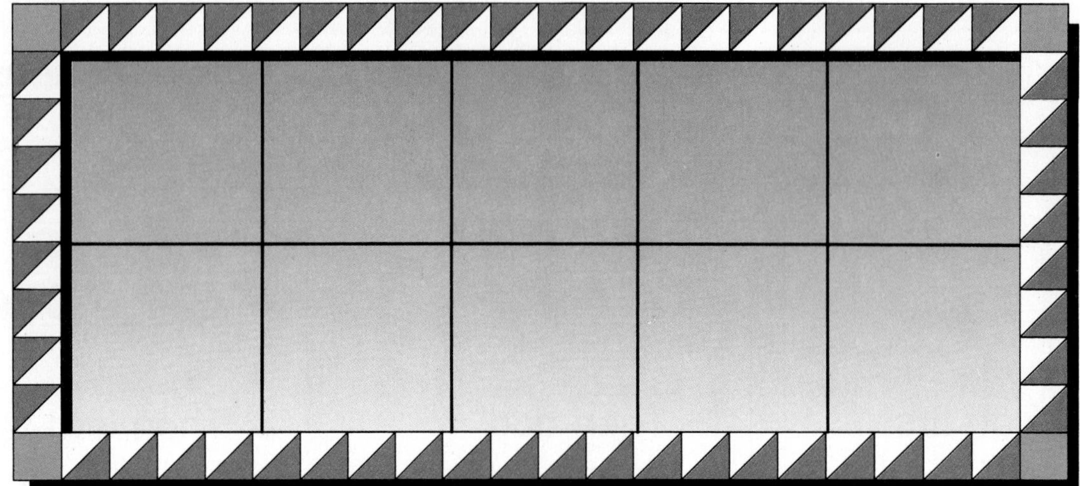

Use counters.
First add to 10.
Then find how many in all.

4.						
4	7	9	7	7	7	8
+ 7	+ 6	+ 7	+ 5	+ 8	+ 4	+ 4
11						

5.						
8	6	7	4	5	8	5
+ 7	+ 7	+ 9	+ 7	+ 7	+ 7	+ 8

6.			
9	7	8	6
+ 8	+ 4	+ 6	+ 7

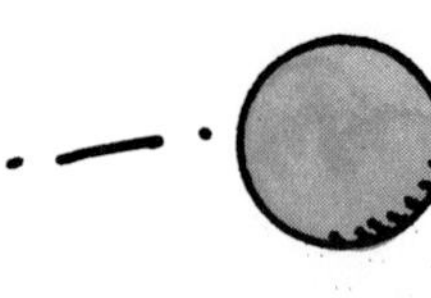

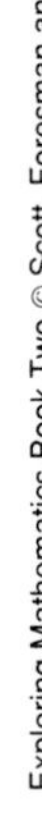
Exploring Mathematics Book Two © Scott, Foresman and Company

Notes for Home Children explore at the CONCRETE level using counters to find sums.

Name

Using 10 When Adding 9

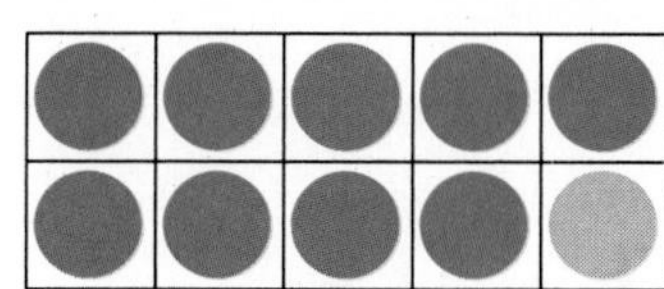

1. To add 9 + 4, you can first add 9 + 1 to make 10.

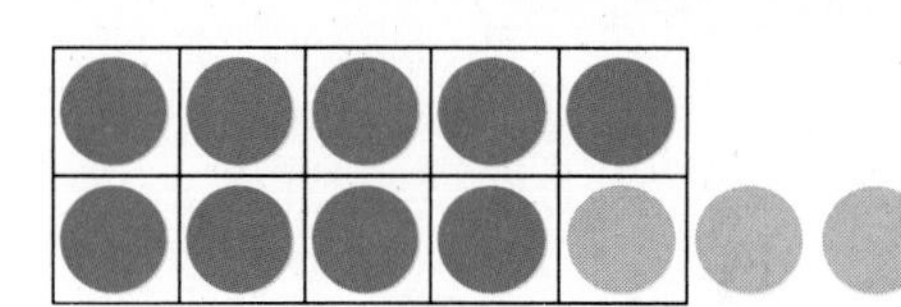

2. Then add 3 more to find the sum.

9 + 4 = 13

Add.

1.

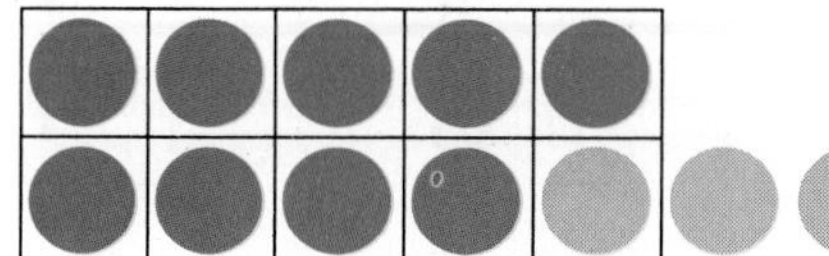

9 + 3 = ____

2.

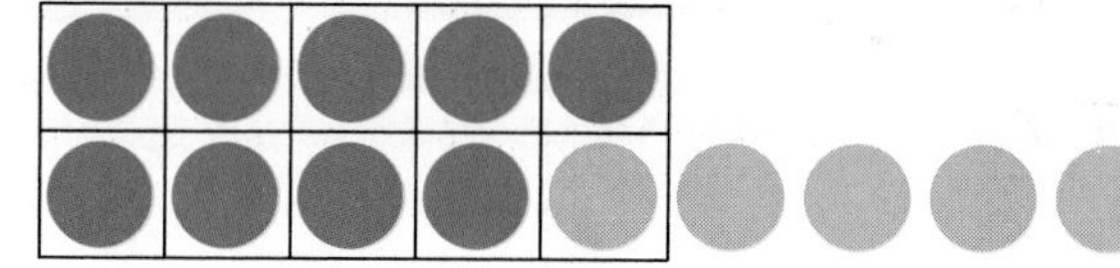

9 + 5 = ____

3.

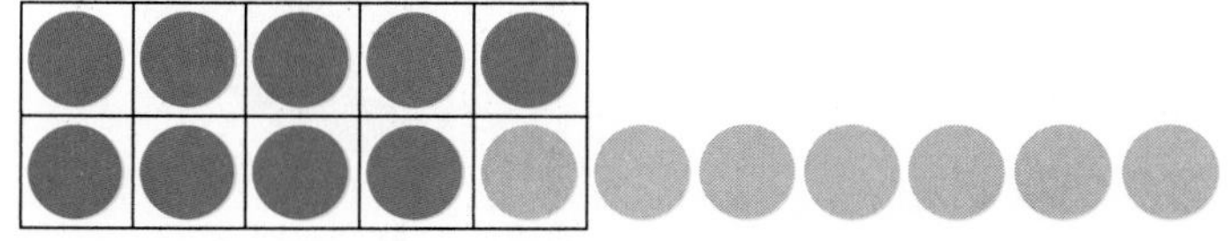

9 + 7 = ____

4.

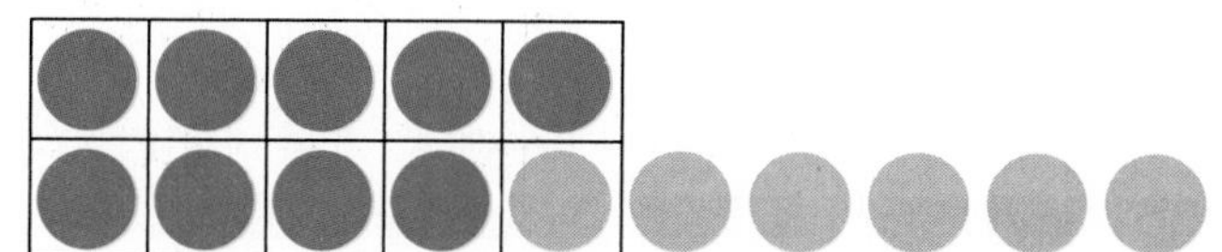

9 + 6 = ____

Notes for Home Children use a fact of 10 to find sums when one of the addends is 9.

Add.

5.

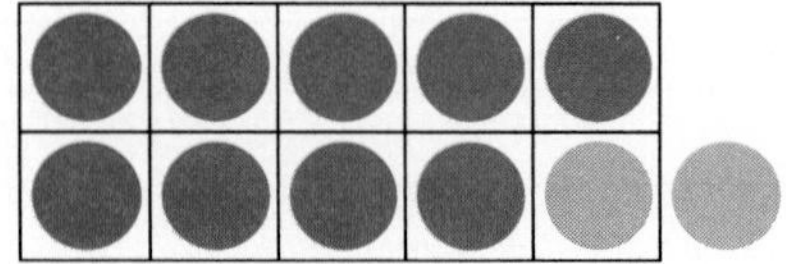

$9 + 2 =$ 11

6.

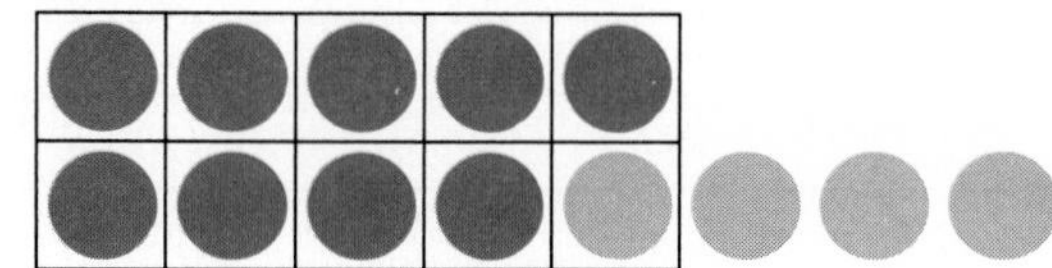

$9 + 4 =$ ____

7.	$9 + 3$	$8 + 9$	$9 + 6$	$4 + 9$	$9 + 2$	$3 + 9$	$9 + 7$
8.	$9 + 7$	$5 + 9$	$9 + 4$	$7 + 9$	$8 + 9$	$9 + 5$	$9 + 3$
9.	$6 + 7$	$8 + 3$	$6 + 9$	$9 + 8$	$7 + 5$	$4 + 8$	$9 + 9$
10.	$7 + 8$	$5 + 9$	$4 + 7$	$8 + 7$	$5 + 8$		

Critical Thinking How is your answer different when you add 9 to a number from when you add 10 to the same number?

Notes for Home Children use a fact of 10 to find sums when one addend is 9. They practice finding sums through 18. Then they discuss how adding 9 to a number is different from adding 10 to the same number.

Exploring Mathematics Book Two © Scott, Foresman and Company

Name

Addition Through 18

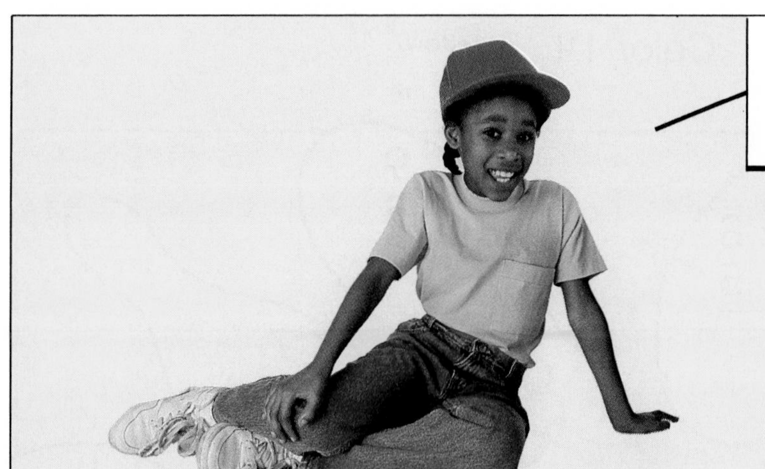

I know different names for 11. These are some of them.

$7 + 4 = 11$

$9 + 2 = 11$

$5 + 6 = 11$

Ring the facts for each number.

1.

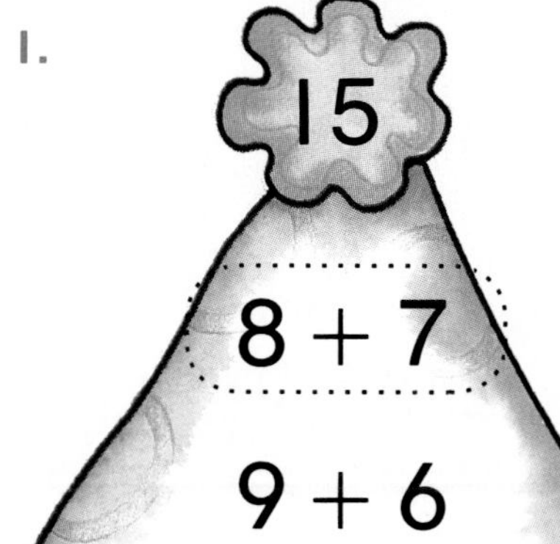

2.

3.

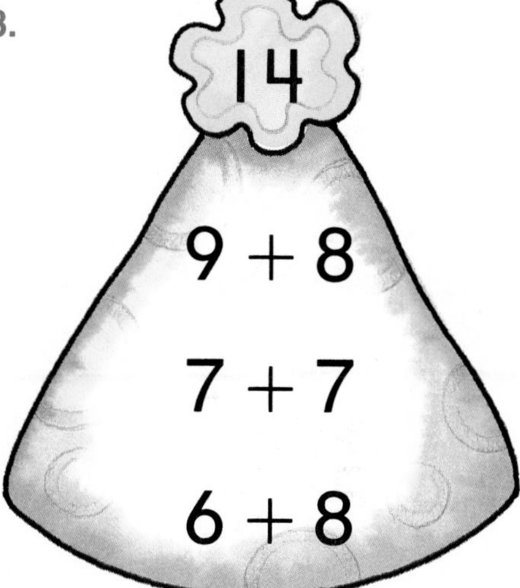

4.

5.

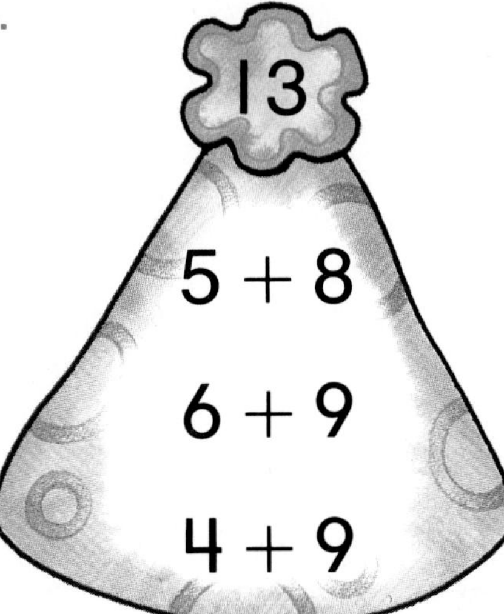

6.

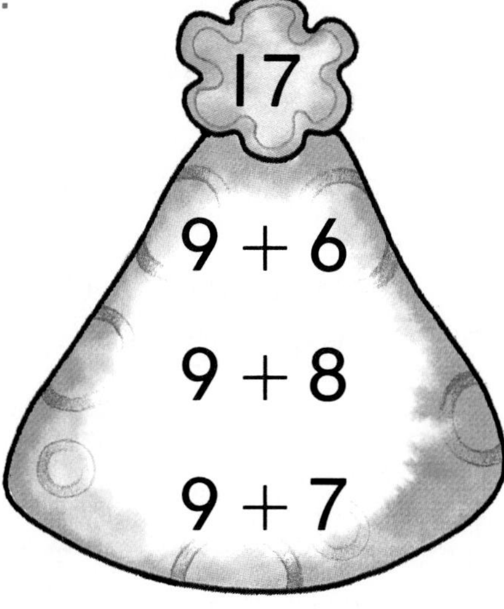

Notes for Home Children practice addition through 18 by identifying facts for a given number.

7. Find the sums.

Color 11 red.
Color 12 green.
Color 13 blue.
Color 14 yellow.

$\begin{array}{r} 5 \\ +\ 9 \\ \hline \end{array}$ $\begin{array}{r} 8 \\ +\ 5 \\ \hline \end{array}$ $\begin{array}{r} 9 \\ +\ 5 \\ \hline \end{array}$

$\begin{array}{r} 7 \\ +\ 5 \\ \hline \end{array}$ $\begin{array}{r} 7 \\ +\ 4 \\ \hline \end{array}$

$\begin{array}{r} 8 \\ +\ 3 \\ \hline \end{array}$ $\begin{array}{r} 6 \\ +\ 5 \\ \hline \end{array}$ $\begin{array}{r} 4 \\ +\ 8 \\ \hline \end{array}$

$\begin{array}{r} 9 \\ +\ 4 \\ \hline \end{array}$ $\begin{array}{r} 6 \\ +\ 8 \\ \hline \end{array}$

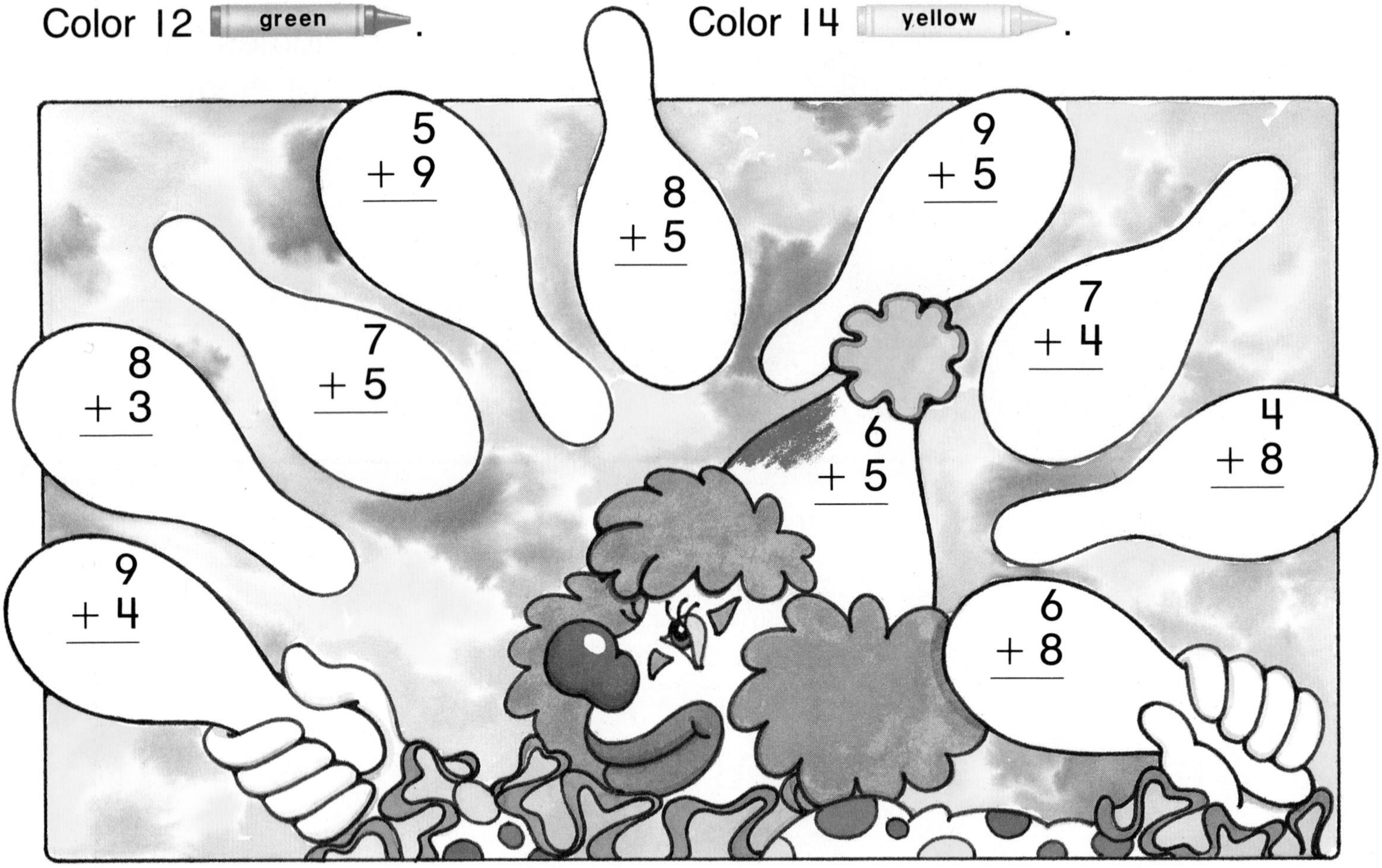

Problem Solving

Solve.

8. The clown has 7 .

He drops 2 .

How many does he have left?

_____ pins

9. The clown has 6 red  .

He has 7 blue .

How many does he have in all?

_____ hats

Exploring Mathematics Book Two © Scott, Foresman and Company

Notes for Home Children practice finding sums through 18. Then they solve problems involving addition and subtraction.

See More Practice Set B on page 69.

Name

PROBLEM-SOLVING GUIDE
Understand
Plan and Solve
Look Back

Use Data from a Graph

The Bike Club went riding for a week.
This graph shows the hours they rode each day.

Biking Hours

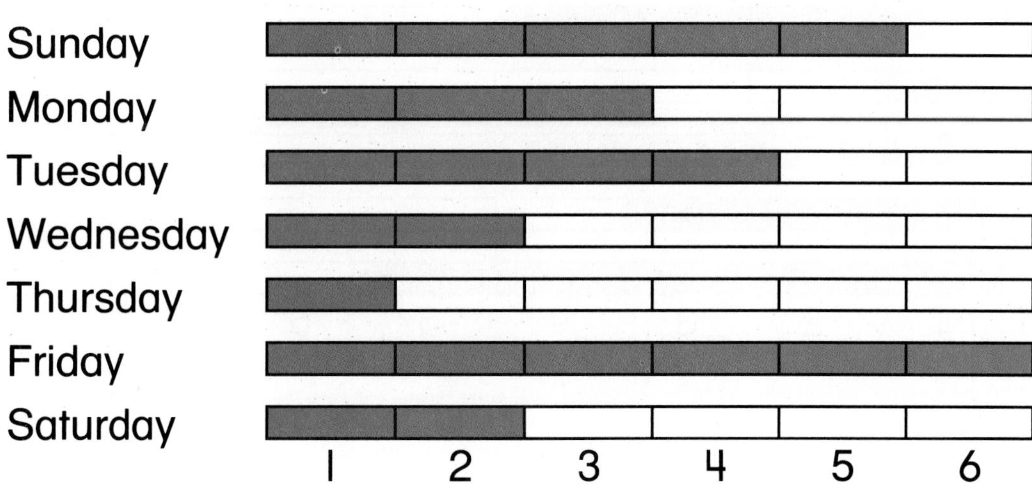

Solve.

1. On which day did they ride the most hours?

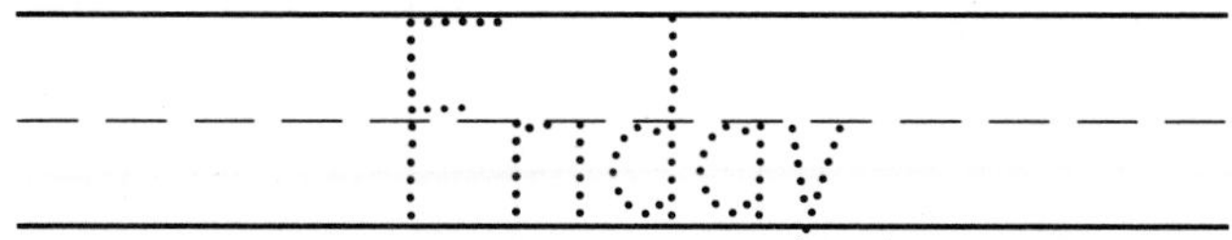

2. On which day did they ride the fewest hours?

3. On which day did they ride for 4 hours?

4. On which two days did they ride for 2 hours?

Notes for Home Children solve problems by using data from a bar graph.

The Rocky Mountain Hiking Club hiked for a week.
This graph shows the hours they hiked each day.

Hiking Hours

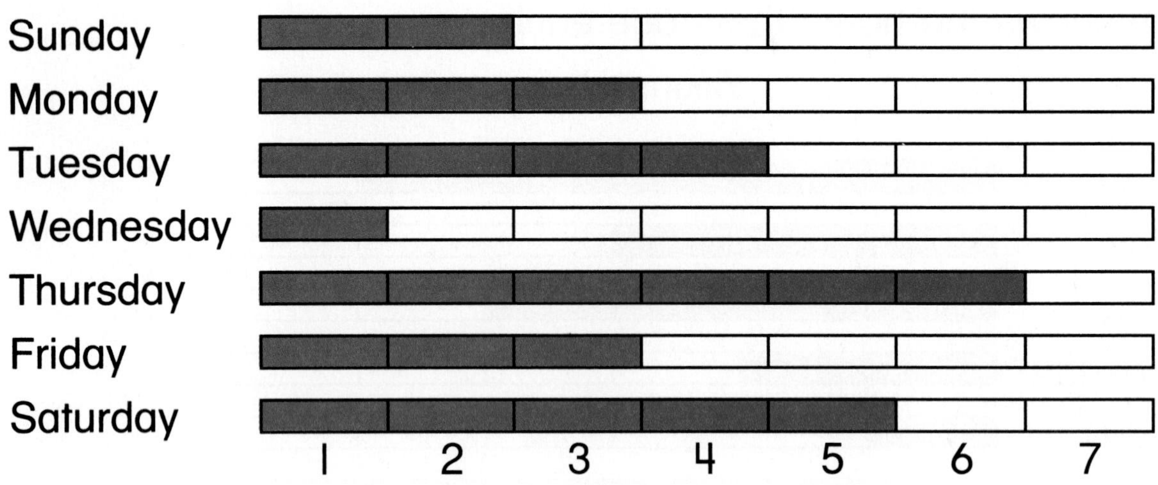

Solve.

5. On which day did they hike the most hours?

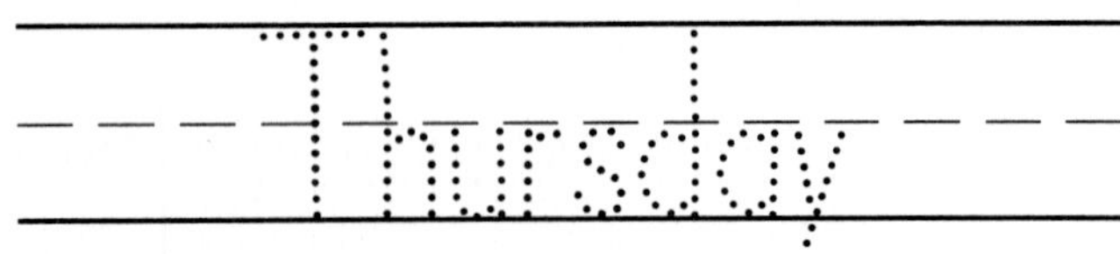

6. On which day did they hike the fewest hours?

7. On which day did they hike for 5 hours?

8. On which two days did they hike for 3 hours?

Notes for Home Children solve problems by using data from a bar graph.

Exploring Mathematics Book Two © Scott, Foresman and Company

Name

Problem-Solving Workshop

Explore as a Team

1. Work with a partner.
2. Use numbers 1 through 9.
3. Make each row add up to 15.
4. Make each column add up to 15.
5. You may use each number only once.

2		
	5	
	3	

Let's do some more!

Do the activity again.
Put each number but the 5 in a different place.

Notes for Home Children explore with a partner to solve a problem.

Problem-Solving Workshop

Explore with a Calculator

Use a [calculator] to solve.

Find different ways to write each sum.
Write 1, 2, 3, 4, or 5 to complete each number sentence.

1.	1	0	+	1	+	4	=	15
2.	1	0	+		+		=	15
3.	1	0	+		+		=	15
4.	1	0	+		+		=	15
5.	1	0	+	4	+	3	=	17
6.	1	0	+		+		=	17
7.	1	0	+		+		=	17
8.	1	0	+		+		=	17

Exploring Mathematics Book Two © Scott, Foresman and Company

Notes for Home Children explore with a calculator. They write missing numbers to complete number sentences.

Name

More Practice

Set A Use after page 58.

Add.

1.	4	6	6	5	6	9	3
	5	0	5	2	2	0	3
	+ 3	+ 7	+ 1	+ 1	+ 3	+ 3	+ 4
	12						
2.	3	0	5	2	4	3	2
	2	1	2	4	2	6	5
	+ 5	+ 0	+ 6	+ 2	+ 6	+ 0	+ 4

Set B Use after page 64.

Add and connect the dots. Find the path.

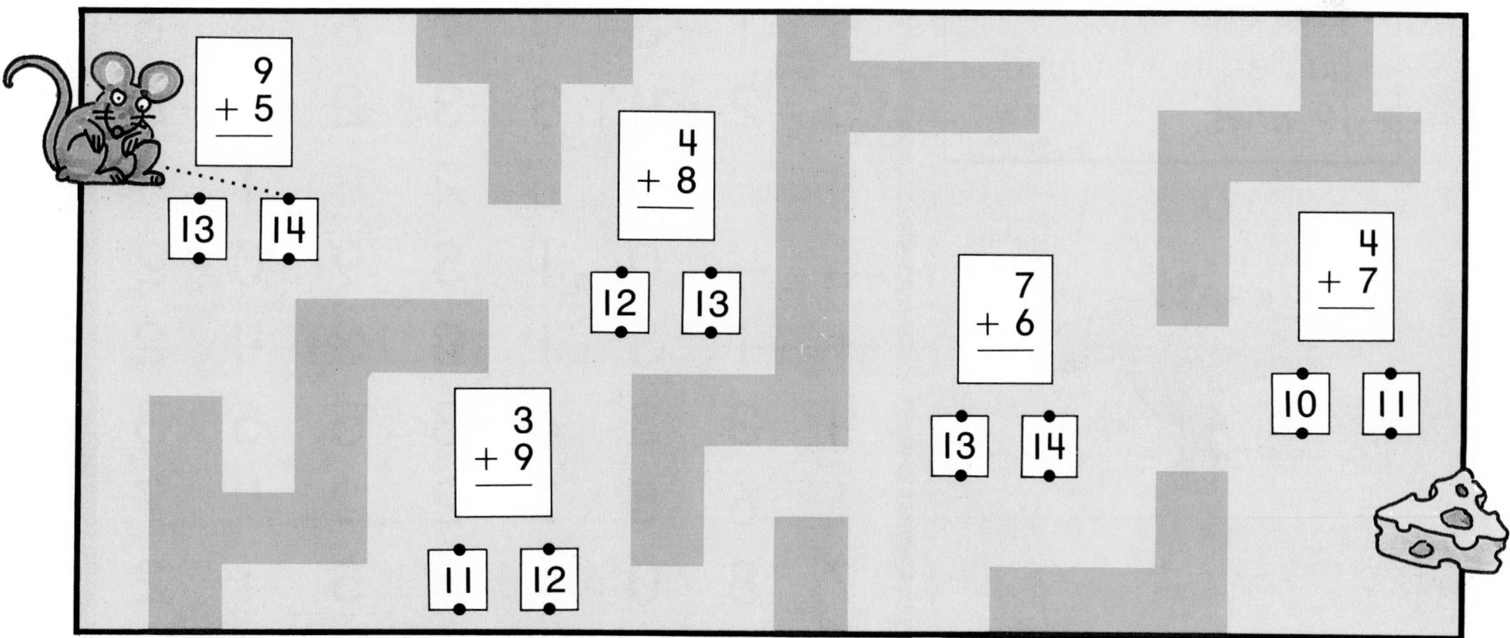

Notes for Home Set A: Children practice finding sums through 18 with three addends.
Set B: Children travel through a maze by finding sums through 18.

Enrichment

1. Ring four numbers that add up to 10.
The numbers must be next to each other.
You may go across or down.

8	2	3	5	1	1	4	6
0	9	4	3	2	0	1	7
2	4	3	2	3	3	3	1
0	1	1	5	4	1	3	3
6	3	2	5	3	4	4	1
3	4	2	2	1	0	2	2
2	6	1	1	1	5	0	4

I found 10 ways to do it.

2. Ring four numbers that add up to 16.
The numbers must be next to each other.
You may go across or down.

This one was harder, but I found 12 ways.

5	1	3	0	7	6	4	6
5	2	4	8	3	2	3	0
4	8	5	6	2	8	1	4
6	4	0	1	5	9	0	2
1	1	3	1	8	3	4	2
4	3	3	6	3	5	5	3
1	6	5	7	2	2	4	7
7	8	0	1	8	5	1	2

Exploring Mathematics Book Two © Scott, Foresman and Company

Notes for Home Children are challenged to find four adjacent numbers that equal 10 and then four adjacent numbers that equal 16.

Name ____________________

Chapter 2 Review/Test

Add.

1.

$$\begin{array}{r} 9 \\ +\ 2 \\ \hline \end{array} \quad \begin{array}{r} 7 \\ +\ 7 \\ \hline \end{array} \quad \begin{array}{r} 7 \\ +\ 6 \\ \hline \end{array} \quad \begin{array}{r} 5 \\ +\ 6 \\ \hline \end{array} \quad \begin{array}{r} 4 \\ +\ 9 \\ \hline \end{array} \quad \begin{array}{r} 9 \\ +\ 6 \\ \hline \end{array}$$

2.

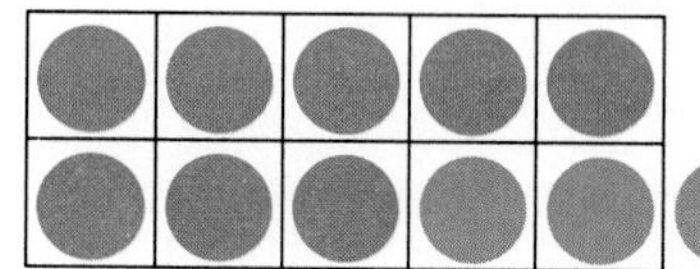

$$\begin{array}{r} 8 \\ +\ 5 \\ \hline \end{array}$$

3.

$$\begin{array}{r} 3 \\ 1 \\ +\ 5 \\ \hline \end{array} \quad \begin{array}{r} 2 \\ 0 \\ +\ 7 \\ \hline \end{array} \quad \begin{array}{r} 4 \\ 5 \\ +\ 3 \\ \hline \end{array}$$

4. How many of each fish?
Make a bar graph.

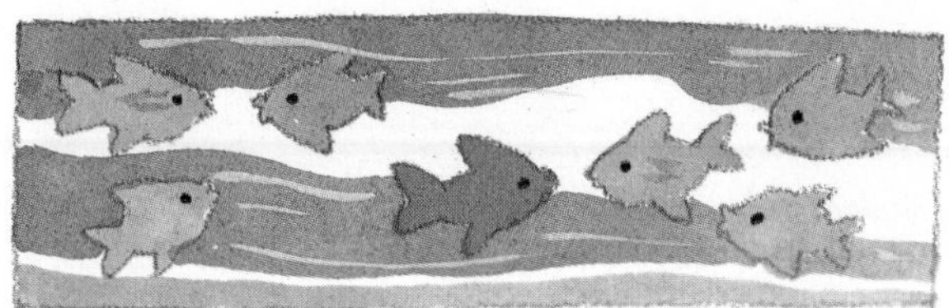

Fish

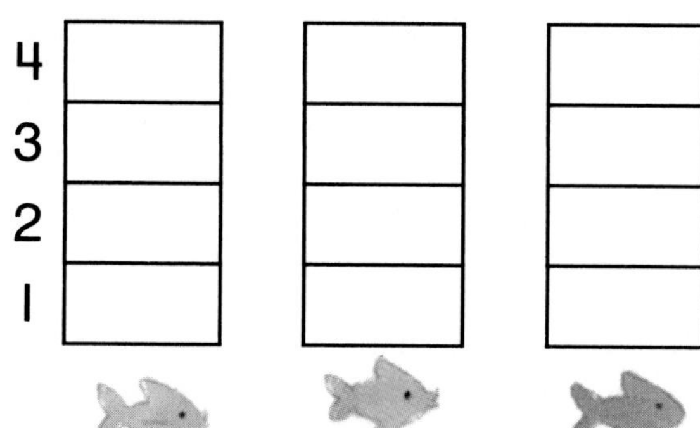

5. How many more  than  ? ____

Read the bar graph.

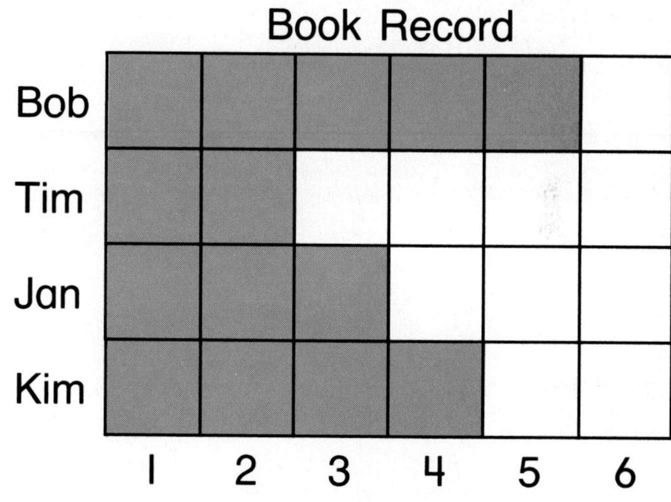

6. Who read 5 books? ____________

7. How many books did Jan read?

____ books

Notes for Home Children are assessed on Chapter 2 concepts, skills, and problem solving.

Exploring Math at Home

Dear Family,

In this chapter I have learned to add through 18. I have solved problems using a graph. Please help me practice these skills by helping me with the activities below.

Love, ______________________

1.

Make flash cards for sums of 11 through 18. Practice a few minutes daily.

2.

Shuffle the addition flash cards. Then match facts that make a related pair.

Coming Attractions

In the next chapter I will learn the value of numbers through 99 and how to compare numbers. I will also learn about ordinal numbers through twentieth.

Exploring Mathematics Book Two © Scott, Foresman and Company

Listen to the math story, "The Hippo and the Hats."
The hippo put on 50 hats in different colors.
Why did he put on so many?

Notes for Home Children listen to a math story introducing chapter concepts and skills. Then they answer a question about the story.

Name

Decade Numbers

Count and write the number of tens.
Write the number.

1.  1 ten 

2. 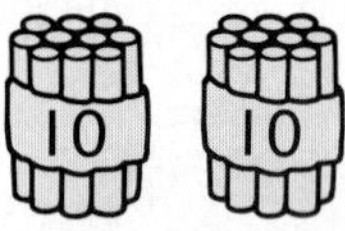 ______ tens ______

3. 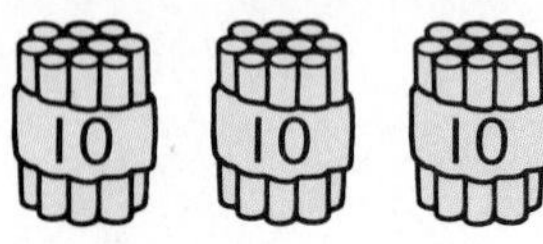 ______ tens ______

4.  ______ tens ______

5.  ______ tens ______

6.  ______ tens ______

7. 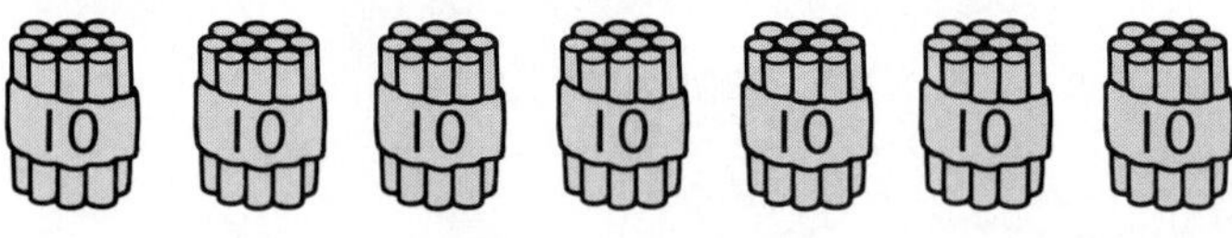 ______ tens ______

8. 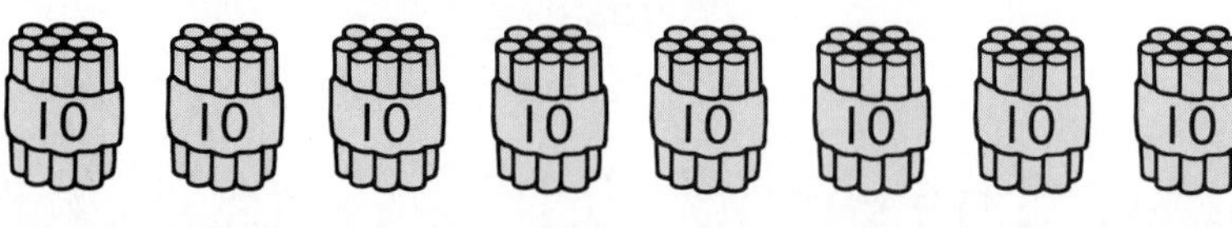 ______ tens ______

9. 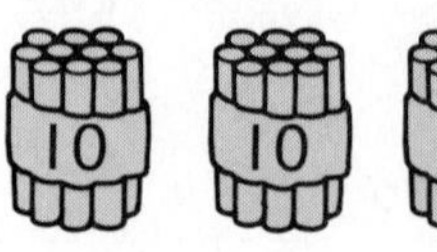  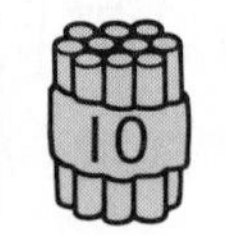 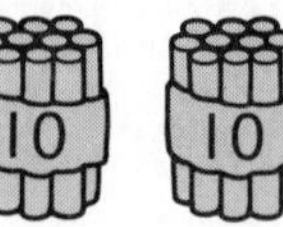   ______ tens ______

Notes for Home Children identify decade numbers through 90.

Exploring Mathematics Book Two © Scott, Foresman and Company

Name

Understanding Tens and Ones

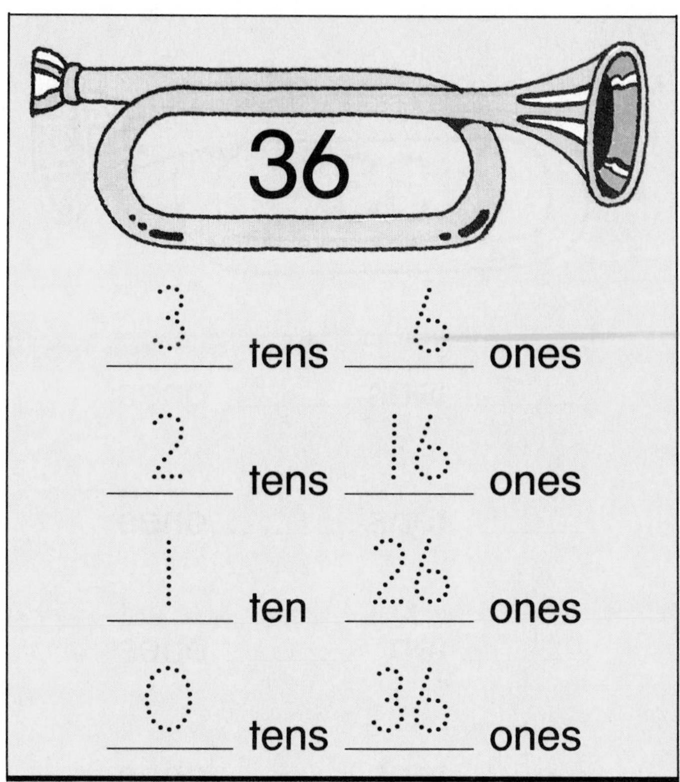

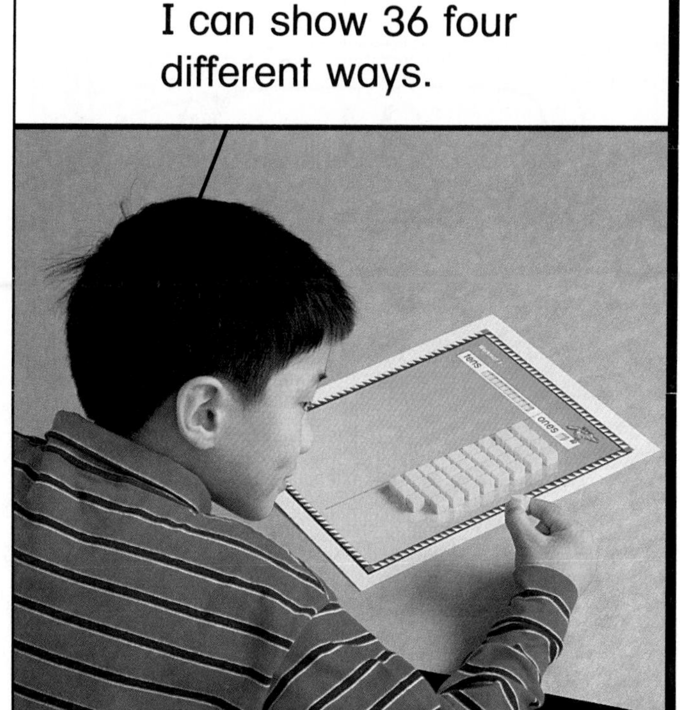

Use Workmat 1.
Use tens and ones counters.
Show each number in different ways.

1. 

_____ tens _____ ones

_____ ten _____ ones

_____ tens _____ ones

2. 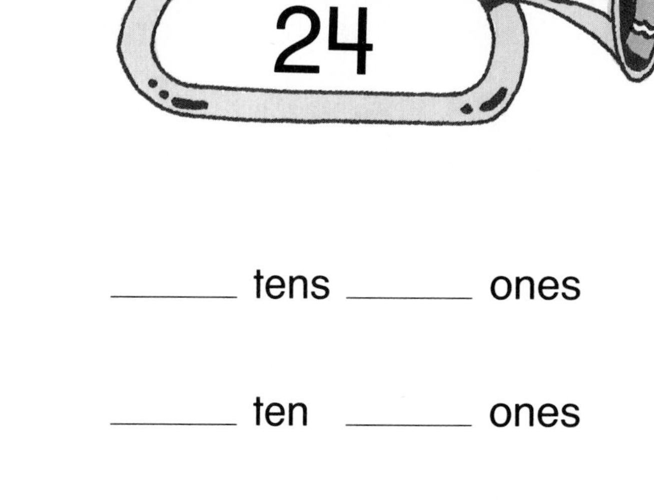

_____ tens _____ ones

_____ ten _____ ones

_____ tens _____ ones

Notes for Home Children explore at the CONCRETE level using tens and ones counters and a place-value mat to find different ways of naming two-digit numbers.

Use Workmat 1.
Use tens and ones counters.
Show each number in different ways.

3.

3 tens 1 one

_____ tens _____ ones

_____ ten _____ ones

_____ tens _____ ones

4.

_____ tens _____ ones

_____ tens _____ ones

_____ ten _____ ones

_____ tens _____ ones

5.

_____ tens _____ ones

_____ tens _____ ones

_____ ten _____ ones

_____ tens _____ ones

6.

_____ tens _____ ones

_____ tens _____ ones

_____ tens _____ ones

_____ ten _____ ones

_____ tens _____ ones

Exploring Mathematics Book Two © Scott, Foresman and Company

Notes for Home Children explore at the CONCRETE level using tens and ones counters and a place-value mat to find different ways of naming two-digit numbers.

Name

Tens and Ones Through 99

How many boxes of 10 crayons are there?
How many crayons are not in boxes?
How many crayons are there in all?

How many?

1.

_____ tens and _____ ones

_____

2.

_____ tens and _____ ones

_____

3.

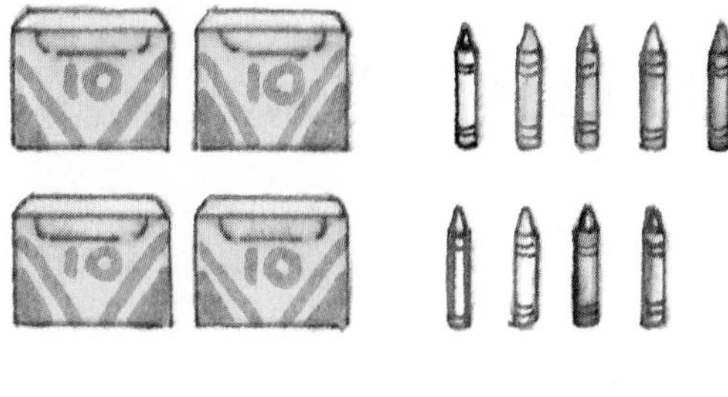

_____ tens _____ ones

_____

4.

_____ tens _____ ones

_____

Notes for Home Children identify and write how many tens and ones for numbers through 99.

How many?

5. 38 — 3 tens, 8 ones

6. 41 — ___ tens, ___ one

7. 60 — ___ tens, ___ ones

8. 23 — ___ tens, ___ ones

9.  16 — ___ ones, ___ ten

10. 87 — ___ tens, ___ ones

11. 21 — ___ tens, ___ one

12. 12 — ___ ones, ___ ten

Problem Solving

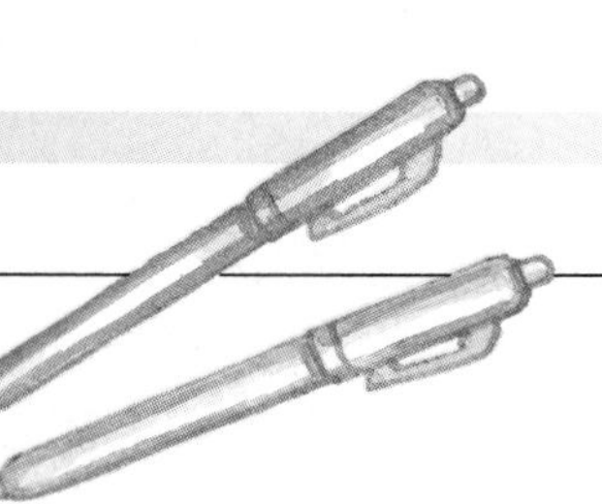

Solve.

13. Ben has 6 boxes of pens. There are 10 pens in each box. Sue gives him 2 more pens. How many pens does Ben have now? ___ pens

14. Jean has 5 empty boxes. Ten pens can fit in each box. She has 70 pens. How many more boxes does Jean need? ___ boxes

Exploring Mathematics Book Two © Scott, Foresman and Company

Notes for Home Children identify and write how many tens and ones for numbers through 99. Then they solve problems about place value.

Name

Order Through 99

1. Complete the chart.

0	1	2	3		5				9
10	11								
		22							
	31								
					45				
				54					
							67		
						76			
								88	
									99

2. Color the boxes with 6 in the ones place red.
3. Color the boxes with 4 in the tens place blue.

4. Which box has 2 colors? ______

Notes for Home Children order numbers through 99 using a hundreds chart.

Write the missing numbers.

5.

After	
31	32
56	
77	
70	
45	
92	
9	
59	

6.

Before	
	79
	44
	16
	27
	89
	63
	20
	50

7.

Between		
23		25
64		66
88		90
75		77
41		43
96		98
50		52
39		41

Talk About Math

What number comes after these numbers?

19

29

89

What number comes before these numbers?

40

70

90

Exploring Mathematics Book Two © Scott, Foresman and Company

Notes for Home Children practice ordering numbers through 99 by identifying numbers after, before, and between. Then they talk about decade numbers.

Name

Comparing Numbers Through 99

To compare numbers, first look at the number of tens.

If the number of tens is the same, then look at the number of ones.

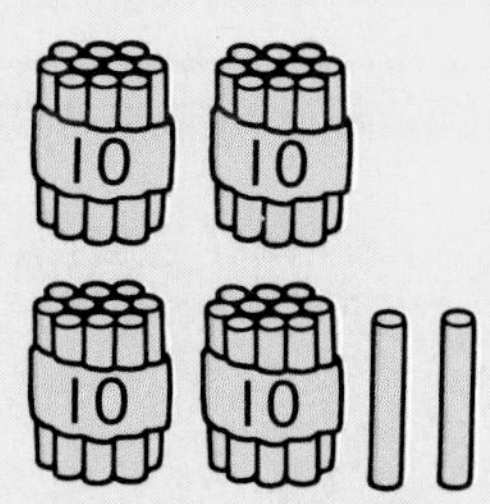
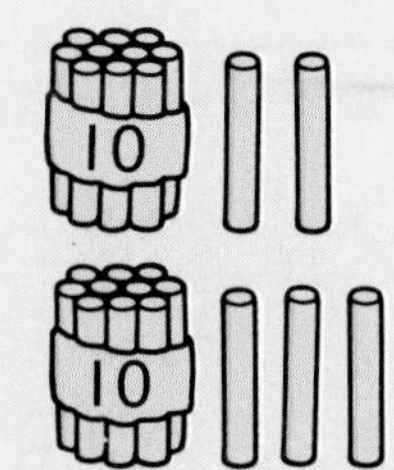

42 is **greater than** 25.

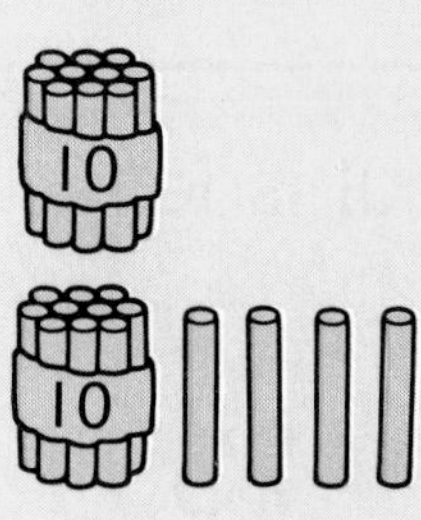
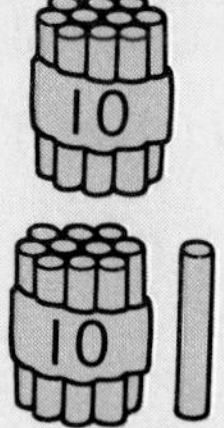

24 is **greater than** 21.

Ring the greater number.

1.	42	32
2.	26	22
3.	65	72
4.	45	53
5.	61	41
6.	28	68
7.	7	71
8.	84	48

Notes for Home Children learn to compare the value of two numbers by identifying the greater number.

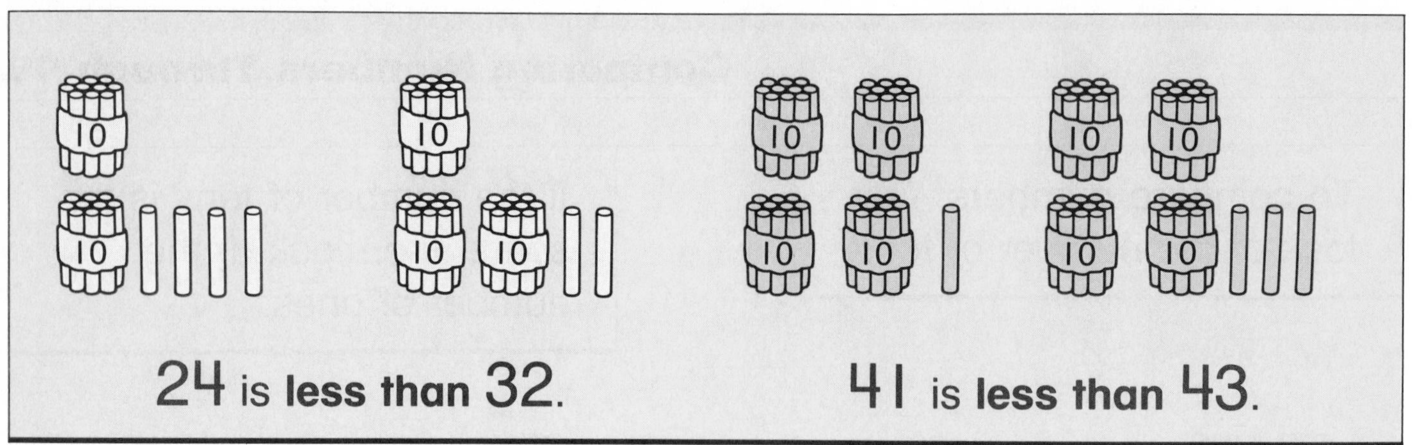

Ring the number that is less.

9.	38	73	**10.**	23	28
11.	84	34	**12.**	50	20
13.	76	65	**14.**	95	9
15.	23	13	**16.**	67	76

17. **Estimation** There are 12 peanuts in the jar with the red lid. Ring the jar that shows about 20 peanuts.

Notes for Home Children practice comparing the value of two numbers by identifying the lesser number. Then they estimate to find the jar with 20 peanuts.

See More Practice Set A on page 99.

Exploring Mathematics Book Two © Scott, Foresman and Company

Using > and < to Compare Numbers

Write the numbers.

1. **23, 24**

   ______ is greater than ______.

   ______ > ______

2. **29, 32**

   ______ is greater than ______.

   ______ > ______

3. **30, 21**

   ______ is less than ______.

   ______ < ______

4. **63, 36**

   ______ is less than ______.

   ______ < ______

Notes for Home Children learn to use the greater-than and less-than symbols when comparing numbers.

Write $>$ or $<$ in the ◯.

5.	8 ◯ 9 (example: $<$)	18 ◯ 16	42 ◯ 40
6.	6 ◯ 19	42 ◯ 40	66 ◯ 68
7.	55 ◯ 51	36 ◯ 41	27 ◯ 75
8.	83 ◯ 73	33 ◯ 23	7 ◯ 17
9.	28 ◯ 79	37 ◯ 75	55 ◯ 50
10.	66 ◯ 44	63 ◯ 91	20 ◯ 30

Talk About Math

Is 40 greater than 4?
How do you know?

Exploring Mathematics Book Two © Scott, Foresman and Company

Notes for Home Children learn to use the greater-than and less-than symbols when comparing numbers. Then they talk about place-value concepts.

Name

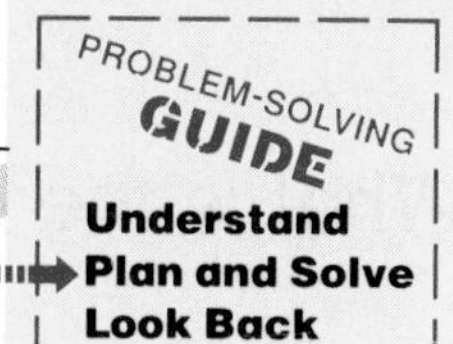

Find a Pattern

What is the pattern?

1. Color more numbers to complete the pattern.

0	1	2	3	4	5	6	7	8	9
10	11	12	13	14	15	16	17	18	19
20	21	22	23	24	25	26	27	28	29
30	31	32	33	34	35	36	37	38	39
40	41	42	43	44	45	46	47	48	49
50	51	52	53	54	55	56	57	58	59
60	61	62	63	64	65	66	67	68	69
70	71	72	73	74	75	76	77	78	79
80	81	82	83	84	85	86	87	88	89
90	91	92	93	94	95	96	97	98	99

2. Write all the numbers in the pattern.

0 10 ____ ____ ____

____ ____ ____ ____ ____

3. Describe the pattern. ______________________

Notes for Home Children solve a problem by finding and completing a pattern.

What is the pattern?

4. Color more numbers to complete the pattern.

0	1	2	3	4	5	6	7	8	9
10	11	12	13	14	15	16	17	18	19
20	21	22	23	24	25	26	27	28	29
30	31	32	33	34	35	36	37	38	39
40	41	42	43	44	45	46	47	48	49
50	51	52	53	54	55	56	57	58	59
60	61	62	63	64	65	66	67	68	69
70	71	72	73	74	75	76	77	78	79
80	81	82	83	84	85	86	87	88	89
90	91	92	93	94	95	96	97	98	99

5. Write all the numbers in the pattern.

0 ____ 5 ____ 10 ____ ____ ____ ____ ____

____ ____ ____ ____ ____ ____ ____

____ ____ ____ ____ ____ ____

6. Describe the pattern. ____________________

Notes for Home Children solve a problem by finding and completing a pattern.

Exploring Mathematics Book Two © Scott, Foresman and Company

Name

Number Sense

How many baby fingers and toes do you see in all?

How many different ways can you count them?

Let's do some more!

How many fingers and toes does your family have?

Notes for Home Children develop number understanding by counting groups of 10.

SKILLS REVIEW

Skills Review

Fill in the correct ◯.
Add.

1. 0 + 8 + 1
   - (A) 0
   - (B) 8
   - (C) 9

2. 2 + 7 + 3
   - (A) 12
   - (B) 13
   - (C) 14

3. 5 + 4 + 1
   - (A) 5
   - (B) 7
   - (C) 10

4. 6 + 3 + 5
   - (A) 13
   - (B) 14
   - (C) 15

5. 3 + 2 + 5
   - (A) 10
   - (B) 12
   - (C) 14

6. 1 + 8 + 6
   - (A) 9
   - (B) 15
   - (C) 17

Vocabulary

Write the missing word.

subtract	add	fact	same

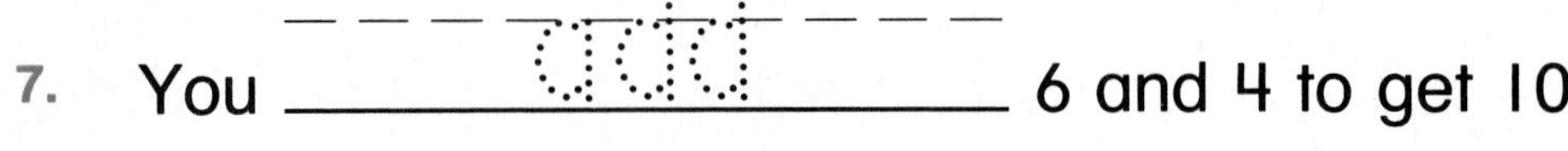

7. You ______ 6 and 4 to get 10.

8. If you ______ 8 from 10, you get 2.

9. 7 + 2 is the ______ as 2 + 7.

10. 4 + 5 = 9 is an addition ______.

Notes for Home Children review finding sums through 18 with three addends. Then they review math terms by completing sentences.

Exploring Mathematics Book Two © Scott, Foresman and Company

Name

Special number words tell order.
The car that says **first** is number 1 in line.
The car that says **eleventh** is number 11 in line.

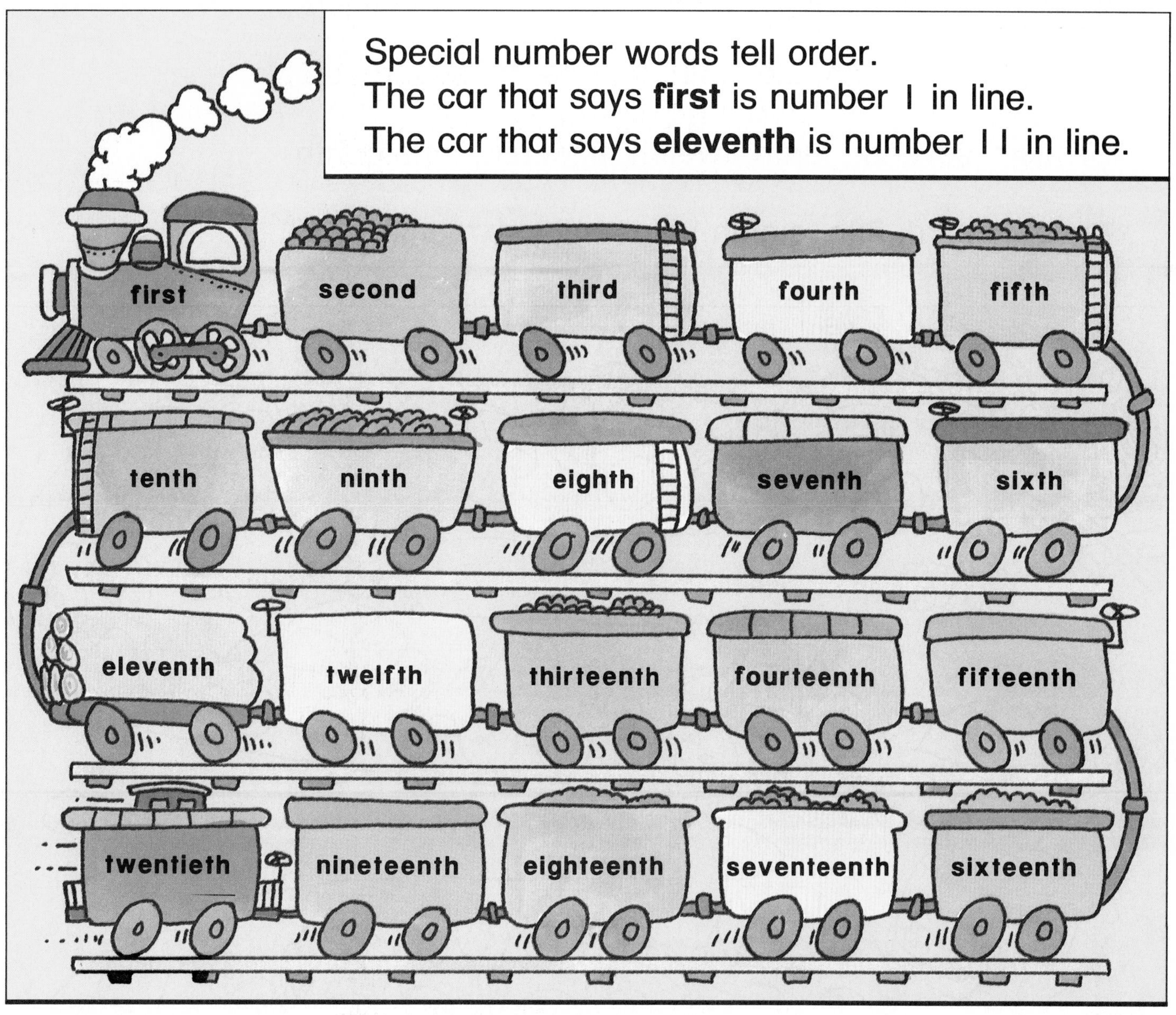

Write the number next to each word.

1. first ______ second ______ third ______
2. seventh ______ twelfth ______ twentieth ______
3. eleventh ______ nineteenth ______ sixteenth ______

Notes for Home Children use cardinal numbers through twenty to identify ordinal numbers through twentieth.

4. Color the cars.

red — second, fourth, ninth, eighteenth, twentieth

blue — first, sixth, eleventh, fourteenth, seventeenth

green — seventh, tenth, twelfth, fifteenth, nineteenth

yellow — third, fifth, eighth, thirteenth, sixteenth

Exploring Mathematics Book Two © Scott, Foresman and Company

Notes for Home Children use ordinal numbers through twentieth to identify positions of objects.

Name

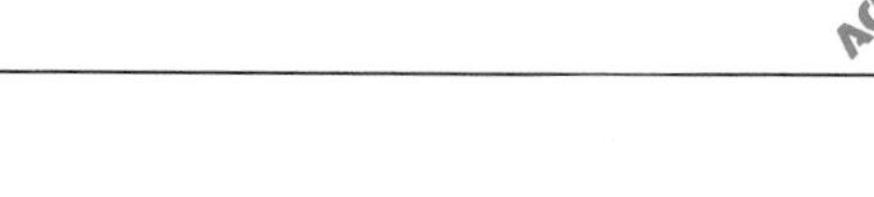

Counting Dimes, Nickels, and Pennies

dime

nickel

penny

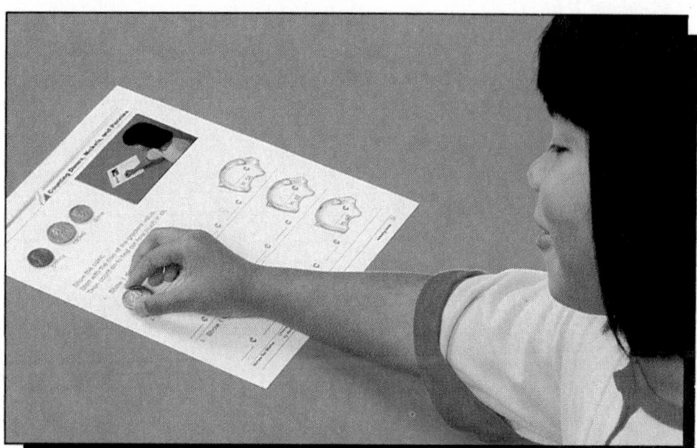

Show the coins.
Start with the coin of greatest value.
Then count on to find how many in all.

1. Show 1 nickel and 4 pennies.

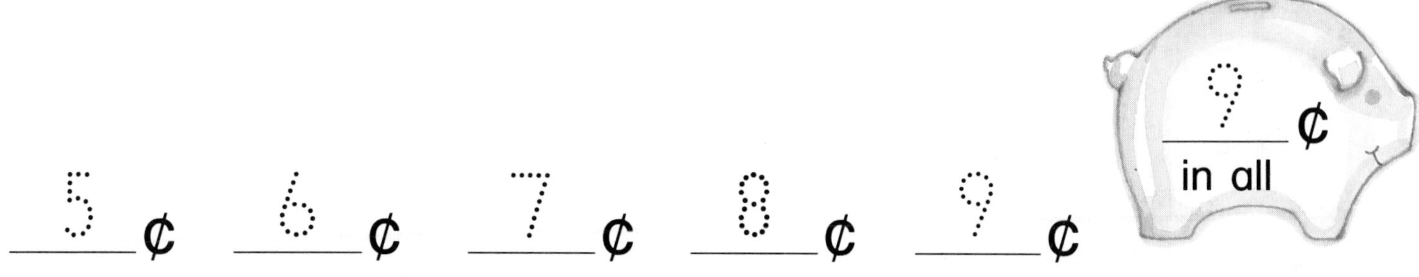

2. Show 3 nickels and 2 pennies.

3. Show 3 dimes, 1 nickel, and 1 penny.

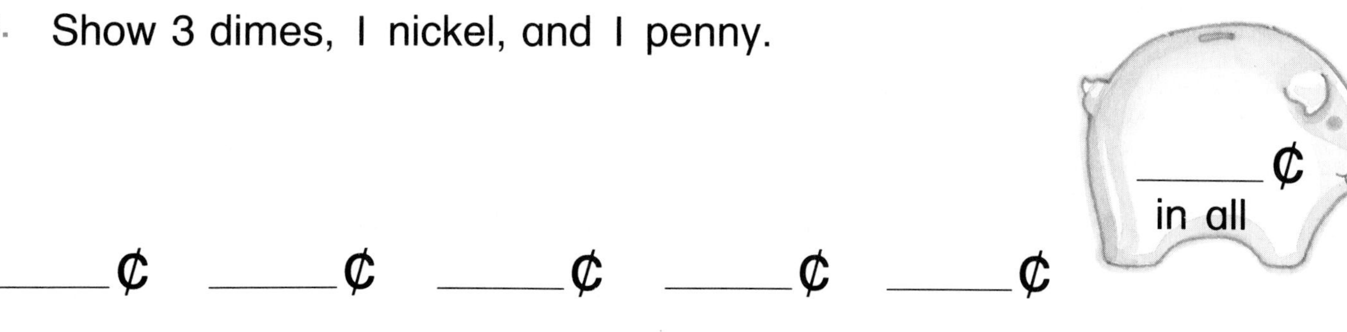

Notes for Home Children use manipulatives to count money amounts by starting with the coin of greatest value.

How much in all?

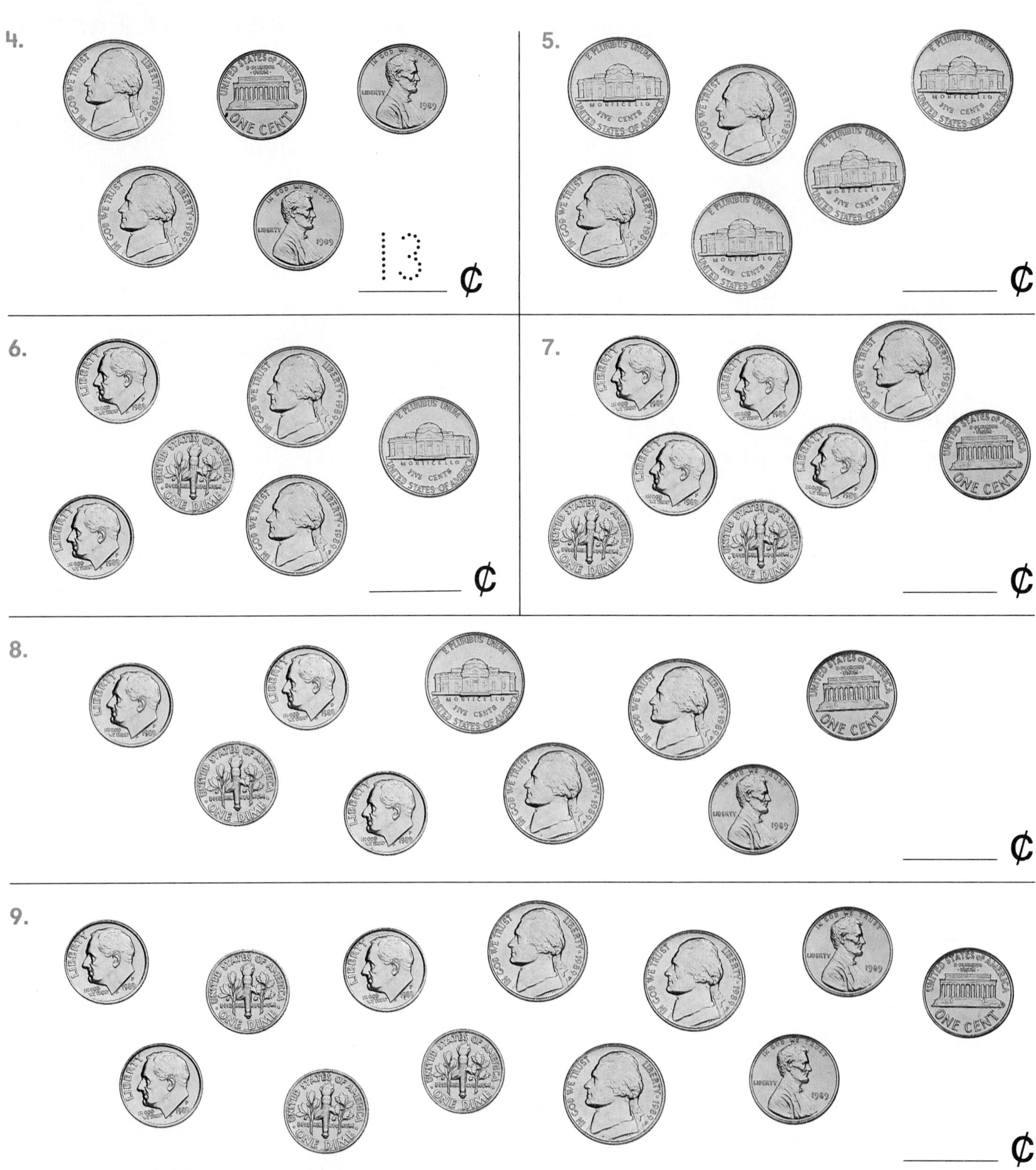

4. 13 ¢

5. ____ ¢

6. ____ ¢

7. ____ ¢

8. ____ ¢

9. ____ ¢

Critical Thinking You have 7 coins worth 36¢. What are they?

Notes for Home Children practice counting dimes, nickels, and pennies by counting on from the coin of greatest value. Then they discuss coins with a value of 36¢.

Exploring Mathematics Book Two © Scott, Foresman and Company

Name

Counting Coins Through 99¢

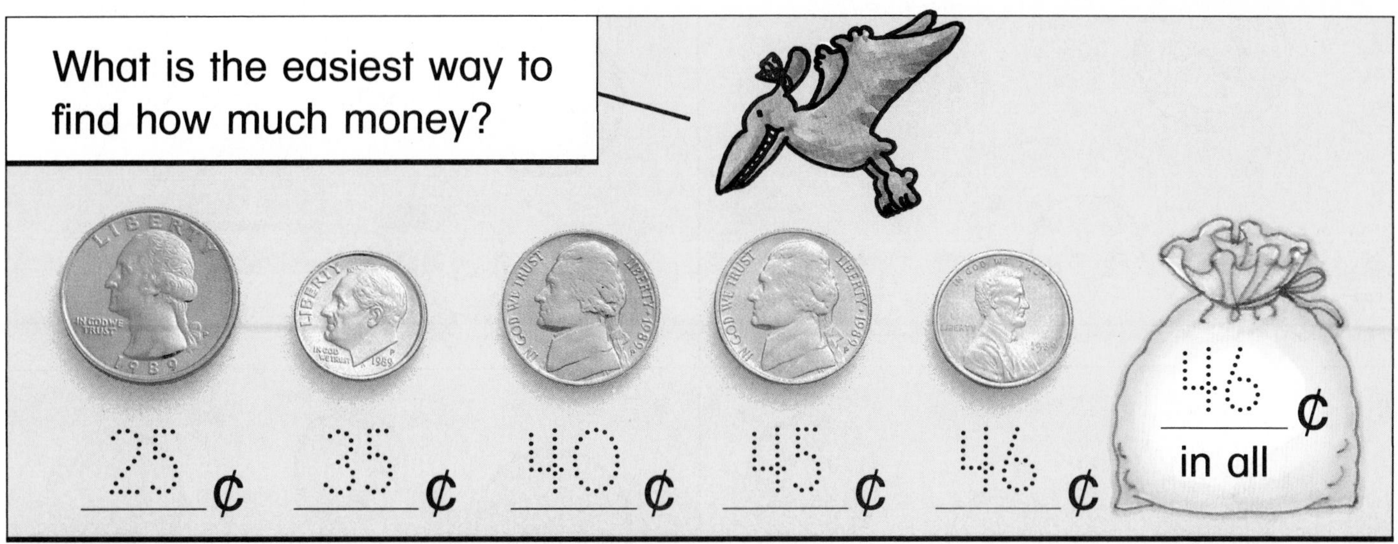

Start with the coin of greatest value.
Count on to find how much.

1.

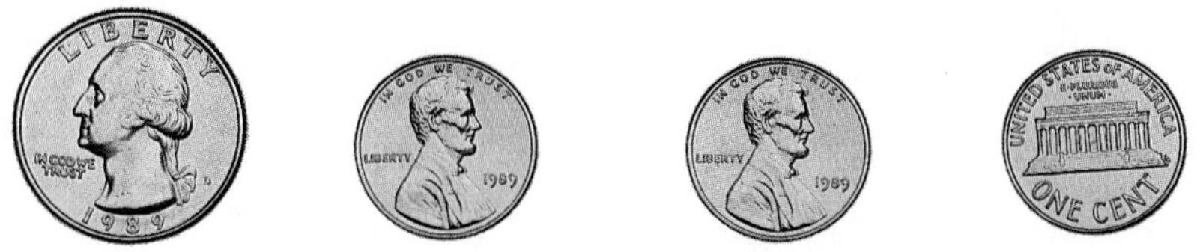

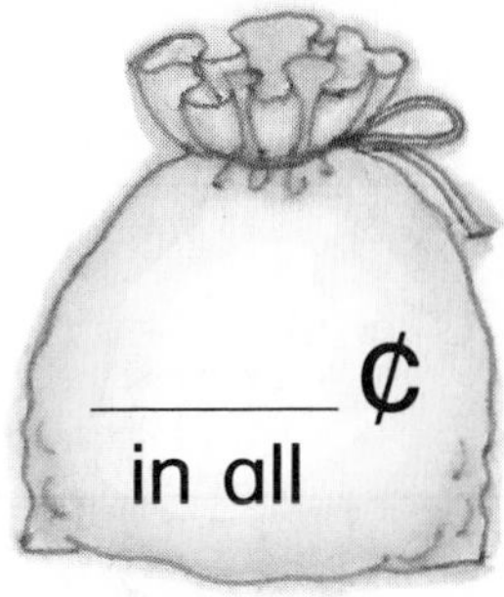

___ ¢ ___ ¢ ___ ¢ ___ ¢

___ ¢ in all

2.

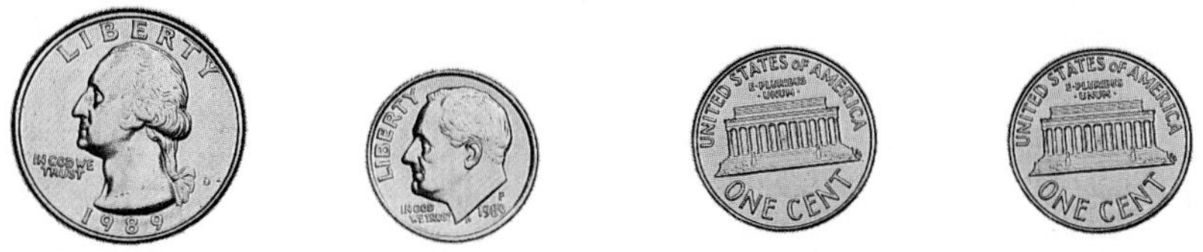

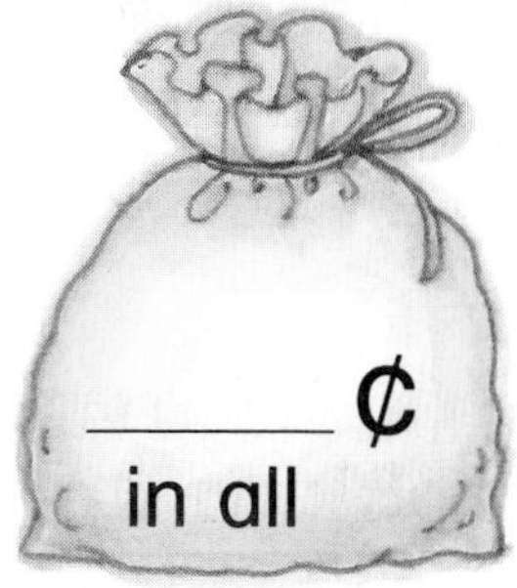

___ ¢ ___ ¢ ___ ¢ ___ ¢

___ ¢ in all

3.

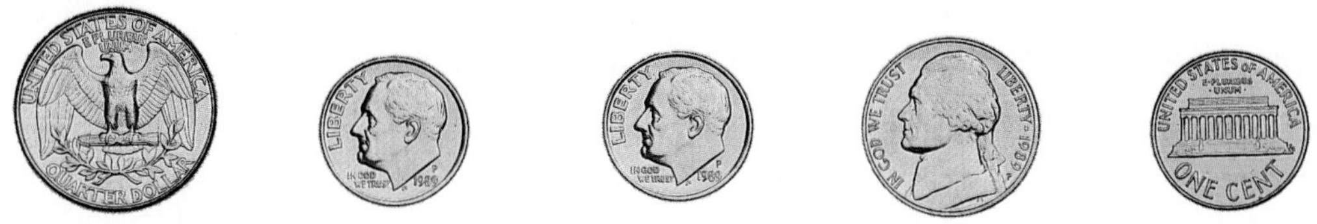

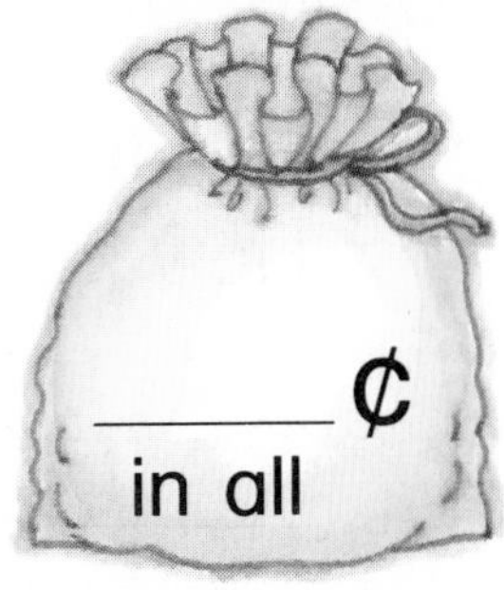

___ ¢ ___ ¢ ___ ¢ ___ ¢ ___ ¢

___ ¢ in all

Notes for Home Children identify amounts of money through 99¢ by counting on from the coin of greatest value.

How much in all?

4.

45 ¢

5.

_____ ¢

6.

_____ ¢

7.

_____ ¢

8.

_____ ¢

Problem Solving

Solve.

9. Eric has 76¢. He has only dimes and pennies. How many dimes and pennies could he have?

_____ dimes _____ pennies

Exploring Mathematics Book Two © Scott, Foresman and Company

Notes for Home Children practice counting coins through 99¢ by counting on from the coin of greatest value. Then they solve a problem involving money.

See More Practice Set B on page 99.

Name

Use Data from a Picture

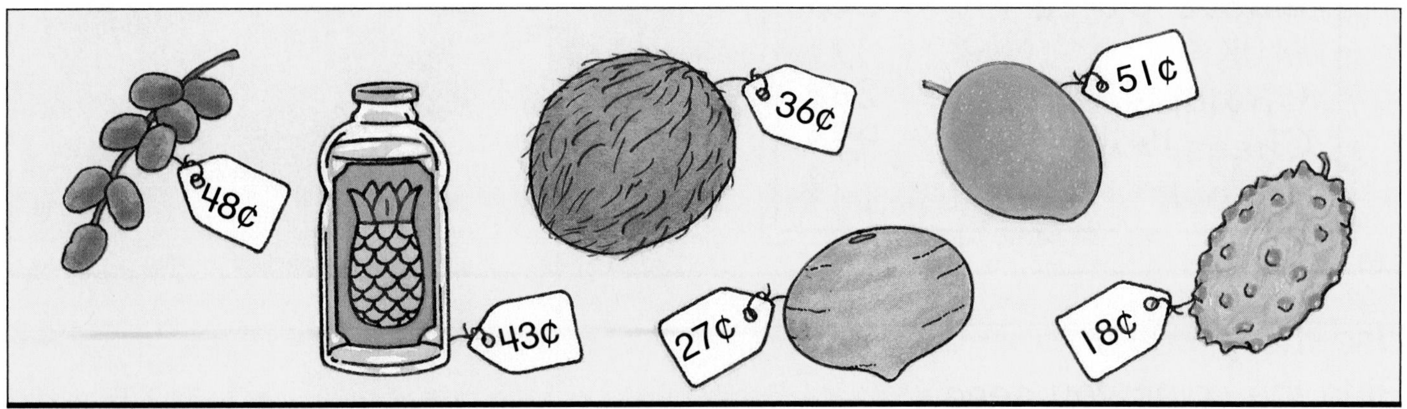

Use the picture of the food.
Ring the coins you need.

1.

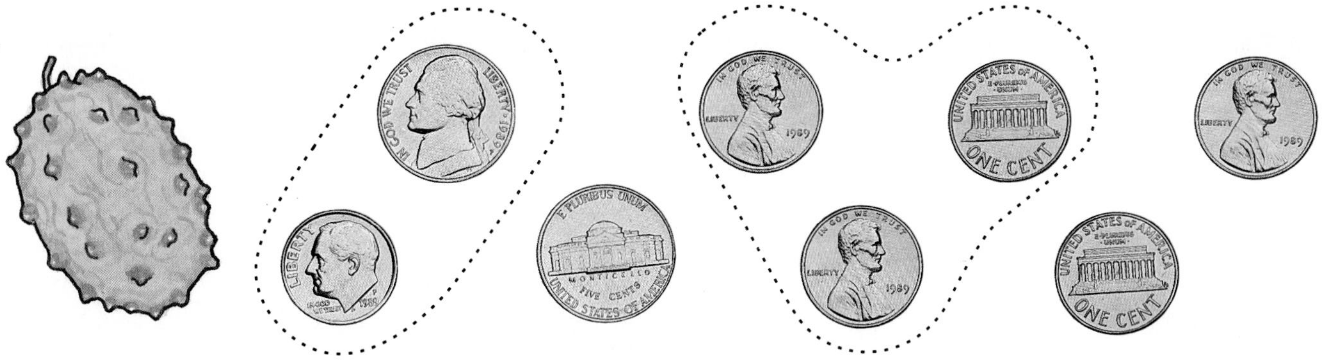

2.

3.

Notes for Home Children solve problems by using data from a picture.

Price List

Guava Juice	26¢
Milk	37¢
Chalupa	29¢
Cheeseburger	42¢
Egg Roll	17¢

Use the price list.
Ring the coins you need.

4.

5.

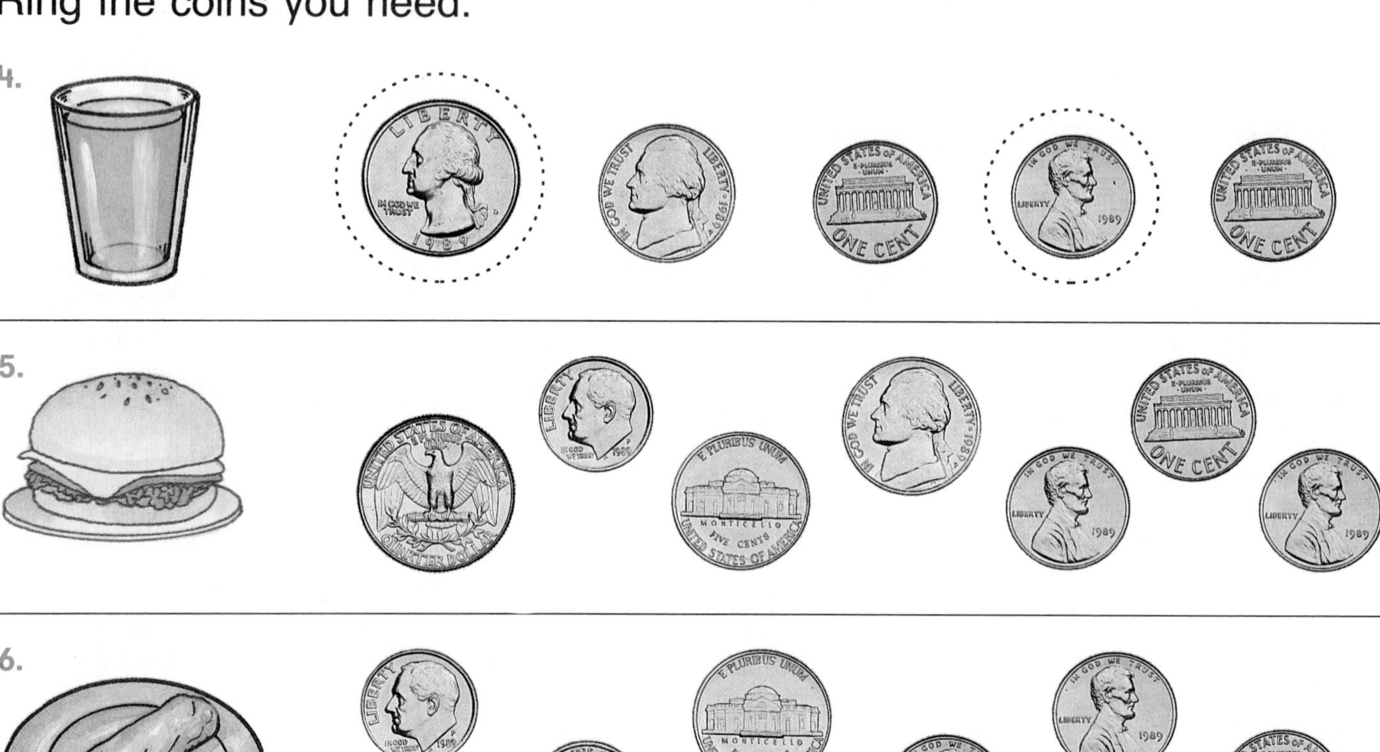

6.

7.

Notes for Home Children solve problems by using data from a picture.

Exploring Mathematics Book Two © Scott, Foresman and Company

Name

Problem-Solving Workshop

Explore as a Team

Work with a partner.
Complete the money puzzle.
Put 1¢, 5¢, 10¢, or 25¢
in each square.

		1.		
	2.		3.	
4.		25¢		
	5.			

Down
1. 55¢
2. 20¢
3. 11¢

Across
2. 25¢
4. 45¢
5. 16¢

Let's do some more!

Try to make your own money puzzle.
Use different amounts of money.

Notes for Home Children explore with a partner to solve a puzzle involving amounts of money.

Problem Solving WORKSHOP

Problem-Solving Workshop

Explore with a Calculator

Use a calculator to solve.

Question | Keys Pressed | Answer

1. What number is one more than seventy-six?

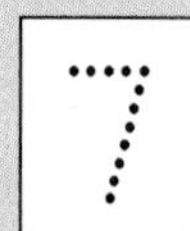
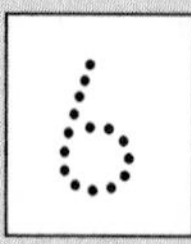
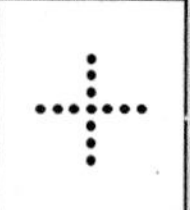
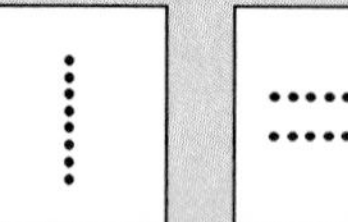

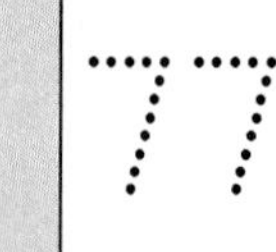

2. What number is one less than ninety-nine?

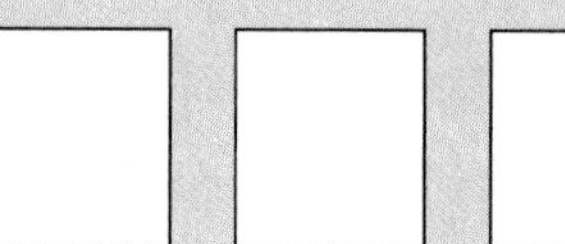
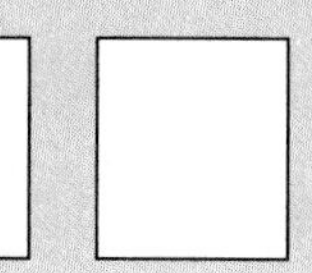

3. What number is one more than fifty-nine?

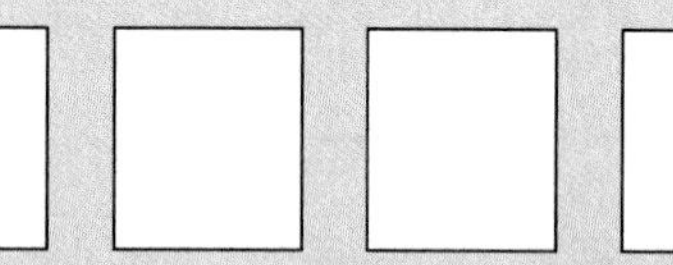

4. What number is one less than forty?

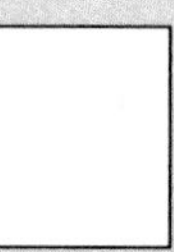
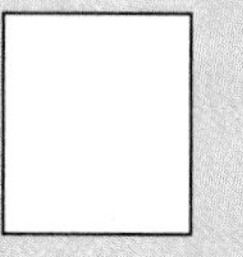
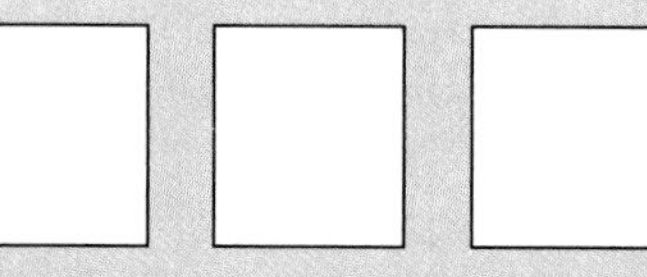

5. What number is ten more than thirty-two?

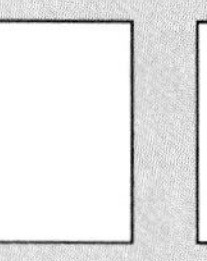
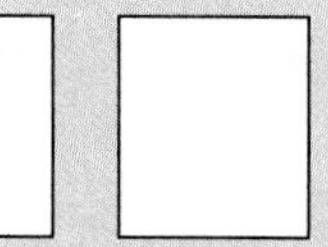
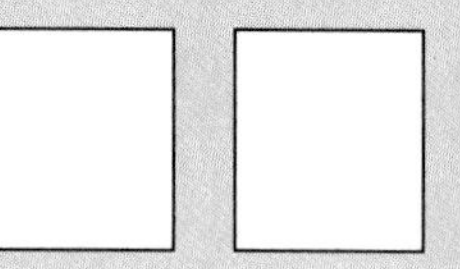

6. What number is ten less than eighty-six?

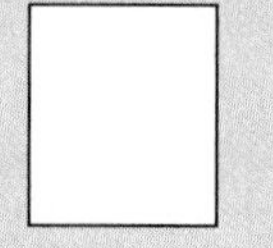
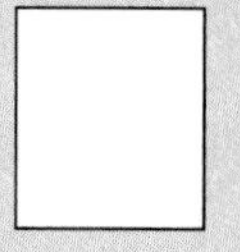

Exploring Mathematics Book Two © Scott, Foresman and Company

Notes for Home Children explore with a calculator to solve problems involving place value.

Name

More Practice

Set A Use after page 82.

Ring the greater number.

1.	63	53	2.	28	29
3.	54	41	4.	67	76

Ring the number that is less.

5.	9	19	6.	98	88
7.	31	13	8.	17	71

Set B Use after page 94.

How much?

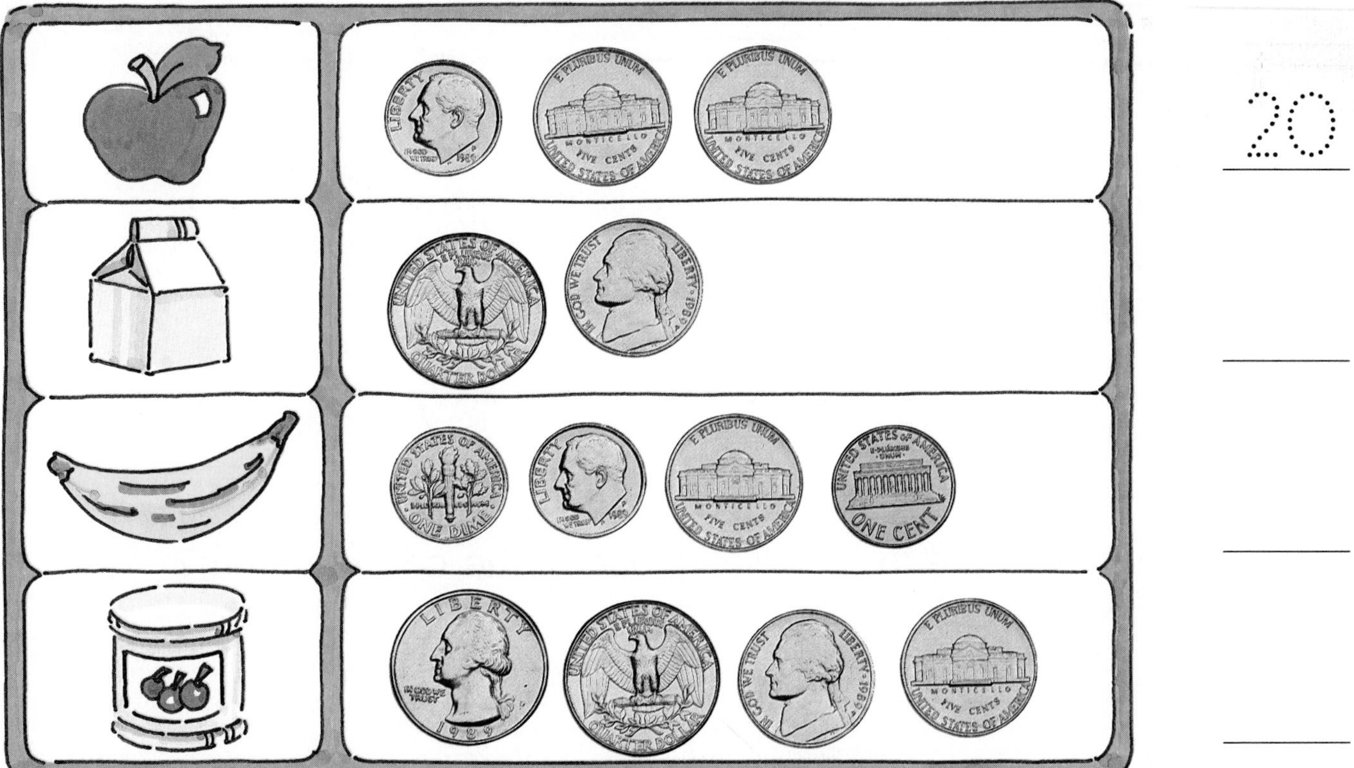

20 ¢

___ ¢

___ ¢

___ ¢

Notes for Home Set A: Children practice comparing the value of two numbers.
Set B: Children practice counting coins through 99¢.

Independent Study ENRICHMENT

Enrichment

The red numbers are odd numbers.

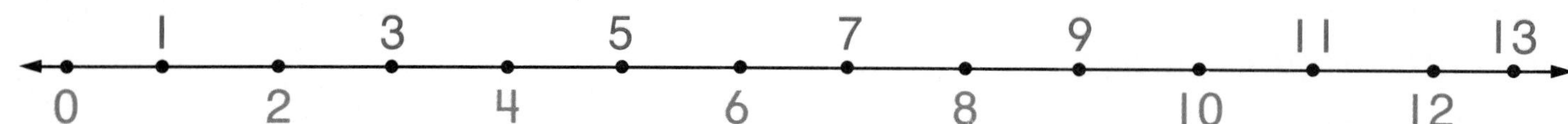

The blue numbers are even numbers.

Write the missing even numbers.

1. 4, 6, 8, 10, 12, ____, 16, ____, ____

2. 26, 28, 30, 32, ____, ____, ____, 40, ____

3. What numerals are in the ones place of the even numbers?

____

Write the missing odd numbers.

4. 5, 7, 9, 11, ____, 15, ____, ____, ____

5. 17, 19, 21, 23, ____, ____, ____, 31, ____

6. What numerals are in the ones place of the odd numbers?

____

Exploring Mathematics Book Two © Scott, Foresman and Company

Notes for Home Children are challenged to write even and odd numbers.

Name ______________________________

Chapter 3 Review/Test

1. How many tens and ones?

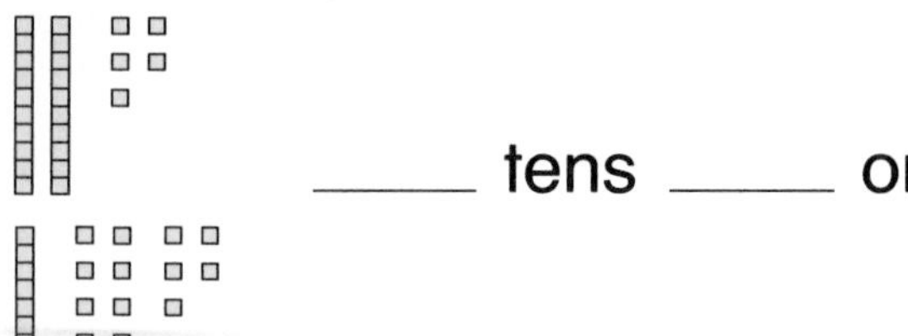

_____ tens _____ ones

_____ ten _____ ones

2. How many tens and ones?

_____ tens _____ ones

3. What number comes after?

38, _____ 83, _____

4. Write $>$ or $<$ in the ○.

39 ○ 45 12 ○ 21

5. Ring the boat that is twelfth in line.

6. How much?

_____ ¢

7. Ring to complete the pattern.

40 41 (42) 43 44 (45) 46 47 (48) 49

50 51 52 53 54 55 56 57 58 59

8. What coins do you need? Ring.

Notes for Home Children are assessed on Chapter 3 concepts, skills, and problem solving.

Exploring Math at Home

Dear Family,

In this chapter I have learned about numbers through 99 and how to compare numbers. I have also learned to use ordinals through twentieth and to count coins through 99¢. Please help me practice these skills by helping me with the activities below.

Love, ______________________________

1.

Look through a newspaper for numbers less than 100. Tell how many tens and ones are in each number.

2.

Find two items that cost 99¢ or less. Tell which item costs more.

3.

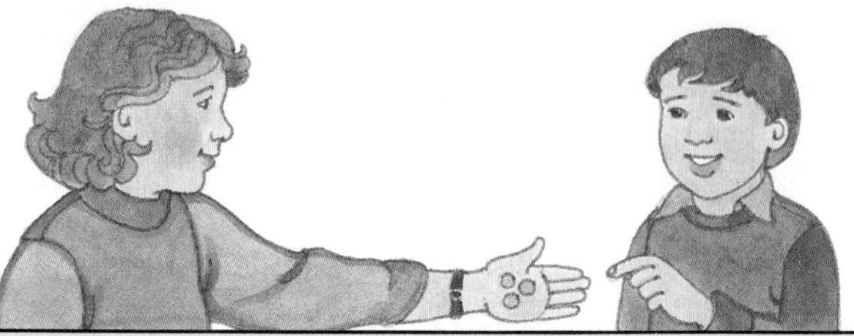

25¢

35¢

45¢

50¢

51¢

52¢

Count coins through 99¢ by counting on from the coin of greatest value.

Coming Attractions

In the next chapter I will learn subtraction facts through 18.

Exploring Mathematics Book Two © Scott, Foresman and Company

Name

Cumulative Review/Test

Fill in the correct ⬭.
Add or subtract.

1. $3 + 6$ (A) 7 (B) 8 (C) 9

2. $7 - 5$ (A) 1 (B) 2 (C) 3

3. $8 - 3$ (A) 5 (B) 6 (C) 7

4. $9 + 3$ (A) 12 (B) 13 (C) 14

5. $9 + 8$ (A) 15 (B) 16 (C) 17

6. $10 - 4$ (A) 3 (B) 5 (C) 6

7. $7 - 0$ (A) 7 (B) 4 (C) 0

8. $2 + 7$ (A) 5 (B) 9 (C) 11

9. $10 - 9$ (A) 9 (B) 2 (C) 1

10. $9 - 5$ (A) 6 (B) 5 (C) 4

11. $6 + 8$ (A) 12 (B) 13 (C) 14

12. $2 + 4 + 7$ (A) 13 (B) 16 (C) 12

Find the greater number.

13. 46 (A) 21 (B)

14. 63 (A) 93 (B)

15. 35 (A) 53 (B)

Notes for Home Children are assessed on Chapters 1–3 concepts, skills, and problem solving using a multiple-choice format.

CUMULATIVE REVIEW/TEST

Fill in the correct ◯.
How many?

16.

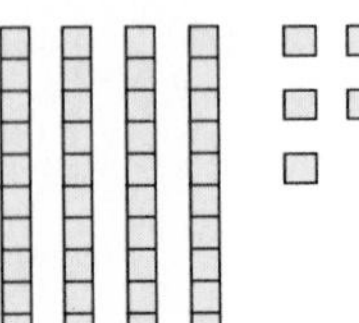

45 Ⓐ 54 Ⓑ

17.

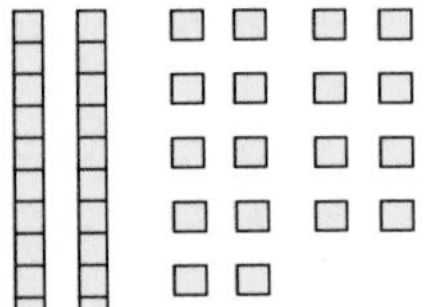

28 Ⓐ 38 Ⓑ

18.

7 tens
4 ones

47 Ⓐ 74 Ⓑ

How much?

19.

7¢ Ⓐ 12¢ Ⓑ

20.

50¢ Ⓐ 55¢ Ⓑ

21. Sara lost 2 dimes and 1 penny. How much money did she lose?

11¢ Ⓐ 21¢ Ⓑ

Solve.

22. Ray has 6 boxes of crayons. There are 10 crayons in a box. Tom gives him 5 more crayons. How many crayons does Ray have?

65 Ⓐ 56 Ⓑ

23. Pulin has 9 marbles. He gives 2 to Faye. How many marbles does he have left?

7 Ⓐ 11 Ⓑ

24. In which place is Sue?

fourth Ⓐ fifth Ⓑ

Exploring Mathematics Book Two © Scott, Foresman and Company

Notes for Home Children are assessed on Chapters 1–3 concepts, skills, and problem solving using a multiple-choice format.

Chapter

4

Subtraction Through 18

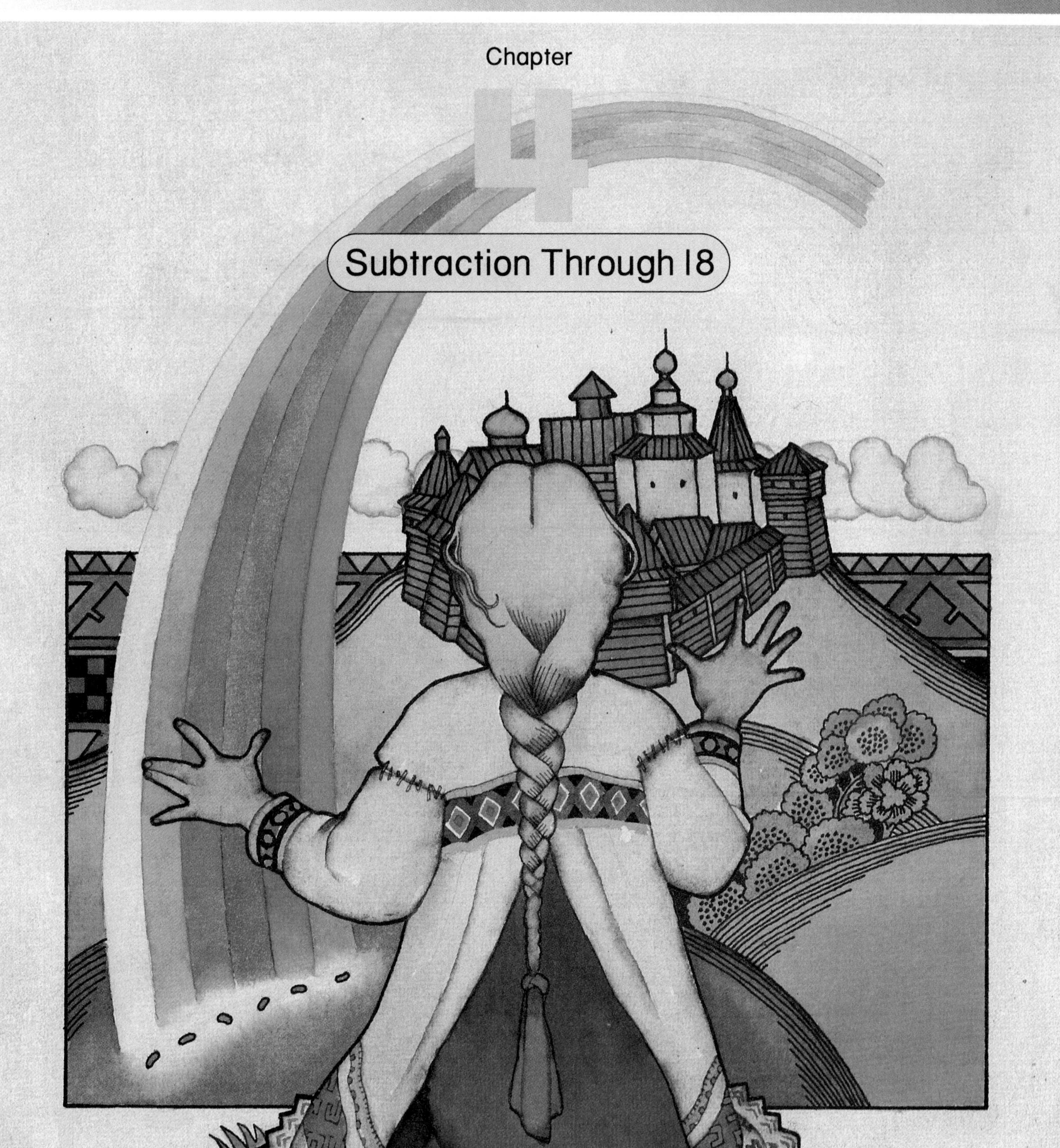

Listen to the math story, "The Golda Rule."
Golda gave away 6 of her 12 magic seeds.
What happened when she dropped the other seeds?

Notes for Home Children listen to a math story introducing chapter concepts and skills. Then they answer a question about the story.

Name

Subtraction Through 10

Subtract.

1.	6 − 3 = ____	7 − 4 = ____	5 − 5 = ____
2.	8 − 7 = ____	9 − 5 = ____	8 − 2 = ____
3.	10 − 3 = ____	8 − 3 = ____	6 − 0 = ____
4.	9 − 8 = ____	8 − 6 = ____	9 − 3 = ____
5.	9 − 2 = ____	10 − 8 = ____	8 − 4 = ____
6.	10 − 2 = ____	9 − 4 = ____	10 − 6 = ____
7.	8 − 5 = ____	10 − 1 = ____	9 − 7 = ____
8.	6 − 2 = ____	10 − 7 = ____	7 − 3 = ____

Exploring Mathematics Book Two © Scott, Foresman and Company

Notes for Home Children review subtraction facts through 10.

Name

Subtracting with Doubles

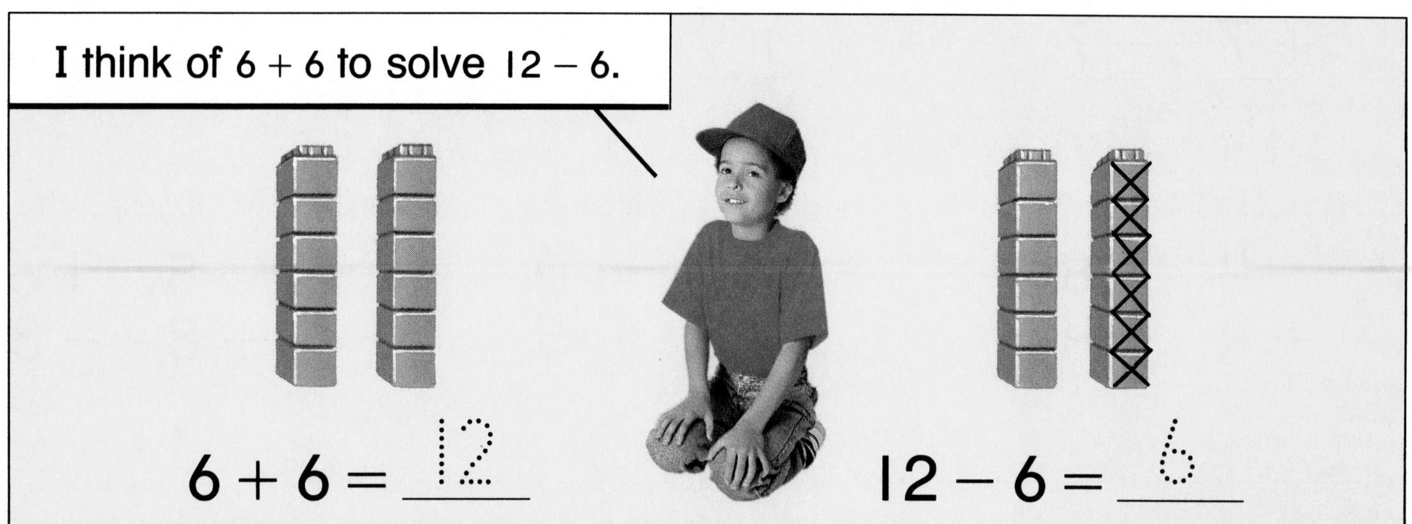

Add or subtract.

1.

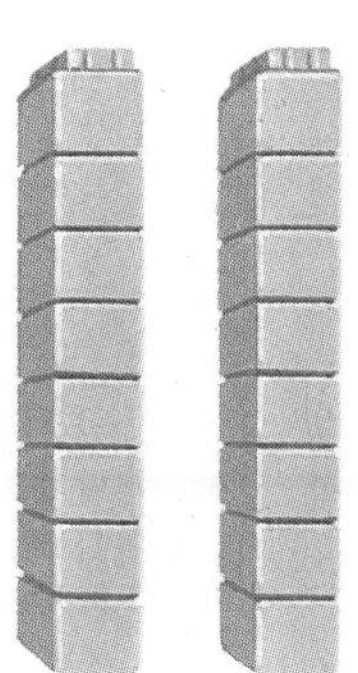

$8 + 8 =$ ____ $16 - 8 =$ ____

2.

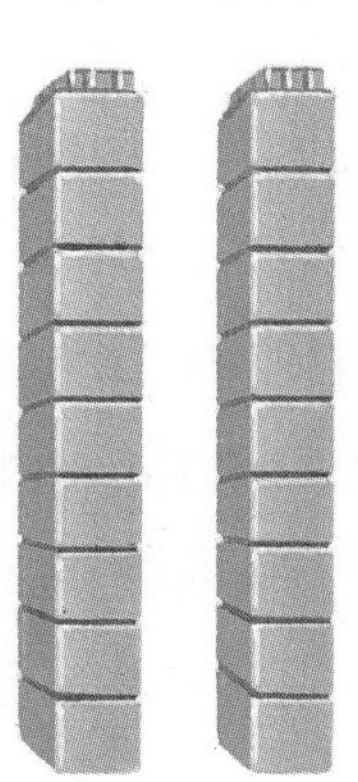

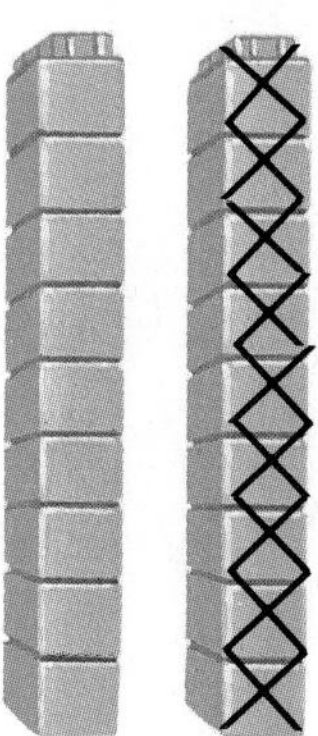

$9 + 9 =$ ____ $18 - 9 =$ ____

Notes for Home Children learn to use a known addition doubles fact to solve a related subtraction fact.

Add or subtract.

3. $\begin{array}{r} 7 \\ +\ 7 \\ \hline 14 \end{array}$ $\begin{array}{r} 14 \\ -\ 7 \\ \hline \end{array}$

4. $\begin{array}{r} 9 \\ +\ 9 \\ \hline \end{array}$ $\begin{array}{r} 18 \\ -\ 9 \\ \hline \end{array}$

5. $\begin{array}{r} 6 \\ +\ 6 \\ \hline \end{array}$ $\begin{array}{r} 12 \\ -\ 6 \\ \hline \end{array}$

6. $\begin{array}{r} 4 \\ +\ 4 \\ \hline \end{array}$ $\begin{array}{r} 8 \\ -\ 4 \\ \hline \end{array}$

7. $\begin{array}{r} 5 \\ +\ 5 \\ \hline \end{array}$ $\begin{array}{r} 10 \\ -\ 5 \\ \hline \end{array}$

8. $\begin{array}{r} 8 \\ +\ 8 \\ \hline \end{array}$ $\begin{array}{r} 16 \\ -\ 8 \\ \hline \end{array}$

9. $\begin{array}{r} 9 \\ -\ 4 \\ \hline \end{array}$ $\begin{array}{r} 16 \\ -\ 8 \\ \hline \end{array}$ $\begin{array}{r} 10 \\ -\ 6 \\ \hline \end{array}$ $\begin{array}{r} 10 \\ -\ 7 \\ \hline \end{array}$ $\begin{array}{r} 9 \\ -\ 6 \\ \hline \end{array}$ $\begin{array}{r} 18 \\ -\ 9 \\ \hline \end{array}$ $\begin{array}{r} 9 \\ -\ 5 \\ \hline \end{array}$

10. $\begin{array}{r} 12 \\ -\ 6 \\ \hline \end{array}$ $\begin{array}{r} 8 \\ -\ 3 \\ \hline \end{array}$ $\begin{array}{r} 14 \\ -\ 7 \\ \hline \end{array}$ $\begin{array}{r} 10 \\ -\ 5 \\ \hline \end{array}$

Problem Solving

Solve.

11. Dan has 14 flowers.
He gives 7 flowers to Pam.
How many flowers does he keep?

_____ flowers

12. Pedro has 6 flowers.
Jean has 6 flowers.
How many flowers do they have in all?

_____ flowers

Exploring Mathematics Book Two © Scott, Foresman and Company

Notes for Home Children practice subtraction facts through 18. Then they solve problems involving addition and subtraction.

Name

Multiple-Step Problems

6 ducks were swimming.
7 ducks joined them.
How many ducks are there now?

8 ducks swam away.
How many ducks are left?

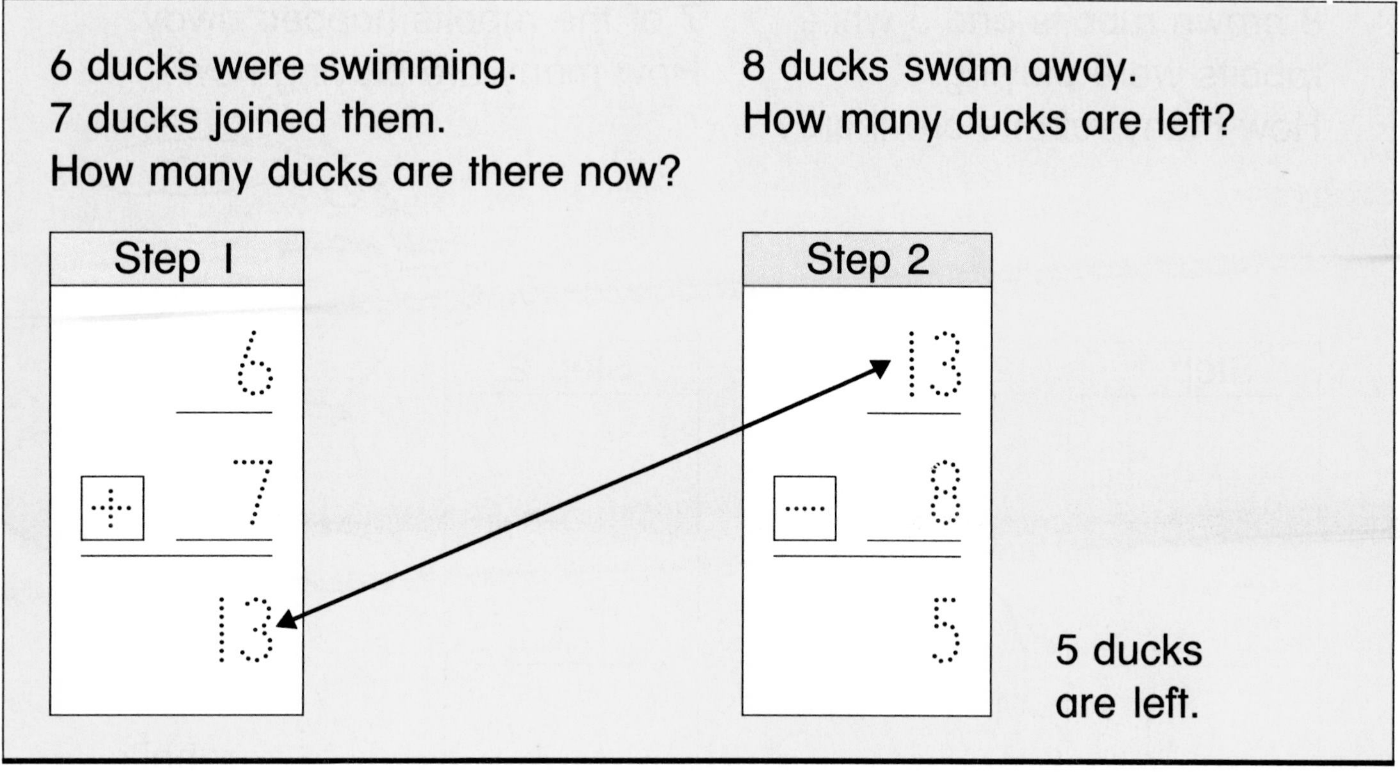

Show each step.
Then solve.

1. 17 beetles sat on a leaf.
8 beetles crawled away.
How many are left?

3 more beetles crawled away.
How many are now on the leaf?

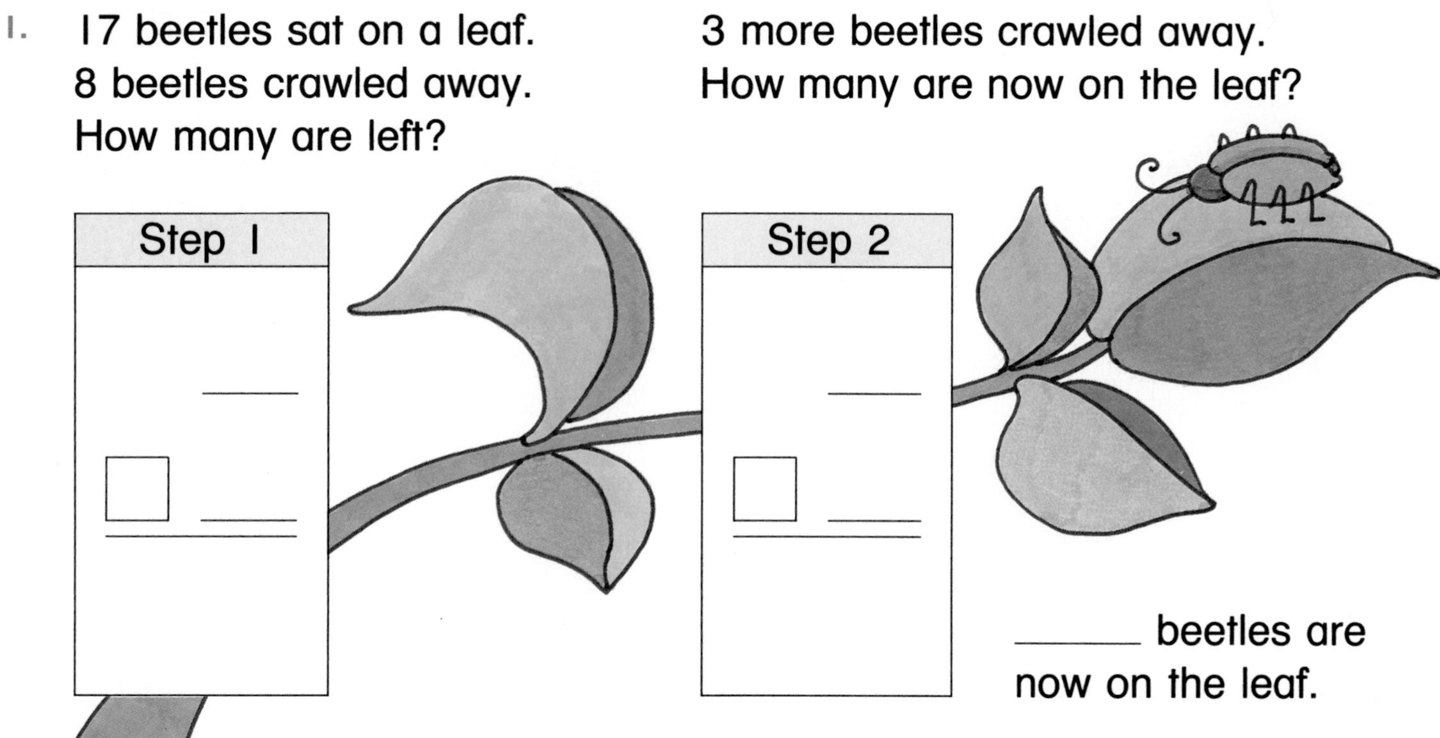

Notes for Home Children learn to solve multiple-step problems involving addition and subtraction.

Show each step.
Then solve.

2. 8 brown rabbits and 5 white rabbits were playing. How many rabbits are there?

7 of the rabbits hopped away. How many are playing now?

6 rabbits are playing.

3. 15 butterflies were on a flower. 7 butterflies flew away. How many are left?

4 more butterflies flew away. How many are still on the flower?

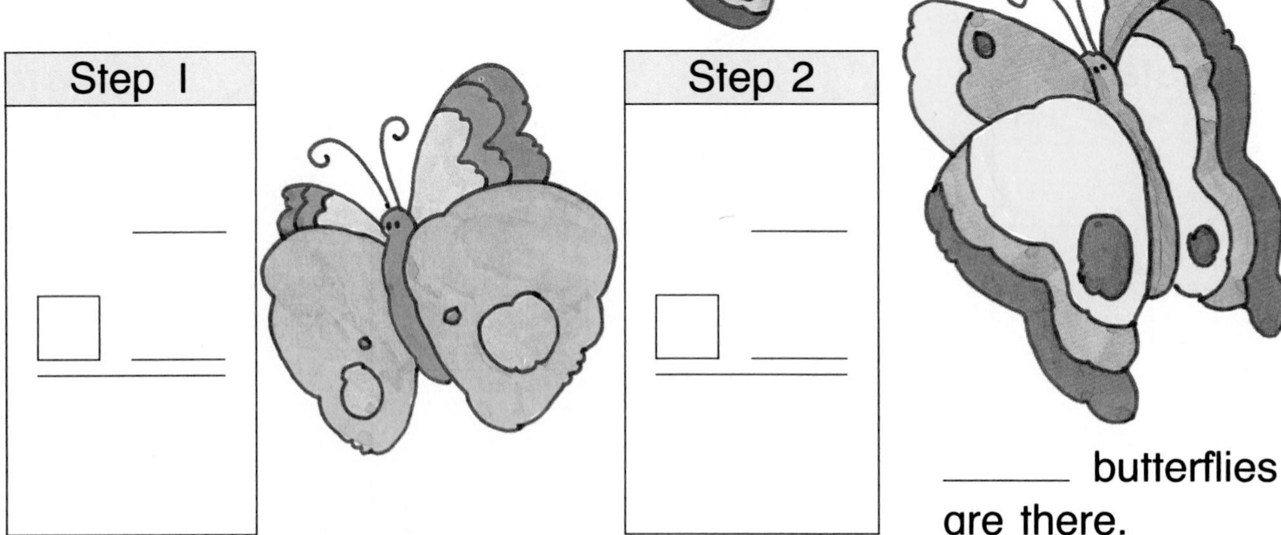

_____ butterflies are there.

Exploring Mathematics Book Two © Scott, Foresman and Company

Notes for Home Children solve multiple-step problems involving addition and subtraction.

Name

Number Sense

Write as many subtraction sentences as you can using the number 7 in each one.

Let's do some more!

Write a subtraction story about 7 flamingos.

Notes for Home Children develop number understanding by writing subtraction sentences using the number 7.

SKILLS REVIEW

Skills Review

Fill in the correct ◯.
Find the greater number.

1. 39 Ⓐ 21 Ⓑ	2. 46 Ⓐ 59 Ⓑ	3. 76 Ⓐ 66 Ⓑ

Find the number that is less.

4. 33 Ⓐ 43 Ⓑ	5. 98 Ⓐ 89 Ⓑ	6. 22 Ⓐ 12 Ⓑ

How much?

7.    

____¢ in all

8.     

____¢ in all

Vocabulary

Write the words in order.

fifth second fourteenth

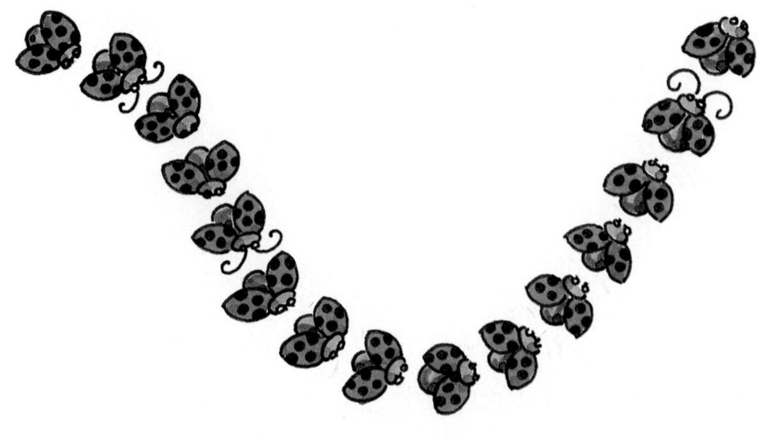

second

____

____

Exploring Mathematics Book Two © Scott, Foresman and Company

Notes for Home Children compare the value of two numbers and review amounts of money through 99¢. Then they write ordinal numbers in order.

Name

Related Subtraction Facts for 11 and 12

8 and 3 are parts of 11.

11 − 3 = 8

11 − 8 = 3

Subtract.

1.

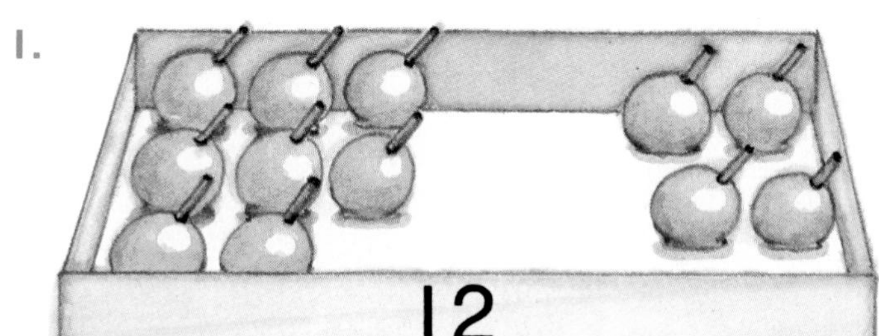

12 − 4 = ___

12 − 8 = ___

2.

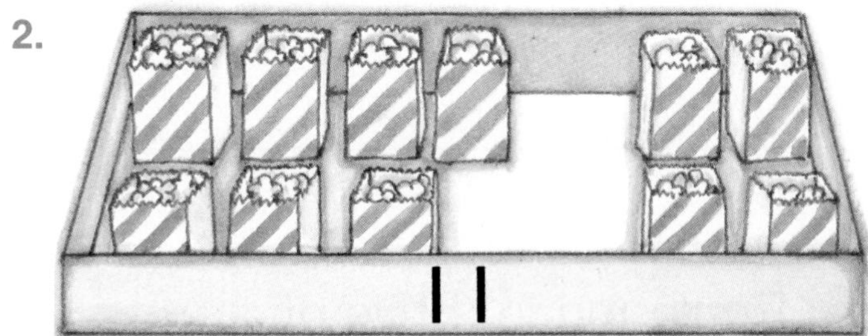

11 − 4 = ___

11 − 7 = ___

3.

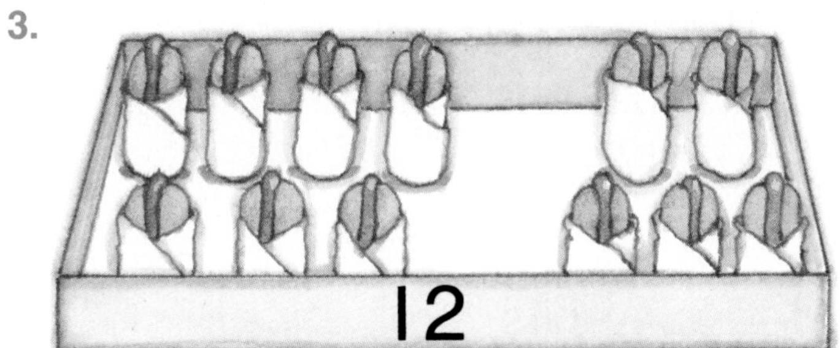

12 − 5 = ___

12 − 7 = ___

Notes for Home Children learn related subtraction facts for 11 and 12.

Subtract.

4.	$\begin{array}{r} 11 \\ -\ 5 \\ \hline 6 \end{array}$	$\begin{array}{r} 11 \\ -\ 6 \\ \hline \end{array}$	5.	$\begin{array}{r} 11 \\ -\ 2 \\ \hline \end{array}$	$\begin{array}{r} 11 \\ -\ 9 \\ \hline \end{array}$	6.	$\begin{array}{r} 12 \\ -\ 3 \\ \hline \end{array}$	$\begin{array}{r} 12 \\ -\ 9 \\ \hline \end{array}$

7. $\begin{array}{r} 12 \\ -\ 6 \\ \hline \end{array}$ $\begin{array}{r} 11 \\ -\ 3 \\ \hline \end{array}$ $\begin{array}{r} 12 \\ -\ 4 \\ \hline \end{array}$ $\begin{array}{r} 12 \\ -\ 5 \\ \hline \end{array}$ $\begin{array}{r} 16 \\ -\ 8 \\ \hline \end{array}$ $\begin{array}{r} 11 \\ -\ 4 \\ \hline \end{array}$ $\begin{array}{r} 18 \\ -\ 9 \\ \hline \end{array}$

8. $\begin{array}{r} 10 \\ -\ 4 \\ \hline \end{array}$ $\begin{array}{r} 12 \\ -\ 3 \\ \hline \end{array}$ $\begin{array}{r} 12 \\ -\ 7 \\ \hline \end{array}$ $\begin{array}{r} 11 \\ -\ 5 \\ \hline \end{array}$ $\begin{array}{r} 12 \\ -\ 8 \\ \hline \end{array}$ $\begin{array}{r} 11 \\ -\ 2 \\ \hline \end{array}$ $\begin{array}{r} 11 \\ -\ 6 \\ \hline \end{array}$

9. $\begin{array}{r} 11 \\ -\ 7 \\ \hline \end{array}$ $\begin{array}{r} 10 \\ -\ 6 \\ \hline \end{array}$ $\begin{array}{r} 12 \\ -\ 7 \\ \hline \end{array}$ $\begin{array}{r} 14 \\ -\ 7 \\ \hline \end{array}$

Problem Solving

Solve.

10. Paula's team plays 12 games this month. They have 7 games left to play. How many games have they played already?

    ______ games

11. Paula made 4 hits on Monday and 7 hits on Wednesday. How many hits did she make in all?

    ______ hits

Exploring Mathematics Book Two © Scott, Foresman and Company

Notes for Home Children practice subtraction facts. Then they solve problems involving addition and subtraction.

Name ______________________

Related Subtraction Facts for 13 and 14

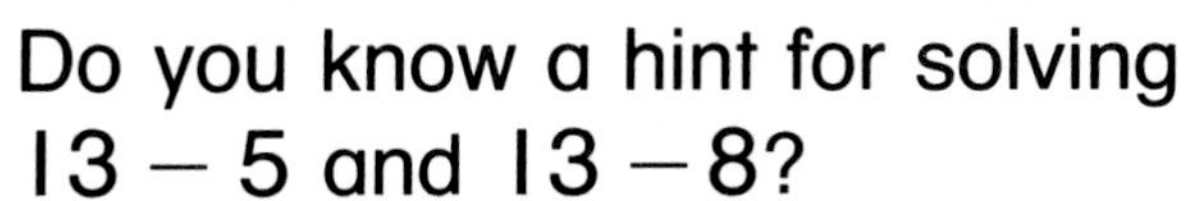

13 − 5 = 8

13 − 8 = 5

Subtract.

1.

14 − ____ = ____

14 − ____ = ____

2.

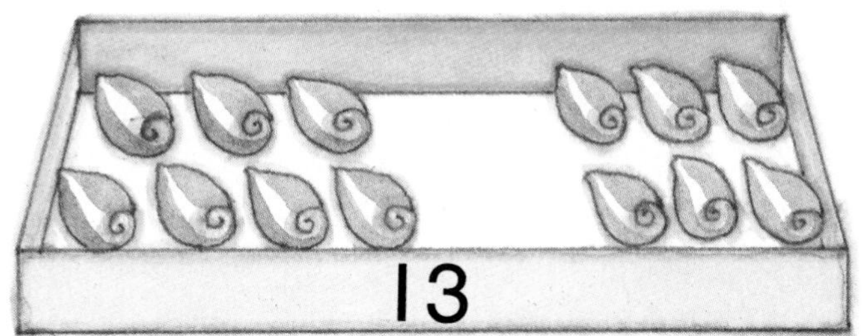

13 − ____ = ____

13 − ____ = ____

3.

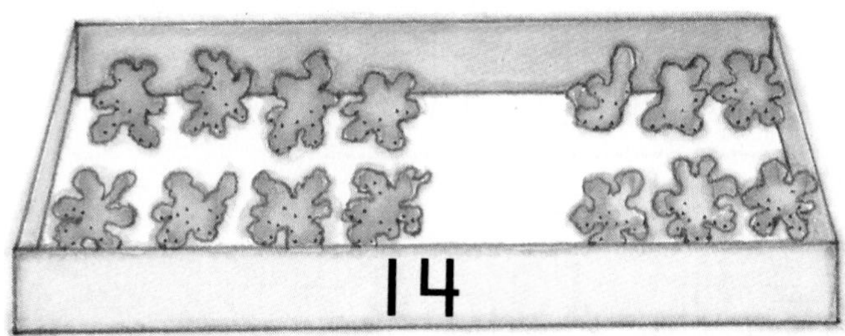

14 − ____ = ____

14 − ____ = ____

Notes for Home Children learn related subtraction facts for 13 and 14.

Subtract.

4. $13 - 4 = 9$ $13 - 9$	5. $13 - 5$ $13 - 8$	6. $14 - 9$ $14 - 5$

7.	$14 - 8$	$12 - 3$	$11 - 6$	$12 - 8$	$13 - 6$	$11 - 8$	$14 - 9$
8.	$11 - 4$	$13 - 9$	$11 - 7$	$12 - 5$	$11 - 2$	$13 - 4$	$14 - 5$
9.	$12 - 9$	$13 - 7$	$13 - 8$	$11 - 5$	$14 - 6$	$12 - 7$	$13 - 5$
10.	$12 - 4$	$11 - 9$	$11 - 3$	$12 - 6$	$14 - 7$	$13 - 4$	$14 - 8$

Talk About Math

Look at the facts below.
Why are they related facts?

$13 - 5 = 8$ $13 - 8 = 5$

Notes for Home Children practice subtraction facts. Then they talk about related facts.

Exploring Mathematics Book Two © Scott, Foresman and Company

Name

Related Subtraction Facts for 15 Through 18

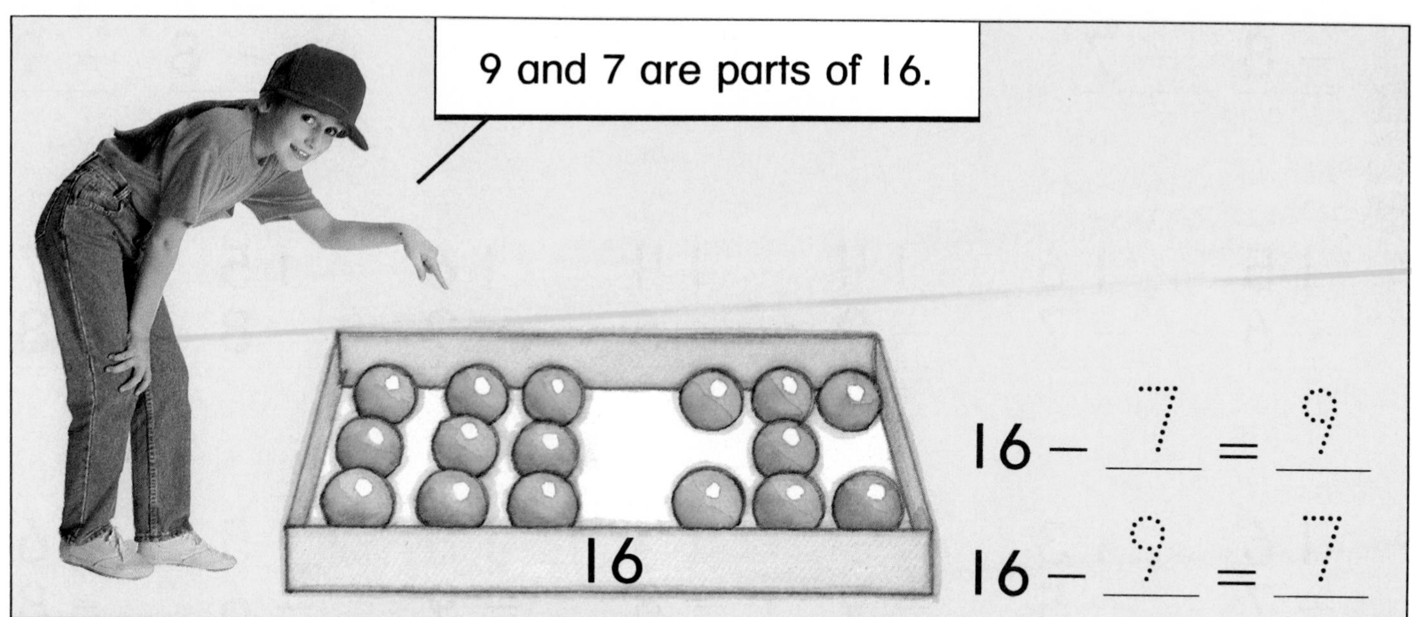

16 − 7 = 9

16 − 9 = 7

Complete the number sentence.

1.

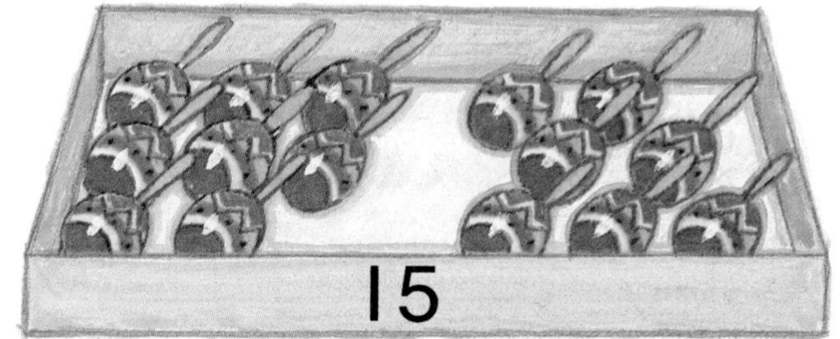

15 − ___ = ___

15 − ___ = ___

2.

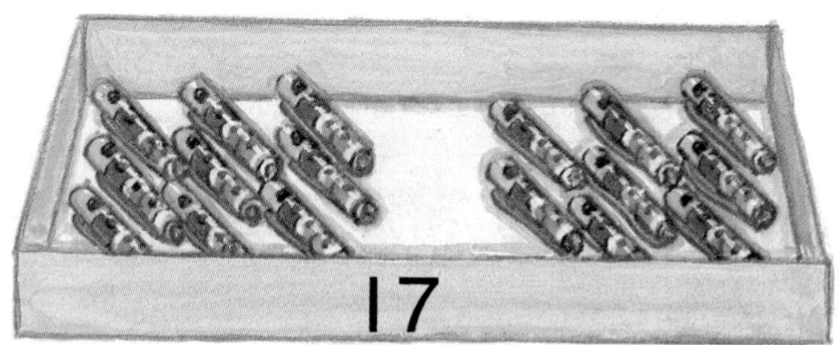

17 − ___ = ___

17 − ___ = ___

3.

15 − ___ = ___

15 − ___ = ___

Notes for Home Children learn related subtraction facts for 15, 16, 17, and 18.

Write the difference.

4. $15 - 8 = 7$ $\quad 15 - 7$

5. $13 - 6$ $\quad 13 - 7$

6. $17 - 8$ $\quad 17 - 9$

7. $15 - 6$ $\quad 16 - 7$ $\quad 14 - 9$ $\quad 14 - 6$ $\quad 16 - 9$ $\quad 15 - 8$ $\quad 17 - 8$

8. $16 - 7$ $\quad 13 - 5$ $\quad 17 - 9$ $\quad 14 - 8$ $\quad 18 - 9$ $\quad 15 - 6$ $\quad 16 - 8$

9. $13 - 8$ $\quad 15 - 9$ $\quad 14 - 5$ $\quad 15 - 7$ $\quad 15 - 9$ $\quad 16 - 9$ $\quad 13 - 7$

Problem Solving

Do you add or subtract?
Ring. Then solve.

10. There are 15 children on the playground. 6 children go home. How many children stay on the playground?

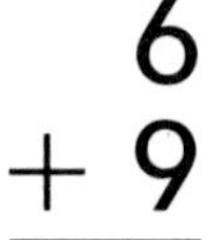

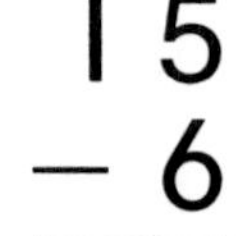

Notes for Home Children practice subtraction facts through 18. Then they solve a problem involving facts.

See More Practice Set A on page 127.

Exploring Mathematics Book Two © Scott, Foresman and Company

Name ______________________________

Families of Facts

5, 9, and 14 make a family of facts.

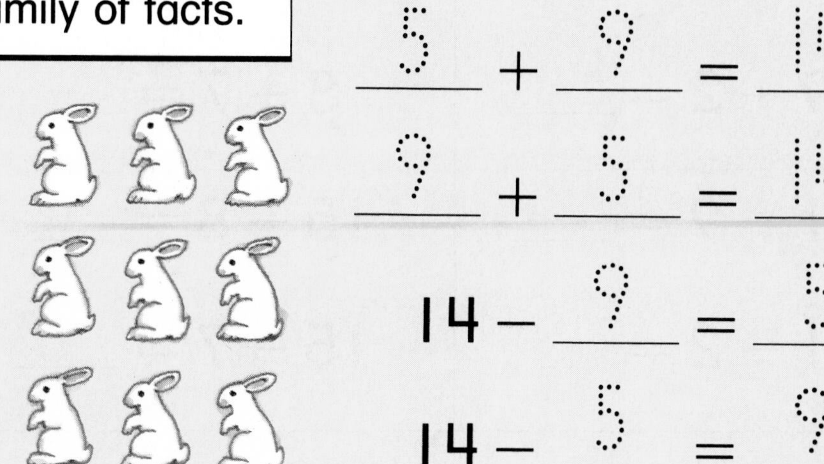

5 + 9 = 14

9 + 5 = 14

14 − 9 = 5

14 − 5 = 9

Use the pictures to complete the number sentences.

1\.

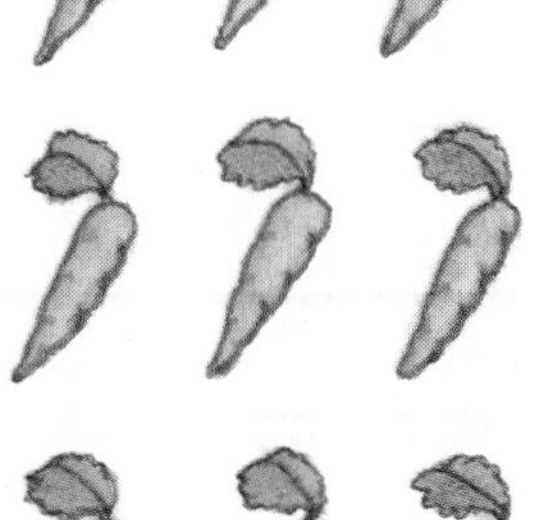

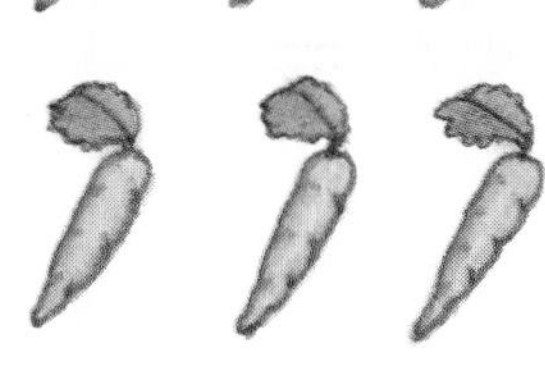

____ + ____ = ____

____ + ____ = ____

17 − ____ = ____

17 − ____ = ____

2\.

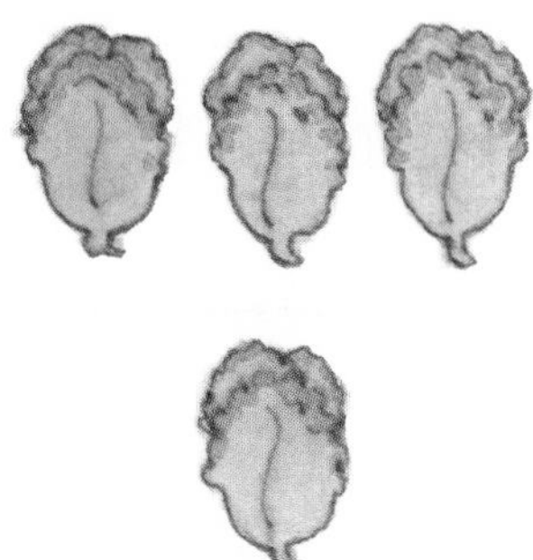

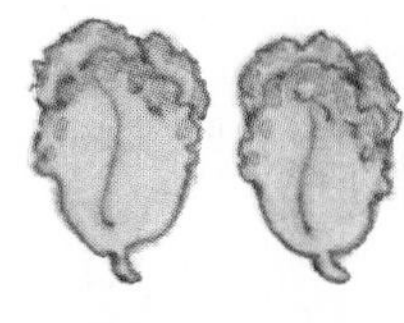

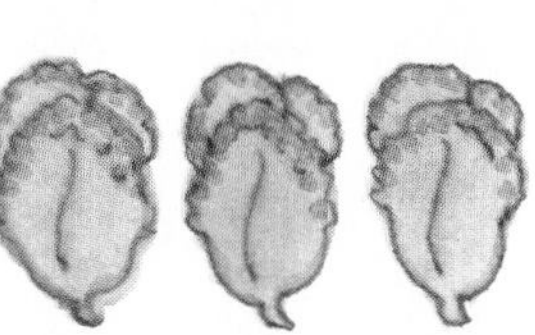

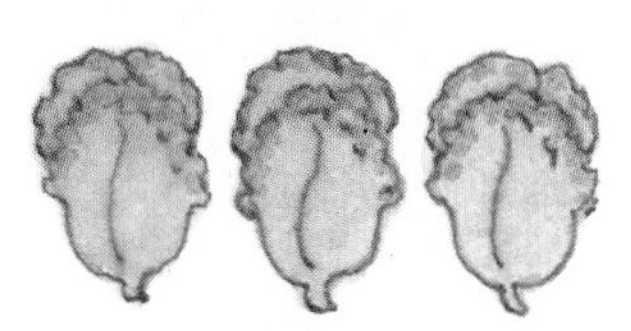

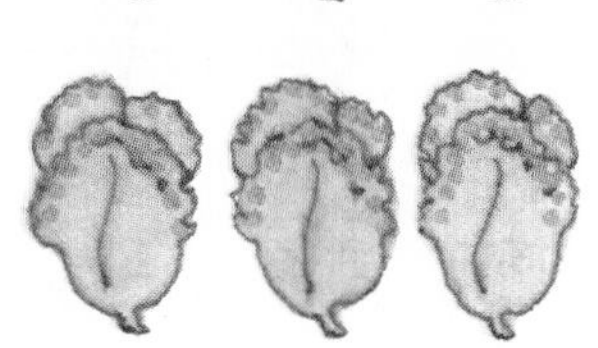

____ + ____ = ____

____ + ____ = ____

16 − ____ = ____

16 − ____ = ____

Notes for Home Children complete number sentences for families of facts.

Add or subtract.

3. $2 + 9 =$ ____
$9 + 2 =$ ____
$11 - 9 =$ ____
$11 - 2 =$ ____

4. $7 + 8 =$ ____
$8 + 7 =$ ____
$15 - 8 =$ ____
$15 - 7 =$ ____

5. $6 + 8 =$ ____
$8 + 6 =$ ____
$14 - 8 =$ ____
$14 - 6 =$ ____

6. $3 + 8 =$ ____
$8 + 3 =$ ____
$11 - 8 =$ ____
$11 - 3 =$ ____

7. $6 + 7 =$ ____
$7 + 6 =$ ____
$13 - 7 =$ ____
$13 - 6 =$ ____

8. $5 + 8 =$ ____
$8 + 5 =$ ____
$13 - 8 =$ ____
$13 - 5 =$ ____

Talk About Math

Why are there only two facts in this family?

$8 + 8 = 16$ $16 - 8 = 8$

Exploring Mathematics Book Two © Scott, Foresman and Company

Notes for Home Children practice finding sums and differences for families of facts. Then they talk about why a doubles family has only two facts.

Name

Addition and Subtraction Through 18

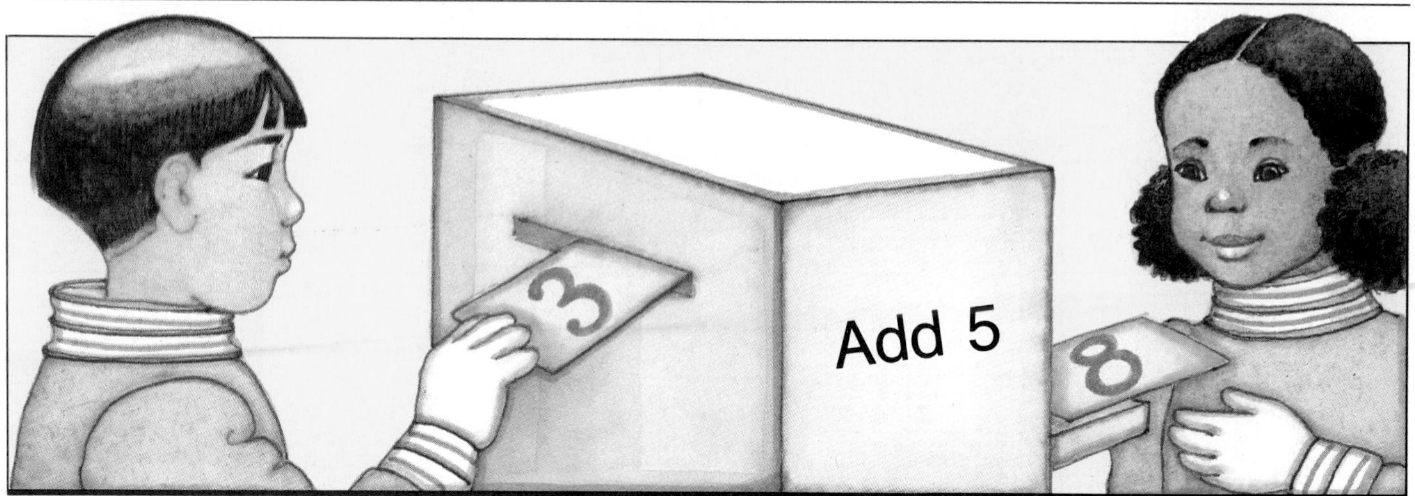

Add or subtract.

1.

Add 5	
3	8
7	
5	
6	

2.

Add 3	
4	
9	
6	
8	

3.

Add 9	
9	
7	
4	
8	

4.

Subtract 4	
9	5
12	
8	
11	

5.

Subtract 6	
10	
14	
12	
15	

6.

Subtract 3	
8	
12	
10	
11	

Notes for Home Children practice finding sums and differences through 18.

Add or subtract.

7.

Add 4	
7	⁞⁞
5	
9	
8	

8.

Subtract 9	
14	
13	
12	
15	

9.

Add 7	
6	
4	
8	
7	

10.

Subtract 5	
13	
11	
12	
14	

11.

Add 8	
3	
9	
7	
5	

12.

Subtract 8	
16	
11	
17	
12	

13.

Subtract 5	
10	
14	
12	
11	

14.

Add 4	
4	
9	
7	
8	

15.

Subtract 9	
16	
13	
17	
12	

Exploring Mathematics Book Two © Scott, Foresman and Company

Notes for Home Children practice finding sums and differences through 18.

See More Practice Set B on page 127.

Name

Choose an Operation

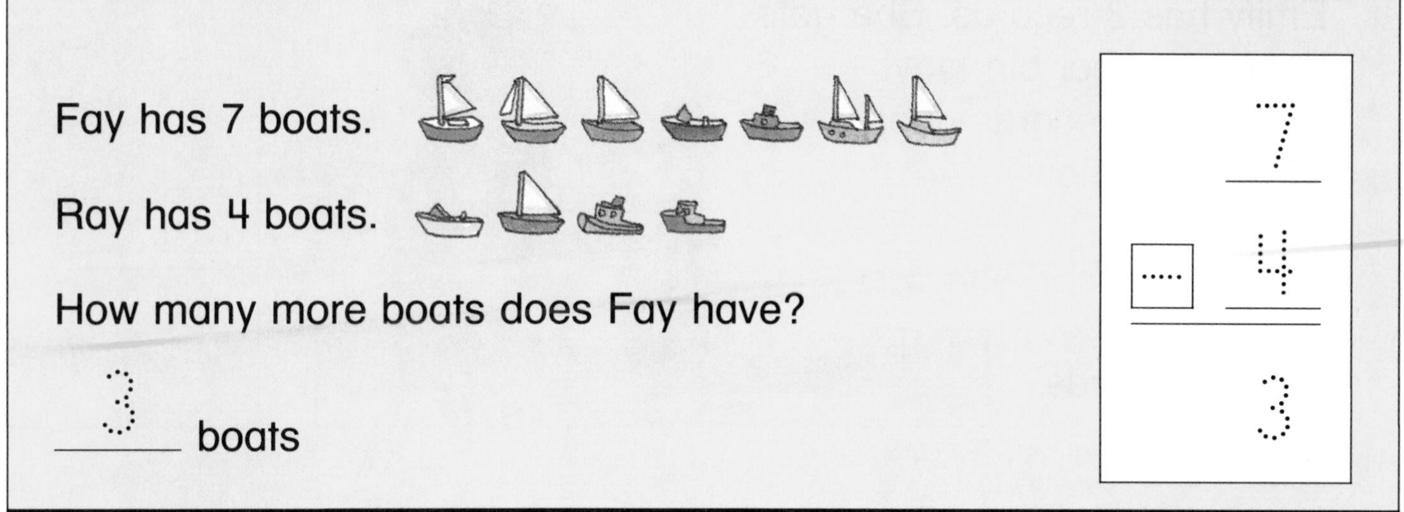

Decide if you need to add or subtract.
Then solve.

1. Karen has 8 toy bears. She buys 7 more toy bears. How many toy bears does she have in all?

_____ bears

2. Jon has 15 books on his shelf. He takes 8 books to the library. How many books are left on the shelf?

_____ books

Notes for Home Children solve problems by deciding whether to add or subtract.

Decide if you need to add or subtract.
Then solve.

3. Emily has 3 records. She gets 4 more for her birthday. How many records does Emily have now?

7 records

	3
+	4
	7

4. Joyce has 8 games. Alex has 3 games less than Joyce. How many games does Alex have?

_____ games

5. Dolly has 9 puzzles. Hans has 6 puzzles. How many more puzzles does Dolly have?

_____ puzzles

Exploring Mathematics Book Two © Scott, Foresman and Company

Notes for Home Children solve problems by deciding whether to add or subtract.

Name

Problem-Solving Workshop

Explore as a Team

Work with a partner.
Ring the hidden subtraction sentence in each box.
Put the − and = in the sentence.

1. | 3 | 12 − 3 = 9 | 1 |

2. | 3 | 12 | 14 | 8 | 6 |

3. | 16 | 7 | 9 | 4 | 12 |

4. | 15 | 12 | 5 | 7 | 9 |

5. | 13 | 6 | 7 | 9 | 10 |

6. | 15 | 9 | 13 | 8 | 5 |

7. | 18 | 9 | 11 | 6 | 5 |

8. | 14 | 6 | 8 | 10 | 4 |

Let's do some more!

Write your own number boxes.
Use subtraction facts through 18.
Have your partner ring the hidden subtraction sentence in each.

Notes for Home Children explore with a partner to solve subtraction problems.

Problem-Solving Workshop

Explore with a Calculator

Use a calculator to solve.

	Start at	Press	Write the pattern
1.	1 8	− 2 = = =	16 14 12   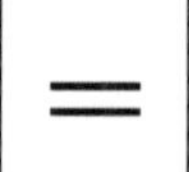 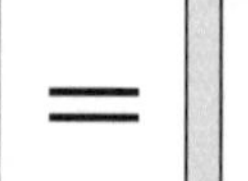 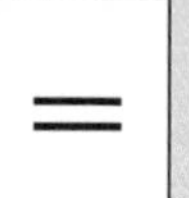   
2.	1 6	− 3 = = =	  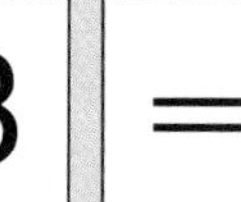 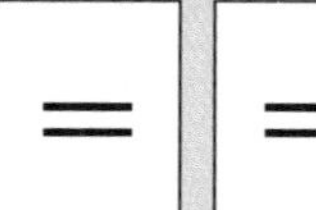  
3.	1 5	− 5 = = =	  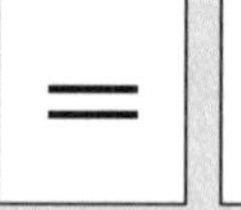 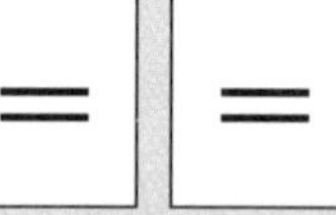  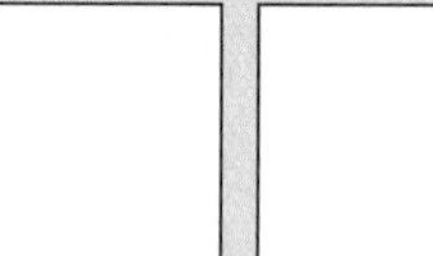
4.	1 6	− 4 = = =	 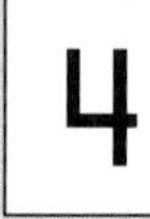 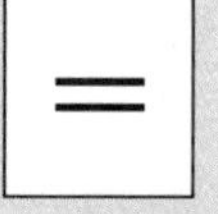 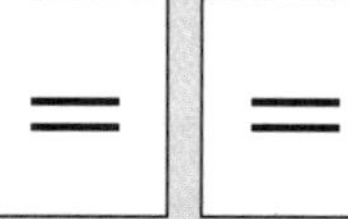  
5.	1 8	− 6 = = =	   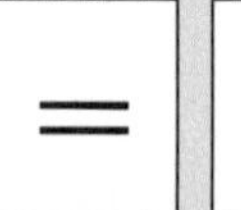 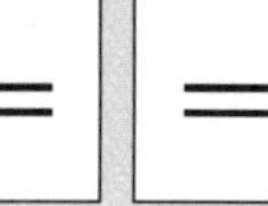  
6.	1 5	− 2 = = =	 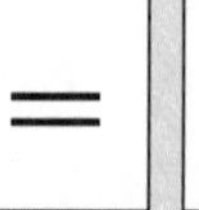   

Exploring Mathematics Book Two © Scott, Foresman and Company

Notes for Home Children explore with a calculator to solve subtraction problems using repeated subtraction.

Name

More Practice

Set A Use after page 118.

Write the difference.

1.	17 − 9 = 8	15 − 9	14 − 5	16 − 8	13 − 8	13 − 7	15 − 8
2.	13 − 6	18 − 9	17 − 8	15 − 7	13 − 9	16 − 7	14 − 8

Set B Use after page 122.

Solve the puzzle. Add or subtract.

Across

1. $9 + 8$
2. $13 - 5$
3. $11 - 5$
6. $6 + 7$
7. $9 + 3$
8. $4 + 4$
9. $12 - 7$

1. 1	7	■	2.	■
5	■	3.	■	4.
■	5.	■	6.	
7.		■		■
	■	8.	■	9.

Down

1. $6 + 9$
2. $16 - 8$
3. $15 - 9$
4. $8 + 5$
5. $4 + 8$
6. $9 + 5$
7. $7 + 4$
8. $17 - 9$
9. $13 - 8$

Notes for Home Set A: Children practice subtraction facts for 15 through 18.
Set B: Children practice adding and subtracting facts through 18.

Independent Study ENRICHMENT

Enrichment

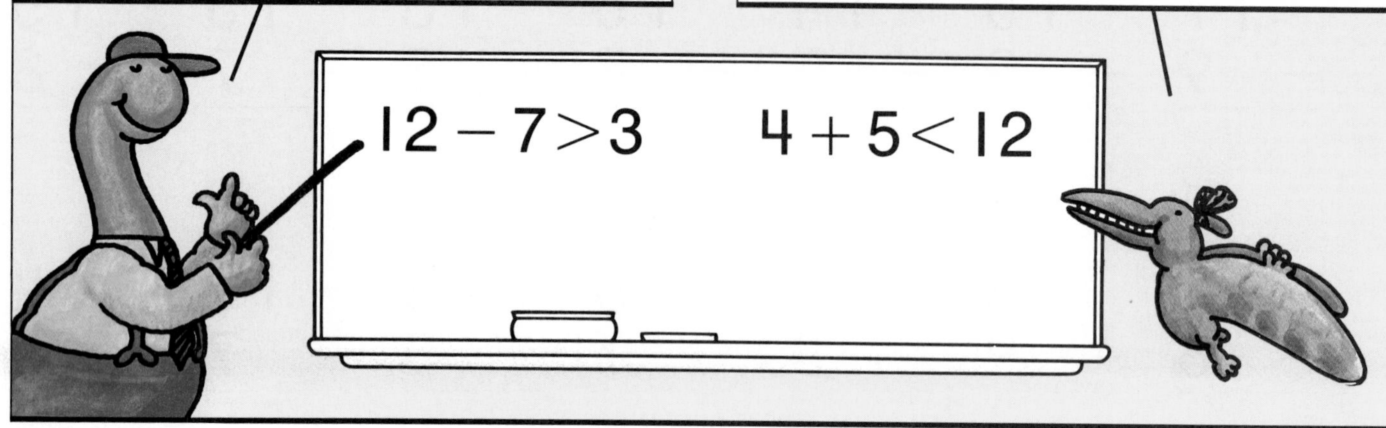

Ring yes or no.

1. $15 - 6 < 7$ yes (no)	2. $4 + 9 > 15$ yes no
3. $6 + 2 = 4 + 4$ yes no	4. $6 + 5 < 15$ yes no
5. $12 - 3 > 10$ yes no	6. $9 + 6 > 8$ yes no
7. $6 + 7 < 5$ yes no	8. $4 + 5 = 3 + 3$ yes no
9. $17 - 8 > 7$ yes no	10. $16 - 8 < 8$ yes no

Notes for Home Children are challenged to use >, <, and = in number sentences.

Exploring Mathematics Book Two © Scott, Foresman and Company

Name

Chapter 4 Review/Test

Subtract.

1. $\begin{array}{r} 12 \\ -\ 6 \\ \hline \end{array}$ $\begin{array}{r} 18 \\ -\ 9 \\ \hline \end{array}$ $\begin{array}{r} 14 \\ -\ 7 \\ \hline \end{array}$

2. $\begin{array}{r} 11 \\ -\ 8 \\ \hline \end{array}$ $\begin{array}{r} 13 \\ -\ 7 \\ \hline \end{array}$ $\begin{array}{r} 14 \\ -\ 6 \\ \hline \end{array}$

3. $\begin{array}{r} 11 \\ -\ 6 \\ \hline \end{array}$ $\begin{array}{r} 11 \\ -\ 5 \\ \hline \end{array}$

4. $\begin{array}{r} 14 \\ -\ 6 \\ \hline \end{array}$ $\begin{array}{r} 14 \\ -\ 8 \\ \hline \end{array}$

5. $\begin{array}{r} 16 \\ -\ 9 \\ \hline \end{array}$ $\begin{array}{r} 16 \\ -\ 7 \\ \hline \end{array}$

Add or subtract.

6. $9+5=$____ $5+9=$____ $14-5=$____ $14-9=$____

7. Decide if you need to add or subtract. Then solve.

Tootsie has 9 puppies. Cooky has 7 puppies. How many more puppies does Tootsie have?

____ puppies

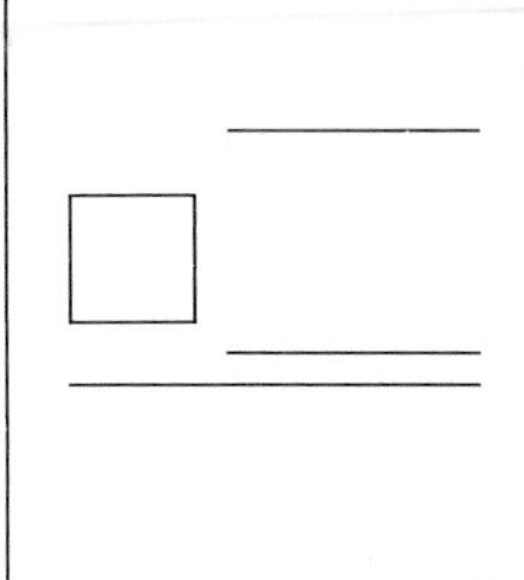

8. Show each step. Solve.

14 puppies are taking a nap. 8 puppies wake up. How many are still sleeping?

Step 1

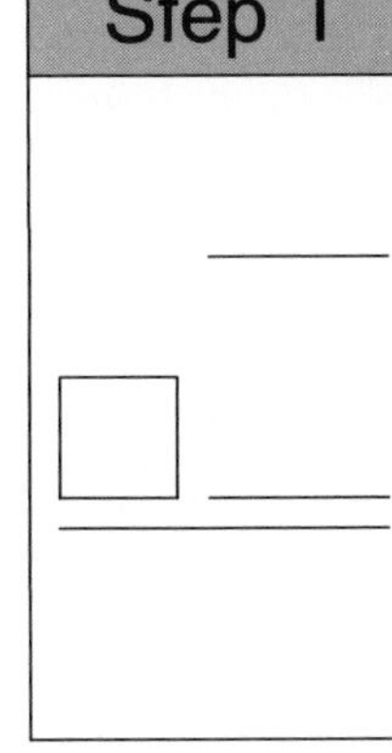

4 more puppies wake up. Now how many are asleep?

Step 2

____ puppies

Notes for Home Children are assessed on Chapter 4 concepts, skills, and problem solving.

Exploring Math at Home

Dear Family,

In this chapter I have reviewed addition and subtraction facts through 18. Please help me with the activities below.

Love, ______________________

1.

Make flash cards for subtraction facts of 11 through 18. Use them daily for a few minutes.

2.

Shuffle the same flash cards. Find pairs of related facts.

Coming Attractions

In the next chapter I will learn about telling time and the calendar. I will also learn to measure the lengths and heights of objects.

Exploring Mathematics Book Two © Scott, Foresman and Company

Listen to the math story, "Keeping Time."
A girl invented a new way to tell time.
What did the villagers call her invention?

Notes for Home Children listen to a math story introducing chapter concepts and skills. Then they answer a question about the story.

Name

Time Duration

About how long does each take?
Ring hour or minute.

1.

hour minute

2.

hour minute

3.

hour minute

4.

hour minute

Notes for Home Children identify whether an activity takes about an hour or about a minute to complete.

Exploring Mathematics Book Two © Scott, Foresman and Company

Name

Number Sense

About how many minutes does it take you to do each of these activities? How can you check to see if you are correct?

1. 

2. 

3. 

4. 

Let's do some more!

Name some activities that you wish would take less time.
Name some activities that you wish would take more time.

Notes for Home Children develop number understanding by first guessing then timing themselves to see how long it takes to do familiar activities.

Skills Review

Fill in the correct ◯.
Add or subtract.

1. $17 - 9$ Ⓐ 7 Ⓑ 8 Ⓒ 9	2. $4 + 8 =$ Ⓐ 4 Ⓑ 8 Ⓒ 12	3. $15 - 9$ Ⓐ 6 Ⓑ 7 Ⓒ 8
4. $7 + 8 =$ Ⓐ 15 Ⓑ 16 Ⓒ 17	5. $13 - 5$ Ⓐ 7 Ⓑ 8 Ⓒ 9	6. $18 - 9$ Ⓐ 7 Ⓑ 8 Ⓒ 9
7. $16 - 8$ Ⓐ 4 Ⓑ 6 Ⓒ 8	8. $7 + 6 =$ Ⓐ 13 Ⓑ 14 Ⓒ 15	9. $14 - 9$ Ⓐ 5 Ⓑ 7 Ⓒ 9

Vocabulary

Ring the sentence if it is correct.

10. 4, 9, and 13 make a family of facts.
11. Subtract 3 from 12 to get 8.
12. 21 is less than 11.
13. 3 tens and 9 ones are the same as 39.
14. 72 is greater than 64.
15. A quarter is the same as 10 cents.

Exploring Mathematics Book Two © Scott, Foresman and Company

Notes for Home Children review addition and subtraction facts through 18. Then they review math terms.

Name

Measuring Inches

Use an inch ruler.
Guess the length of each object.
Then measure to check.

1. 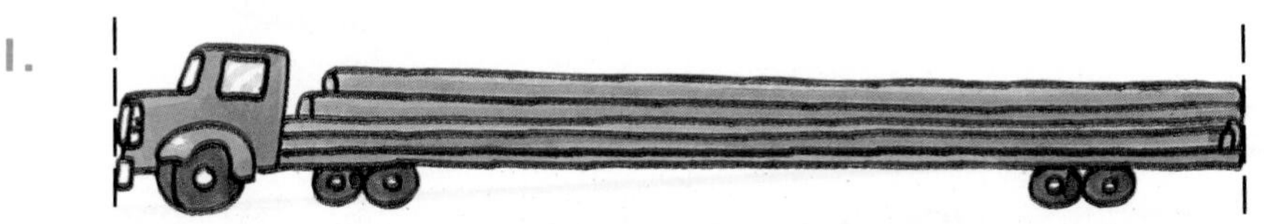

Guess: ______ inches Measure: __4__ inches

2. 

Guess: ______ inches Measure: ______ inches

3. 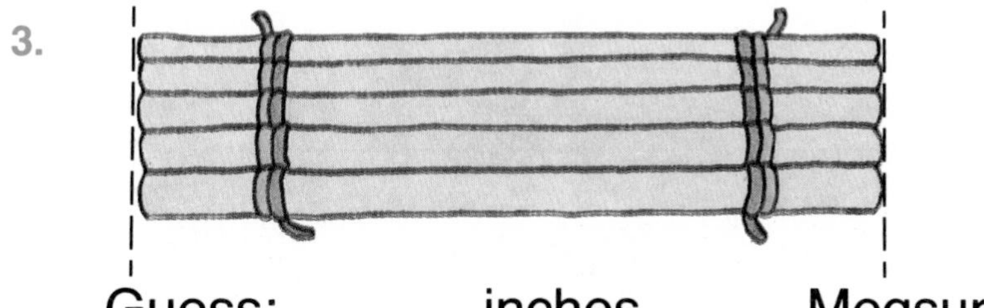

Guess: ______ inches Measure: ______ inches

Notes for Home Children explore at the CONCRETE level. They estimate lengths of objects and then use an inch ruler to measure.

Use an inch ruler.
Guess the height of each object.
Then measure to check.

4.

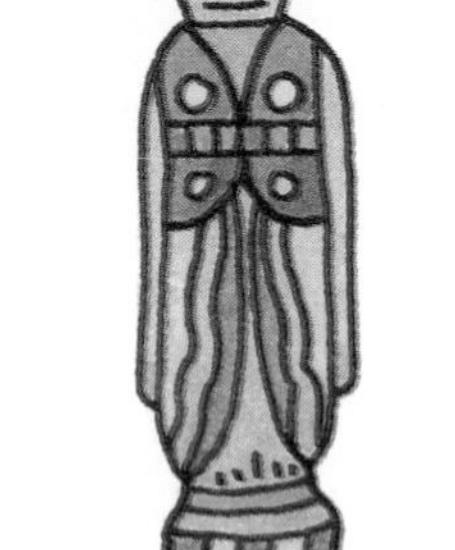

Guess: _____ inches

Measure: 2 inches

5.

Guess: _____ inches

Measure: _____ inches

6.

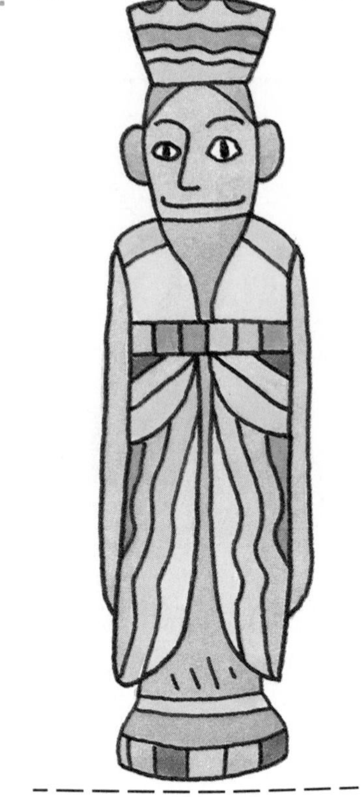

Guess: _____ inches

Measure: _____ inches

Talk About Math

Lori thought her pencil was 4 inches long.
What mistake did she make when she measured it?

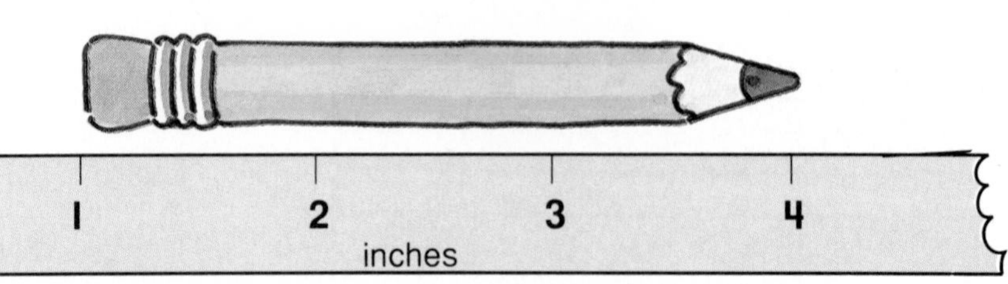

Exploring Mathematics Book Two © Scott, Foresman and Company

Notes for Home Children explore at the CONCRETE level estimating heights of objects and using an inch ruler to measure. Then they talk about measurement.

Name

Measuring to the Nearest Inch

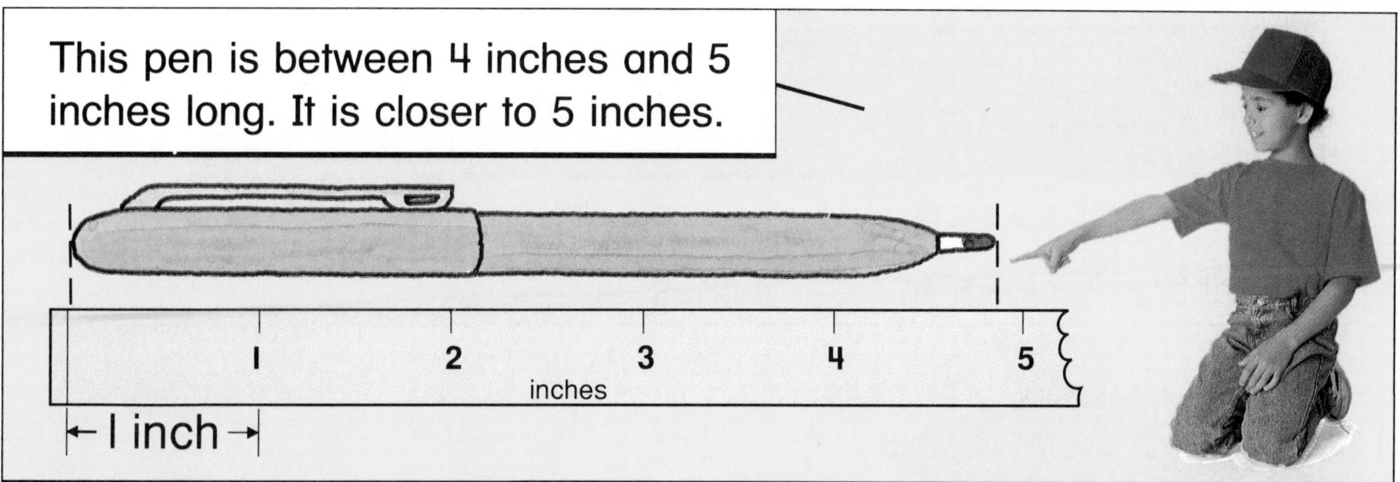

Use an inch ruler.
Find the length to the closer inch.

1. 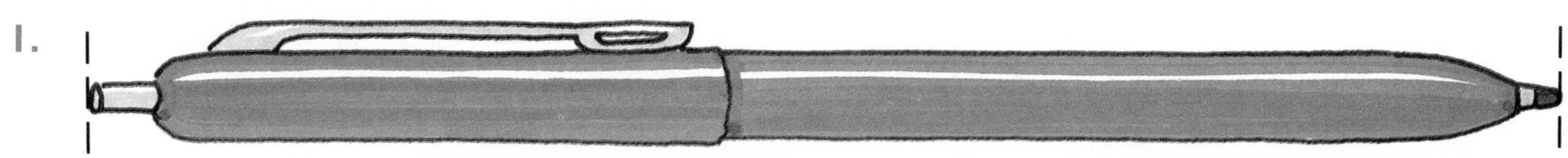

The pen is between 6 inches and 7 inches.

It is closer to 6 inches.

2. 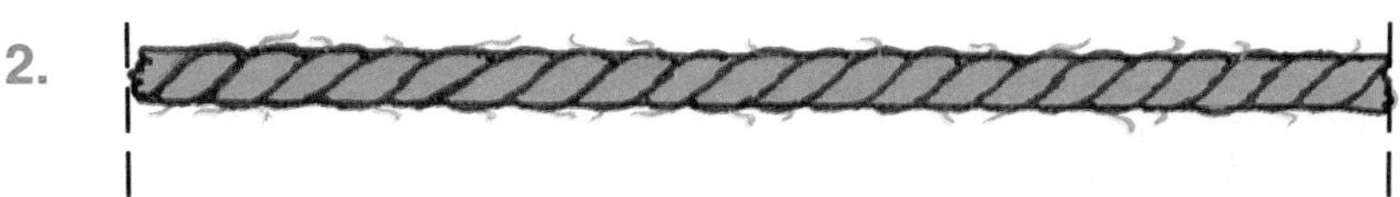

The yarn is between _____ inches and _____ inches.

It is closer to _____ inches.

3. 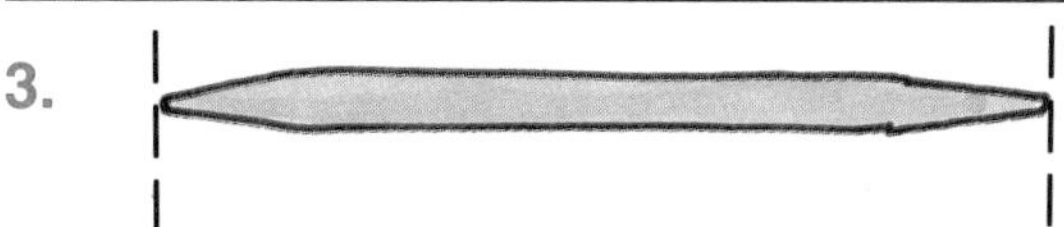

The toothpick is between _____ inches and _____ inches.

It is closer to _____ inches.

Notes for Home Children explore at the CONCRETE level measuring lengths of objects to the nearest inch.

Use an inch ruler.
Find the length to the closer inch.

4. 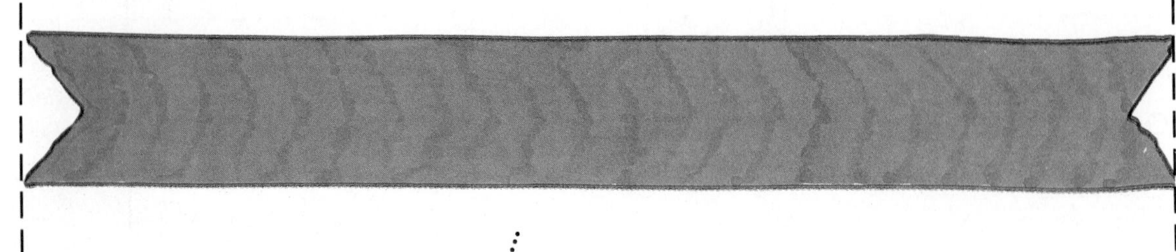

The ribbon is closer to 6 inches.

5. 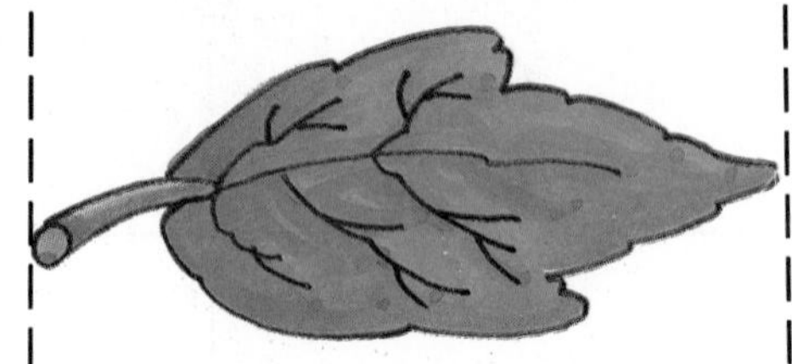

The leaf is closer to ____ inches.

6. 

The watch is closer to ____ inches.

7. 

The feather is closer to ____ inches.

8. 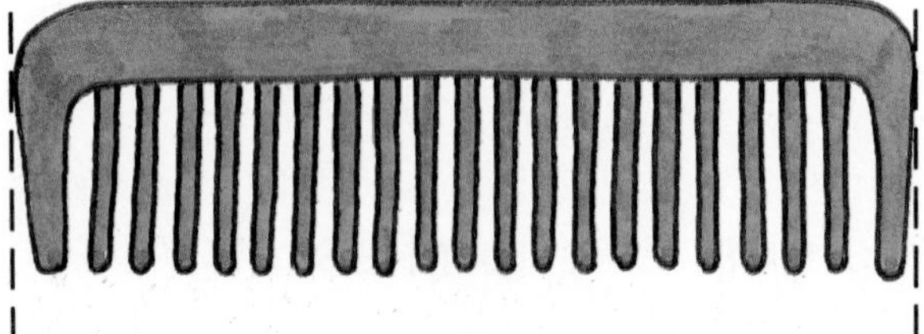

The comb is closer to ____ inches.

Exploring Mathematics Book Two © Scott, Foresman and Company

Notes for Home Children explore at the CONCRETE level measuring lengths of objects to the nearest inch.

 See More Practice Set B on page 165.

Name

Feet

1. Name objects in your classroom that are about 1 foot long.

2. Name objects that are shorter than 1 foot.

3. Name objects that are longer than 1 foot.

Notes for Home Children identify classroom objects that are about 1 foot long, shorter than 1 foot, and longer than 1 foot.

4. Ring the objects that are shorter than 1 foot.

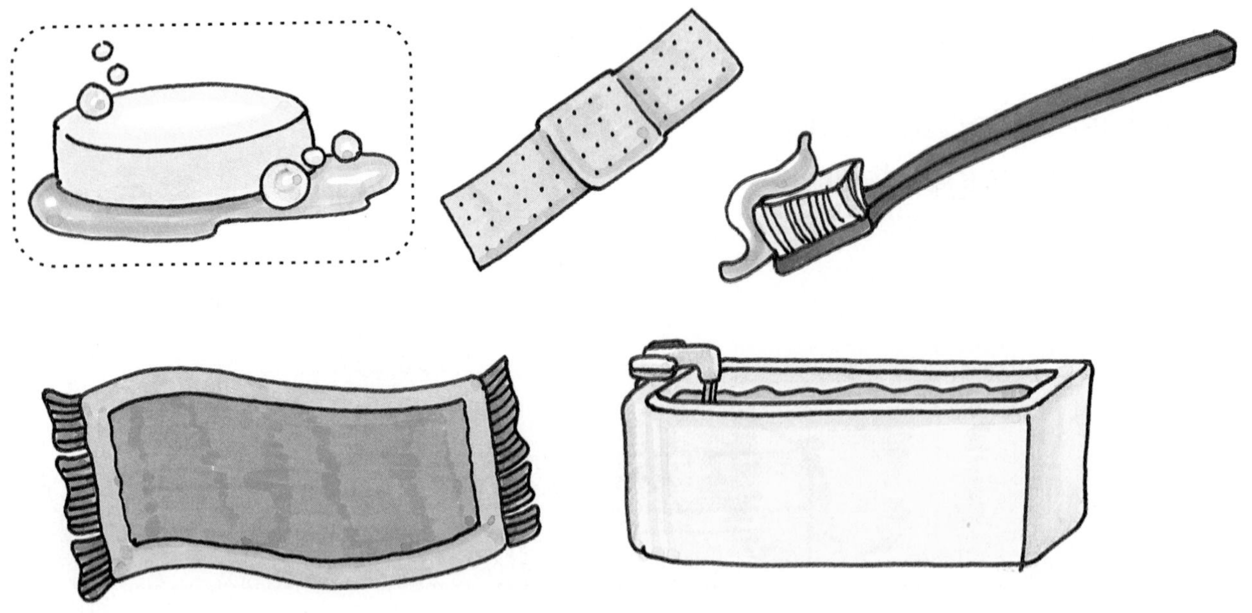

5. Ring the objects that are taller than 1 foot.

Critical Thinking Name some things you would measure in inches. Name some things you would measure in feet. Tell why.

Exploring Mathematics Book Two © Scott, Foresman and Company

Notes for Home Children practice estimating whether objects are shorter or taller than 1 foot. Then they discuss appropriate units of measure.

Name

Measuring Centimeters

ACTIVITY

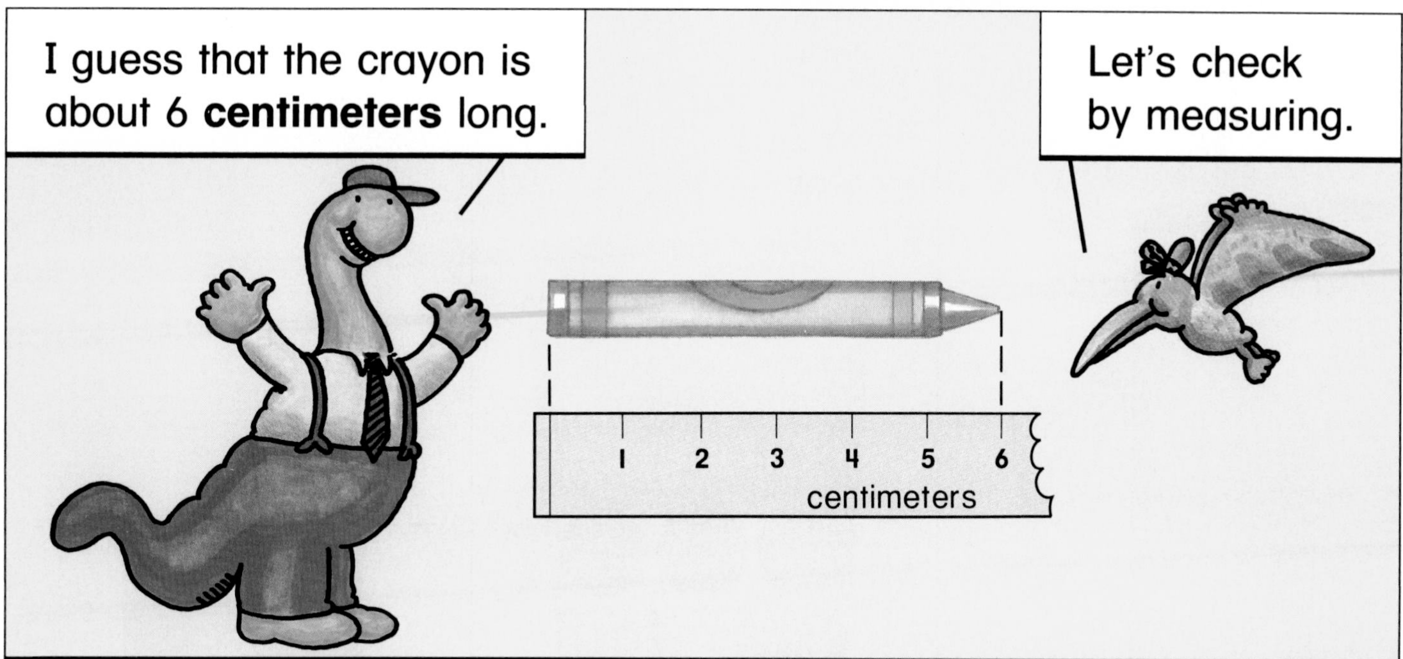

Use a centimeter ruler.
Guess the length of each object.
Then measure to check.

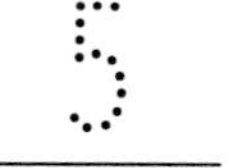

Guess: ______ cm Measure: ______ cm

2.

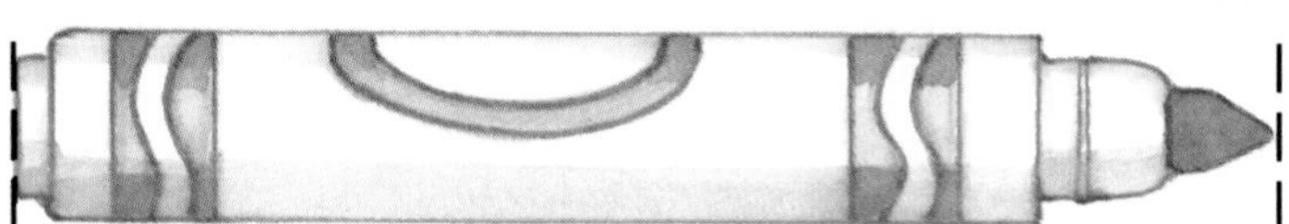

Guess: ______ cm Measure: ______ cm

3.

Guess: ______ cm Measure: ______ cm

Notes for Home Children explore at the CONCRETE level. They estimate lengths of objects and then use a centimeter ruler to measure.

Use a centimeter ruler.
Guess the height of each object.
Then measure to check.

4.

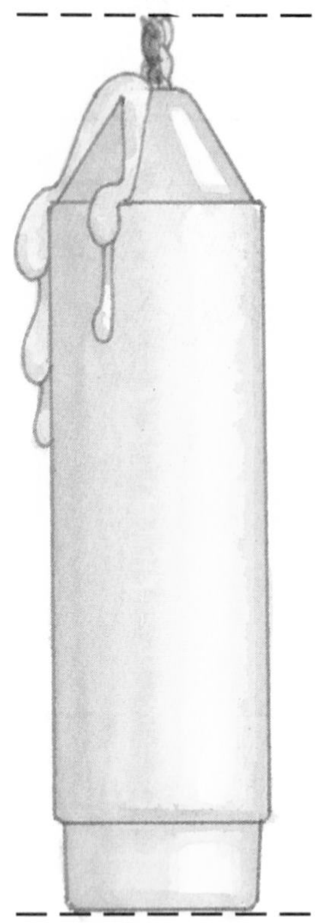

Guess: ____ cm

Measure: 10 cm

5.

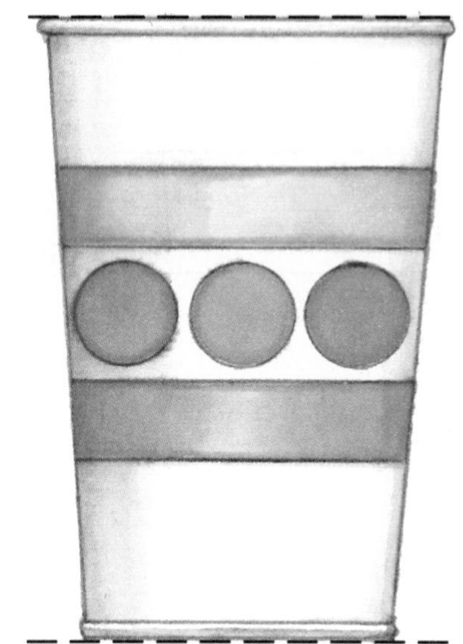

Guess: ____ cm

Measure: ____ cm

6.

Guess: ____ cm

Measure: ____ cm

Problem Solving

Solve.

7. Peter guesses that his pencil is 12 centimeters long. It measures 9 centimeters long. What is the difference?

____ centimeters

Exploring Mathematics Book Two © Scott, Foresman and Company

Notes for Home Children explore at the CONCRETE level estimating heights of objects and using a centimeter ruler to measure. Then they solve a problem about measurement.

Name

Measuring to the Nearest Centimeter

This pen is between 11 centimeters and 12 centimeters long.
It is closer to 11 centimeters long.

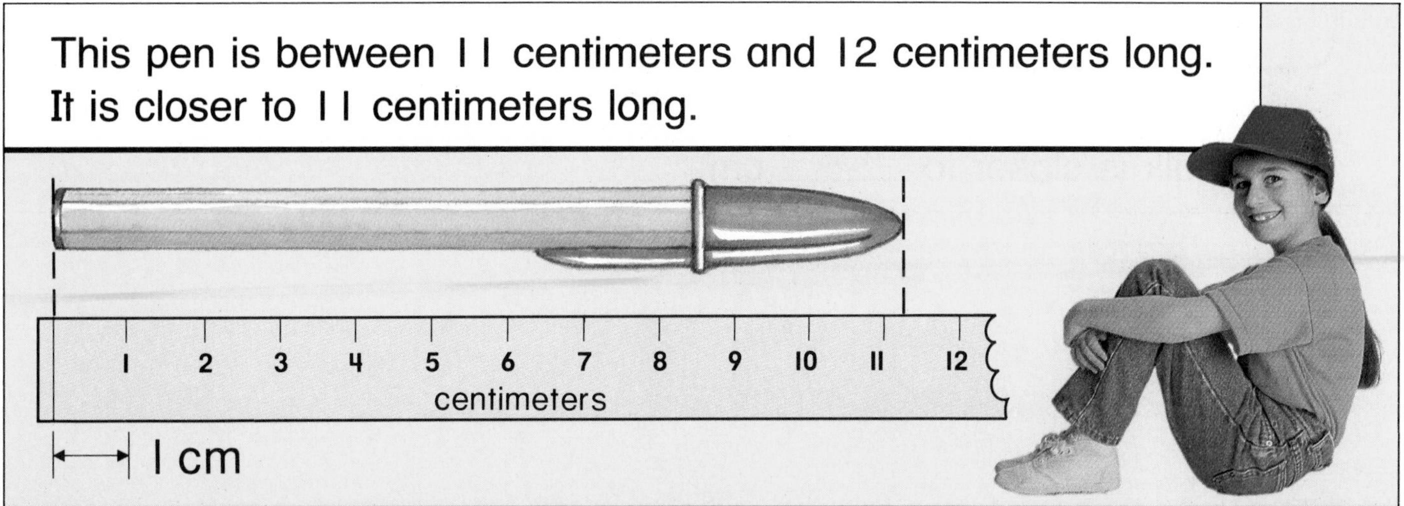

Use a centimeter ruler.
Find the length to the closer centimeter.

1. 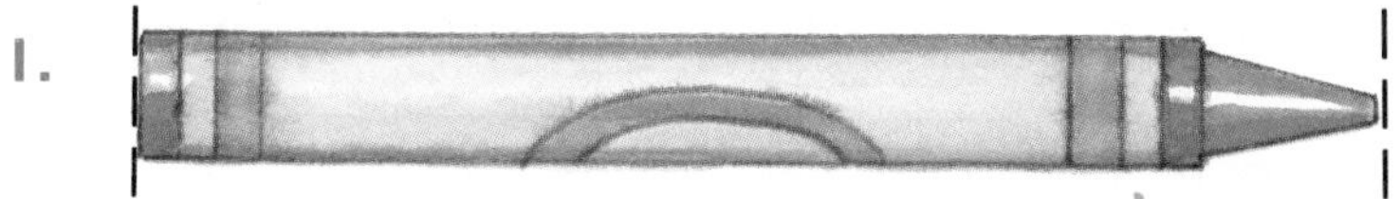

The crayon is between 8 cm and 9 cm.

It is closer to 9 cm.

2. 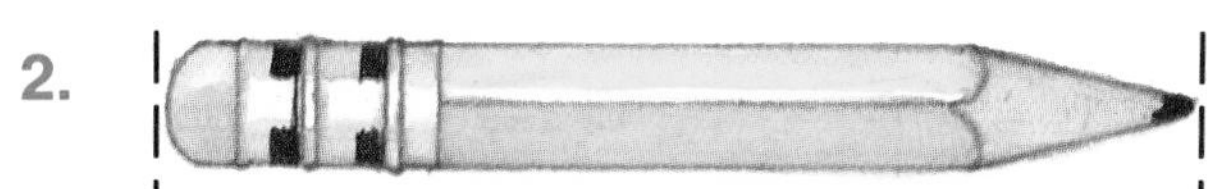

The pencil is between ____ cm and ____ cm.

It is closer to ____ cm.

3. 

The paintbrush is between ____ cm and ____ cm.

It is closer to ____ cm.

Notes for Home Children explore at the CONCRETE level measuring lengths of objects to the nearest centimeter.

Use a centimeter ruler.
Find the length to the closer centimeter.

4\.

The chalk is closer to 12 cm.

5\.

The tickets are closer to ______ cm.

6\.

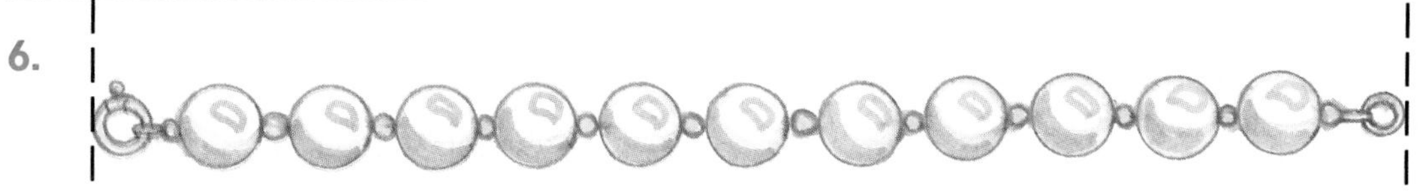

The bracelet is closer to ______ cm.

7\.

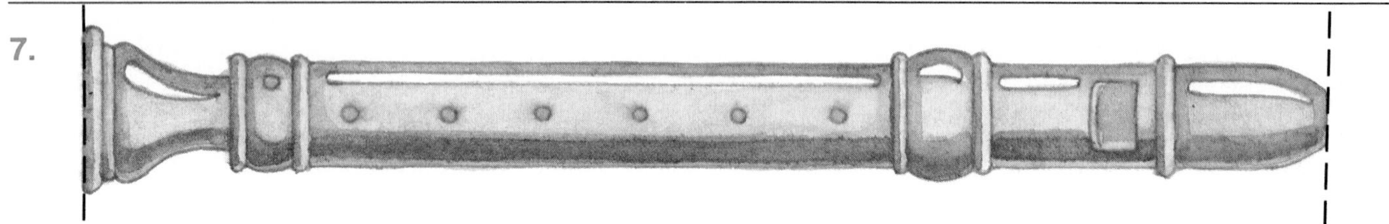

The recorder is closer to ______ cm.

8\. **Estimation** The blue pen is about 10 cm long.

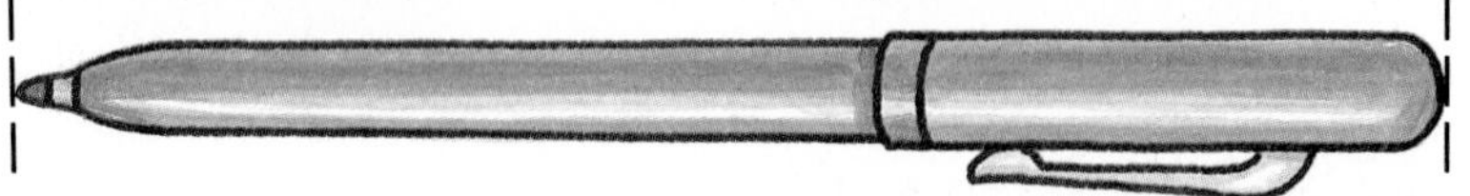

Guess how long the green pen is. Then measure it.

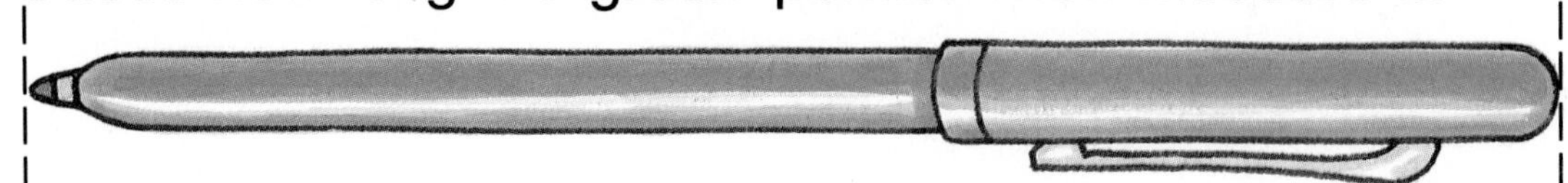

My guess is ______ cm. It measures ______ cm.

Notes for Home Children explore at the CONCRETE level measuring lengths of objects to the nearest centimeter. Then they estimate and measure an object in centimeters.

Exploring Mathematics Book Two © Scott, Foresman and Company

Name

Meters

1. Name objects in your classroom that are about 1 meter long.

2. Name objects that are shorter than 1 meter.

3. Name objects that are longer than 1 meter.

Notes for Home Children identify classroom objects that are about 1 meter long, shorter than 1 meter, and longer than 1 meter.

4. Ring the objects that are shorter than 1 meter.

5. Ring the objects that are taller than 1 meter.

Exploring Mathematics Book Two © Scott, Foresman and Company

Notes for Home Children practice estimating whether objects are shorter or taller than 1 meter.

Name

Use Logical Reasoning

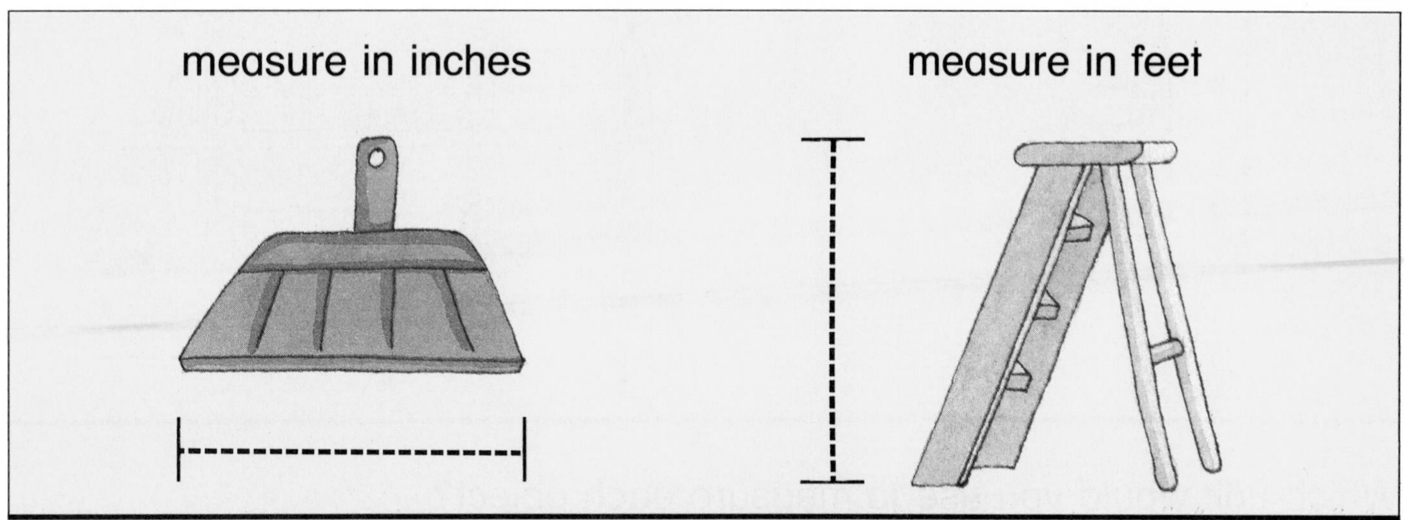

Which unit would you use to measure each object?
Ring the better unit.

1. inches feet

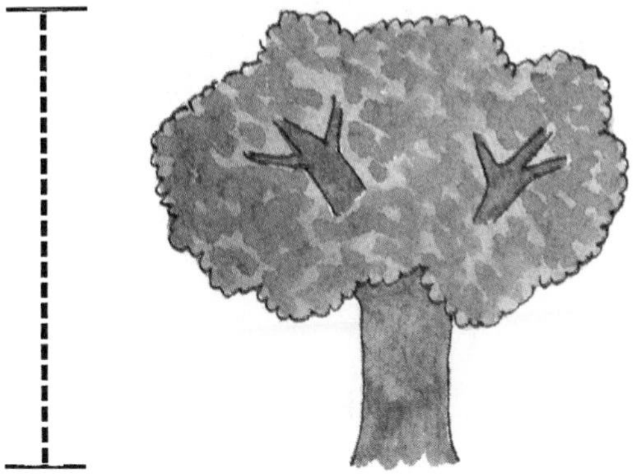

2. inches feet

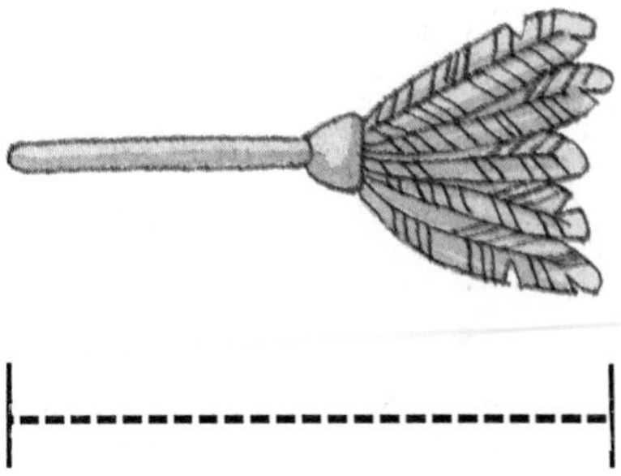

3. inches feet

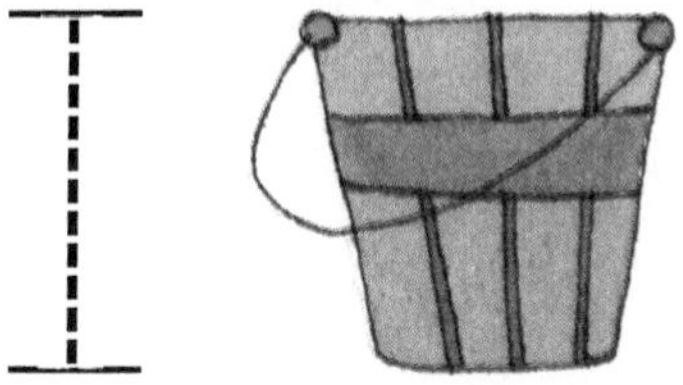

4. inches feet

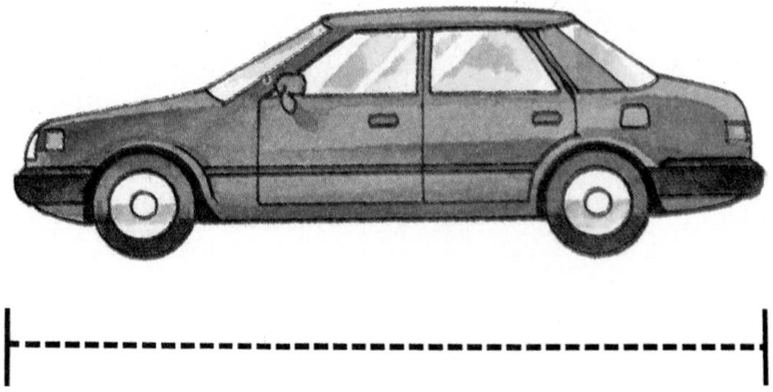

Notes for Home Children solve problems by choosing a sensible measure.

measure in centimeters

measure in meters

Which unit would you use to measure each object?
Ring the better unit.

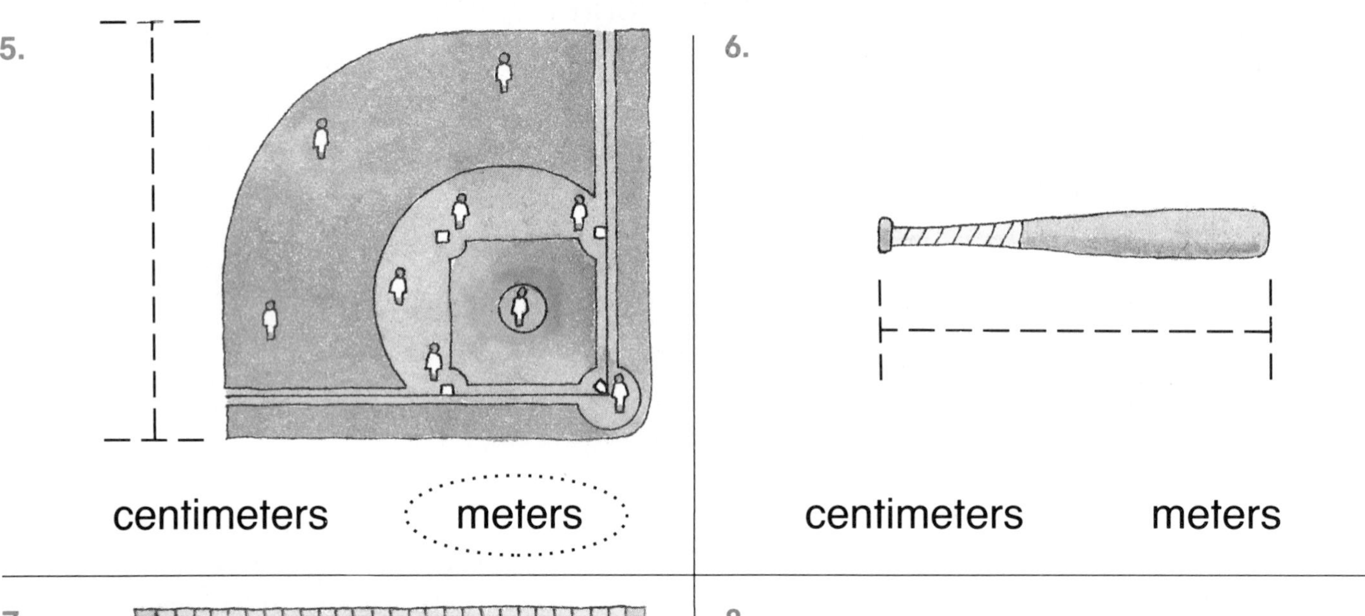

5. centimeters meters

6. centimeters meters

7. centimeters meters

8. centimeters meters

Exploring Mathematics Book Two © Scott, Foresman and Company

Notes for Home Children solve problems by choosing a sensible measure.

Name

Problem-Solving Workshop

Explore as a Team

Work with a partner.
Use a clock to help you.
Draw the hands on the clock to show the time.

1. Sue went to her dance class at 3:00.
The class was an hour long.
It took her 10 minutes to change clothes.
She stayed 20 minutes to talk to a friend.
It took her 15 minutes to walk home.
What time did Sue get home?

2. Bob had a baseball game at 4:30.
The game took 2 hours.
Then Bob and his father went to dinner.
It took 50 minutes to eat.
It took 25 minutes to drive home.
What time did Bob get home?

Notes for Home Children explore with a partner to solve problems involving telling time.

Problem-Solving Workshop

Explore with a Computer

Money and Time Project

1. At the computer, start the stopwatch. Jump 6 times.

Stop the stopwatch.
Write the time.

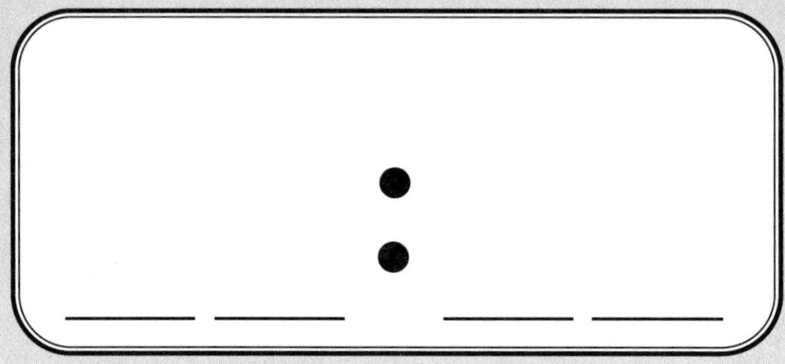

2. Start the stopwatch.
See how long you can stand on one leg.

Stop the stopwatch.
Write how long you stood on one leg.

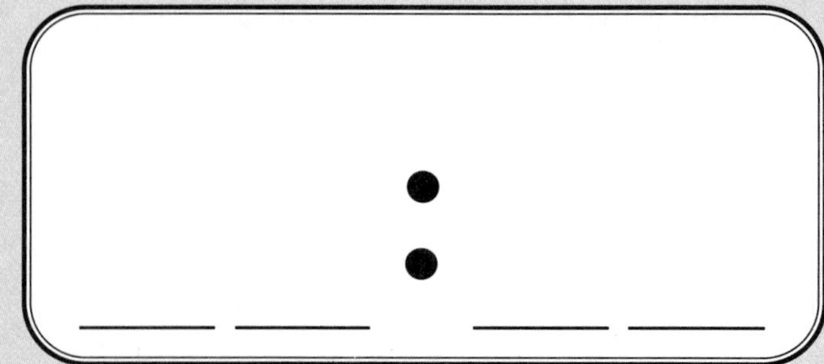

Exploring Mathematics Book Two © Scott, Foresman and Company

Notes for Home Children use the computer's timer to record elapsed time for the activities in this workshop.

Name

More Practice

Set A Use after page 140.

What time is it?

1\.

:

:

:

2\.

:

:

:

:

Set B Use after page 152.

Find the length to the nearest inch.

1\.

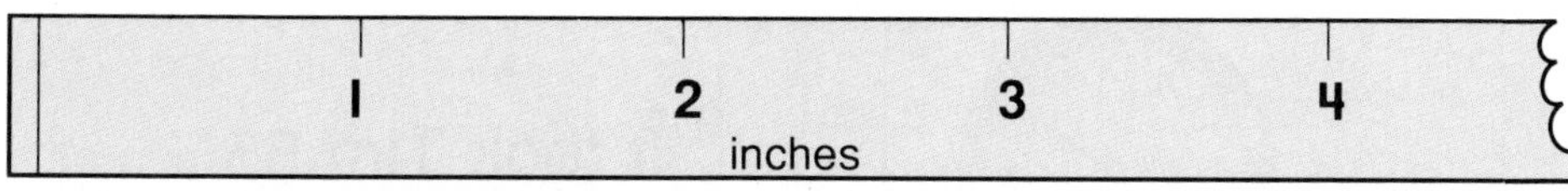

nearest inch ____

2\.

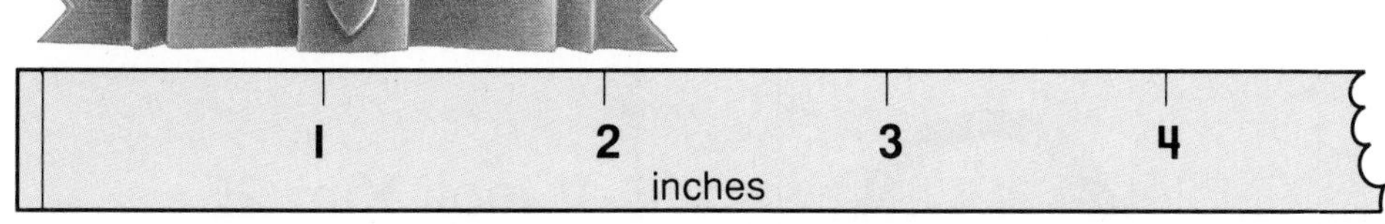

nearest inch ____

3\.

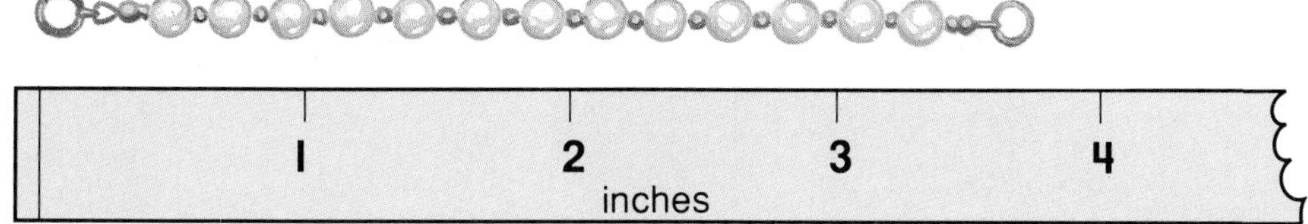

nearest inch ____

Notes for Home Set A: Children practice telling time to the hour, half hour, quarter hour, and 5 minutes.
Set B: Children measure lengths of objects to the nearest inch.

Enrichment

Write the name of the person who finished first.

	Activity	Starting Time	Time Taken
1.			It took Karen 20 minutes.
			It took Jim 10 minutes.

Who finished first? ____________________

	Activity	Starting Time	Time Taken
2.			It took Tim 35 minutes.
			It took Kim 25 minutes.

Who finished first? ____________________

Notes for Home Children are challenged to compare elapsed time events.

Exploring Mathematics Book Two © Scott, Foresman and Company

Name

Chapter 5 Review/Test

1. Write the time.

______

2. How many days in May?

______

3. How many months in 1 year?

______

4. About how long?

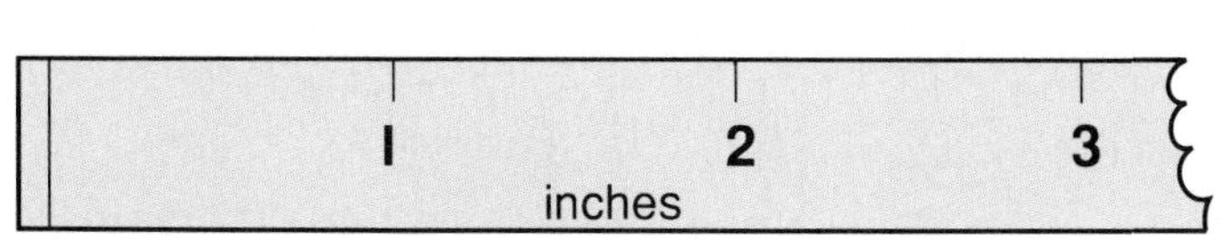

Closer to ______ inches long.

5. About how long?

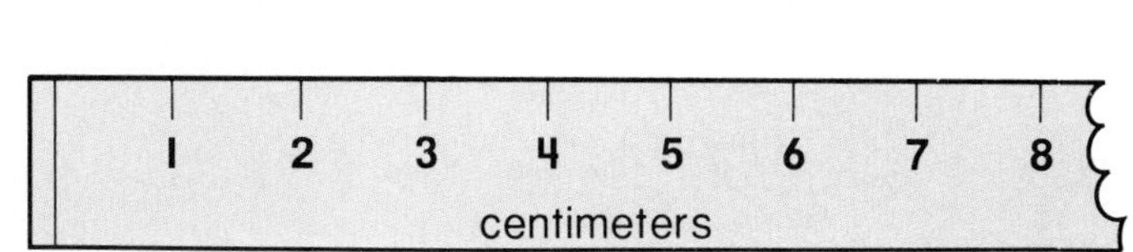

Closer to ______ centimeters long.

Ring yes or no.

6. 

The mug is shorter than 1 foot.

yes no

7. The dog is taller than 1 meter.

yes no

Write the time when the job will end.

8.

Job	Time	Amount of Time
Make bed	7:30	10 minutes

______

Ring the best measure.

9. 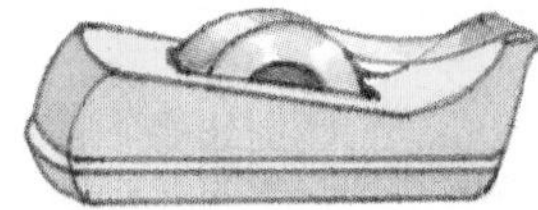

inches feet

Notes for Home Children are assessed on Chapter 5 concepts, skills, and problem solving.

Exploring Math at Home

Dear Family,

In this chapter I have learned how to tell time and how to use a calendar. I have also learned to measure lengths and heights of objects. Please help me with the activities below.

Love, ______________________

1.

When beginning new activities throughout the day, tell the time to the nearest hour, half hour, or quarter hour.

2.

Make a calendar for each month. Mark holidays, family birthdays, and school activities. Look at the calendar every day.

3.

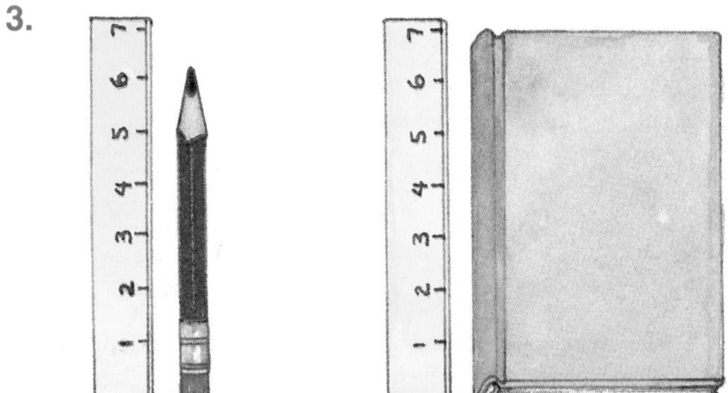

Use both inch and centimeter rulers to measure lengths and heights of objects around the house.

Coming Attractions

In the next chapter I will learn how and when to trade ones and tens in order to join and separate groups. I will also learn about tables and graphs.

Exploring Mathematics Book Two © Scott, Foresman and Company

Listen to the math story, "Bottles of Fun."
The old man used 10 bottles.
What did he do with the bottles?

Notes for Home Children listen to a math story introducing chapter concepts and skills. Then they answer a question about the story.

Name

Trading 10 Ones for 1 Ten

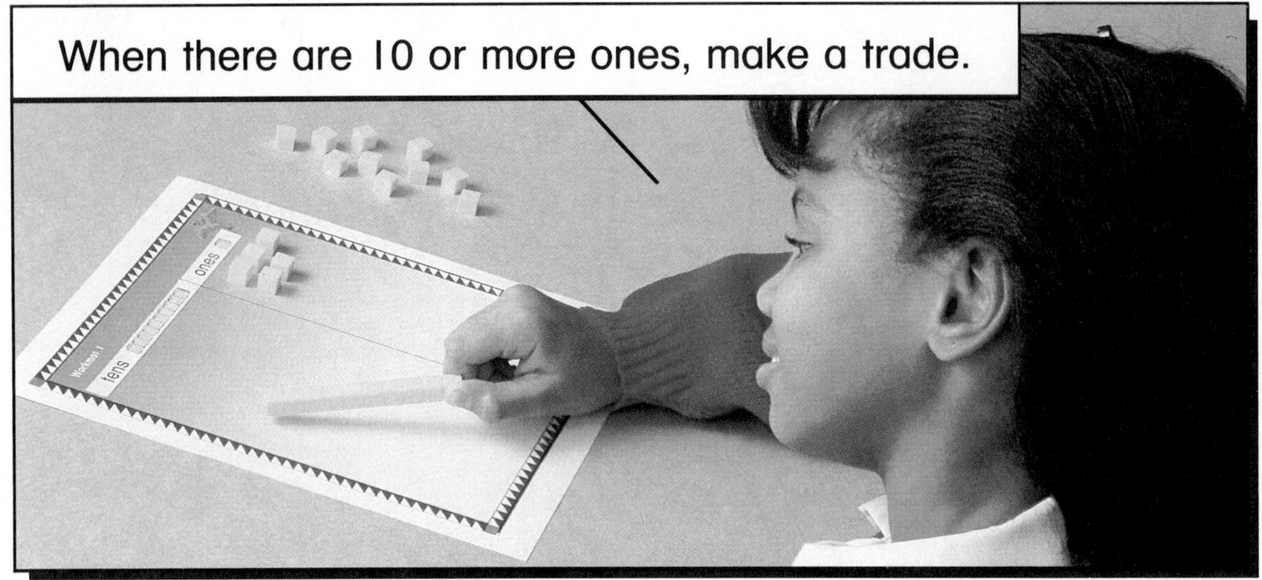

Use Workmat 1.
Use tens and ones counters.

Take this many.	Can you make a trade?	Write the number of tens and ones.
1. 15 ones	yes	1 ten 5 ones
2. 17 ones	_____	_____ ten _____ ones
3. 8 ones	_____	_____ ten _____ ones
4. 14 ones	_____	_____ ten _____ ones

Exploring Mathematics Book Two © Scott, Foresman and Company

Notes for Home Children explore at the CONCRETE level using tens and ones counters and a place-value workmat. They trade 10 ones for 1 ten when necessary.

Name

ACTIVITY

Determining If a Trade Is Necessary

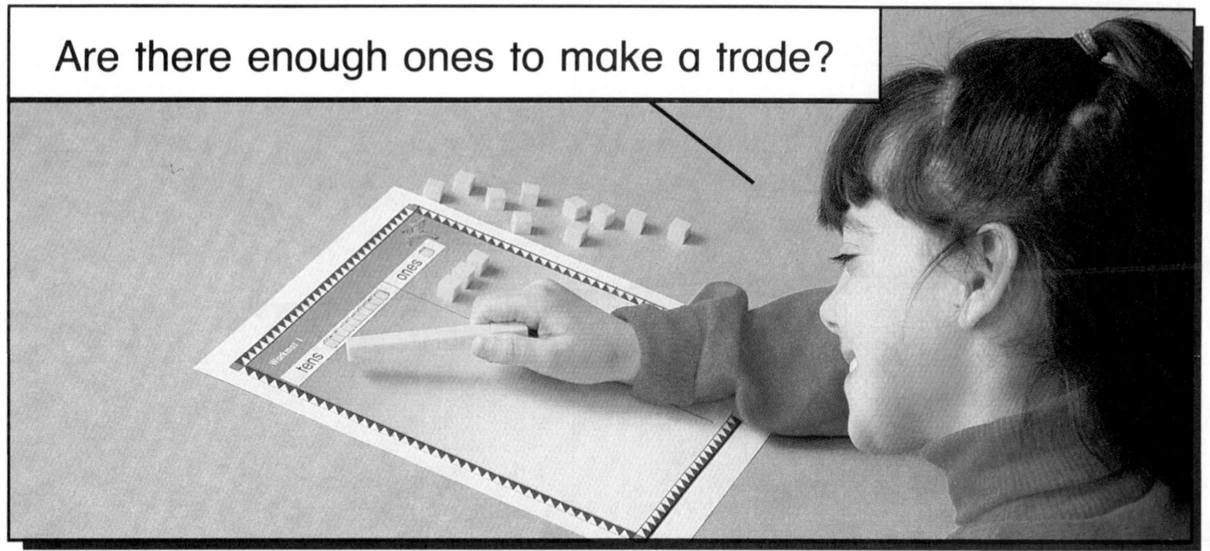

Use Workmat 1.
Use tens and ones counters.

Take this many.	Can you make a trade?	Write the number of tens and ones.
1. 6 ones and 7 ones	yes	1 ten 3 ones
2. 5 ones and 6 ones	______	______ ten ______ one
3. 4 ones and 5 ones	______	______ ten ______ ones
4. 7 ones and 5 ones	______	______ ten ______ ones

Notes for Home Children explore at the CONCRETE level using tens and ones counters and a place-value workmat to combine two single-digit quantities and determine if a trade is necessary.

Use Workmat 1.
Use tens and ones counters.

Take this many.	Can you make a trade?	Write the number of tens and ones.
5. 3 ones and 5 ones	no	___ ten 8 ones
6. 8 ones and 2 ones	___	___ ten ___ ones
7. 7 ones and 7 ones	___	___ ten ___ ones
8. 9 ones and 8 ones	___	___ ten ___ ones
9. 7 ones and 2 ones	___	___ ten ___ ones

Exploring Mathematics Book Two © Scott, Foresman and Company

Notes for Home Children explore at the CONCRETE level using tens and ones counters and a place-value workmat to combine two single-digit quantities and determine if a trade is necessary.

Name

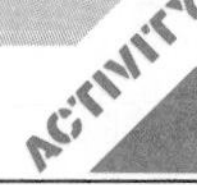

Trading with Larger Numbers

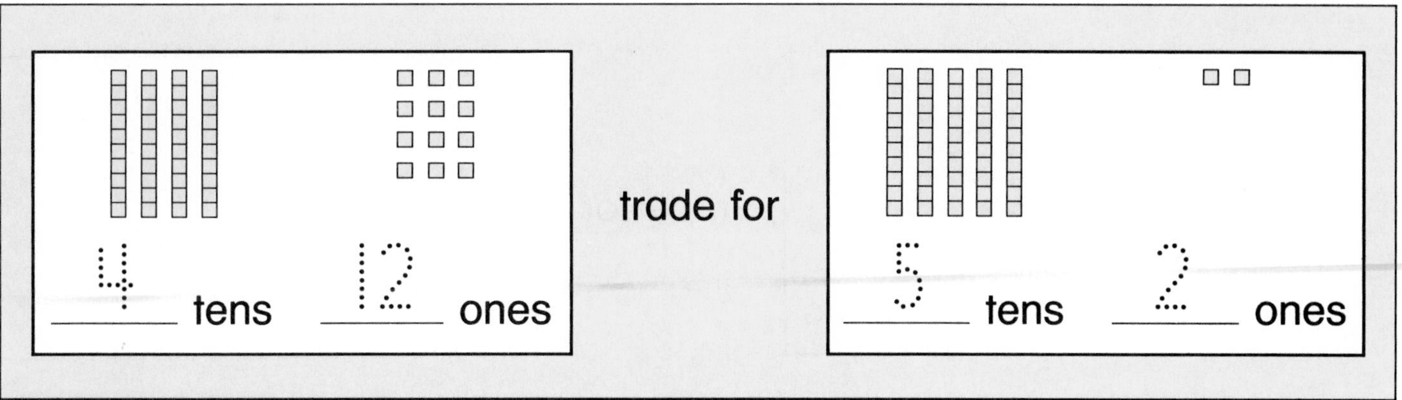

Cut out the pictures of tens and ones on page 175.
Match to show each trade. Then paste.
Write how many tens and ones.

1. ______ tens ______ ones

trade for

2.

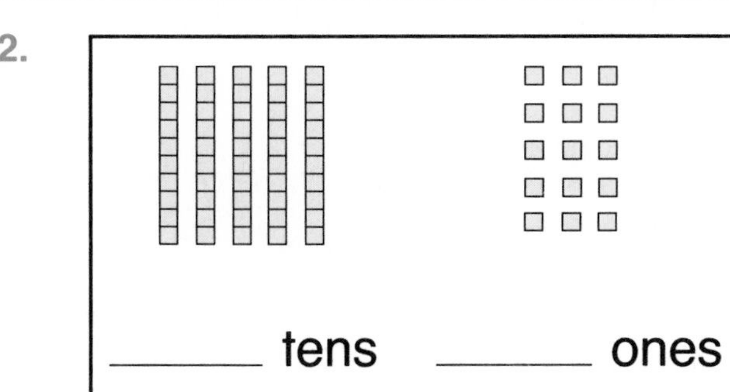

trade for

3.

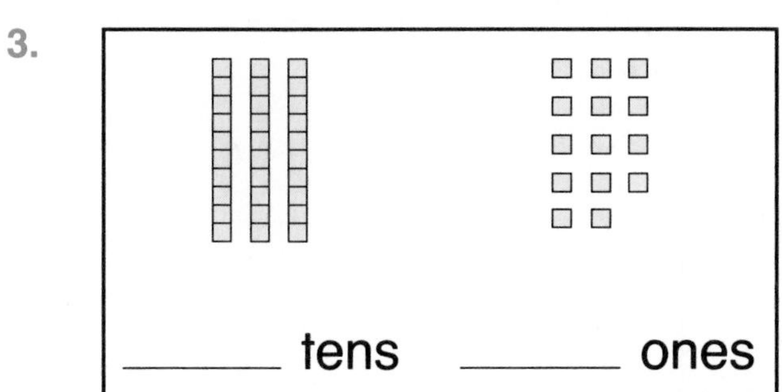

trade for

Notes for Home Children cut out and paste pictures of tens and ones from page 175 to show trades. They write the number of tens and ones shown in each picture.

Cut out the pictures of tens and ones on page 175.
Match to show each trade. Then paste.
Write how many tens and ones.

4.

5 tens 16 ones

trade for

5.

_____ tens _____ ones

trade for

6.

_____ tens _____ ones

trade for

7.

_____ tens _____ ones

trade for

Exploring Mathematics Book Two © Scott, Foresman and Company

Notes for Home Children cut out and paste pictures of tens and ones from page 175 to show trades. They write the number of tens and ones shown in each picture.

Use with page 173.

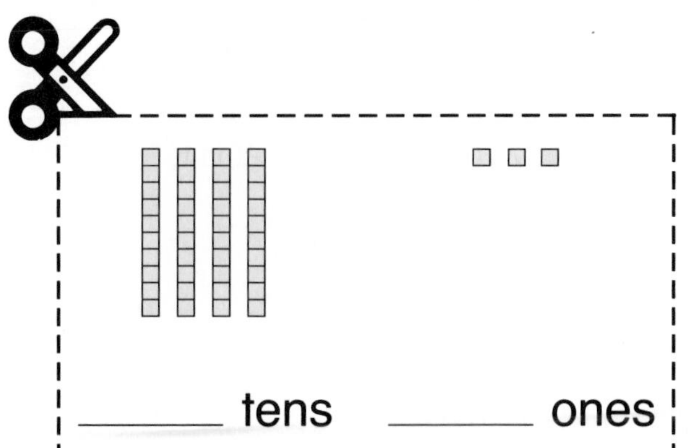

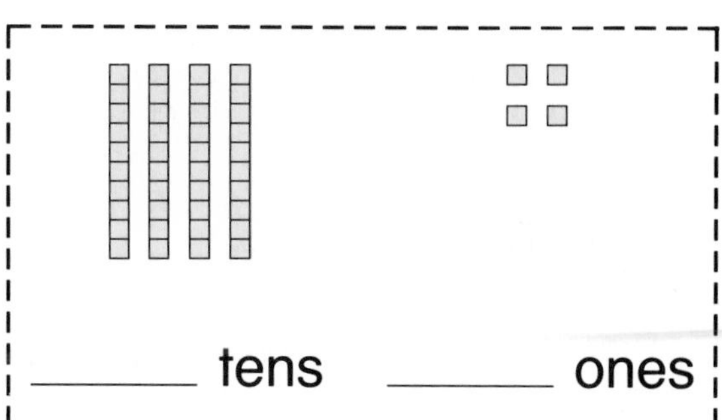

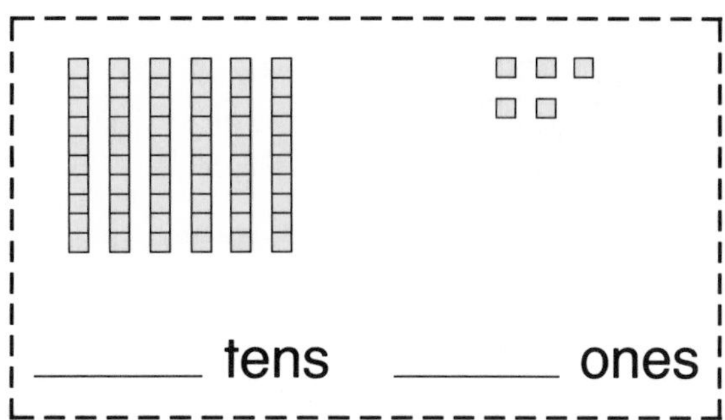

Use with page 174.

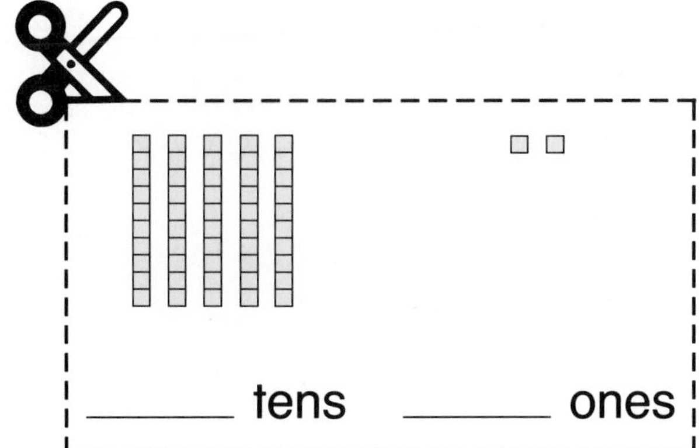

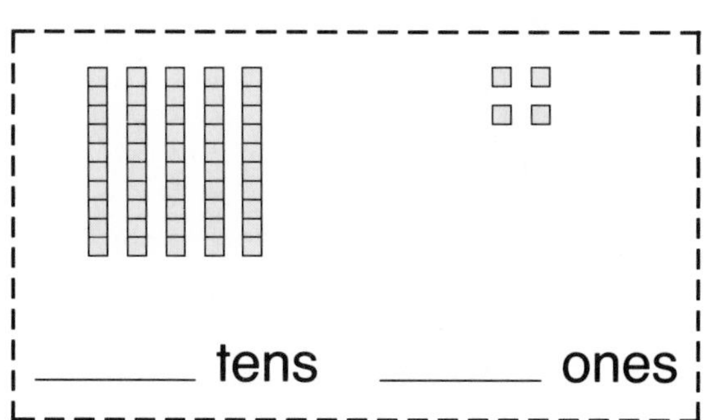

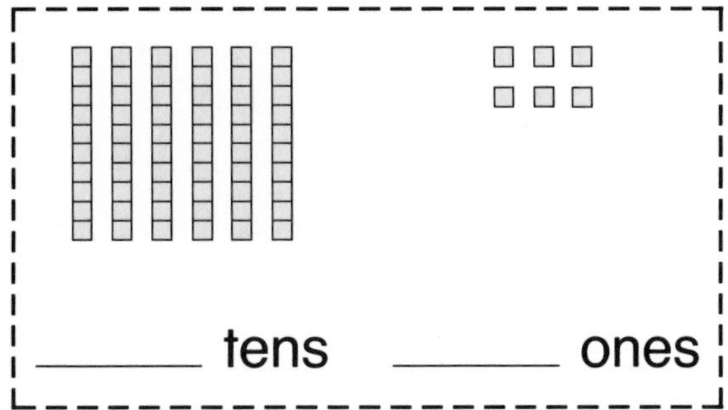

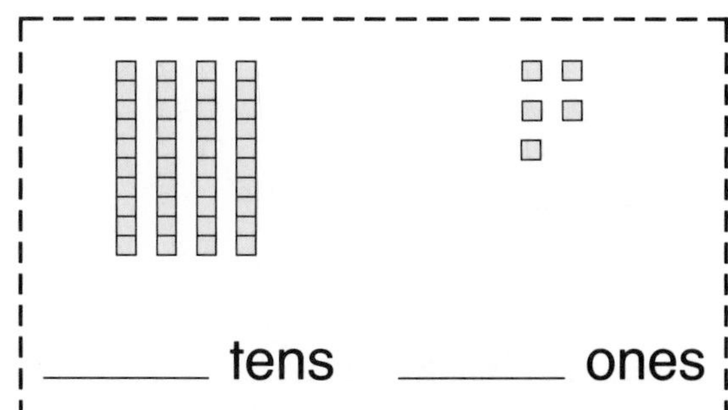

Use with page 173.

_____ tens _____ ones

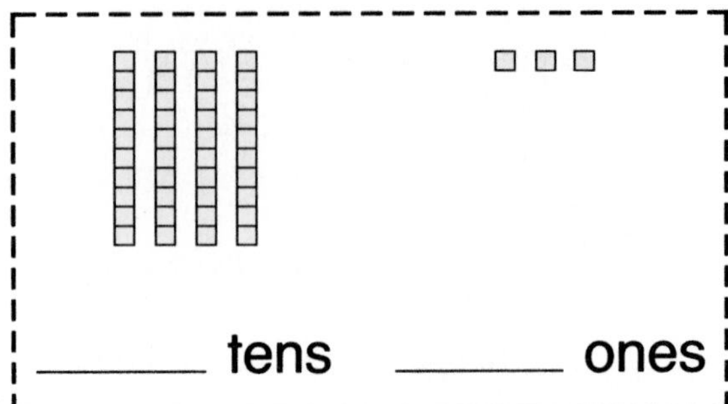

_____ tens _____ ones

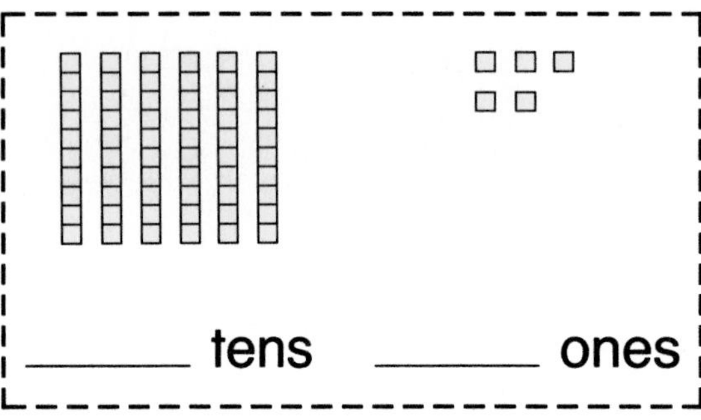

_____ tens _____ ones

Use with page 174.

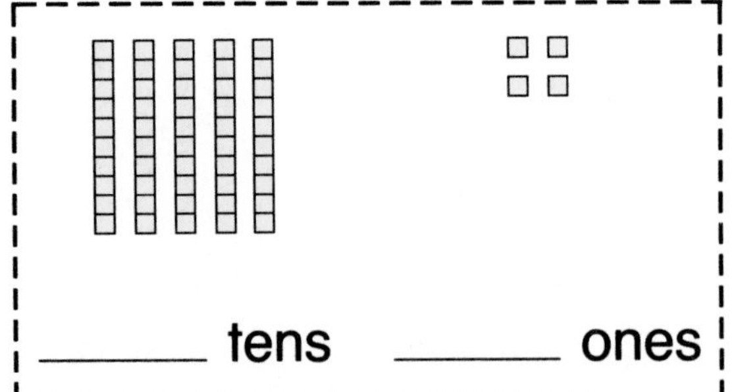

_____ tens _____ ones

_____ tens _____ ones

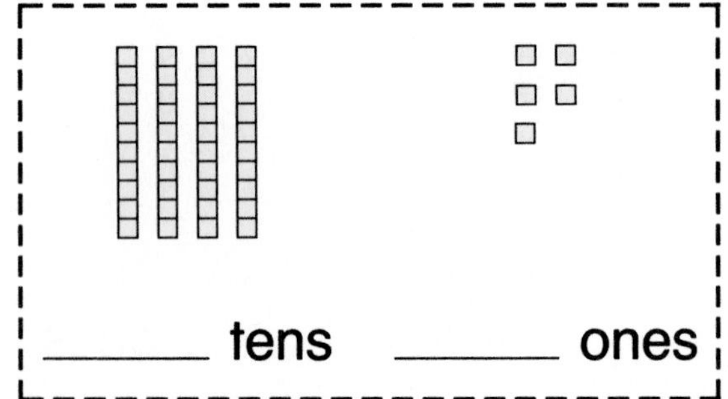

_____ tens _____ ones

_____ tens _____ ones

Exploring Mathematics Book Two © Scott, Foresman and Company

Name ______________________________

Trading with Larger Numbers

If I join these two groups, I can make another group of ten.

25 and 7

32 in all

Write how many in each group.
Ring another group of ten if you can.
Write how many in all.

1.

______ and ______

______ in all

2.

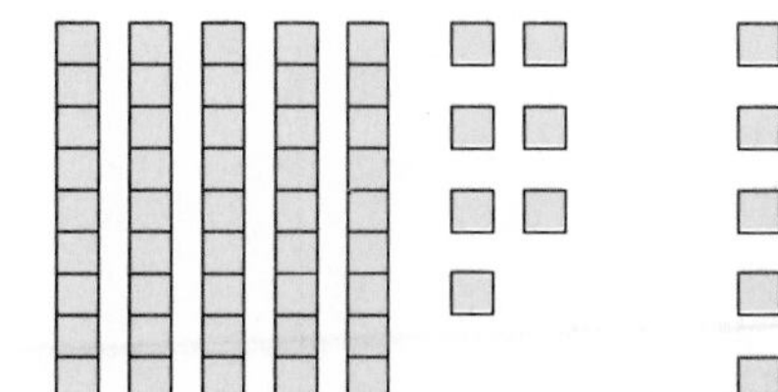

______ and ______

______ in all

3.

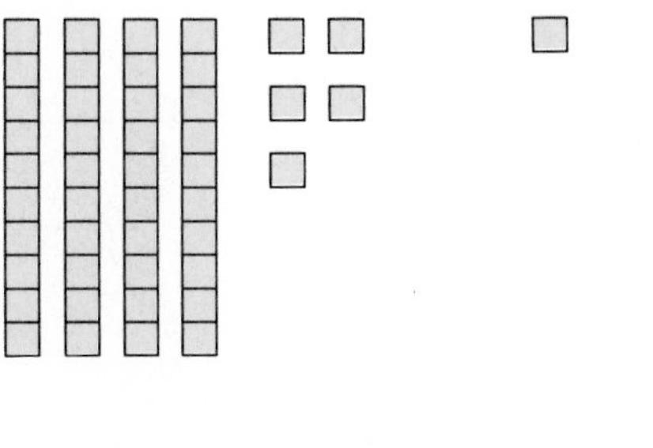

______ and ______

______ in all

4.

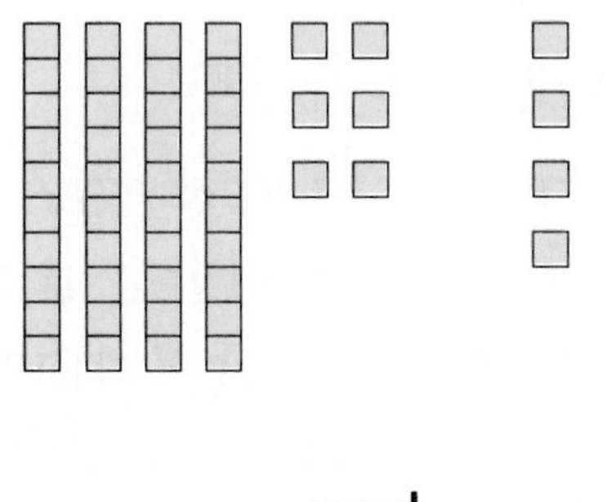

______ and ______

______ in all

Notes for Home Children write the number of objects shown in each group and ring a ten when possible. They write how many in all.

Write how many in each group.
Ring another group of ten if you can.
Write how many in all.

5. 42 and 5
47 in all

6. ______ and ______
______ in all

7. ______ and ______
______ in all

8. ______ and ______
______ in all

9. ______ and ______
______ in all

10. ______ and ______
______ in all

Problem Solving

Solve. Ring yes or no.

11. 10 marbles fit in a tray.
Kim has 17 marbles in trays.
If Andy gives her 4 marbles, will Kim need another tray?

yes no

Exploring Mathematics Book Two © Scott, Foresman and Company

Notes for Home Children write the number of objects shown in each group, ring a ten when possible, and write how many in all. Then they solve a problem involving trading with larger numbers.

See More Practice Set A on page 195.

Name

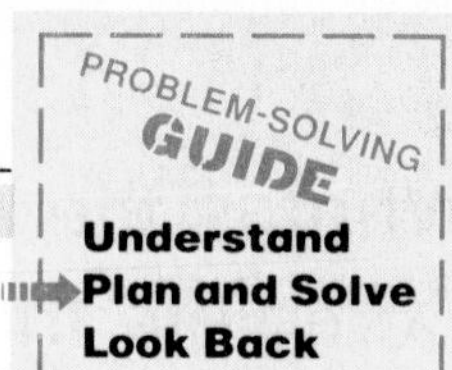

Make a Table

Andy and Lily make sandwiches with pita bread.
Andy makes 1 less sandwich than Lily.
Write the number that Andy makes.

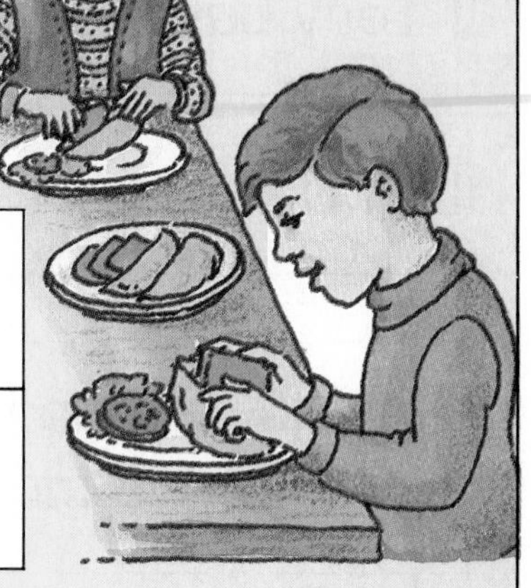

If Lily makes	3	4	5	6	7
then Andy makes	2	3	4	5	6

What is the number?
Complete the table.

1. Chico and Tina eat breadsticks.
Chico eats 1 more breadstick than Tina.

If Tina eats	0	4	5	6	8
then Chico eats	1				

2. Suzy and Sam like muffins.
Sam eats 1 less muffin than Suzy.

If Suzy eats	1	3	5	7
then Sam eats				

Notes for Home Children solve problems by making a table for addition or subtraction.

What is the number?
Complete the table.

3. Tony and Niki buy bagels.
Niki buys 2 more than Tony.

If Tony buys	1	2		4	
then Niki buys	3		5		8

4. Margo and Lin bake rolls.
Lin bakes 3 more rolls than Margo.

If Margo bakes	2	4		6	
then Lin bakes			8		10

5. Carl and Maria make tortillas.
Maria makes 4 more than Carl.

If Carl makes	2		4		
then Maria makes		7		9	10

Exploring Mathematics Book Two © Scott, Foresman and Company

Notes for Home Children solve problems by making a table for addition or subtraction.

Number Sense

Chef Dino makes pizzas.
He puts them in large boxes with 10 in each box,
or he puts them in small boxes with one in each box.
Chef Dino made 52 pizzas.
Tell the different ways he can put the pizza in boxes.

Let's do some more!

Make a list of the things that might be sold 10 to a package.

Notes for Home Children develop number understanding by finding groups of tens and ones.

Skills Review

Fill in the correct ◯.
What time is it?

1. 

1:45 Ⓐ 7:45 Ⓑ

2. 

2:00 Ⓐ 3:00 Ⓑ

3. 

6:45 Ⓐ 9:30 Ⓑ

Find the length to the nearest inch.

4. 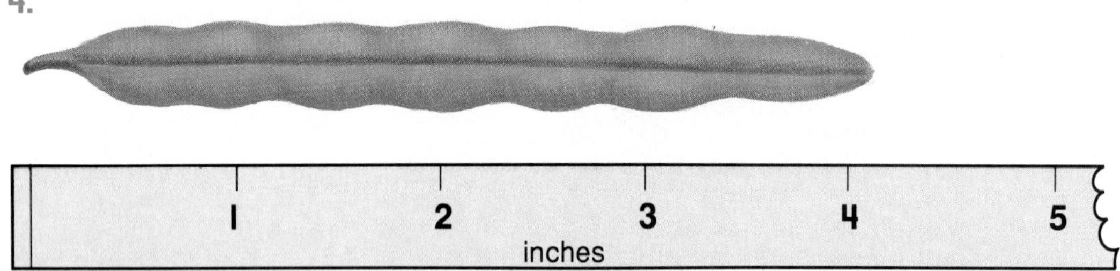

Ⓐ 4 inches
Ⓑ 5 inches
Ⓒ 6 inches

5.

Ⓐ 3 inches
Ⓑ 4 inches
Ⓒ 5 inches

Vocabulary

Match.

month •	• 7 days
day •	• 1991
year •	• July
week •	• Tuesday

JULY

SUN.	MON.	TUES.	WED.	THURS.	FRI.	SAT.
	1	2	3	4	5	6
7	8	9	10	11	12	13
14	15	16	17	18	19	20
21	22	23	24	25	26	27
28	29	30	31			

Notes for Home Children practice telling time and measuring to the nearest inch. Then they review calendar terms.

Exploring Mathematics Book Two © Scott, Foresman and Company

Name

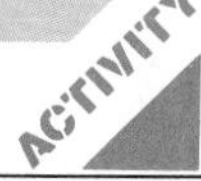

Determining If a Trade Is Necessary

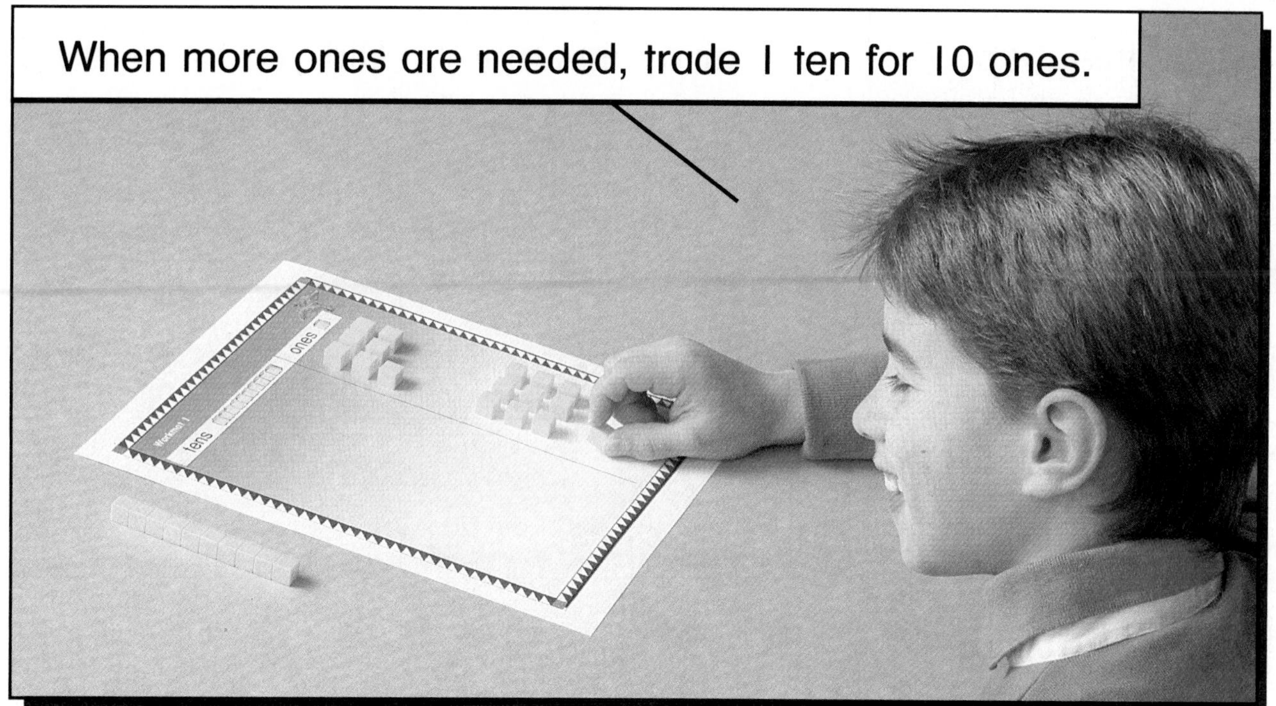

Use Workmat 1.
Use tens and ones counters.

	Show this many.	Take away this many.	Did you need to trade?
1.	1 ten 7 ones	8 ones	yes
2.	1 ten 6 ones	3 ones	______
3.	1 ten 5 ones	7 ones	______
4.	1 ten 2 ones	5 ones	______

Notes for Home Children explore at the CONCRETE level using tens and ones counters and a place-value workmat to discover when it is necessary to trade 1 ten for 10 ones.

Use Workmat 1.
Use tens and ones counters.

	Show this many.	Take away this many.	Did you need to trade?
5.	1 ten 4 ones	9 ones	yes
6.	1 ten 3 ones	5 ones	______
7.	1 ten 6 ones	4 ones	______
8.	1 ten 1 one	4 ones	______
9.	1 ten 0 ones	3 ones	______
10.	1 ten 3 ones	3 ones	______
11.	1 ten 7 ones	8 ones	______

Critical Thinking You have a box of 10 crackers and 4 extra crackers. You wish to give 6 crackers to your friend. Do you need to take crackers from the box? How do you know?

Exploring Mathematics Book Two © Scott, Foresman and Company

Notes for Home Children explore at the CONCRETE level using tens and ones counters and a place-value workmat to discover when it is necessary to trade 1 ten for 10 ones. Then they discuss when to trade.

Name

Trading with Larger Numbers

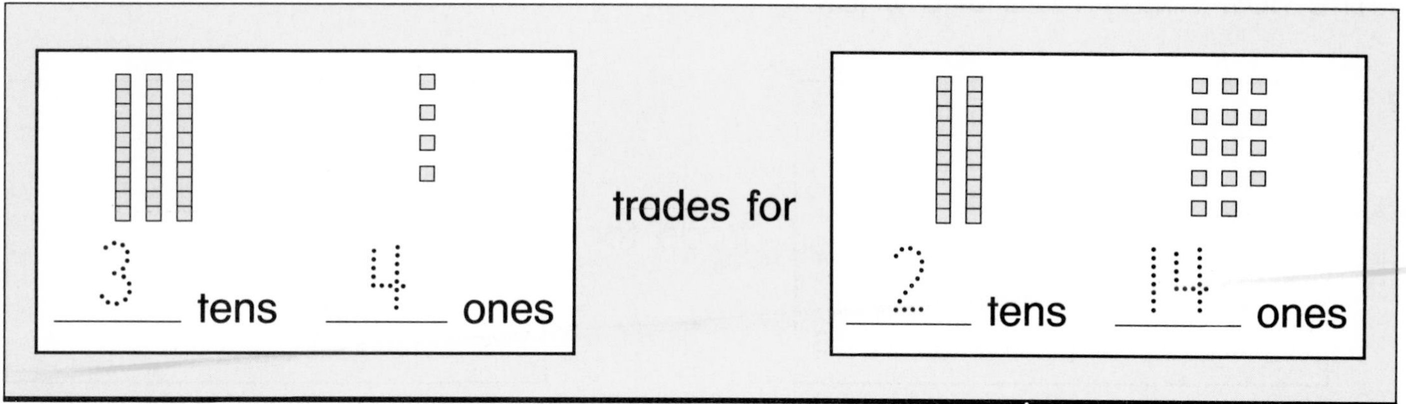

Cut out the pictures of tens and ones on page 187.
Match to show each trade. Then paste.
Write how many tens and ones.

1.

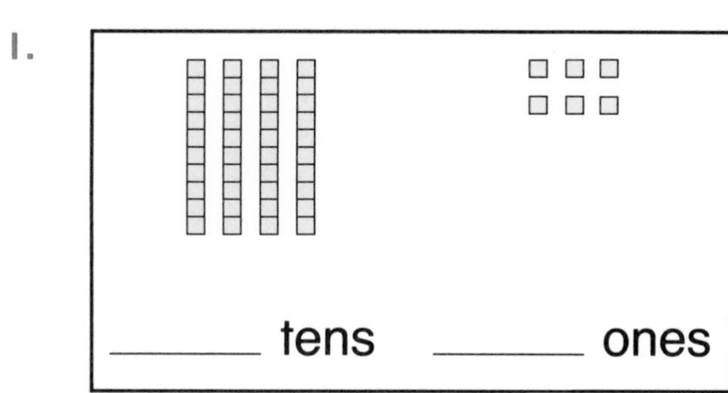

_____ tens _____ ones

trades for

2.

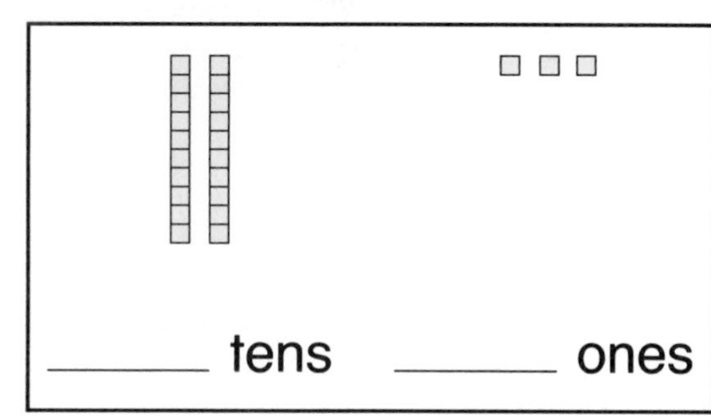

_____ tens _____ ones

trades for

3.

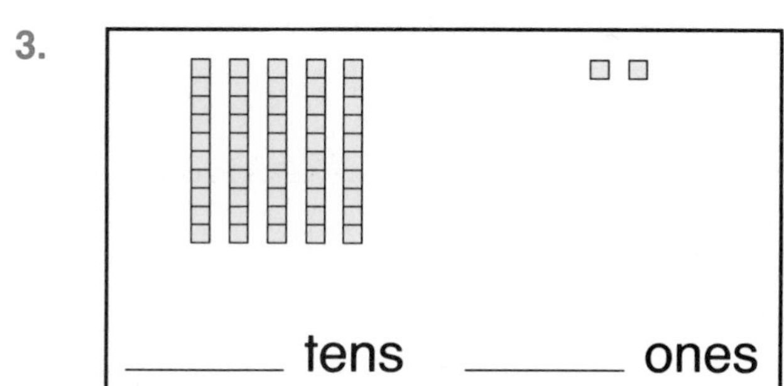

_____ tens _____ ones

trades for

Notes for Home Children cut out and paste pictures of tens and ones from page 187 to show trades. They write the number of tens and ones shown in each picture.

Cut out the pictures of tens and ones on page 187.
Match to show each trade. Then paste.
Write how many tens and ones.

4. 3 tens 1 ones — trade for

5. ____ tens ____ ones — trade for

6. ____ tens ____ ones — trade for

7. ____ tens ____ ones — trade for

Exploring Mathematics Book Two © Scott, Foresman and Company

Notes for Home Children cut out and paste pictures of tens and ones from page 187 to show trades. They write the number of tens and ones shown in each picture.

Use with page 185.

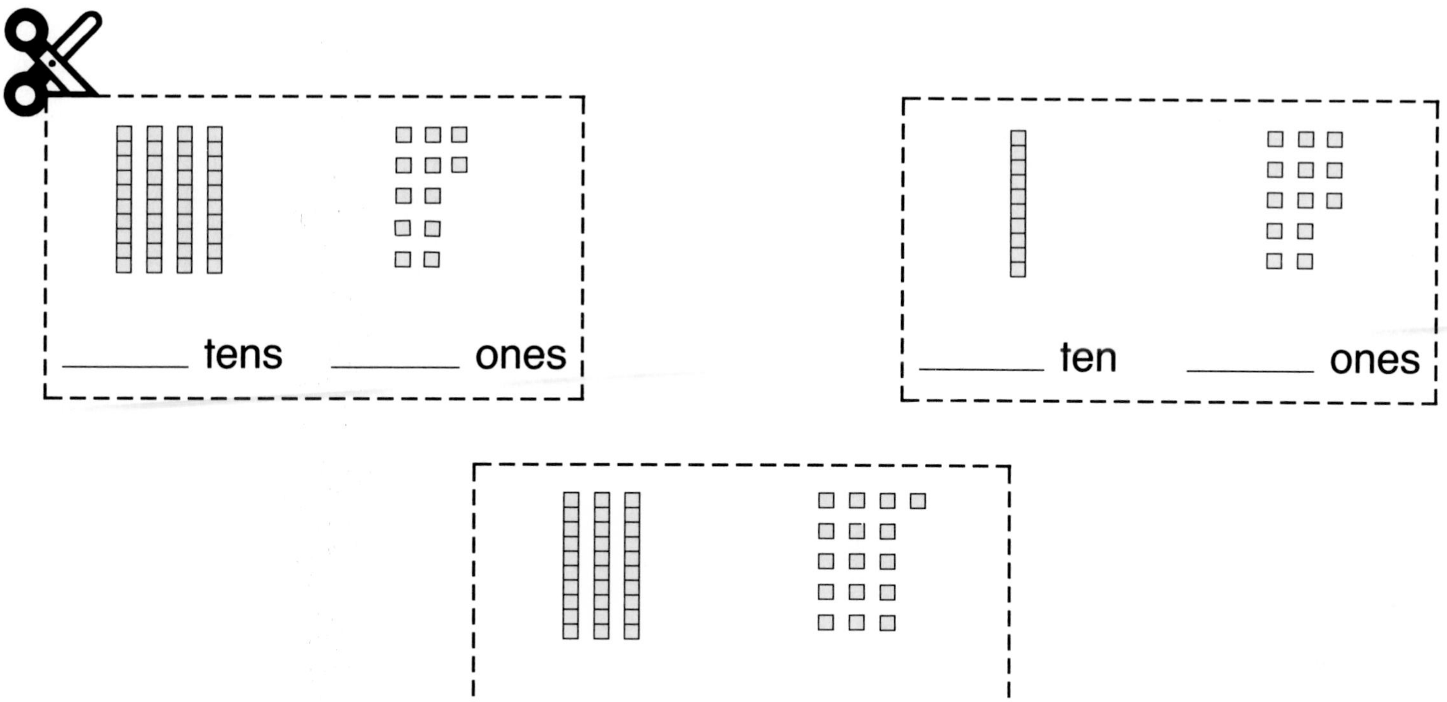

Use with page 186.

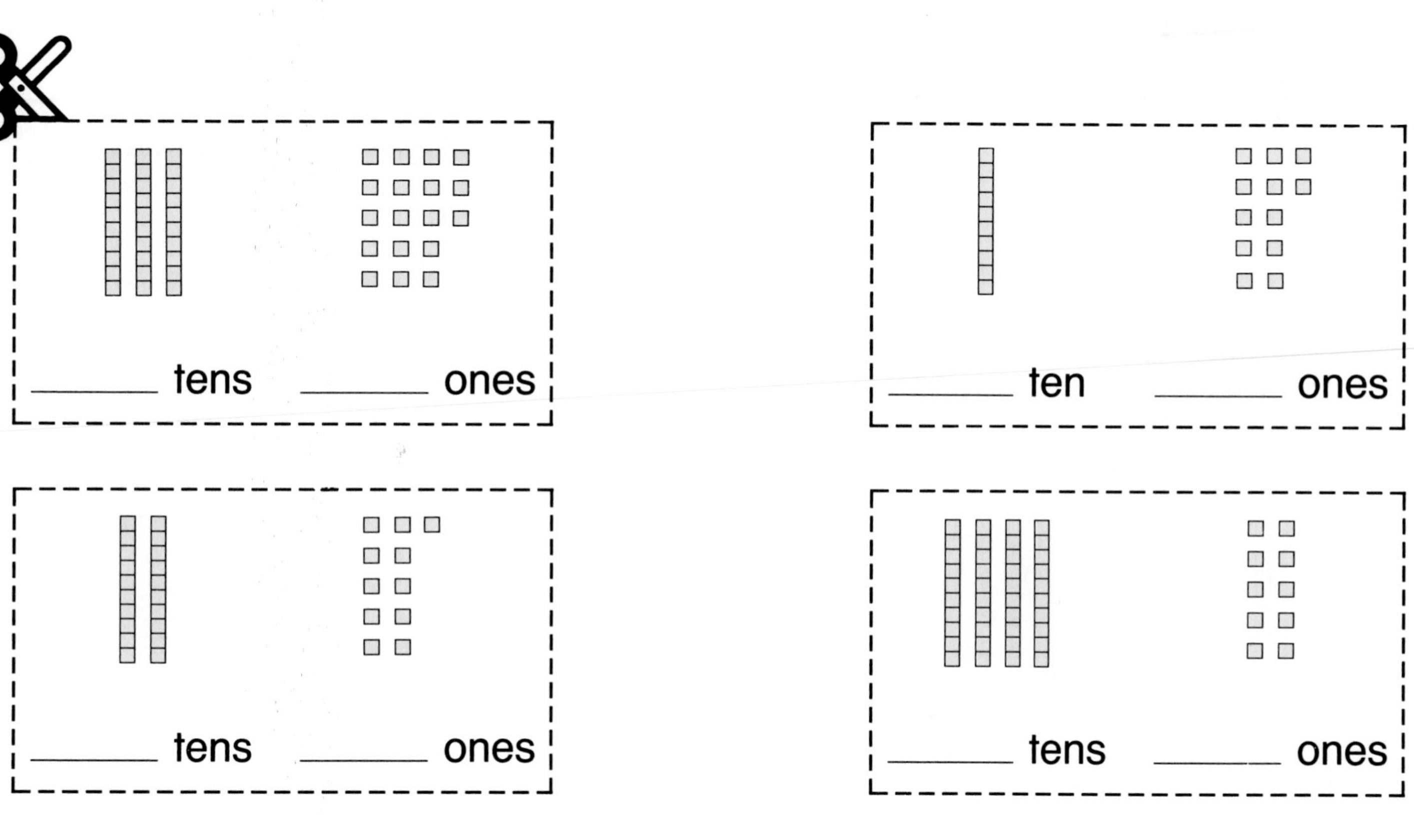

Use with page 185.

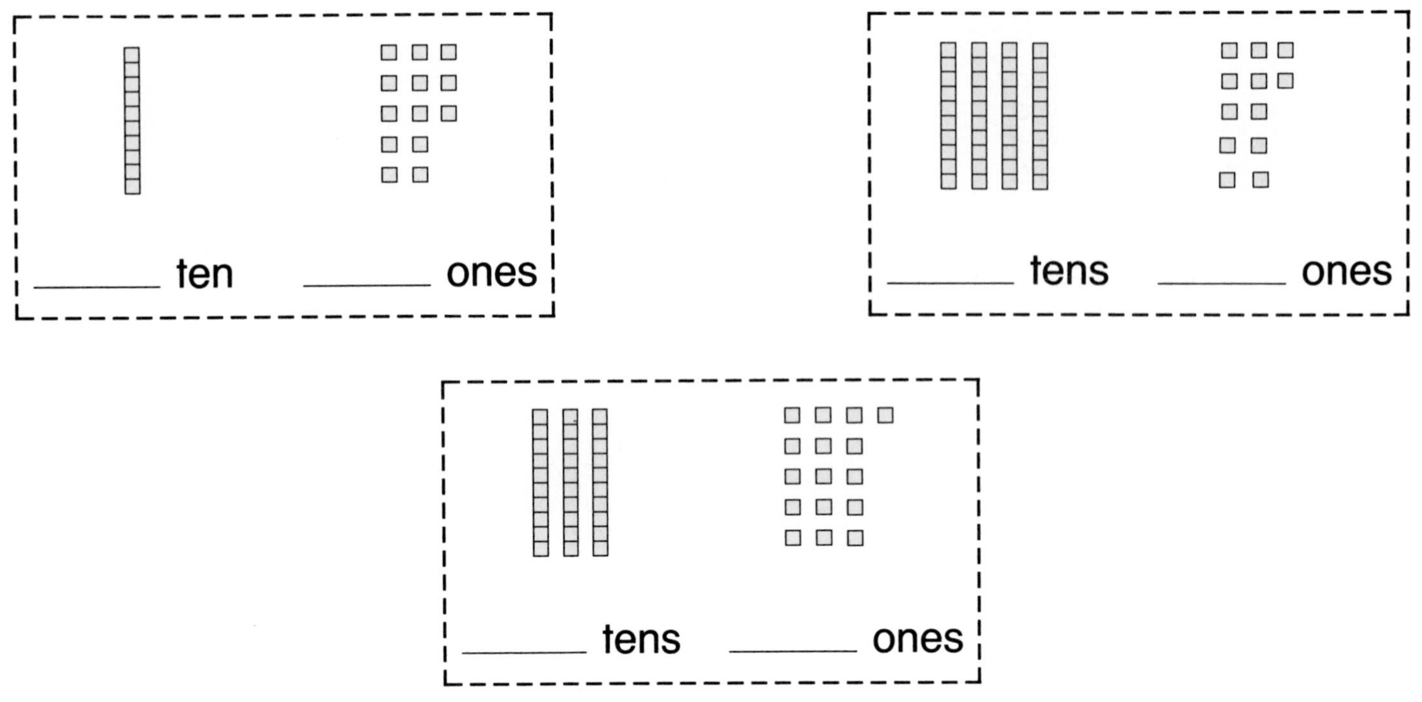

Use with page 186.

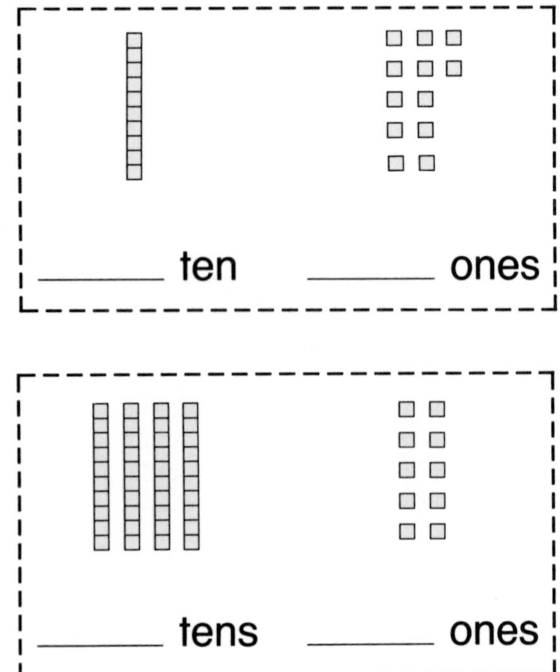

_____ tens _____ ones

_____ tens _____ ones

Exploring Mathematics Book Two © Scott, Foresman and Company

Name

Trading with Larger Numbers

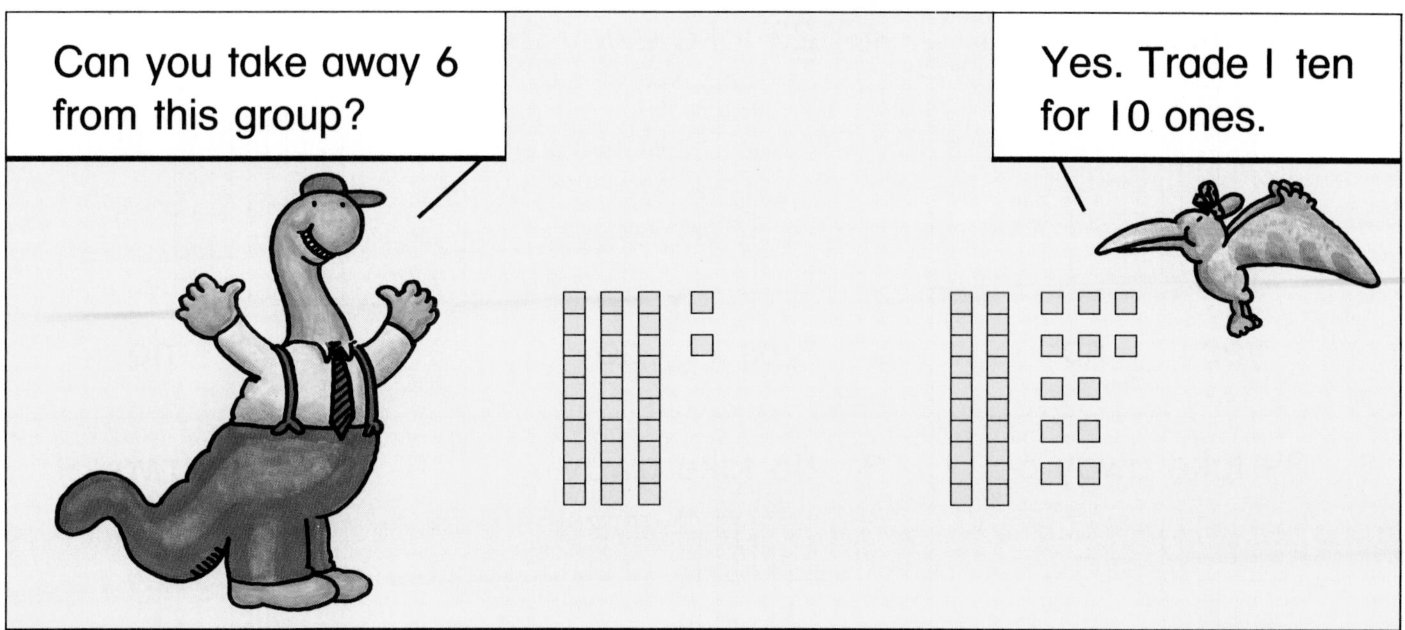

Decide if you need to trade.
Ring yes or no.

1. 43 take away 5

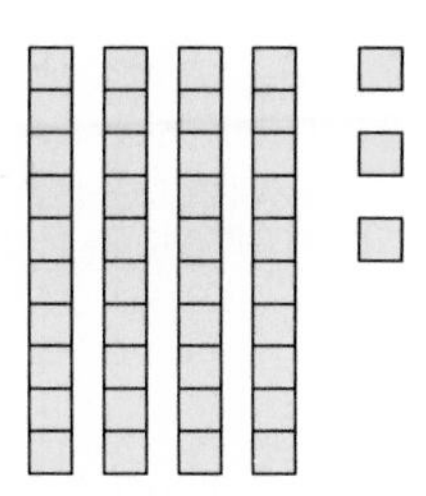

yes no

2. 36 take away 2

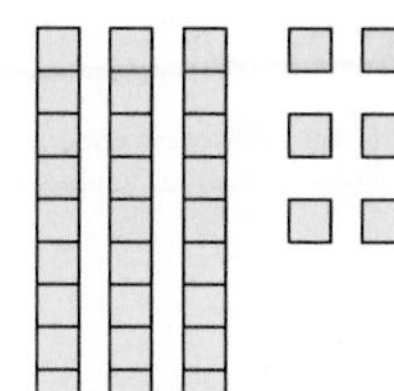

yes no

3. 55 take away 7

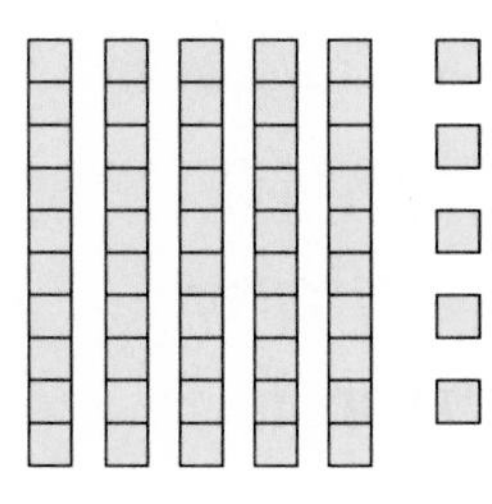

yes no

4. 40 take away 1

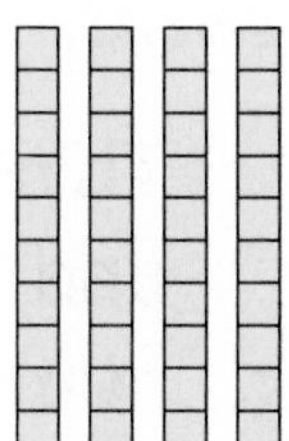

yes no

Notes for Home Children decide if a trade is needed to subtract some ones.

Decide if you need to trade.
Ring yes or no.

5. 45 take away 8

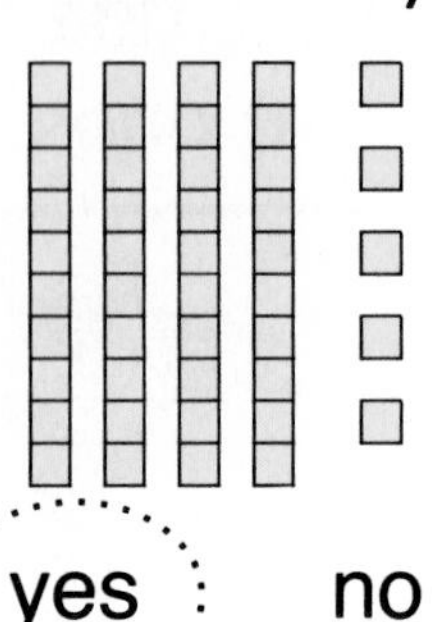

yes no

6. 23 take away 2

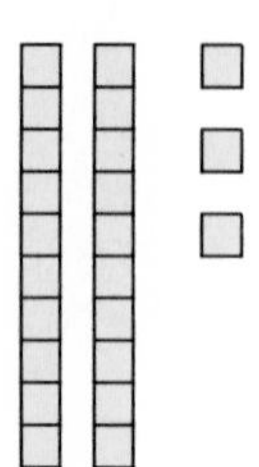

yes no

7. 52 take away 5

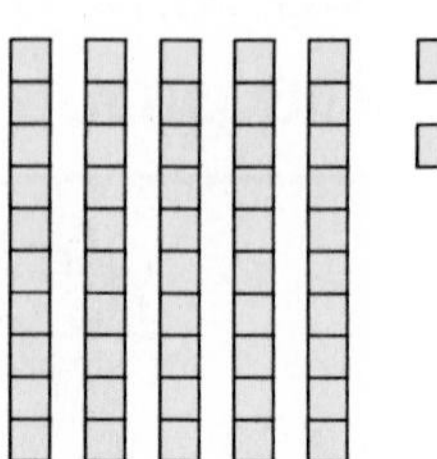

yes no

8. 34 take away 6

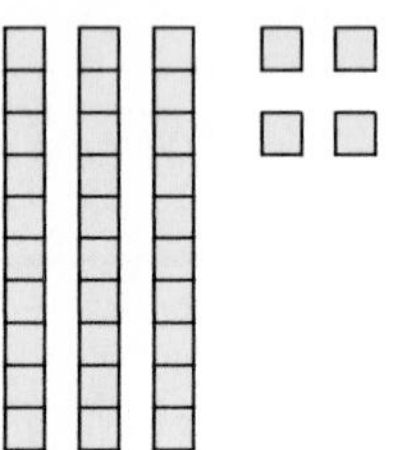

yes no

9. 46 take away 7

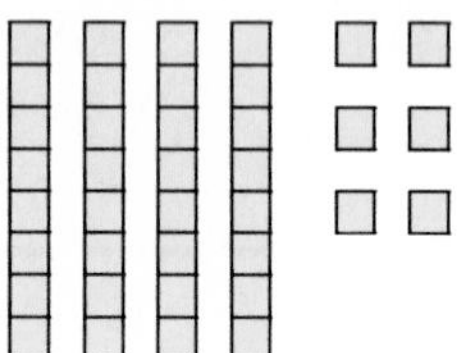

yes no

10. 38 take away 4

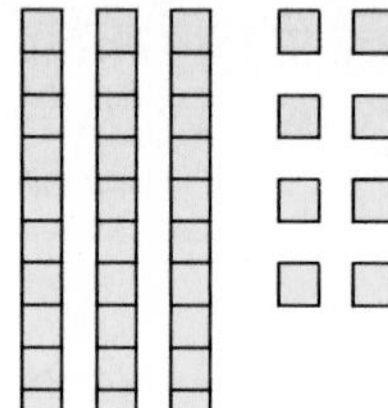

yes no

11. 55 take away 3

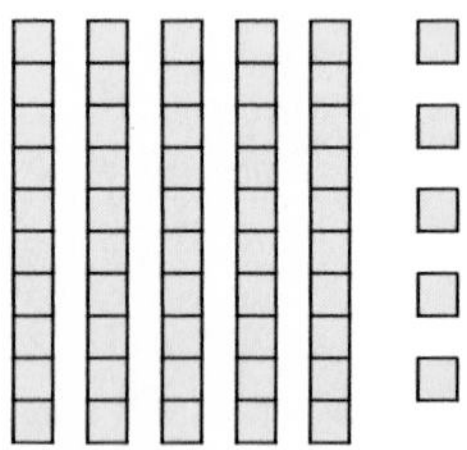

yes no

12. 28 take away 9

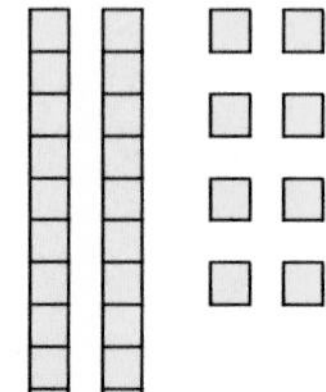

yes no

13. 62 take away 5

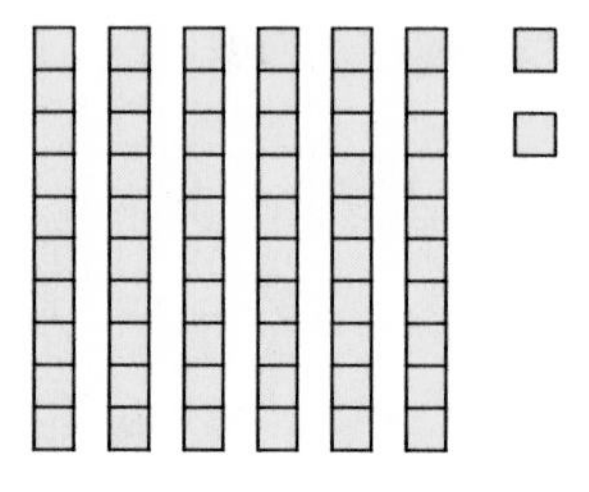

yes no

Write About Math

Think of a number that's more than 10 and less than 20. You can subtract any number of ones from it and you don't need to trade. What is the number? ______

Exploring Mathematics Book Two © Scott, Foresman and Company

Notes for Home Children decide if a trade is needed to subtract some ones. Then they write about trading with larger numbers.

See More Practice Set B on page 195.

Name ____________________

Use Data from a Graph

On this chart, each picture stands for 10 tickets.

You can count by tens to find how many in all.

Ticket Sales	= 10 tickets
Sunday	
Monday	
Tuesday	
Wednesday	
Thursday	
Friday	
Saturday	

How many tickets were sold?

1. Sunday 60

2. Tuesday ______

3. Saturday ______

4. Friday ______

5. On which day were the least tickets sold? ____________________

Notes for Home Children solve problems by reading a pictograph.

Popcorn Sales = 10 boxes	
Sunday	
Monday	
Tuesday	
Wednesday	
Thursday	
Friday	
Saturday	

How many boxes were sold each day?

6. Thursday 40

7. Sunday ______

8. Saturday ______

9. Friday ______

10. On which day were the most boxes sold?

____

11. On which day were the least boxes sold?

____

12. On which 2 days were the popcorn sales the same?

______________________ ______________________

Notes for Home Children solve problems by reading a pictograph.

Exploring Mathematics Book Two © Scott, Foresman and Company

Name

Problem-Solving Workshop

Explore as a Team

1. Work with a partner.
2. Take 12 cards that are the same size.
3. Write this on the cards:

4 tens 13 ones	53
2 tens 17 ones	37
1 ten 11 ones	21
6 tens 10 ones	70
5 tens 12 ones	62
3 tens 14 ones	44

4. Mix the cards.
5. Turn them face down like this.

6. One child turns up 2 cards. If they match by being equal, keep the cards.
7. If they do not match, turn them back down. Do not move them.
8. Take turns with your partner turning up 2 cards at a turn.
9. When all 12 cards are gone, the game is over.

Let's do some more!

Play the game again.
Make more pairs.
Add them to your game.

Notes for Home Children explore with a partner to play a game involving trading.

Problem Solving WORKSHOP

Problem-Solving Workshop

Explore with a Computer

Primary Graphing and Probability Project

1. Ask 10 classmates to tell you their favorite subject. Tally their answers below.

Reading	
Language Arts	
Math	
Science	
Social Studies	

2. At the computer, make a bar graph to show the favorite subjects.

3. Which subject was picked most often? ______________

____

Exploring Mathematics Book Two © Scott, Foresman and Company

Notes for Home Children take a survey and record the results. Then they use the computer to create a bar graph of the data they collected.

Name

More Practice

Set A Use after page 178.

Write how many in each group.
Ring a ten if you can.
How many in all?

1. 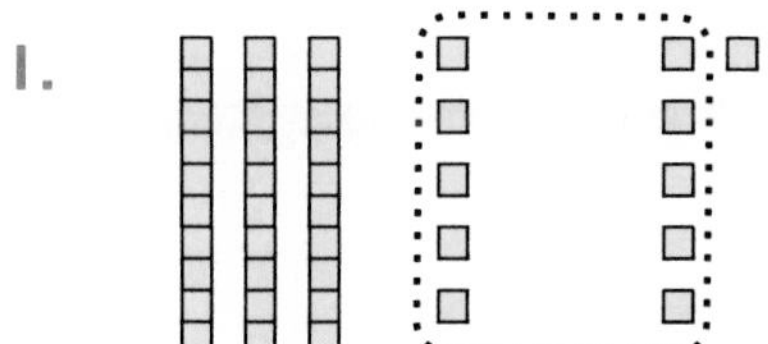

35 and 6

41 in all

2. 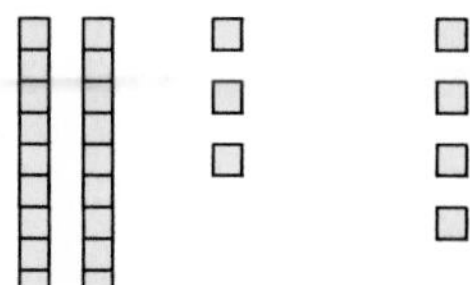

______ and ______

______ in all

3. 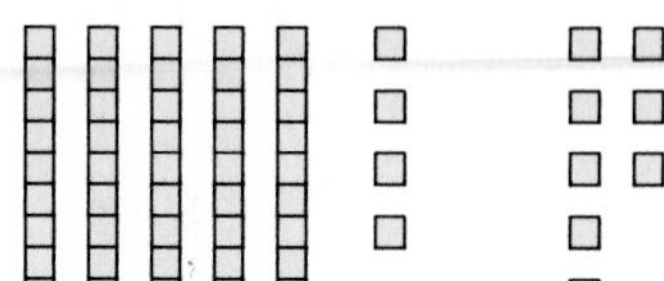

______ and ______

______ in all

4. 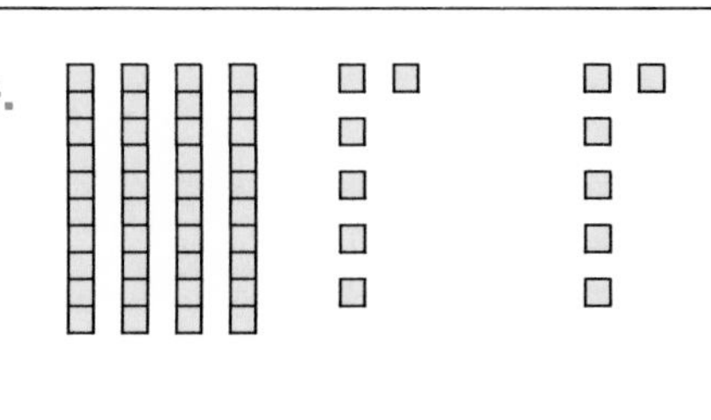

______ and ______

______ in all

5. 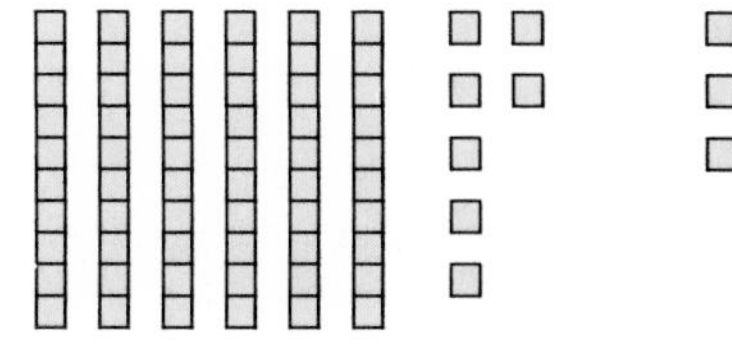

______ and ______

______ in all

6. 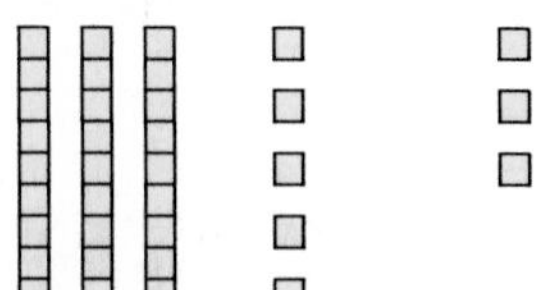

______ and ______

______ in all

Set B Use after page 190.

Decide if you need to trade.
Ring yes or no.

1. 36 take away 5

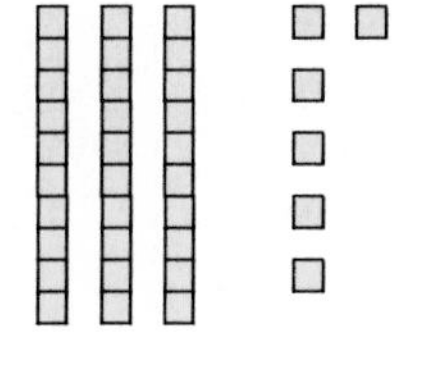

yes no

2. 55 take away 9

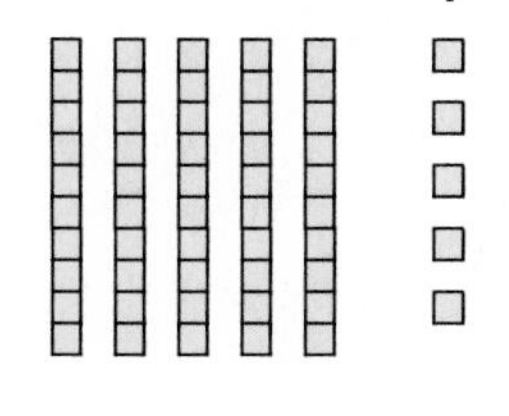

yes no

3. 47 take away 8

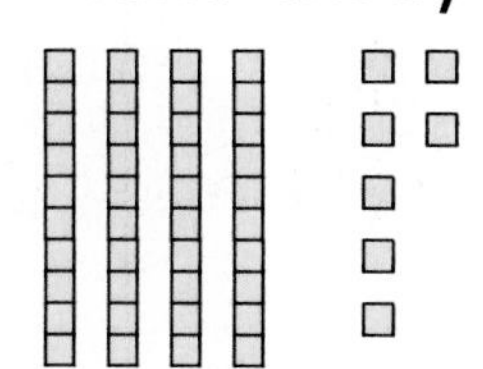

yes no

Notes for Home Set A: Children practice ringing a ten when possible. Then they write how many in all.
Set B: Children decide if a trade is needed to subtract some ones.

Enrichment

Trade 10 pennies for 1 dime.

1.

2.

2 | 14

3.

Notes for Home Children are challenged to develop place-value understanding by trading 10 pennies for 1 dime.

Exploring Mathematics Book Two © Scott, Foresman and Company

Name

Chapter 6 Review/Test

Can you trade 10 ones for 1 ten? Ring yes or no.

1. and

yes no

How many in each group? Ring a ten if you can. Write how many in all.

2.

_____ and _____

_____ in all

Do they match? Ring yes or no.

3.

yes no

4. Decide if you need to trade. Ring yes or no.

24 take away 6

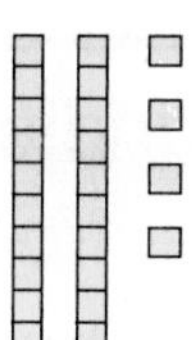

yes no

5. Complete the table.

Bob and Jan like to drink milk. Bob drinks 2 more glasses than Jan every day. Write how many each child drinks a day.

If Jan drinks	1	2	3
then Bob drinks			

6. This graph tells how many pets are in each store. Read the graph. Answer the question.

Store	[cat] = 5 pets
A	[cat] [cat] [cat] [cat]
B	[cat] [cat]

How many more pets are in Store A than in Store B?

_____

Notes for Home Children are assessed on Chapter 6 concepts, skills, and problem solving.

Exploring Math at Home

Dear Family,

In this chapter I have learned how and when to trade ones and tens in order to join and separate groups. Please help me with the activities below.

Love, ________________________

1.

Use some straws. Tell how many in all. Then make tens when possible. Tell how many tens and ones. Repeat the activity with different amounts of straws.

2.

Use straws again. Make bundles of tens. Show extra ones. Count how many tens and ones. Decide if a trade is needed to subtract some ones.

Coming Attractions

In the next chapter I will learn two-digit addition and how to record a trade of 10 ones for 1 ten. I will also learn about adding amounts of money.

Exploring Mathematics Book Two © Scott, Foresman and Company

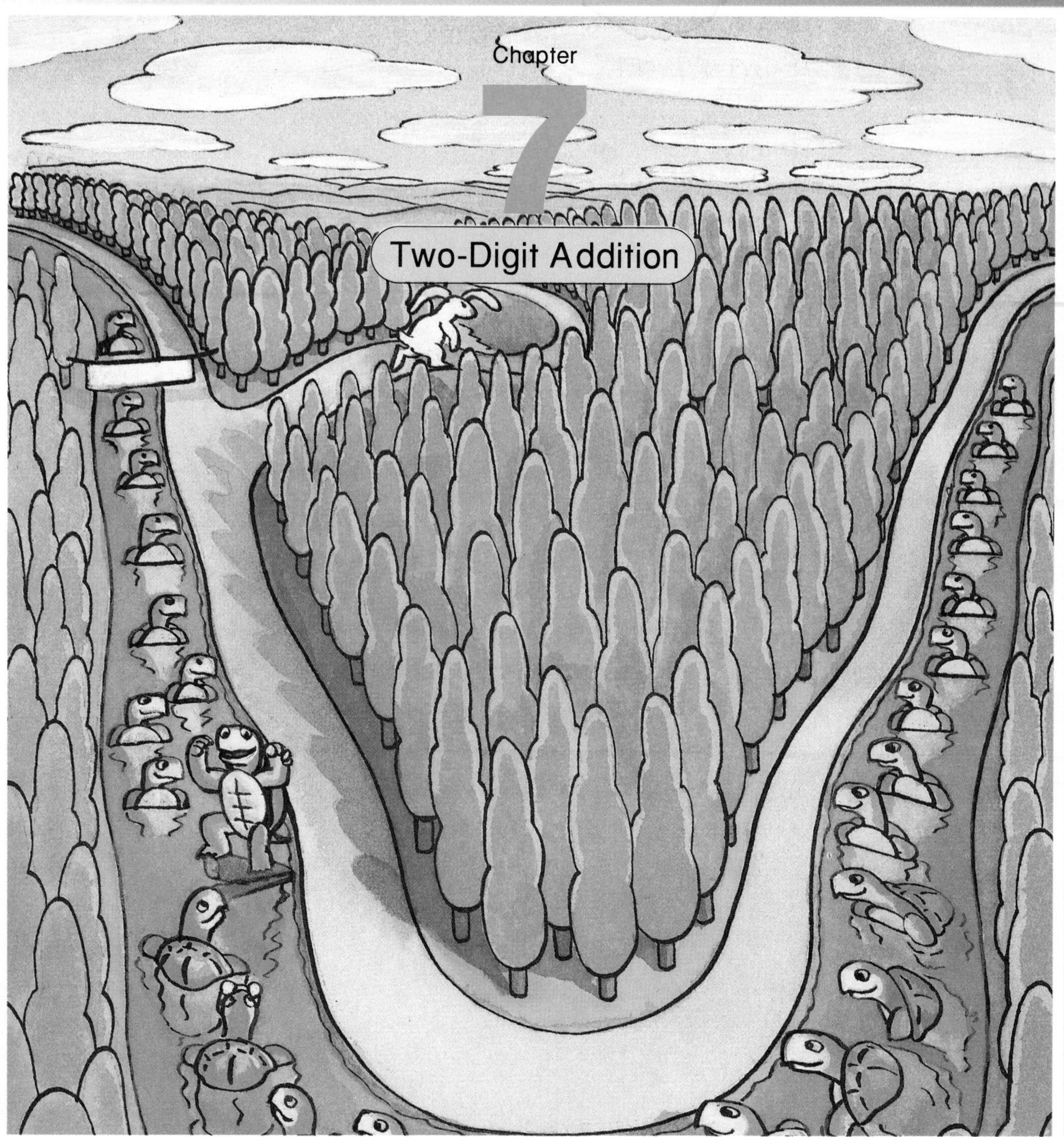

Listen to the math story, "Turtle's Race."
Turtle saw 21 turtles. Then he saw 6 turtles.
How did he find how many turtles in all?

Notes for Home Children listen to a math story introducing chapter concepts and skills. Then they answer a question about the story.

Name

Learning to Record a Trade

Record a trade if you make one.

1.

tens	ones
1	
	7
+	6
	3

tens	ones
	4
+	9

tens	ones
	4
+	5

tens	ones
	3
+	8

2.

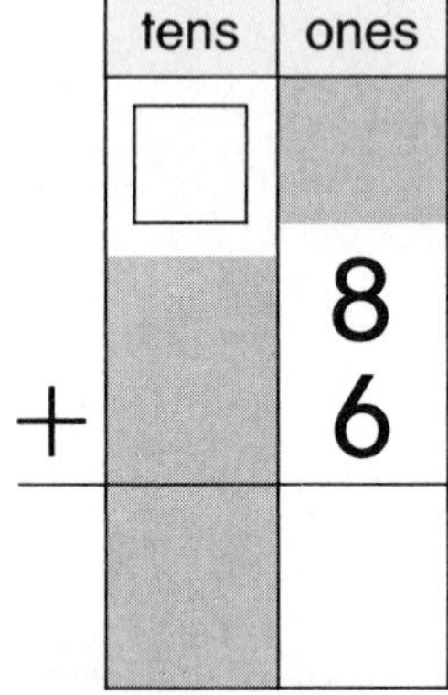

tens	ones
	3
+	4

tens	ones
	6
+	4

tens	ones
	7
+	8

Exploring Mathematics Book Two © Scott, Foresman and Company

Notes for Home Children learn where to record trades when the total number of digits in the ones place is more than 9.

Name

Adding a Two-Digit and a One-Digit Number

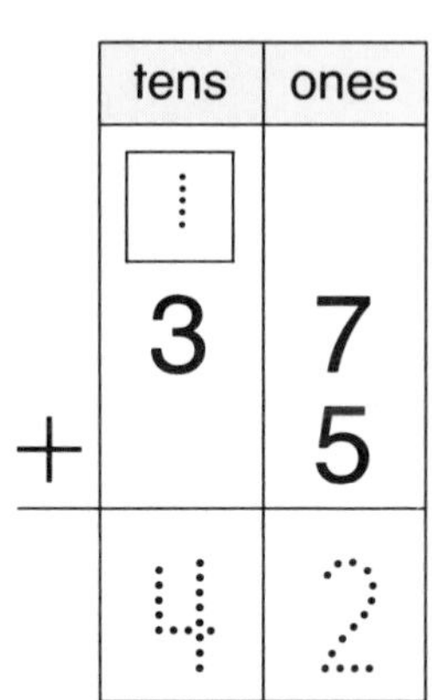

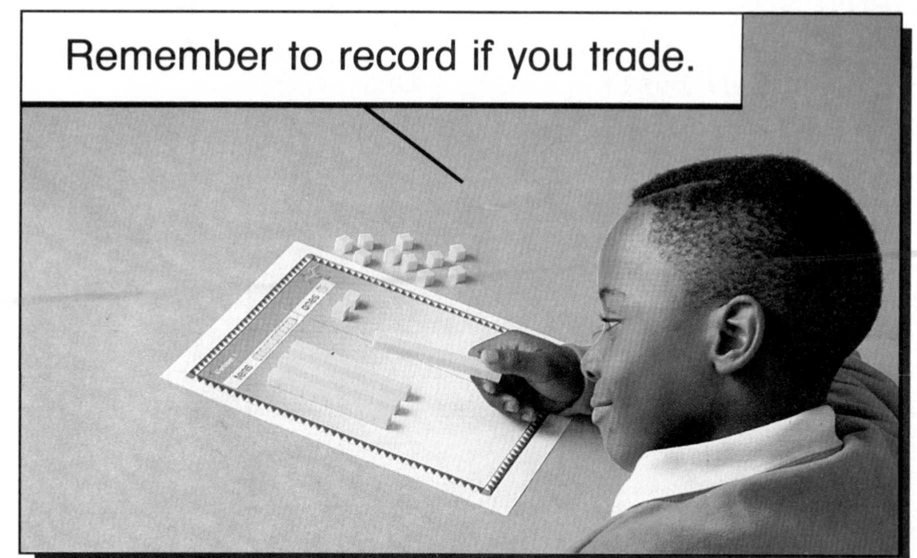

Use Workmat 1.
Use tens and ones counters.
Show each number. Add. Record if you trade.

1.

	tens	ones
	2	7
+		7

	tens	ones
	3	6
+		9

	tens	ones
	5	5
+		4

	tens	ones
	2	8
+		5

2.

	tens	ones
	4	6
+		8

	tens	ones
	5	4
+		6

	tens	ones
	1	3
+		8

	tens	ones
	3	2
+		6

Notes for Home Children explore at the CONCRETE level using tens and ones counters and a place-value workmat to add a one-digit number to a two-digit number.

Use Workmat 1.
Use tens and ones counters.
Show each number. Add. Record if you trade.

3.

tens	ones
1	
5	8
+	4
6	2

tens	ones
3	5
+	9

tens	ones
4	3
+	4

tens	ones
1	7
+	9

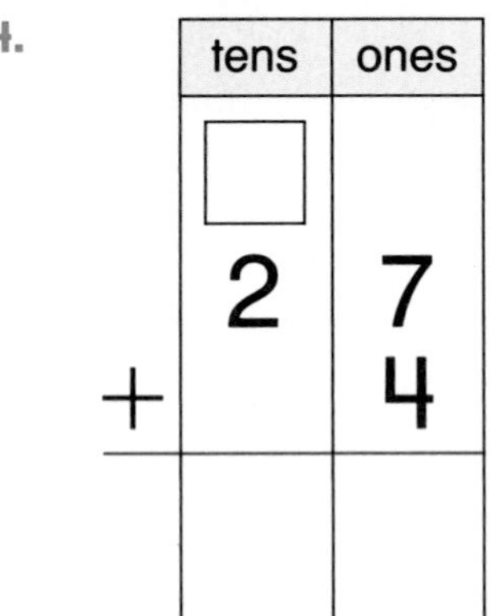

4.

tens	ones
2	7
+	4

tens	ones
4	9
+	8

tens	ones
3	6
+	5

tens	ones
4	3
+	7

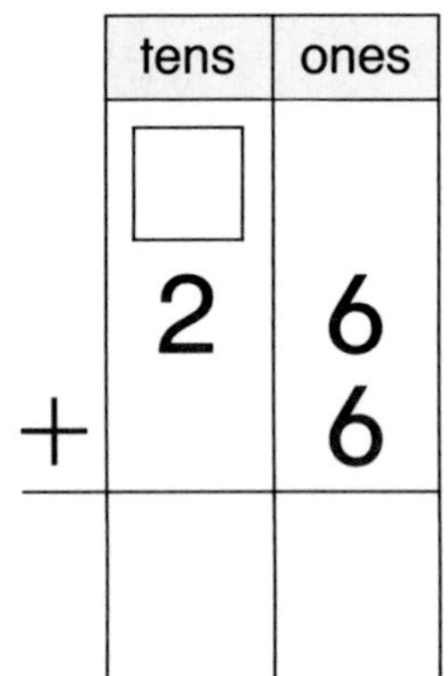

5.

tens	ones
2	6
+	6

tens	ones
5	5
+	8

tens	ones
4	9
+	3

tens	ones
3	2
+	9

Critical Thinking Explain how you use counters to add the ones in 26 + 7.

Notes for Home Children explore at the CONCRETE level using tens and ones counters and a place-value workmat to add a one-digit number to a two-digit number. Then they discuss making a trade.

Exploring Mathematics Book Two © Scott, Foresman and Company

Name

Adding a Two-Digit and a One-Digit Number

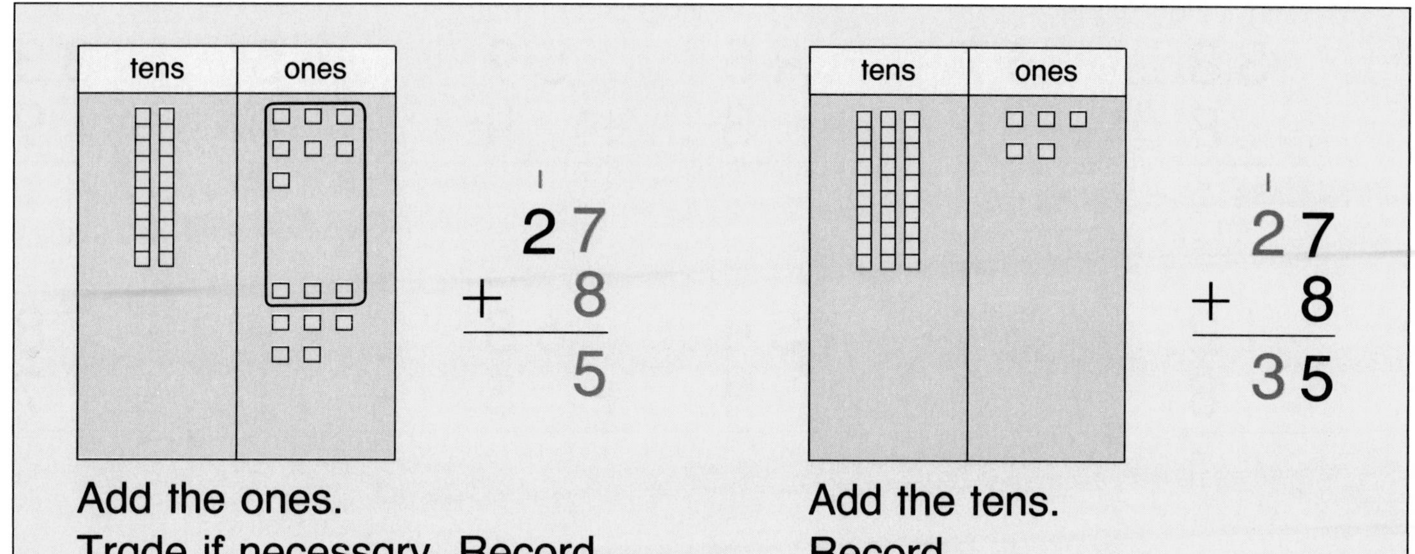

Do you need to trade? Ring yes or no.
Add. Ring the trade.

1\.

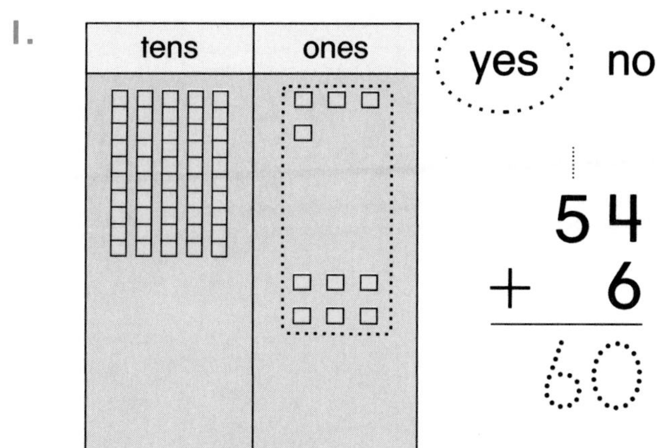

yes no

54
+ 6
60

2\.

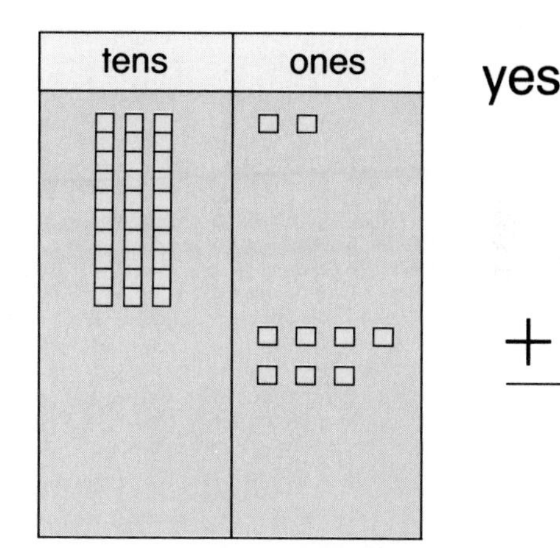

yes no

32
+ 7

3\.

tens | ones

yes no

48
+ 5

4\.

tens | ones

yes no

31
+ 9

Notes for Home Children add a one-digit number to a two-digit number using pictures of place-value materials.

Ring if you need to trade.
Then add.

5.	38 + 8 = 46	67 + 4	45 + 3	59 + 4	65 + 6	83 + 9
6.	12 + 8	37 + 8	34 + 4	68 + 3	49 + 1	78 + 7
7.	39 + 6	42 + 3	75 + 7	29 + 9	34 + 4	56 + 3
8.	55 + 5	71 + 7	37 + 3	49 + 5	86 + 8	67 + 6

Problem Solving

Solve.

9. Lee is 47 inches tall.
How tall will he be if
he grows 7 inches?

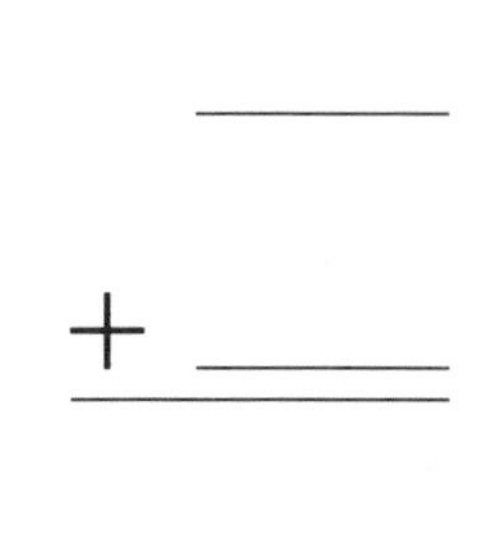

______ inches

Exploring Mathematics Book Two © Scott, Foresman and Company

Notes for Home Children practice adding a one-digit number to a two-digit number. Then they solve a problem involving one- and two-digit numbers.

Name

Adding Two-Digit Numbers

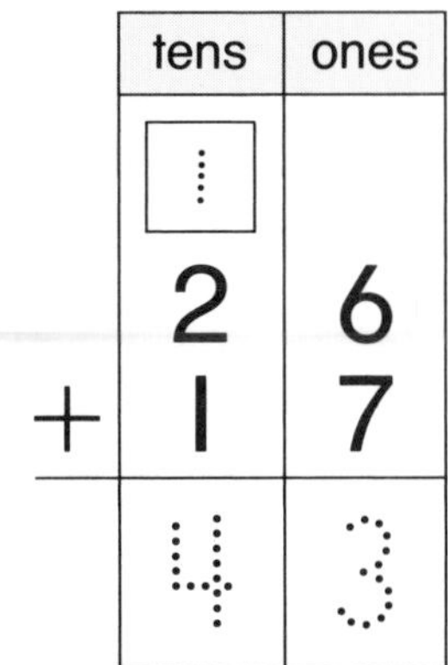

First, add the ones. If you make a trade, record the ten. Then add the tens.

Use Workmat 1.
Use tens and ones counters.
Show each number. Add. Record if you trade.

1.

	tens	ones
	☐	
	1	4
+	2	6

	tens	ones
	☐	
	3	4
+	1	7

	tens	ones
	☐	
	2	7
+	1	6

	tens	ones
	☐	
	2	8
+	4	1

2.

	tens	ones
	☐	
	1	8
+	3	5

	tens	ones
	☐	
	4	1
+	1	9

	tens	ones
	☐	
	3	0
+	1	5

	tens	ones
	☐	
	3	4
+	1	8

Notes for Home Children explore at the CONCRETE level using tens and ones counters and a place-value workmat to find two-digit sums. They determine whether or not they need to trade.

Use Workmat 1.
Use tens and ones counters.
Show each number. Add. Record if you trade.

3.

	tens	ones
	1	
	2	6
+	3	8
	6	4

	tens	ones
	3	6
+	1	5

	tens	ones
	2	3
+	6	5

	tens	ones
	3	7
+		7

4.

	tens	ones
	3	5
+	2	4

	tens	ones
	1	5
+	7	7

	tens	ones
	2	6
+	2	4

	tens	ones
	4	4
+	4	9

5.

	tens	ones
	4	2
+	1	6

	tens	ones
	3	5
+	5	5

	tens	ones
	3	4
+		3

	tens	ones
	1	8
+	5	7

Exploring Mathematics Book Two © Scott, Foresman and Company

Notes for Home Children explore at the CONCRETE level using tens and ones counters and a place-value workmat to find two-digit sums. They determine whether or not they need to trade.

Name

Adding Two-Digit Numbers

Do you need to trade? Ring yes or no.
Add. Ring the trade.

1. tens | ones — yes no

$$\begin{array}{r} 1 \\ 38 \\ +16 \\ \hline 54 \end{array}$$

2. tens | ones — yes no

$$\begin{array}{r} 43 \\ +17 \\ \hline \end{array}$$

3. tens | ones — yes no

$$\begin{array}{r} 26 \\ +22 \\ \hline \end{array}$$

4. tens | ones — yes no

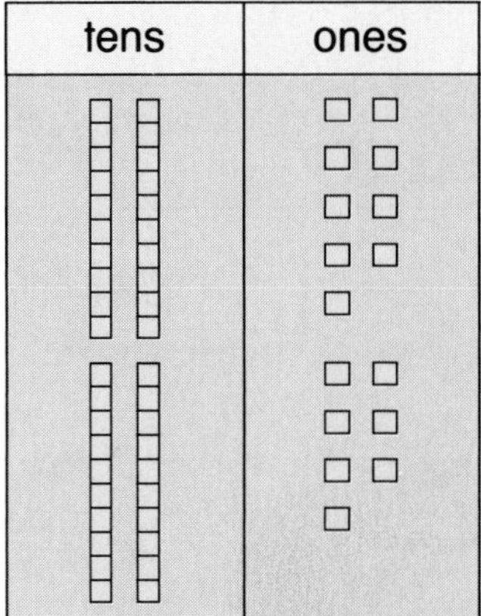

$$\begin{array}{r} 29 \\ +27 \\ \hline \end{array}$$

Notes for Home Children add two-digit numbers using pictures of place-value materials.

Ring if you need to trade.
Then add.

5.	35 + 26 = 61	29 + 42	63 + 24	16 + 49	27 + 64	44 + 31
6.	58 + 35	32 + 35	48 + 17	21 + 36	38 + 52	65 + 16
7.	35 + 53	62 + 17	29 + 61	18 + 38	26 + 37	52 + 27
8.	29 + 25	56 + 14	53 + 29	15 + 42	28 + 59	47 + 28

Talk About Math

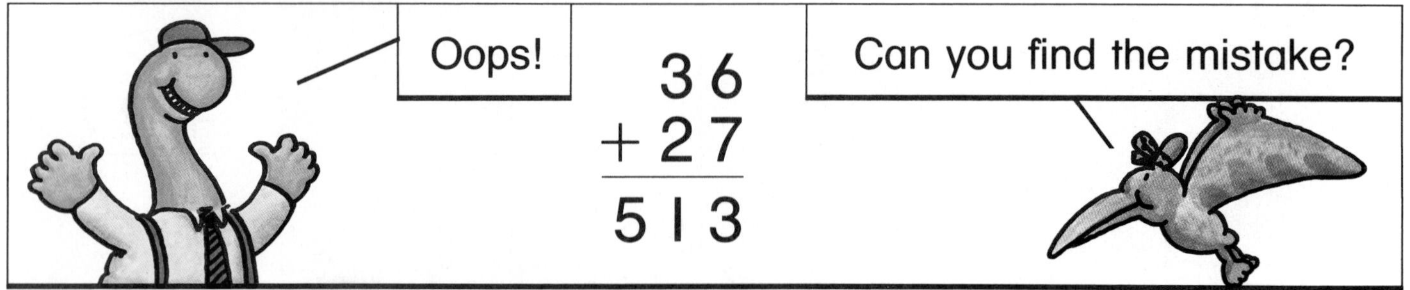

Exploring Mathematics Book Two © Scott, Foresman and Company

Notes for Home Children practice finding sums of two-digit numbers. Then they talk about the importance of trading and place value.

Name

Adding Two-Digit Numbers

Holly has 27 straws. Jordan has 16 straws. How can you find how many straws they have altogether?

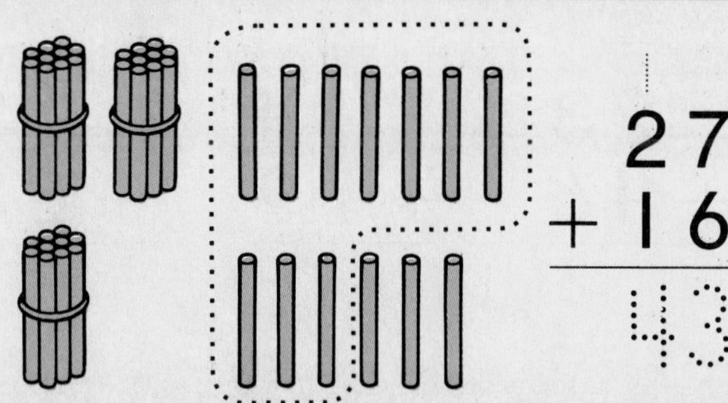

$$\begin{array}{r} 27 \\ +16 \\ \hline 43 \end{array}$$

Ring the ones if you trade. Then add.

1. 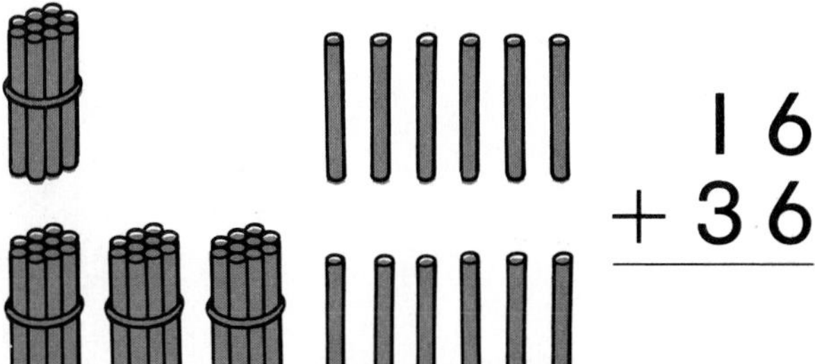

$$\begin{array}{r} 16 \\ +36 \\ \hline \end{array}$$

2. 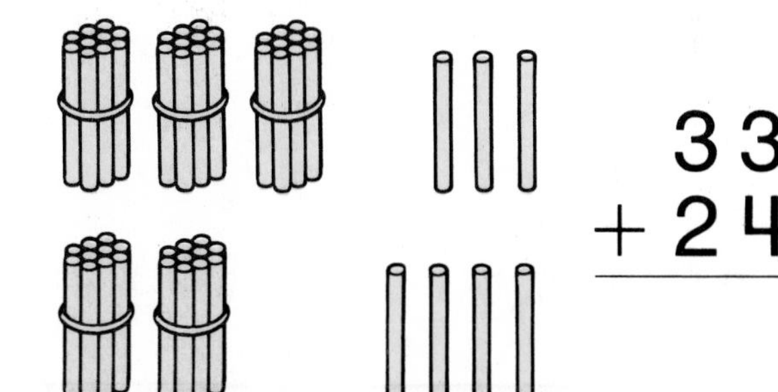

$$\begin{array}{r} 33 \\ +24 \\ \hline \end{array}$$

3. 

$$\begin{array}{r} 25 \\ +15 \\ \hline \end{array}$$

4. 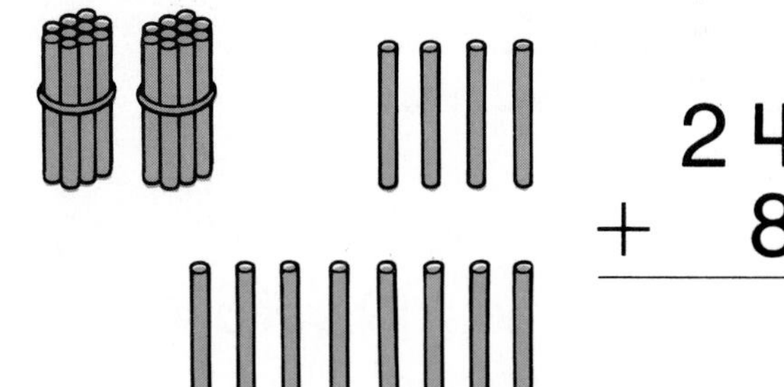

$$\begin{array}{r} 24 \\ +\ 8 \\ \hline \end{array}$$

5. 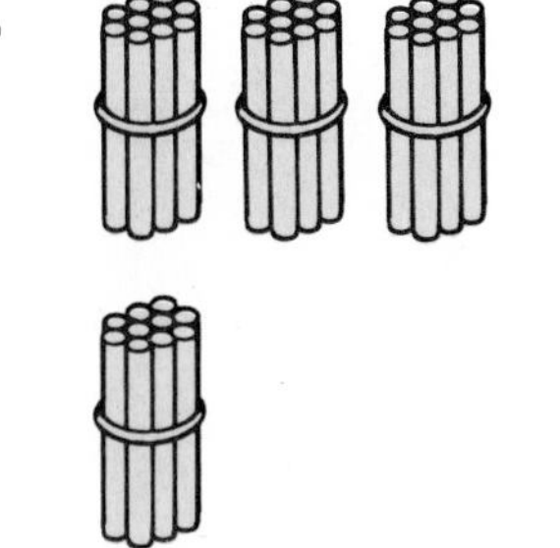

$$\begin{array}{r} 35 \\ +12 \\ \hline \end{array}$$

6. 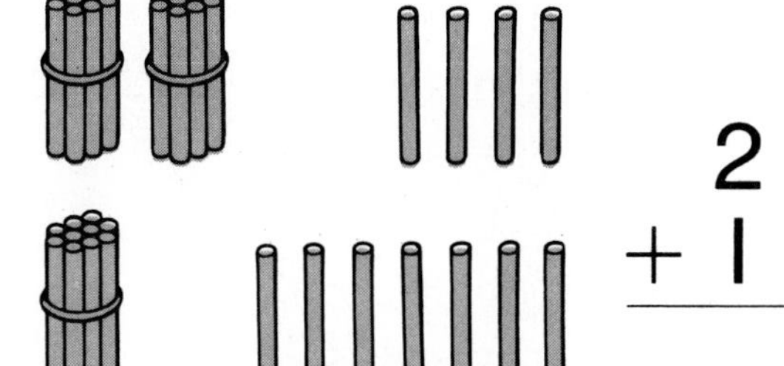

$$\begin{array}{r} 24 \\ +17 \\ \hline \end{array}$$

Notes for Home Children find sums of two-digit numbers.

Ring if you need to trade.
Then add.

7.	33 + 19 = 52	28 + 7	46 + 32	38 + 5	54 + 36	35 + 22
8.	23 + 46	14 + 79	13 + 83	37 + 6	55 + 29	62 + 4
9.	38 + 53	37 + 39	40 + 6	35 + 7	28 + 9	43 + 28
10.	52 + 38	23 + 54	59 + 8	43 + 45	27 + 3	71 + 14

Problem Solving

Solve.

11. Alex has 19 yellow straws and 22 green straws. How many straws does Alex have altogether?

______ straws

12. Lola had 17 blue straws. She used 8 of them. How many straws does she have left?

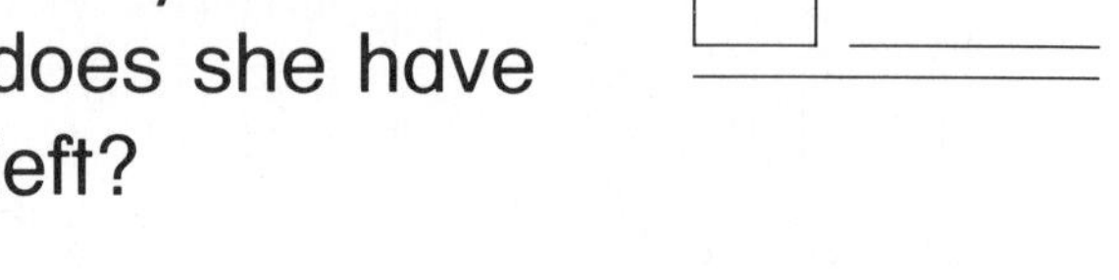

______ straws

Exploring Mathematics Book Two © Scott, Foresman and Company

Notes for Home Children practice finding sums of two-digit numbers. Then they solve problems involving addition and subtraction.

See More Practice Set A on page 227.

Name

Adding Amounts of Money

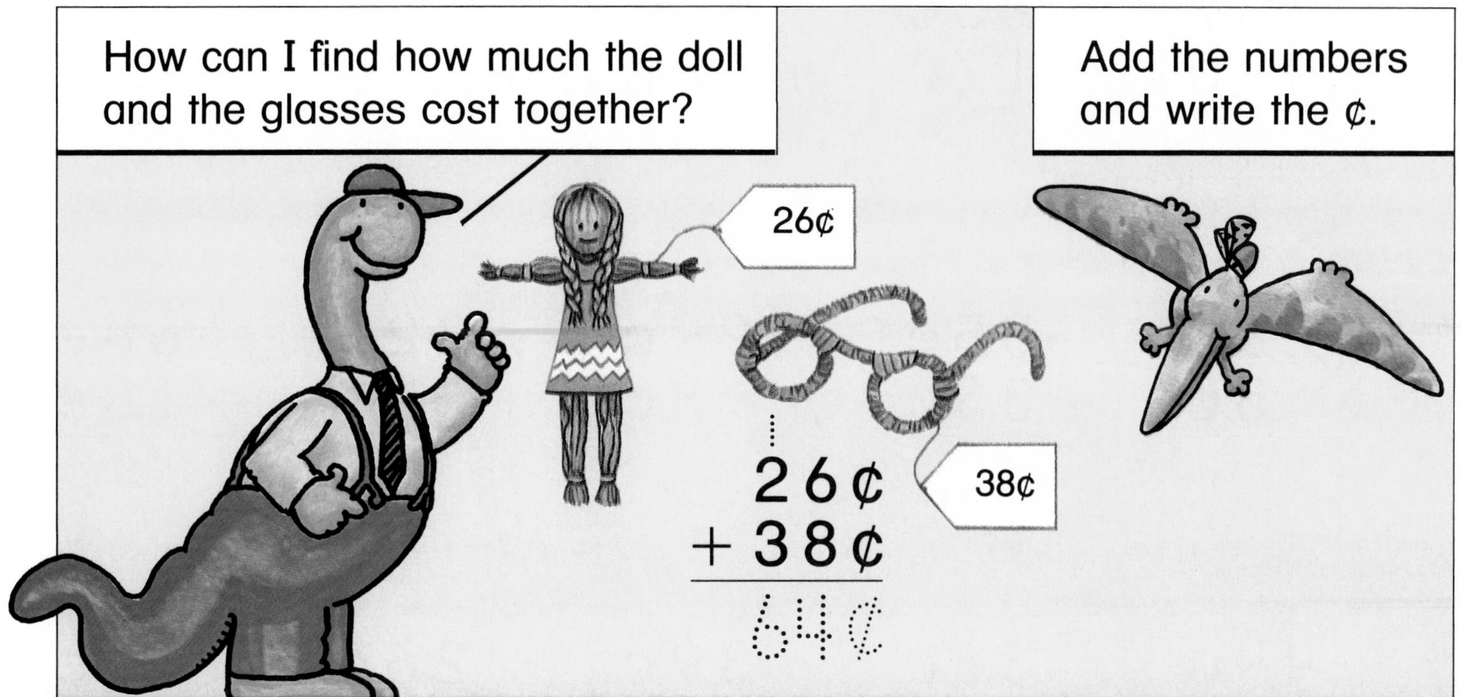

Write the sum. Write the ¢.

1. 32¢ + 18¢   43¢ + 19¢   48¢ + 6¢   19¢ + 6¢   28¢ + 66¢

2. 22¢ + 75¢   43¢ + 56¢   57¢ + 4¢   35¢ + 45¢   29¢ + 19¢

3. 23¢ + 58¢   36¢ + 16¢   59¢ + 28¢   66¢ + 30¢   34¢ + 4¢

Notes for Home Children add amounts of money to find two-digit sums.

Write the sum. Write the ¢.

4.	38¢ + 44¢ = 82¢	23¢ + 17¢	53¢ + 6¢	17¢ + 17¢	35¢ + 14¢
5.	26¢ + 5¢	35¢ + 33¢	29¢ + 8¢	32¢ + 56¢	68¢ + 13¢
6.	44¢ + 13¢	36¢ + 37¢	39¢ + 44¢	26¢ + 52¢	17¢ + 78¢

Problem Solving

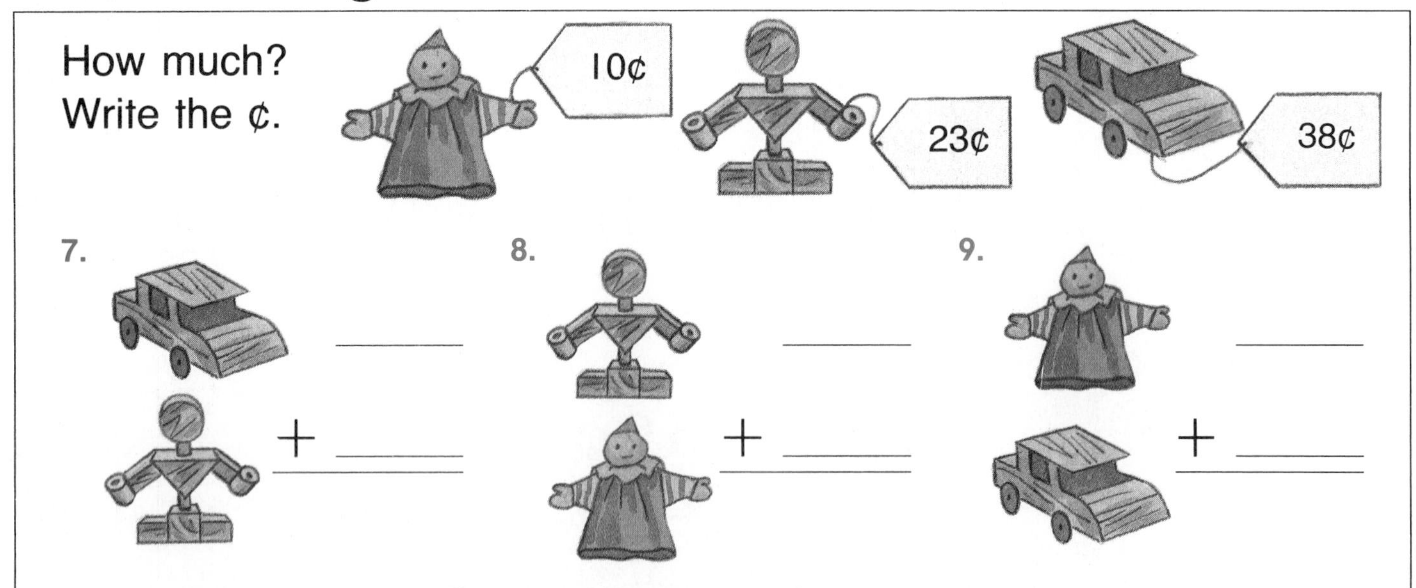

Notes for Home Children add amounts of money to find two-digit sums. Then they solve problems involving money.

Exploring Mathematics Book Two © Scott, Foresman and Company

Name ______________________________

PROBLEM-SOLVING GUIDE
➡ Understand
Plan and Solve
Look Back

Use Data from a Picture

Look at the picture. Solve.

1. Chin buys a plant. He buys a clay pot for the plant. How much does he spend for both?

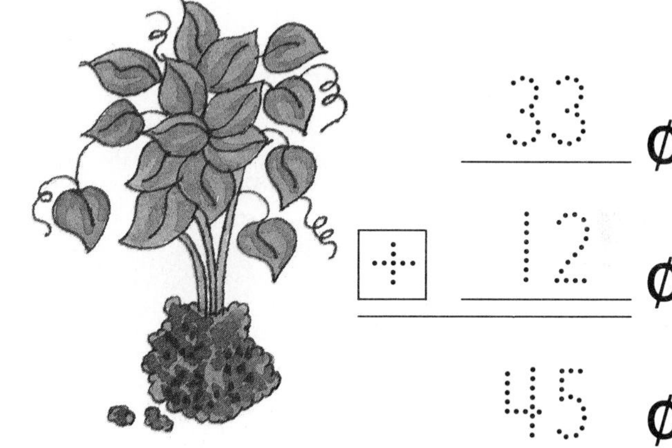

33 ¢
+ 12 ¢
45 ¢

2. How much more does the clay pot cost than the beans?

_____ ¢

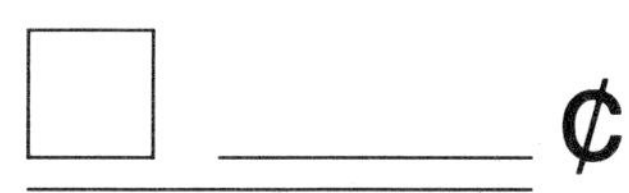
☐ _____ ¢

¢

3. Janice needs a watering can and some soil. How much does she need to spend?

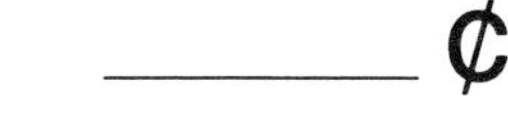
_____ ¢

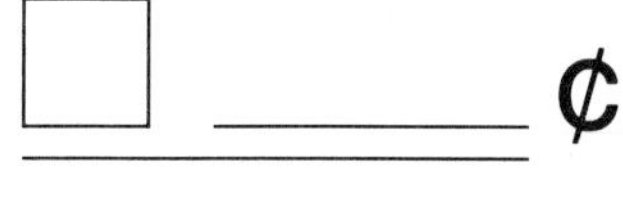
☐ _____ ¢

¢

Notes for Home Children solve problems involving money by using data from a picture.

tulips
38¢ each
roses
50¢ each
daisies
9¢ each
irises
25¢ each
ferns
15¢ each
vase
49¢
basket
45¢

Look at the picture.
Solve.

4. If you buy a fern and a basket, what is the cost altogether?

15 ¢
+ 45 ¢
60 ¢

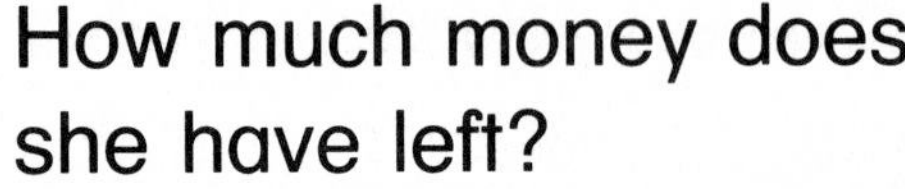

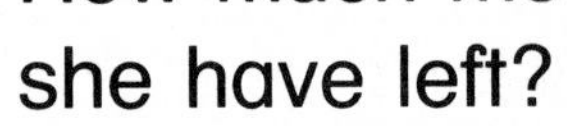

5. Bianca has 15¢. She buys a daisy.
How much money does
she have left?

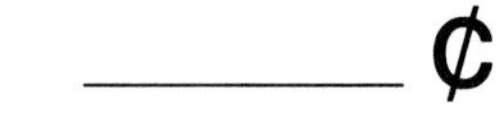

_____ ¢
☐ _____ ¢
¢

6. How much do an iris and a vase cost?

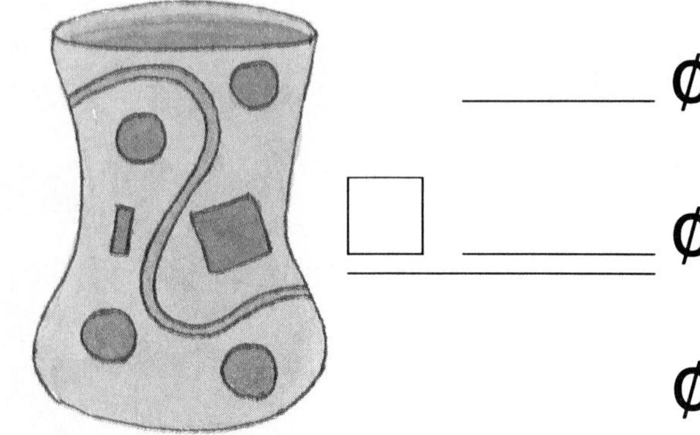

_____ ¢
☐ _____ ¢
¢

Exploring Mathematics Book Two © Scott, Foresman and Company

Notes for Home Children solve problems involving money by using data from a picture.

Name

Number Sense

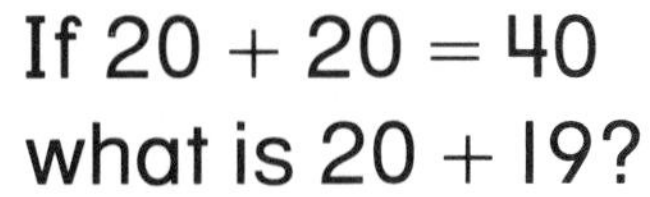

Think of some more stories for adding nines.

Notes for Home Children develop number understanding by discussing number relationships.

SKILLS REVIEW

Skills Review

Fill in the correct ⬭.
Do you need to trade?

1. 30 take away 4

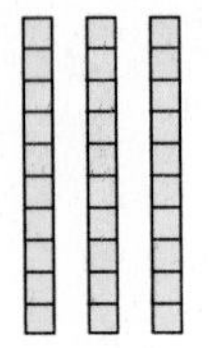

Ⓐ yes
Ⓑ no

2. 26 take away 8

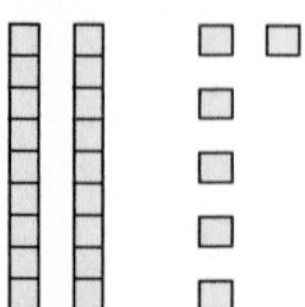

Ⓐ yes
Ⓑ no

3. 52 take away 6

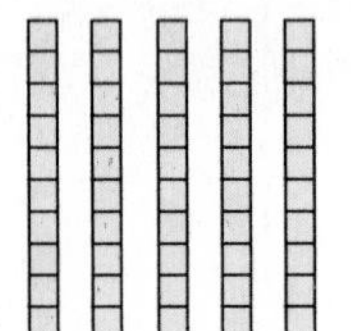

Ⓐ yes
Ⓑ no

4. 48 take away 7

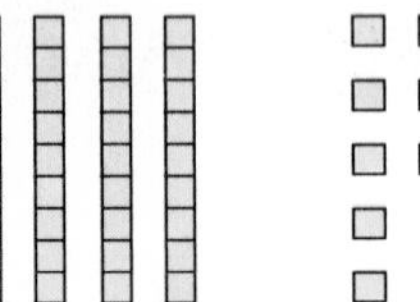

Ⓐ yes
Ⓑ no

Vocabulary

Use the words in the word bank.

subtract	trade	ten	ones

5. Sometimes you need to trade when you subtract.

6. One ten is the same as 10 ________.

7. You can trade 10 ones for 1 ________.

8. You ________ when you take away.

Exploring Mathematics Book Two © Scott, Foresman and Company

Notes for Home Children decide if a trade is needed to subtract some ones. Then they review math terms for trading numbers.

Name

Estimating Two-Digit Sums

How many red marbles does José have?
How many blue marbles does he have?
Does he have more than 40 marbles altogether?

25 + 17 is more than 40.

Estimate the sum. Ring more or less.

1. 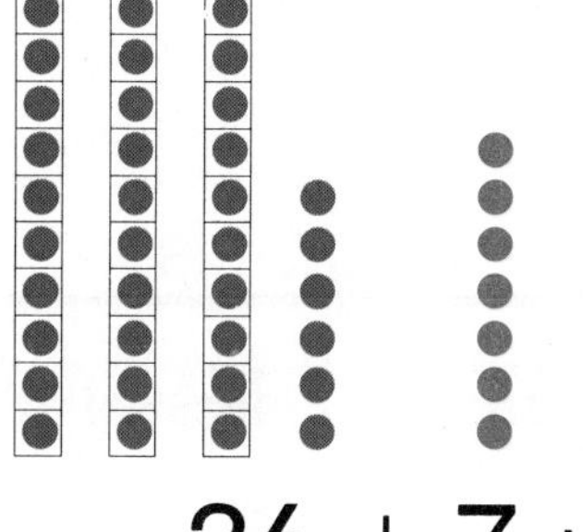

36 + 7 is

more than 40. (ringed) less than 40.

2. 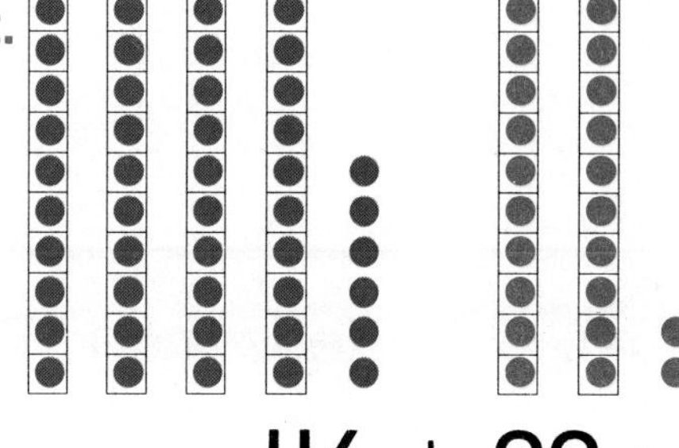

46 + 22 is

more than 70. less than 70.

3. 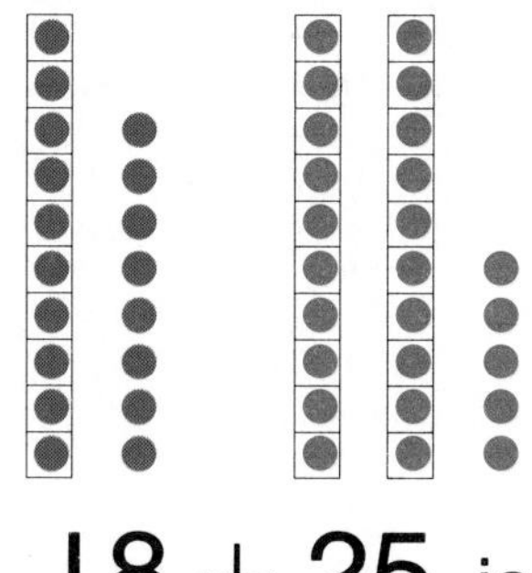

18 + 25 is

more than 40. less than 40.

4. 31 + 23 is

more than 60. less than 60.

Notes for Home Children estimate two-digit sums by determining if there are more or less than 10 ones.

Estimate the sum.
Ring more or less.

5.

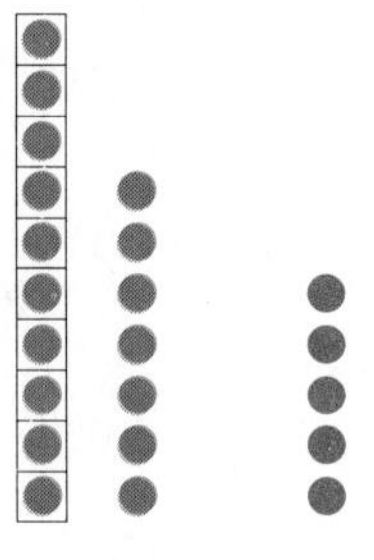

17 + 5 is

more than 20. less than 20.

6.

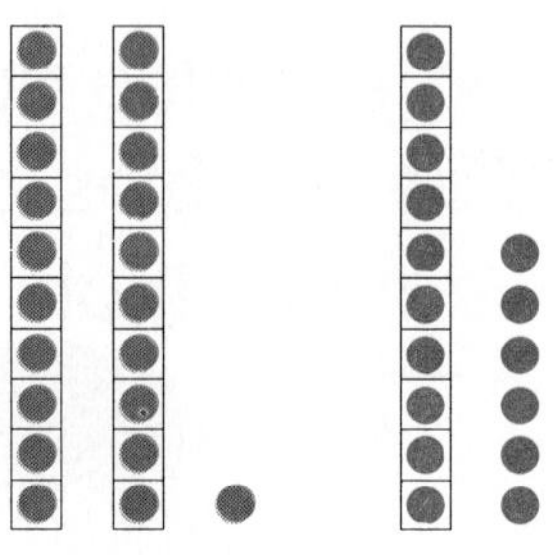

21 + 16 is

more than 40. less than 40.

7.

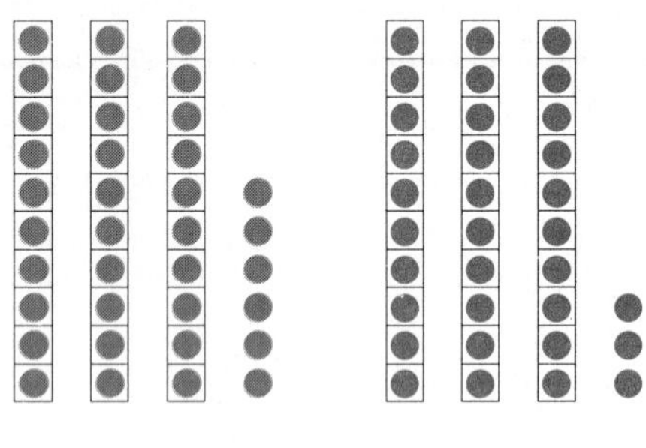

36 + 33 is

more than 70. less than 70.

8.

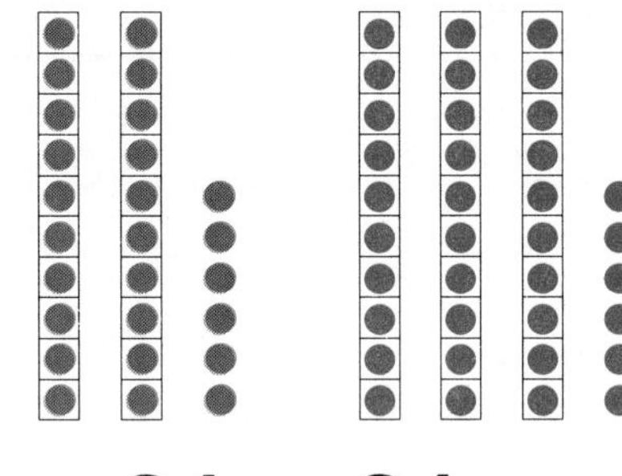

26 + 36 is

more than 60. less than 60.

Write About Math

What numbers can you add to 25 so that the sum is less than 30?

_____ _____ _____ _____ _____

Exploring Mathematics Book Two © Scott, Foresman and Company

Notes for Home Children estimate two-digit sums by determining if there are more or less than 10 ones. Then they find sums that are less than a given number.

Name

Finding Patterns in Addition

I found a pattern in the ones place.

7	17	27	37
+ 5	+ 5	+ 5	+ 5
12	22	32	42

Write the sum.
Look for a pattern.

1.

3	13	23	33	43	53
+ 5	+ 5	+ 5	+ 5	+ 5	+ 5
8					

2.

10	10	10	10	10	10
+ 2	+ 12	+ 22	+ 32	+ 42	+ 52

3.

9	9	9	9	9	9
+ 2	+ 12	+ 22	+ 32	+ 42	+ 52

Notes for Home Children find two-digit sums by looking for number patterns.

4. Color sums

with 5 in the ones place red.

with 2 in the ones place orange.

with 3 in the ones place green.

with 7 in the ones place yellow.

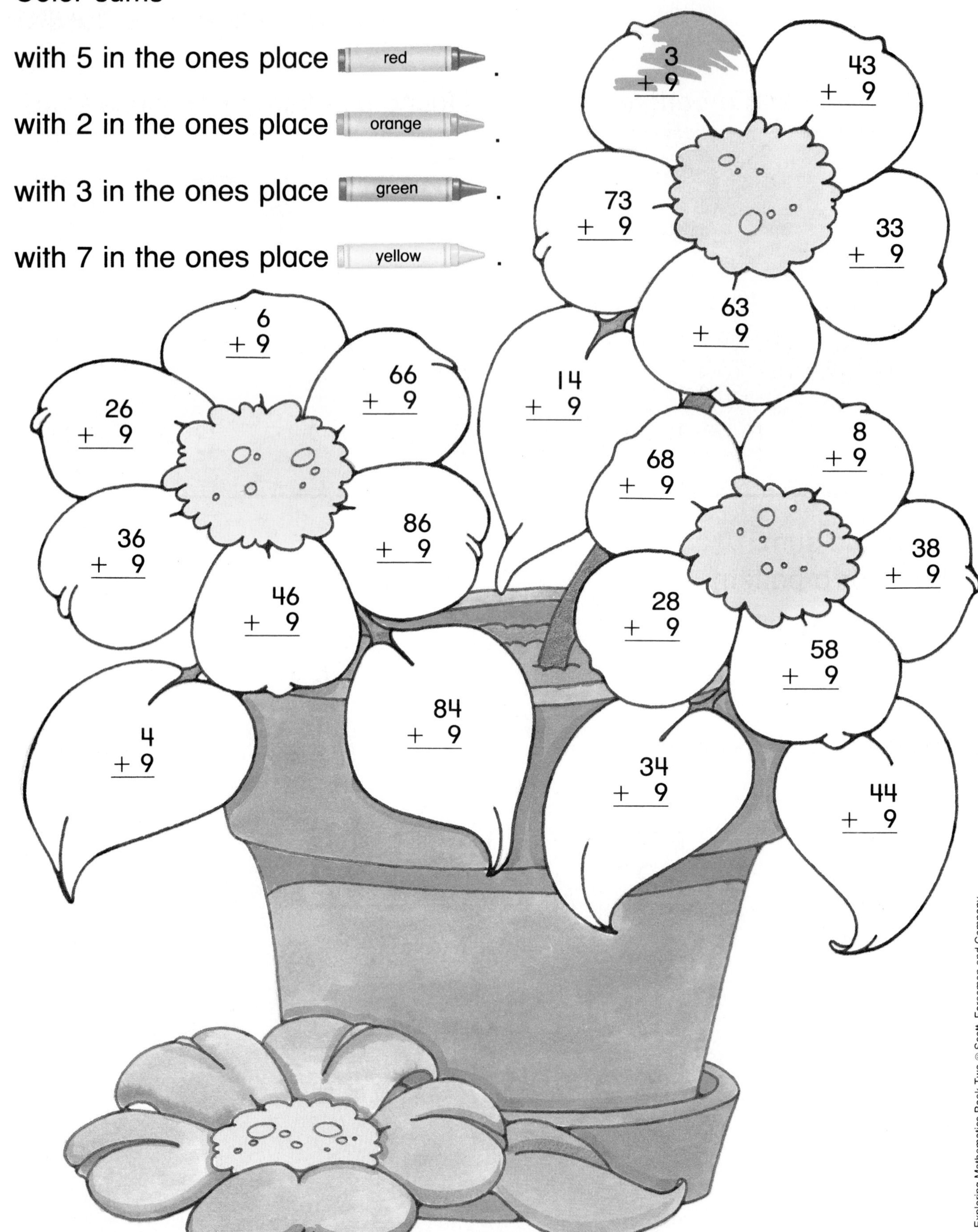

Exploring Mathematics Book Two © Scott, Foresman and Company

Notes for Home Children practice finding sums by looking for number patterns.

Name

Adding in a Column

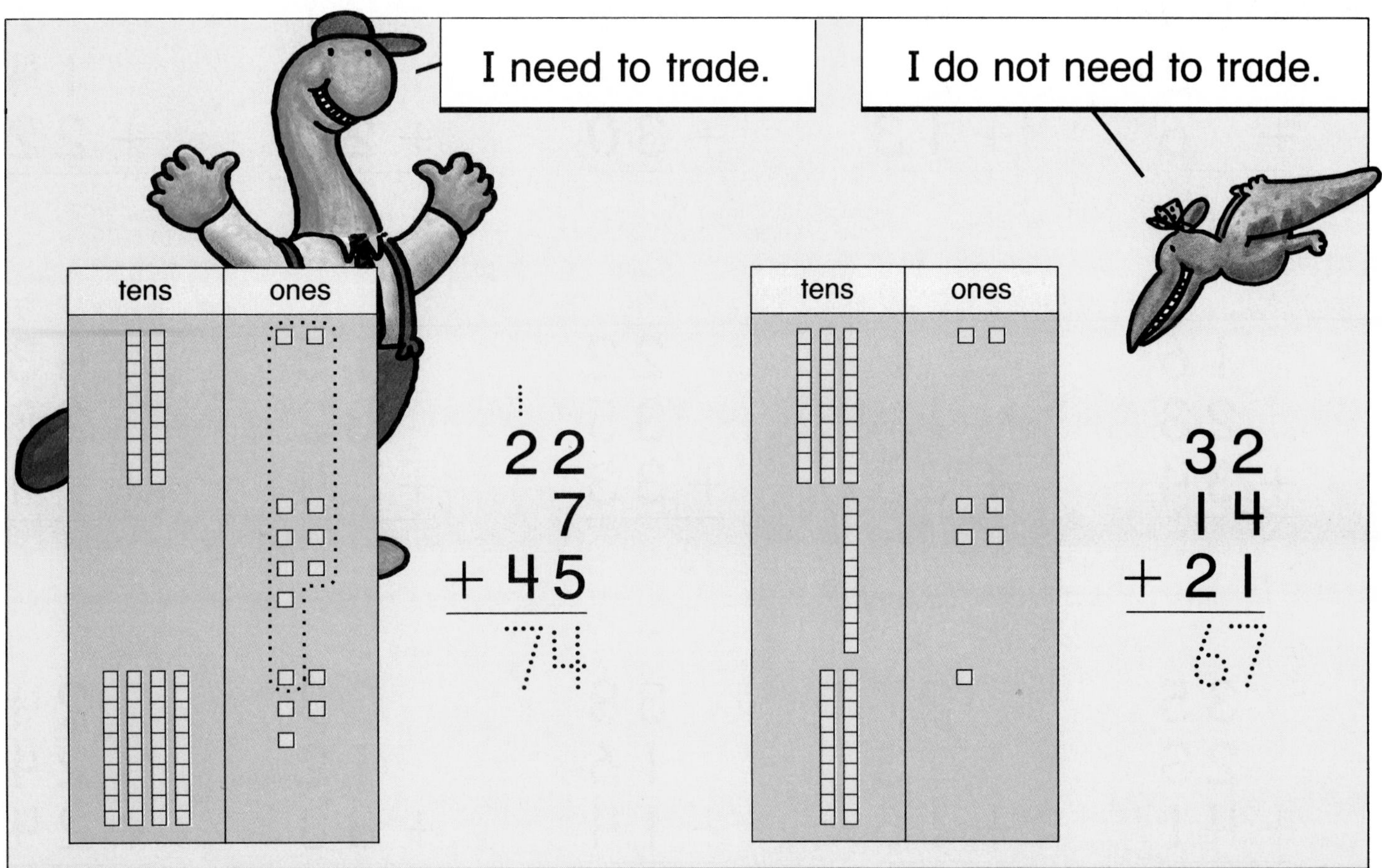

Write the sum.

1.

24	41	32	20	17
26	13	17	3	13
+ 33	+ 18	+ 2	+ 54	+ 25

2.

52	26	47	32	35
8	10	22	41	11
+ 26	+ 32	+ 9	+ 19	+ 3

Notes for Home Children add columns of numbers, trading if necessary, to find two-digit sums.

Write the sum.

3.					
	55	42	48	31	7
	13	22	7	15	14
	+ 6	+ 13	+ 30	+ 26	+ 22
	74				

4.					
	16	2	22	15	43
	23	14	35	32	28
	+ 34	+ 33	+ 33	+ 4	+ 14

5.					
	35	27	38	38	24
	23	3	16	12	24
	+ 41	+ 15	+ 14	+ 38	+ 24

Problem Solving

Solve.

6. The library has 22 books about dogs, 7 books about horses, and 45 books about cats. How many books does the library have about these pets?

______

______

+ ______

______ books

Exploring Mathematics Book Two © Scott, Foresman and Company

Notes for Home Children add columns of numbers to find two-digit sums. Then they solve a problem involving addition of three addends.

See More Practice Set B on page 227.

Name ____________________

Too Much or Too Little Information

Which facts do not help solve this problem?

The second grade class went to the art museum.
They saw 17 oil paintings and 15 watercolor paintings.
~~They also saw 7 statues.~~
How many paintings did they see?

Cross out the facts you do not need.

1. The museum guide gives 8 tours every weekday.
On weekends there are 15 tours.
The museum is open from 9:00 to 5:00.
How many tours are given in one week?

2. The museum has a gift shop.
In one day 15 art books were sold.
In one week 23 pictures and 49 postcards were sold.
How many pictures and postcards were sold?

3. Mary and Alex bought postcards.
Mary bought 17 cards.
Alex bought 8 cards.
He spent 85¢.
How many more cards did Mary buy than Alex?

Notes for Home Children prepare to solve problems by eliminating unneeded information.

I have enough information to solve this problem.

The second grade class rode the bus to the museum. There were 16 girls and 15 boys on the bus. How many children rode on the bus?

enough   not enough

Is there enough information?
Ring enough or not enough.

4. The class saw 35 paintings at the museum. They saw more drawings than paintings. How many drawings did they see?

enough   not enough

5. There are 14 rooms on the second floor of the museum and 29 rooms on the first floor. How many rooms are there on both floors?

enough   not enough

6. The children bought 15 art books. The teacher bought fewer books than the children. How many books did the teacher buy?

enough   not enough

Exploring Mathematics Book Two © Scott, Foresman and Company

Notes for Home Children prepare to solve problems by determining if there is enough information.

Name

Problem-Solving Workshop

Explore as a Team

Work with a partner.
Write the missing number.
Look in the ones place first.

1.
$$\begin{array}{r} 3\ \boxed{7} \\ +\ \boxed{2}\ 2 \\ \hline 5\ 9 \end{array}$$

2.
$$\begin{array}{r} 4\ \square \\ +\ \square\ 3 \\ \hline 6\ 6 \end{array}$$

3.
$$\begin{array}{r} 2\ 5 \\ +\ \square\ \square \\ \hline 7\ 9 \end{array}$$

4.
$$\begin{array}{r} 5\ \square \\ +\ \square\ 7 \\ \hline 8\ 2 \end{array}$$

5.
$$\begin{array}{r} \square\ 1 \\ +\ 4\ \square \\ \hline 9\ 0 \end{array}$$

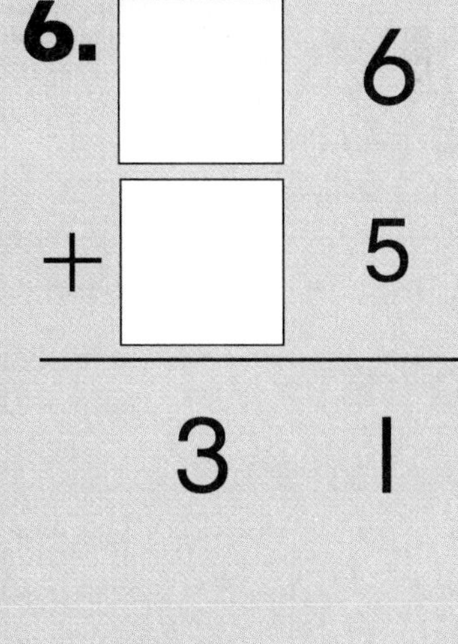

6.
$$\begin{array}{r} \square\ 6 \\ +\ \square\ 5 \\ \hline 3\ 1 \end{array}$$

Let's do some more!

Make up 5 problems for your partner.

Notes for Home Children explore with a partner to find missing numerals.

Problem Solving WORKSHOP

Problem-Solving Workshop

Explore with a Calculator

Use a [calculator] to solve.

Find the distances.

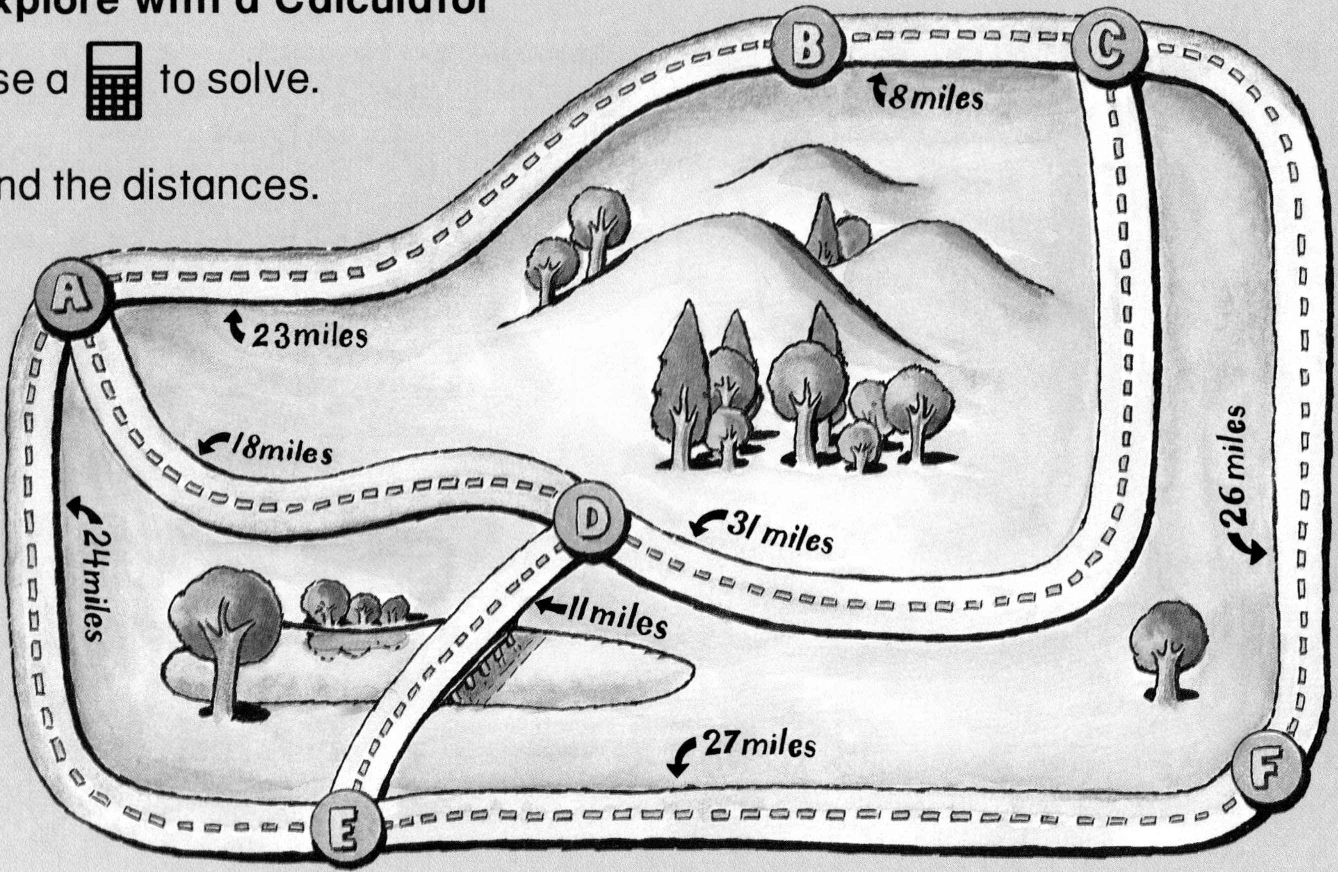

A B C D E F

8 miles
23 miles
18 miles
24 miles
31 miles
26 miles
11 miles
27 miles

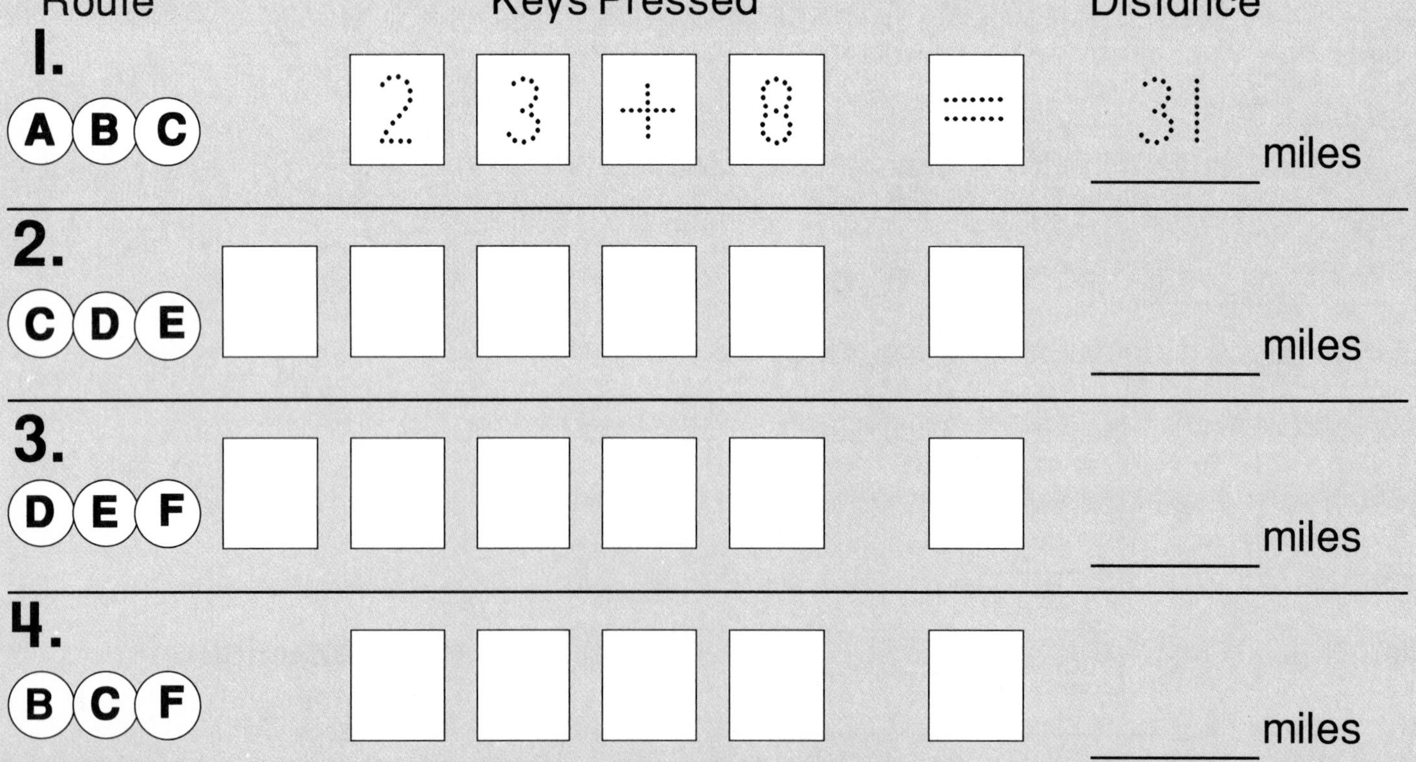

Route	Keys Pressed						Distance
1. A B C		2	3	+	8	=	31 miles
2. C D E							____ miles
3. D E F							____ miles
4. B C F							____ miles

Notes for Home Children explore with a calculator to solve two-digit problems.

Exploring Mathematics Book Two © Scott, Foresman and Company

Name

More Practice

Set A Use after page 210.

Add.

1. 39 + 42 = 81   29 + 16   30 + 5   55 + 21   22 + 7   42 + 19

2. 18 + 56   45 + 24   53 + 28   83 + 8   72 + 12   32 + 39

Set B Use after page 222.

Add. Color those you need to trade.

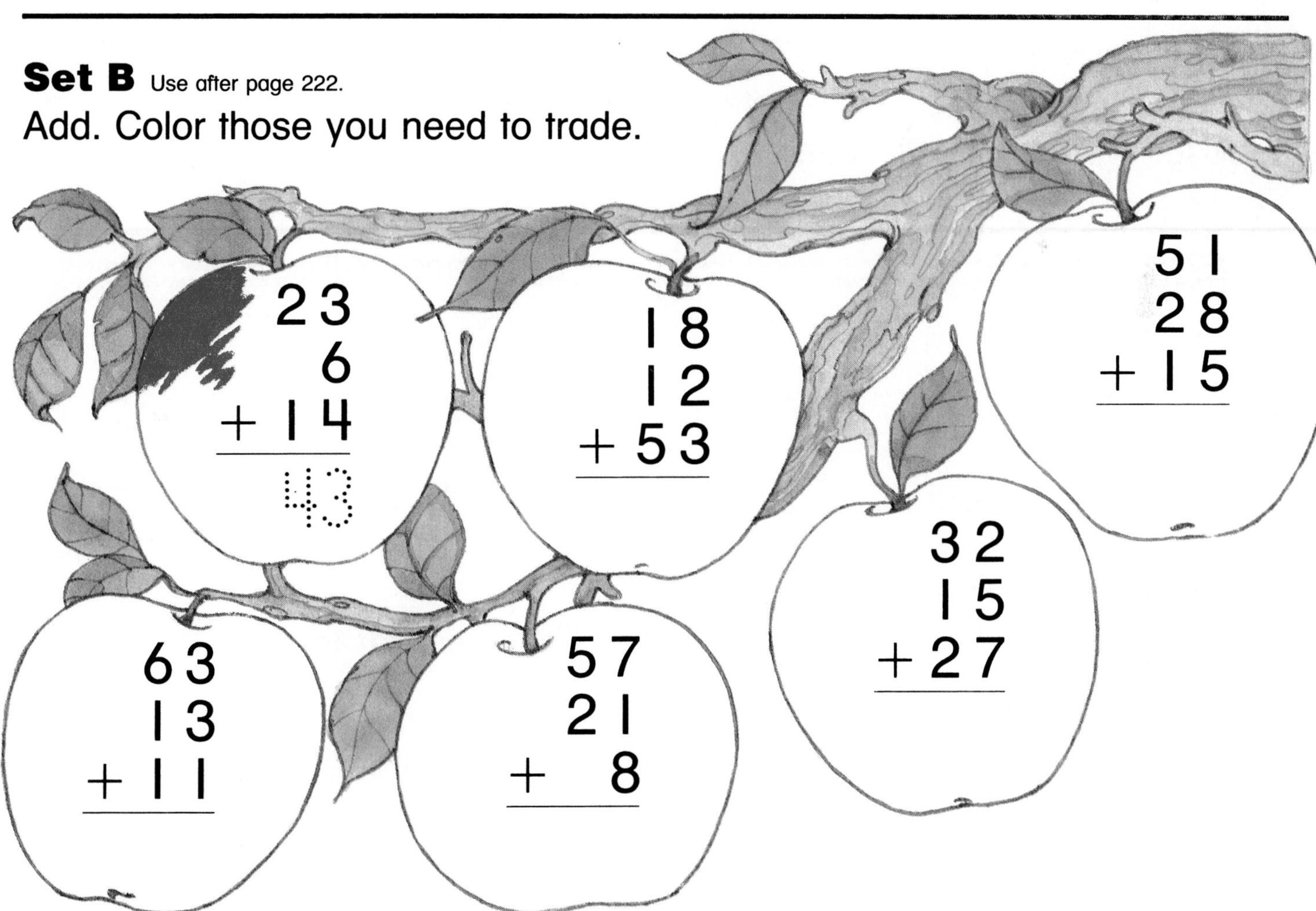

Notes for Home Set A: Children practice adding to find two-digit sums.
Set B: Children add columns of numbers, trading if necessary, to find two-digit sums.

Independent Study MORE PRACTICE

Enrichment

Use the number lines to estimate each number.
Look for the nearer 10. Then estimate the sum.

1. 27 is nearer to 30.

   12 is nearer to 10.

   27 + 12 is about 40.

2. 23 is nearer to ______.

   18 is nearer to ______.

   23 + 18 is about ______.

3. 38 is nearer to ______.

   21 is nearer to ______.

   38 + 21 is about ______.

4. 39 is nearer to ______.

   33 is nearer to ______.

   39 + 33 is about ______.

Exploring Mathematics Book Two © Scott, Foresman and Company

Notes for Home Children are challenged to estimate the sum of two numbers.

Name

Chapter 7 Review/Test

Ring if you can make a trade. Then add.

1.
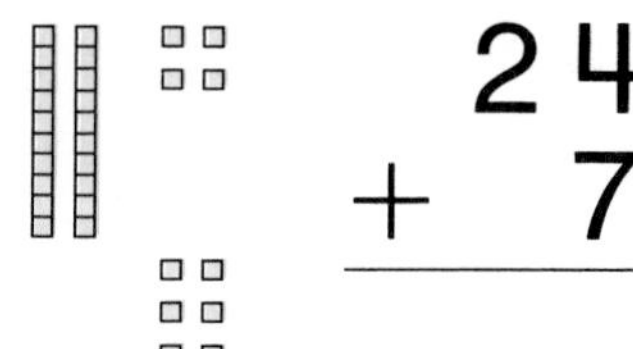

$$\begin{array}{r} 24 \\ +\ \ 7 \\ \hline \end{array}$$

2.
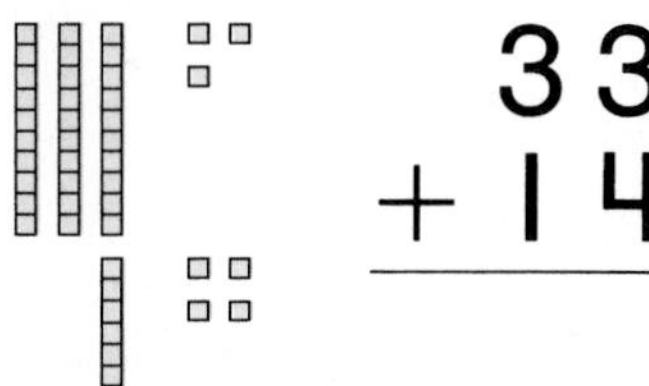

$$\begin{array}{r} 33 \\ +14 \\ \hline \end{array}$$

Add.

3.
$$\begin{array}{r} 33¢ \\ +\ \ 5¢ \\ \hline \end{array}$$

4.
$$\begin{array}{r} 67¢ \\ +28¢ \\ \hline \end{array}$$

Ring.

5.
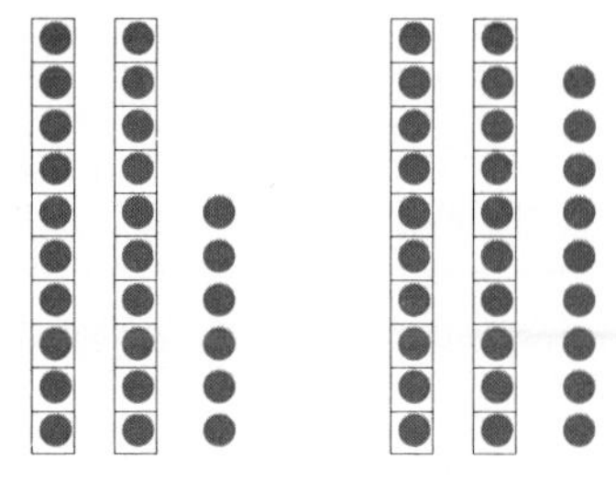

26 + 29

more than 50

less than 50

6. Add.

$$\begin{array}{r} 6 \\ +9 \\ \hline \end{array} \qquad \begin{array}{r} 16 \\ +\ \ 9 \\ \hline \end{array} \qquad \begin{array}{r} 26 \\ +\ \ 9 \\ \hline \end{array}$$

7. Add.

$$\begin{array}{r} 28 \\ 42 \\ +15 \\ \hline \end{array}$$

8. Cross out the facts you do not need.

2 teachers took our class to the zoo. There were 16 boys and 9 girls at the zoo. How many more boys than girls were there?

9. Look at the menu. Then solve.

Lunch Menu			
milk	17¢	pizza	38¢
juice	14¢	sandwich	49¢

Joan buys juice and a piece of pizza for lunch. How much does she spend?

_____ ¢

☐ _____ ¢

¢

Notes for Home Children are assessed on Chapter 7 concepts, skills, and problem solving.

Exploring Math at Home

Dear Family,

In this chapter I have learned two-digit addition and how to record a trade of 10 ones for 1 ten. I also learned about adding amounts of money. Please help me with the activities below.

Love, ______________________

1.

Use straws. Choose a two-digit number. Add some more straws. Make a bundle of ten if you can.

2.

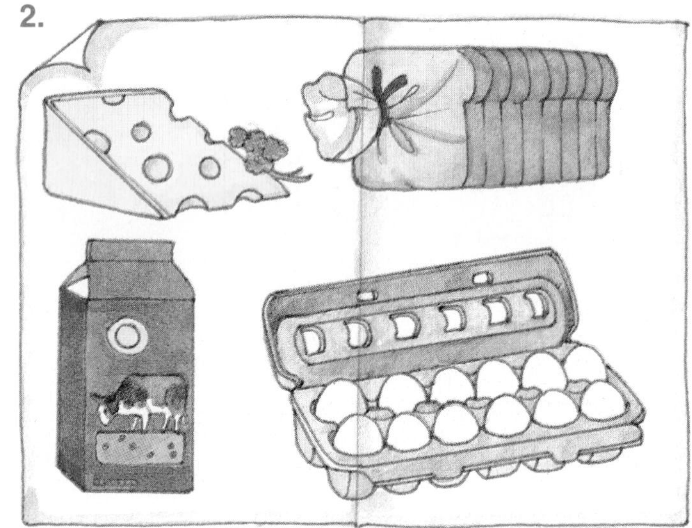

Find two grocery items in newspaper ads that cost less than $1.00 when added.

3.

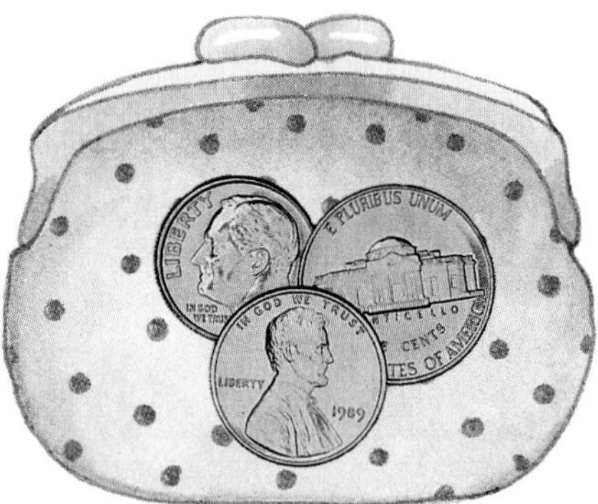

Make three groups of coins with a total value less than $1.00. Add to find the total value.

Coming Attractions

In the next chapter I will learn two-digit subtraction. I will also learn how to record a trade of 1 ten for 10 ones and how to subtract amounts of money.

Exploring Mathematics Book Two © Scott, Foresman and Company

Name

Cumulative Review/Test

Fill in the correct ◯.
Subtract.

1. $10 - 7$
   - (A) 3
   - (B) 2
   - (C) 1

2. $15 - 6$
   - (A) 1
   - (B) 9
   - (C) 11

3. $13 - 7$
   - (A) 8
   - (B) 7
   - (C) 6

4. What time is it?

   - (A) 5:15
   - (B) 3:25

5. How many?

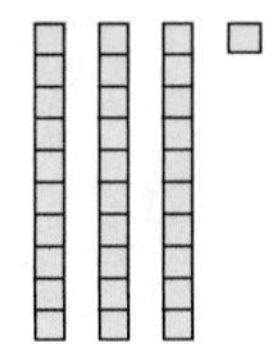

   - (A) 31
   - (B) 13
   - (C) 33

6. The numbers are in order. What number is missing?

   53, ___, 55, 56

   - (A) 52
   - (B) 54
   - (C) 57

7. About how long is the toothpick?

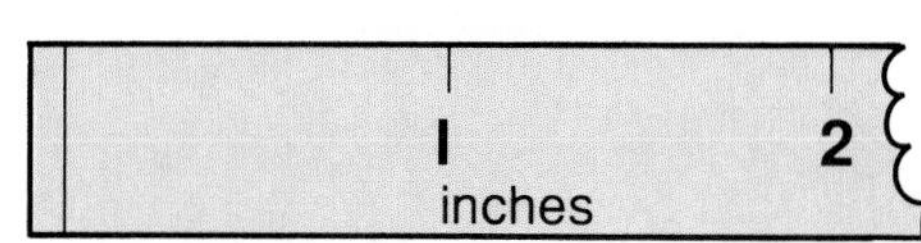

   - (A) 1 inch
   - (B) 2 inches

8. Do you need to trade? Ring yes or no.

   26 and 7

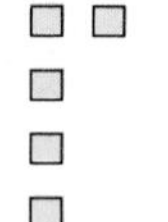

   - (A) yes
   - (B) no

9. Do you need to trade? Ring yes or no.

   43 take away 5

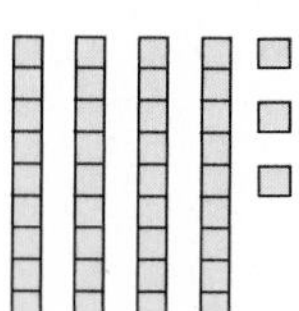

   - (A) yes
   - (B) no

Notes for Home Children are assessed on Chapters 1–7 concepts, skills, and problem solving using a multiple-choice format.

Fill in the correct ⬭.
Add.

10.
$$\begin{array}{r} 7 \\ +9 \\ \hline \end{array}$$
Ⓐ 16
Ⓑ 18
Ⓒ 19

11.
$$\begin{array}{r} 38 \\ +21 \\ \hline \end{array}$$
Ⓐ 69
Ⓑ 67
Ⓒ 59

12.
$$\begin{array}{r} 24 \\ +36 \\ \hline \end{array}$$
Ⓐ 50
Ⓑ 60
Ⓒ 70

13. Solve.

Kelly has 17¢. Tom has 9¢ less than Kelly. How much does Tom have?

26¢ Ⓐ
8¢ Ⓑ

14. How much?

40¢ Ⓐ
45¢ Ⓑ

15. How much?

I have 4 dimes, 1 nickel, and 3 pennies.

48¢ Ⓐ
43¢ Ⓑ

16. Do you add or subtract?

Nellie is 12 years old. Helen is 3 years older than Nellie. How old is Helen?

add Ⓐ
subtract Ⓑ

17. Is there enough information?

On Saturday morning Nino mowed 3 lawns. How much money did he earn?

enough Ⓐ
not enough Ⓑ

18. Mark yes or no.

Ed wants 3 candles. Does he need to take some from a box too?

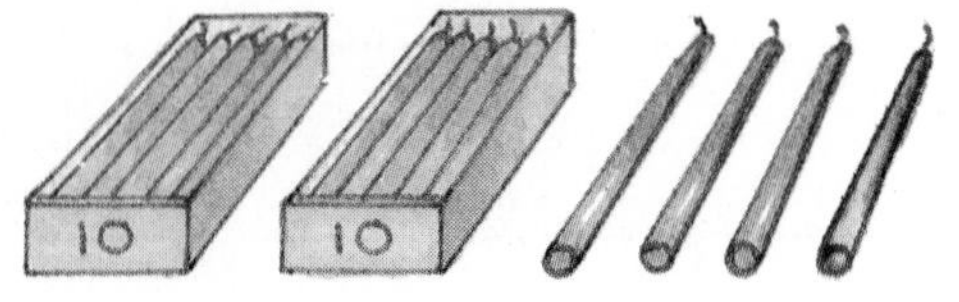

yes Ⓐ
no Ⓑ

Exploring Mathematics Book Two © Scott, Foresman and Company

Notes for Home Children are assessed on Chapters 1–7 concepts, skills, and problem solving using a multiple-choice format.

Listen to the math story, "Funny Business."
The animals sold 33 cookies at the market.
Why was it easy for them to sell the cookies?

Notes for Home Children listen to a math story introducing chapter concepts and skills. Then they answer a question about the story.

Learning to Record a Trade

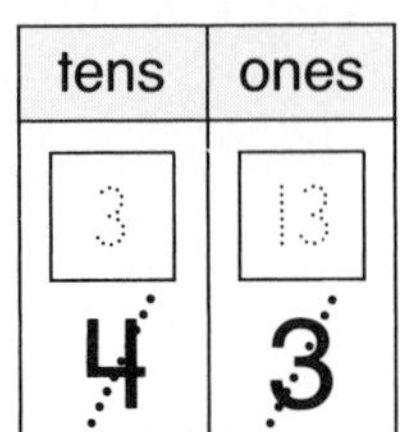

tens	ones
3	13
4	3

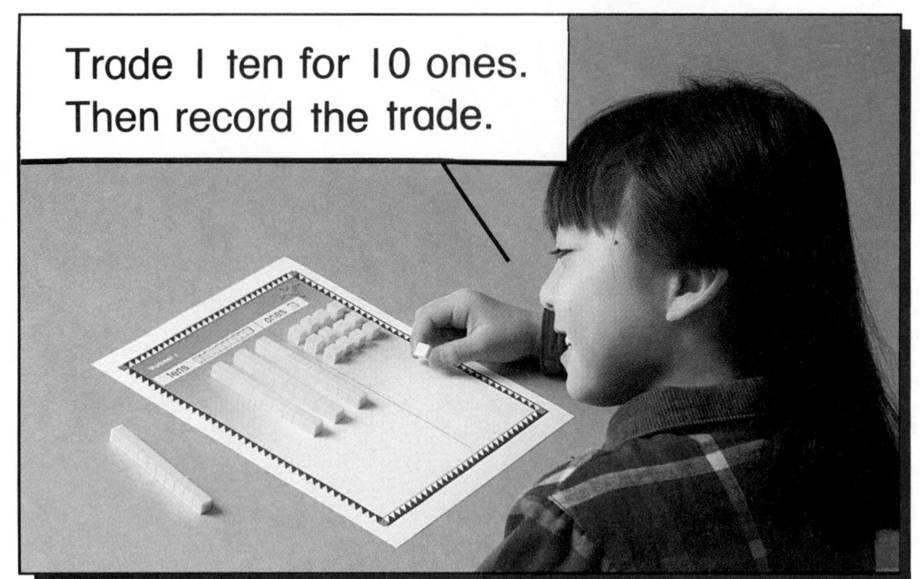

Use Workmat 1.
Use tens and ones counters.
Trade 1 ten for 10 ones. Record.

1.

tens	ones
5	7

tens	ones
2	0

tens	ones
1	8

tens	ones
3	6

2.

tens	ones
2	2

tens	ones
3	5

tens	ones
4	1

tens	ones
5	4

3.

tens	ones
3	0

tens	ones
1	6

tens	ones
2	7

tens	ones
4	4

Exploring Mathematics Book Two © Scott, Foresman and Company

Notes for Home Children explore at the CONCRETE level using tens and ones counters and a place-value workmat to show and record a trade of 1 ten for 10 ones.

Name

Subtracting a One-Digit Number from a Two-Digit Number

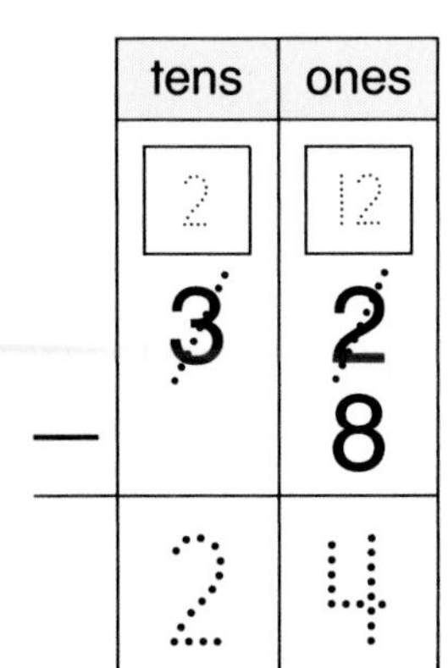

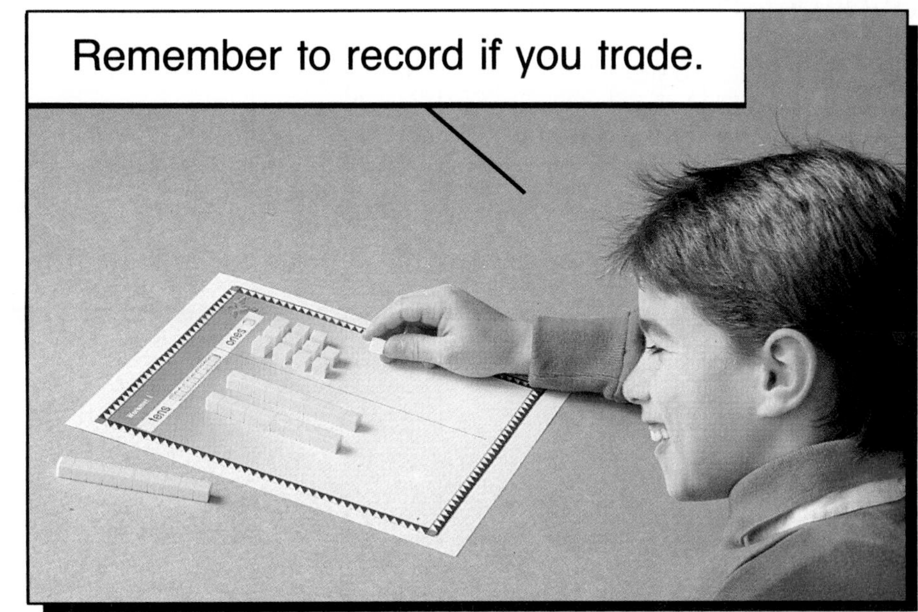

Use Workmat 1.
Use tens and ones counters.
Subtract. Record if you trade.

1.

tens	ones
2	2
−	7

tens	ones
3	3
−	8

tens	ones
1	4
−	2

tens	ones
3	5
−	9

2.

tens	ones
3	1
−	8

tens	ones
2	6
−	5

tens	ones
2	2
−	9

tens	ones
4	2
−	5

Notes for Home Children explore at the CONCRETE level using tens and ones counters and a place-value workmat to subtract one-digit numbers from two-digit numbers.

Use Workmat 1.
Use tens and ones counters.
Subtract. Record if you trade.

3.

tens	ones
2	15
~~3~~	~~5~~
−	8
2	7

tens	ones
2	1
−	9

tens	ones
3	4
−	6

tens	ones
1	7
−	3

4.

tens	ones
3	2
−	7

tens	ones
3	7
−	5

tens	ones
2	3
−	9

tens	ones
2	8
−	9

5.

tens	ones
1	6
−	4

tens	ones
3	1
−	3

tens	ones
2	3
−	6

tens	ones
3	2
−	6

Exploring Mathematics Book Two © Scott, Foresman and Company

Notes for Home Children explore at the CONCRETE level using tens and ones counters and a place-value workmat to subtract one-digit numbers from two-digit numbers.

Name

Subtracting a One-Digit Number from a Two-Digit Number

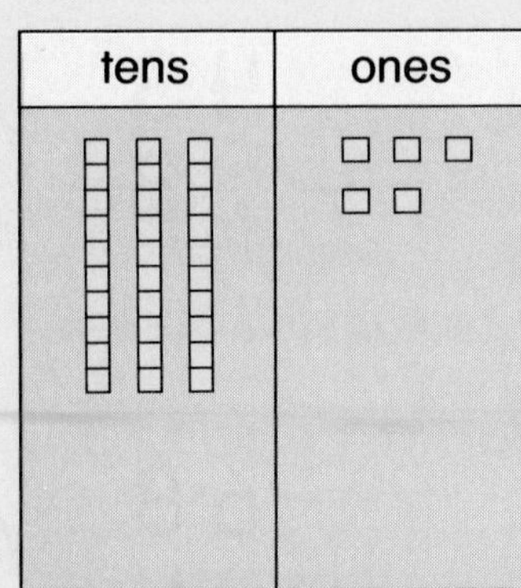

$$\begin{array}{r} 35 \\ -\ \ 8 \\ \hline \end{array}$$

1. Decide if you need to trade.

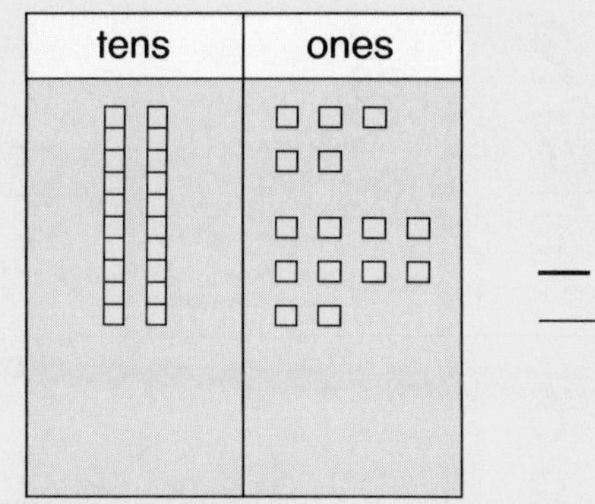

2 15
$$\begin{array}{r} \not{3}\not{5} \\ -\ \ 8 \\ \hline \end{array}$$

2. Trade 1 ten for 10 ones, if needed. Record the trade.

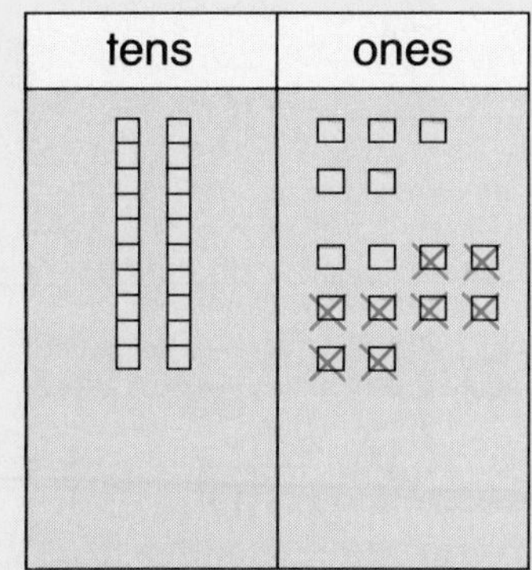

2 15
$$\begin{array}{r} \not{3}\not{5} \\ -\ \ 8 \\ \hline 27 \end{array}$$

3. Subtract the ones and record. Subtract the tens and record.

Cross out to subtract.
Then write the difference.

1.

tens	ones

$$\begin{array}{r} 43 \\ -\ \ 6 \\ \hline 37 \end{array}$$

2.

tens	ones

$$\begin{array}{r} 28 \\ -\ \ 5 \\ \hline \end{array}$$

Notes for Home Children subtract one-digit numbers from two-digit numbers using pictures of place-value materials.

Do you need to trade? Ring yes or no.
Then write the difference.

3. $\begin{array}{r} \overset{4}{5}\overset{12}{2} \\ -\ 7 \\ \hline 45 \end{array}$ (yes) no

$\begin{array}{r} 38 \\ -\ 6 \\ \hline \end{array}$ yes no

$\begin{array}{r} 43 \\ -\ 8 \\ \hline \end{array}$ yes no

4. $\begin{array}{r} 46 \\ -\ 8 \\ \hline \end{array}$ yes no

$\begin{array}{r} 65 \\ -\ 9 \\ \hline \end{array}$ yes no

$\begin{array}{r} 68 \\ -\ 4 \\ \hline \end{array}$ yes no

5. $\begin{array}{r} 72 \\ -\ 8 \\ \hline \end{array}$ yes no

$\begin{array}{r} 55 \\ -\ 7 \\ \hline \end{array}$ yes no

$\begin{array}{r} 76 \\ -\ 4 \\ \hline \end{array}$ yes no

6. $\begin{array}{r} 47 \\ -\ 2 \\ \hline \end{array}$ yes no

$\begin{array}{r} 53 \\ -\ 5 \\ \hline \end{array}$ yes no

$\begin{array}{r} 92 \\ -\ 3 \\ \hline \end{array}$ yes no

Problem Solving

Solve.

7. There are 27 children in Mr. Safer's class. There are 9 boys. How many children are girls?

_____ girls

8. There are 12 girls and 17 boys putting on a play. How many children are in the play?

_____ children

Exploring Mathematics Book Two © Scott, Foresman and Company

Notes for Home Children practice subtracting one-digit numbers from two-digit numbers. Then they solve problems involving addition and subtraction.

Name

Subtracting Two-Digit Numbers

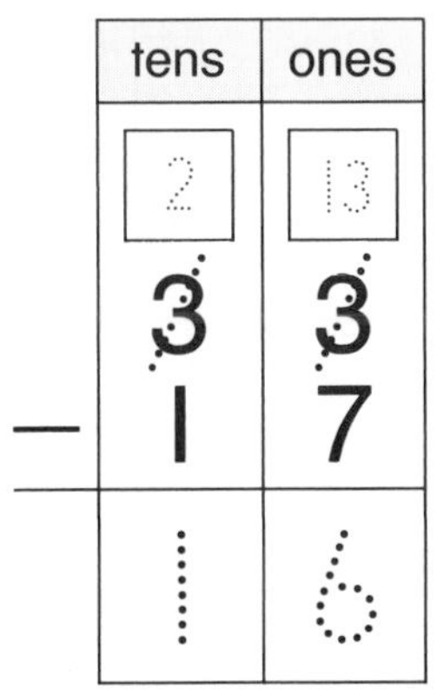

First, decide if a trade is needed. Record if a trade is made. Subtract the ones and then the tens.

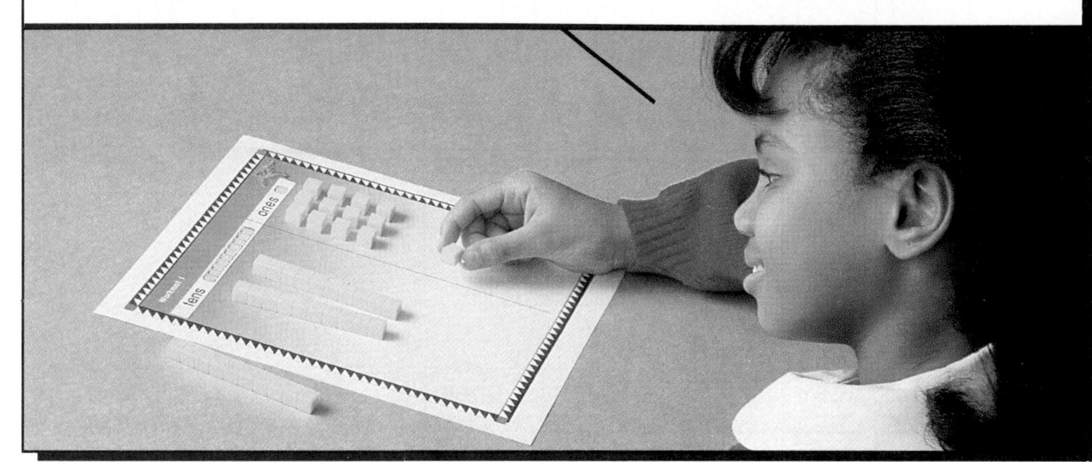

Use Workmat 1.
Use tens and ones counters.
Subtract. Record if you trade.

1.

	tens	ones
	☐	☐
	3	2
–	1	4

	tens	ones
	☐	☐
	2	7
–	1	5

	tens	ones
	☐	☐
	4	1
–	2	9

	tens	ones
	☐	☐
	3	4
–	2	7

2.

	tens	ones
	☐	☐
	2	4
–	1	3

	tens	ones
	☐	☐
	4	2
–	1	9

	tens	ones
	☐	☐
	3	1
–	1	2

	tens	ones
	☐	☐
	3	8
–	1	3

Notes for Home Children explore at the CONCRETE level using tens and ones counters and a place-value workmat to find differences of two-digit numbers.

Use Workmat 1.
Use tens and ones counters.
Subtract. Record if you trade.

3.

tens	ones
1	15
~~2~~	~~5~~
− 1	7
	8

tens	ones
3	1
− 1	3

tens	ones
3	4
− 1	1

tens	ones
3	7
− 1	9

4.

tens	ones
4	4
− 1	7

tens	ones
4	5
− 2	6

tens	ones
3	8
− 2	6

tens	ones
3	6
− 1	7

5.

tens	ones
2	7
− 1	3

tens	ones
3	2
− 1	9

tens	ones
4	3
− 1	4

tens	ones
3	4
− 2	8

Exploring Mathematics Book Two © Scott, Foresman and Company

Notes for Home Children explore at the CONCRETE level using tens and ones counters and a place-value workmat to find differences of two-digit numbers.

Name

Subtracting Two-Digit Numbers

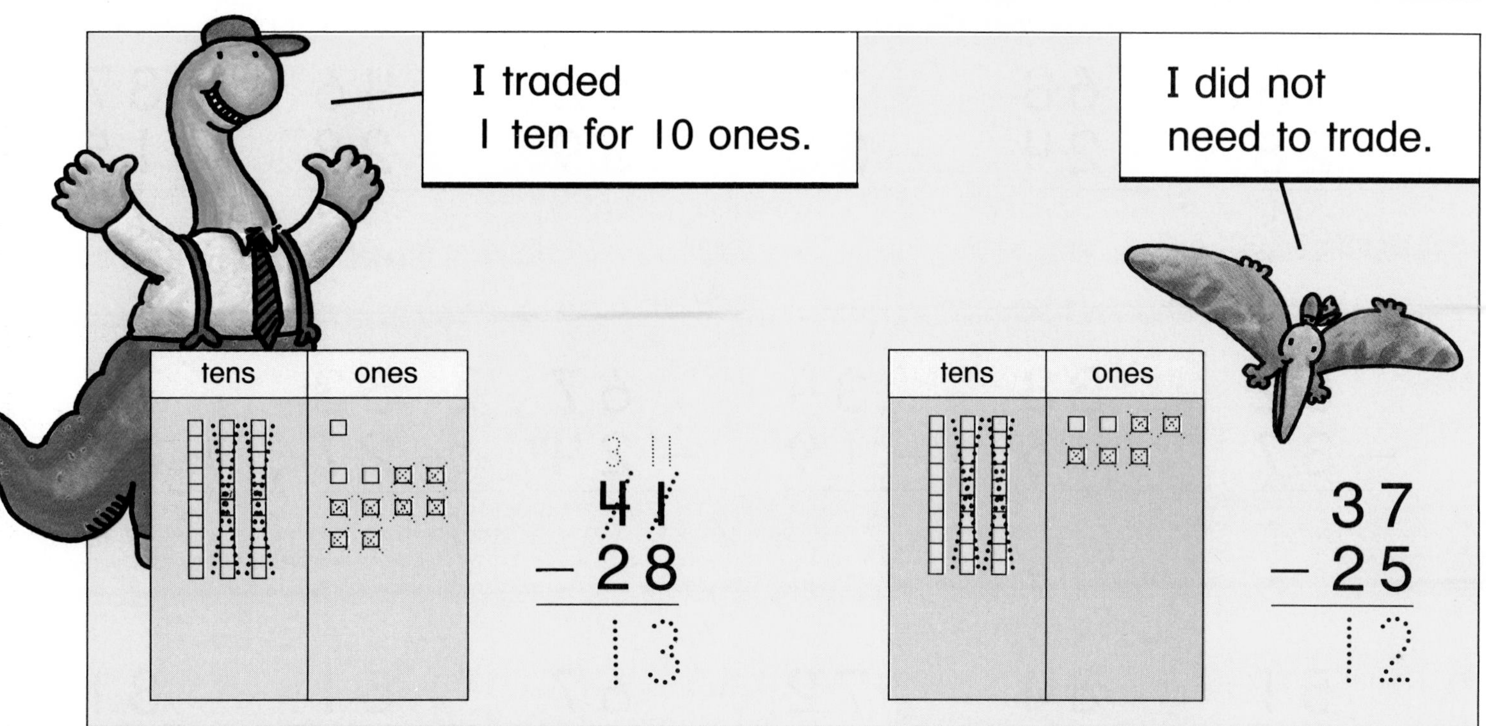

Cross out to subtract.
Write the difference.

1.

tens	ones

$$\begin{array}{r} 53 \\ -\ 36 \\ \hline \end{array}$$

2.

tens	ones

$$\begin{array}{r} 45 \\ -\ 27 \\ \hline \end{array}$$

3.

tens	ones

$$\begin{array}{r} 46 \\ -\ 22 \\ \hline \end{array}$$

4.

tens	ones

$$\begin{array}{r} 54 \\ -\ 28 \\ \hline \end{array}$$

Notes for Home Children find differences of two-digit numbers using pictures of place-value materials.

Ring if you need to trade.
Write the difference.

5.	63 − 28 = 35	68 − 24	74 − 33	62 − 39	46 − 28	37 − 15
6.	52 − 37	38 − 16	34 − 19	67 − 24	53 − 27	75 − 29
7.	51 − 20	84 − 39	72 − 35	67 − 18	51 − 29	81 − 36
8.	66 − 28	47 − 22	63 − 24	91 − 82	85 − 29	59 − 28

Talk About Math

Oops!

$$\begin{array}{r} 53 \\ -\,27 \\ \hline 34 \end{array}$$

Can you find the mistake?

Exploring Mathematics Book Two © Scott, Foresman and Company

Notes for Home Children practice finding differences of two-digit numbers. Then they talk about trading and subtraction.

See More Practice Set A on page 261.

Name

Subtracting with Zero

How many pencils does Mrs. Goldman have?
How many is she giving away?
How many will she have left?

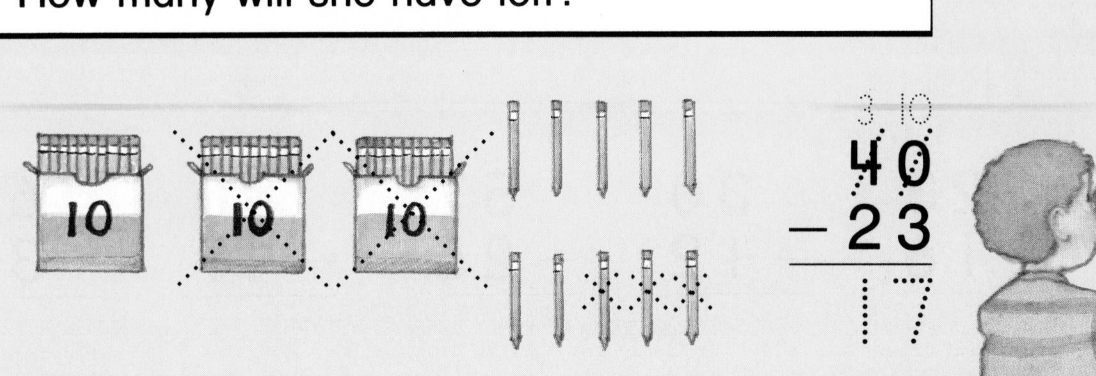

Cross out to subtract.
Write the difference.

1.

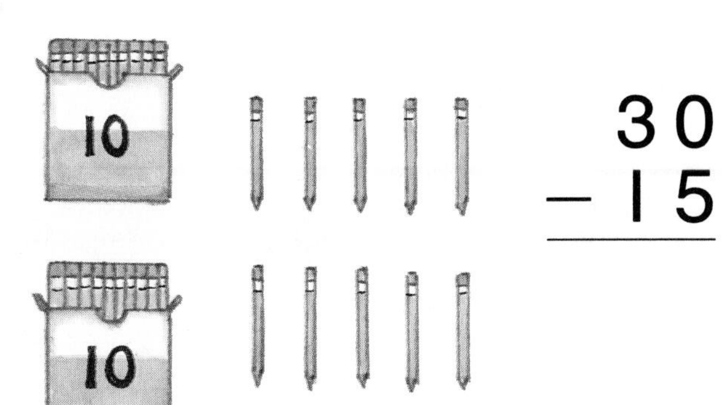

$$\begin{array}{r} 30 \\ -\ 15 \\ \hline \end{array}$$

2.

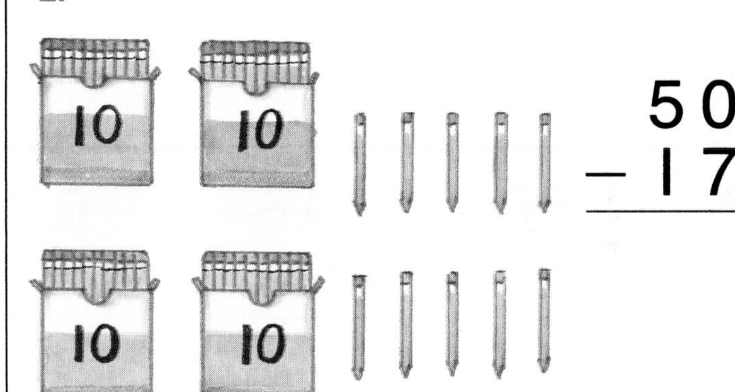

$$\begin{array}{r} 50 \\ -\ 17 \\ \hline \end{array}$$

3.

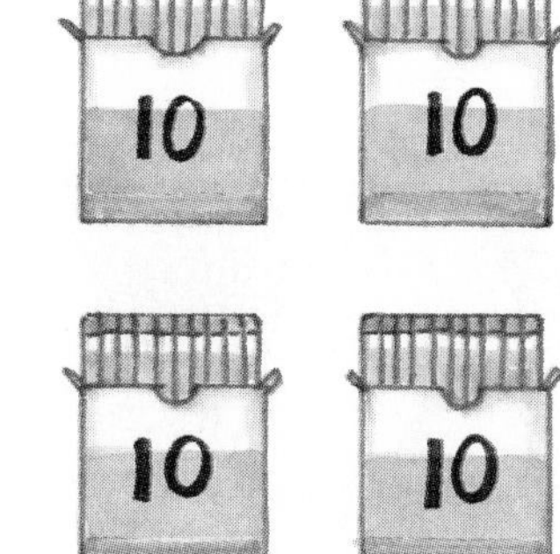

$$\begin{array}{r} 40 \\ -\ 10 \\ \hline \end{array}$$

4.

$$\begin{array}{r} 20 \\ -\ 14 \\ \hline \end{array}$$

Notes for Home Children subtract two-digit numbers to find differences.

Ring if you need to trade.
Write the difference.

5.

6 10 70 − 35 35	38 − 26	60 − 18	32 − 9	45 − 28	53 − 12

6.

51 − 7	23 − 16	30 − 12	57 − 25	80 − 49	68 − 37

7.

51 − 10	40 − 6	82 − 22	20 − 3	67 − 35	71 − 43

8.

50 − 39	46 − 30	93 − 46	37 − 27	90 − 51	89 − 65

9. **Estimation** About how many pens are in the other mugs? Record your estimates on the mugs.

Exploring Mathematics Book Two © Scott, Foresman and Company

Notes for Home Children subtract two-digit numbers to find differences. Then they estimate the number of pens in mugs.

See More Practice Set B on page 261.

Name ____________________

Choose an Operation

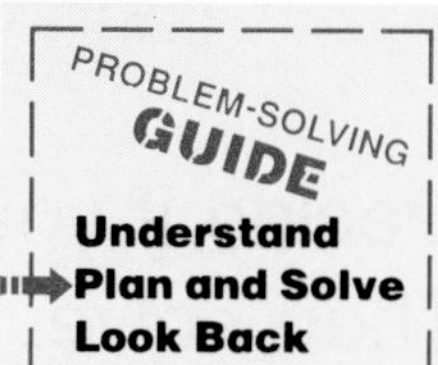

There are 27 classrooms in Swift School. There are 16 more classrooms in Ray School than in Swift School. How many classrooms are there in Ray School?

43 classrooms

$$\begin{array}{r} 27 \\ + \ 16 \\ \hline 43 \end{array}$$

Decide if you need to add or subtract.
Then solve.

1. There are 45 tables in the lunchroom. 16 tables are new. How many old tables are there?

______ tables

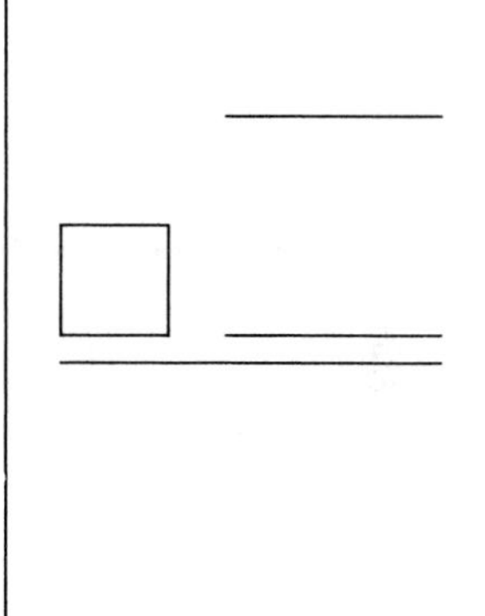

2. The second grade boys have 21 baseballs. The girls have 12 more baseballs than the boys. How many baseballs do the girls have?

______ baseballs

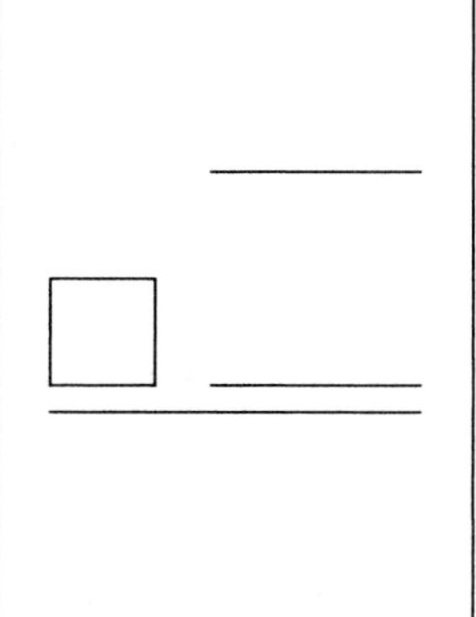

Notes for Home Children solve problems by deciding whether to add or subtract.

Decide if you need to add or subtract.
Then solve.

3. 36 girls enter the school science fair.
29 boys enter the fair.
How many children enter
the science fair in all?

65 children

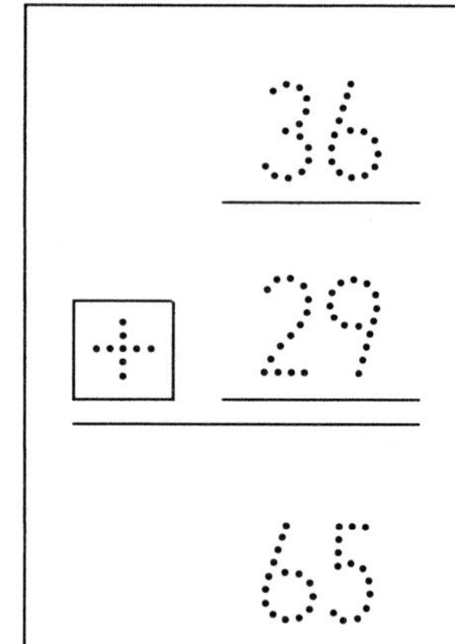

4. 45 children take the bus.
29 children ride their bikes.
How many more children take
the bus than ride bikes?

_____ children

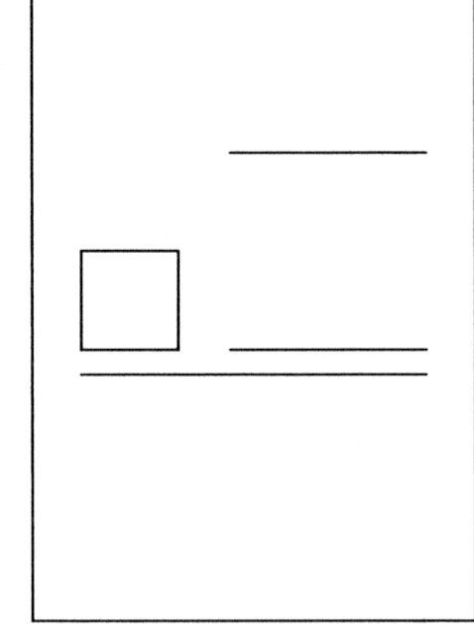

5. The second graders have 38 more
books than the first graders.
The second graders have 87 books.
How many books do the
first graders have?

_____ books

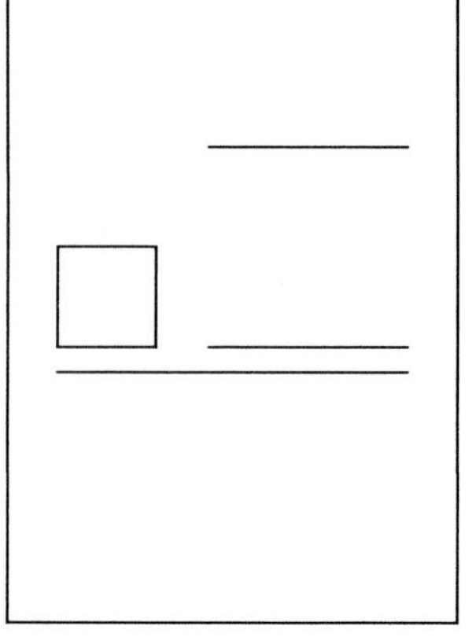

Exploring Mathematics Book Two © Scott, Foresman and Company

Notes for Home Children solve problems by deciding whether to add or subtract.

Name

Number Sense

If 40 - 20 = 20
what is 40 - 19?

Can you tell why this
difference is easy to find?

Let's do some more!

Think of some more stories for subtracting nines.

Notes for Home Children develop number understanding by discussing number relationships.

Skills Review

Fill in the correct ◯.
Add.

1. 34 + 26
Ⓐ 50 Ⓑ 55 Ⓒ 60

2. 52 + 35
Ⓐ 82 Ⓑ 87 Ⓒ 97

3. 27 + 66
Ⓐ 83 Ⓑ 90 Ⓒ 93

4. 44 + 34
Ⓐ 78 Ⓑ 88 Ⓒ 98

5. 16 + 68
Ⓐ 74 Ⓑ 83 Ⓒ 84

6. 45 + 27
Ⓐ 62 Ⓑ 72 Ⓒ 82

Add these money amounts.

7. 52¢ + 43¢
Ⓐ 90¢ Ⓑ 93¢ Ⓒ 95¢

8. 19¢ + 26¢
Ⓐ 35¢ Ⓑ 45¢ Ⓒ 49¢

9. 38¢ + 5¢
Ⓐ 33¢ Ⓑ 43¢ Ⓒ 48¢

Vocabulary

Find words across and down in the puzzle.
Ring them.

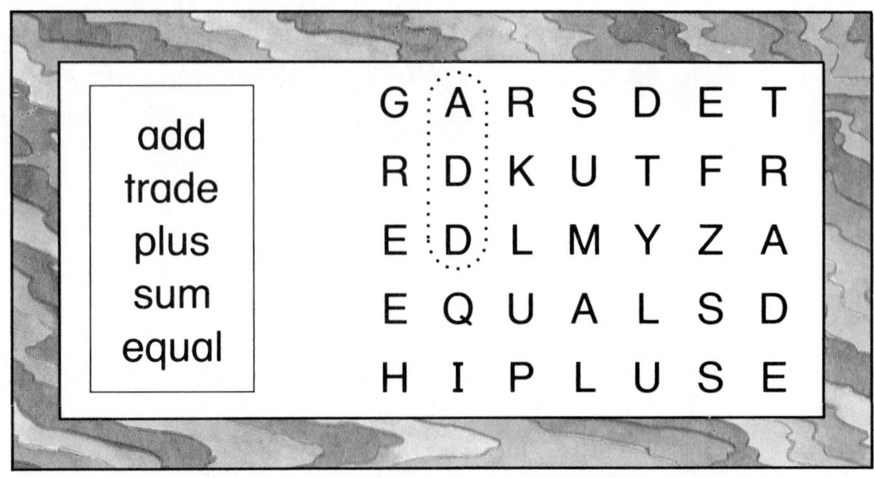

Exploring Mathematics Book Two © Scott, Foresman and Company

Notes for Home Children review adding two-digit sums and amounts of money. Then they find math terms in a puzzle.

Name

Ali has 75¢. She wants to buy some wooden animals.
How much does one animal cost?
How can you find how much money Ali will have left?

$$\begin{array}{r} \overset{6}{7}\overset{15}{5}¢ \\ -\ 28¢ \\ \hline 47¢ \end{array}$$

Subtract.

1. $\begin{array}{r} 50¢ \\ -\ 28¢ \\ \hline \end{array}$ $\begin{array}{r} 48¢ \\ -\ 18¢ \\ \hline \end{array}$ $\begin{array}{r} 56¢ \\ -\ 8¢ \\ \hline \end{array}$ $\begin{array}{r} 62¢ \\ -\ 19¢ \\ \hline \end{array}$ $\begin{array}{r} 25¢ \\ -\ 16¢ \\ \hline \end{array}$

2. $\begin{array}{r} 35¢ \\ -\ 24¢ \\ \hline \end{array}$ $\begin{array}{r} 36¢ \\ -\ 7¢ \\ \hline \end{array}$ $\begin{array}{r} 70¢ \\ -\ 22¢ \\ \hline \end{array}$ $\begin{array}{r} 66¢ \\ -\ 44¢ \\ \hline \end{array}$ $\begin{array}{r} 62¢ \\ -\ 57¢ \\ \hline \end{array}$

3. $\begin{array}{r} 43¢ \\ -\ 35¢ \\ \hline \end{array}$ $\begin{array}{r} 45¢ \\ -\ 22¢ \\ \hline \end{array}$ $\begin{array}{r} 83¢ \\ -\ 62¢ \\ \hline \end{array}$ $\begin{array}{r} 34¢ \\ -\ 25¢ \\ \hline \end{array}$ $\begin{array}{r} 96¢ \\ -\ 9¢ \\ \hline \end{array}$

Notes for Home Children subtract amounts of money to find differences of two-digit numbers.

Subtract.

4.	$\begin{array}{r} \overset{4}{\cancel{5}}\overset{12}{\cancel{2}}¢ \\ -\ 26¢ \\ \hline 26¢ \end{array}$	$\begin{array}{r} 30¢ \\ -\ 13¢ \\ \hline \end{array}$	$\begin{array}{r} 44¢ \\ -\ 3¢ \\ \hline \end{array}$	$\begin{array}{r} 68¢ \\ -\ 34¢ \\ \hline \end{array}$	$\begin{array}{r} 81¢ \\ -\ 67¢ \\ \hline \end{array}$
5.	$\begin{array}{r} 53¢ \\ -\ 6¢ \\ \hline \end{array}$	$\begin{array}{r} 67¢ \\ -\ 29¢ \\ \hline \end{array}$	$\begin{array}{r} 38¢ \\ -\ 29¢ \\ \hline \end{array}$	$\begin{array}{r} 90¢ \\ -\ 7¢ \\ \hline \end{array}$	$\begin{array}{r} 76¢ \\ -\ 10¢ \\ \hline \end{array}$
6.	$\begin{array}{r} 33¢ \\ -\ 29¢ \\ \hline \end{array}$	$\begin{array}{r} 86¢ \\ -\ 24¢ \\ \hline \end{array}$	$\begin{array}{r} 51¢ \\ -\ 49¢ \\ \hline \end{array}$	$\begin{array}{r} 43¢ \\ -\ 5¢ \\ \hline \end{array}$	$\begin{array}{r} 65¢ \\ -\ 23¢ \\ \hline \end{array}$
7.	$\begin{array}{r} 32¢ \\ -\ 16¢ \\ \hline \end{array}$	$\begin{array}{r} 47¢ \\ -\ 20¢ \\ \hline \end{array}$	$\begin{array}{r} 71¢ \\ -\ 55¢ \\ \hline \end{array}$	$\begin{array}{r} 42¢ \\ -\ 8¢ \\ \hline \end{array}$	$\begin{array}{r} 89¢ \\ -\ 47¢ \\ \hline \end{array}$

Problem Solving

Ring the correct example.
Then solve.

8. How much more does the elephant cost than the leopard?

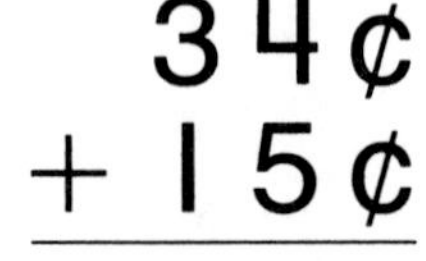

$\begin{array}{r} 34¢ \\ -\ 15¢ \\ \hline \end{array}$

______

Exploring Mathematics Book Two © Scott, Foresman and Company

Notes for Home Children subtract amounts of money to find two-digit differences. Then they solve a problem involving amounts of money.

Name

Estimating Two-Digit Differences

Estimate the difference.
Ring more than or less than.

1.

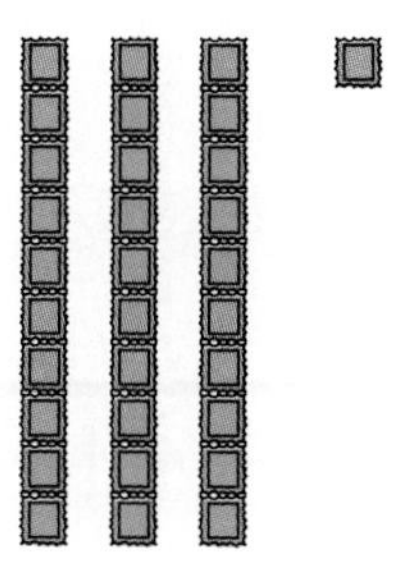

32 − 6 is

more than 30. less than 30.

2.

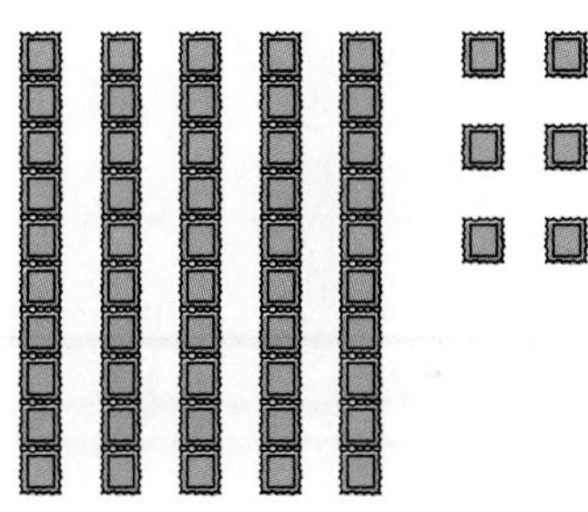

56 − 4 is

more than 50. less than 50.

3.

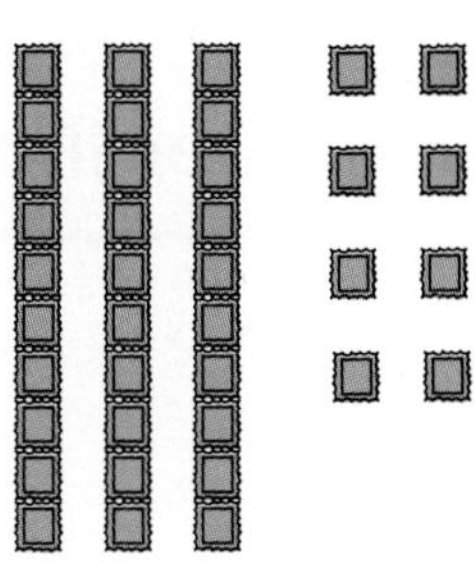

38 − 15 is

more than 20. less than 20.

4.

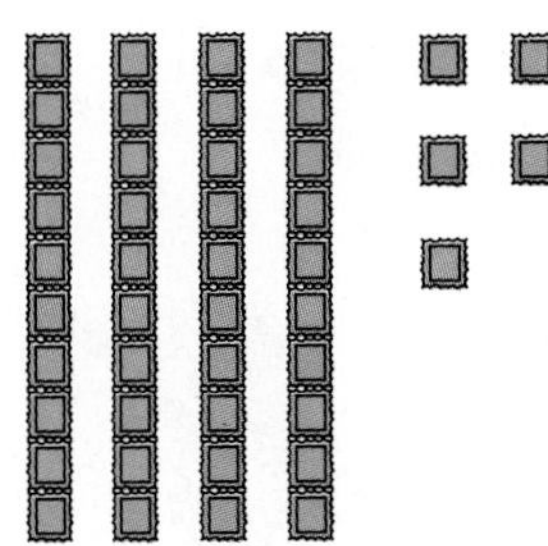

45 − 18 is

more than 30. less than 30.

Notes for Home Children estimate two-digit differences by determining if there are enough ones.

Estimate the difference.
Ring more than or less than.

5.

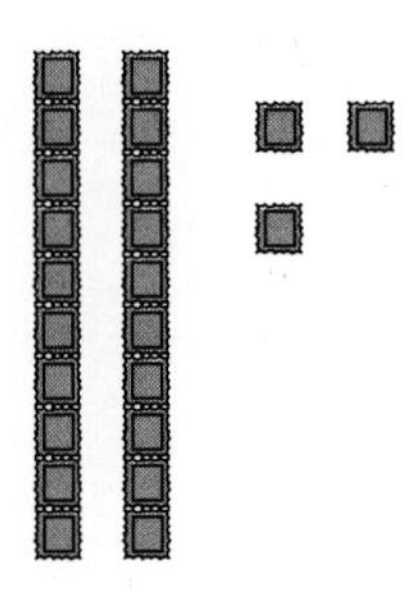

23 − 5 is

more than 20. less than 20.

6.

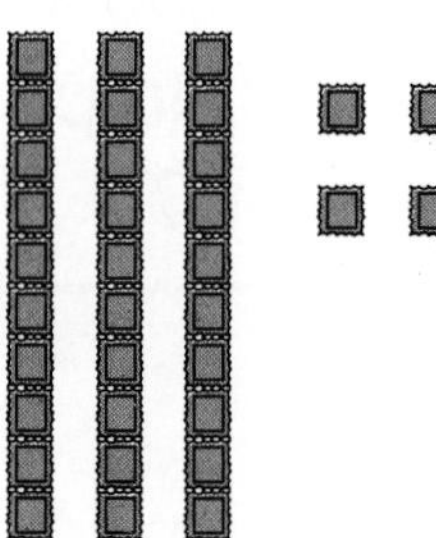

34 − 7 is

more than 30. less than 30.

7.

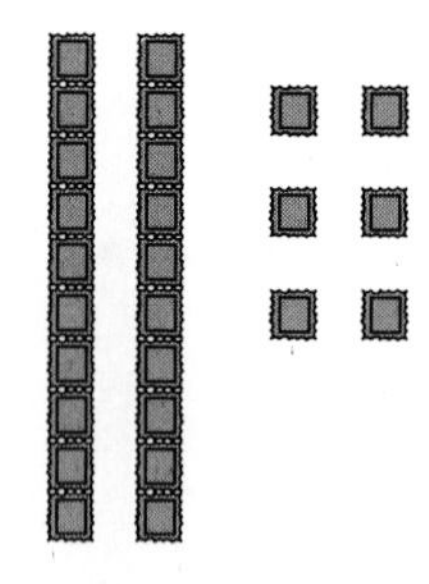

26 − 14 is

more than 10. less than 10.

8.

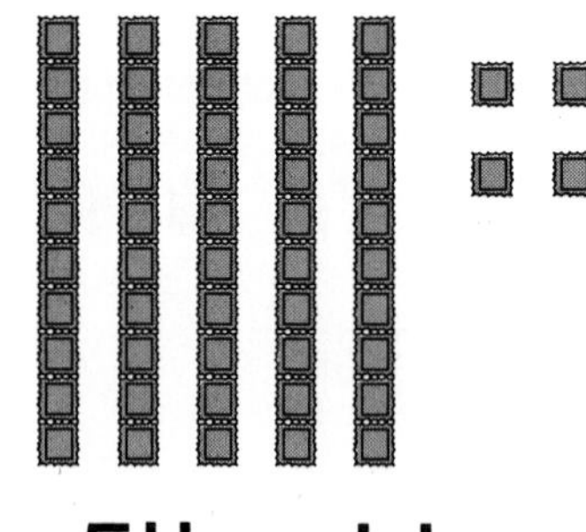

54 − 11 is

more than 40. less than 40.

Talk About Math

What numbers can you subtract from 25 so that the difference is greater than 20?

____ ____ ____ ____ ____

Exploring Mathematics Book Two © Scott, Foresman and Company

Notes for Home Children practice estimating differences by determining if there are enough ones. Then they find differences that are greater than a given number.

Name

Finding Patterns in Subtraction

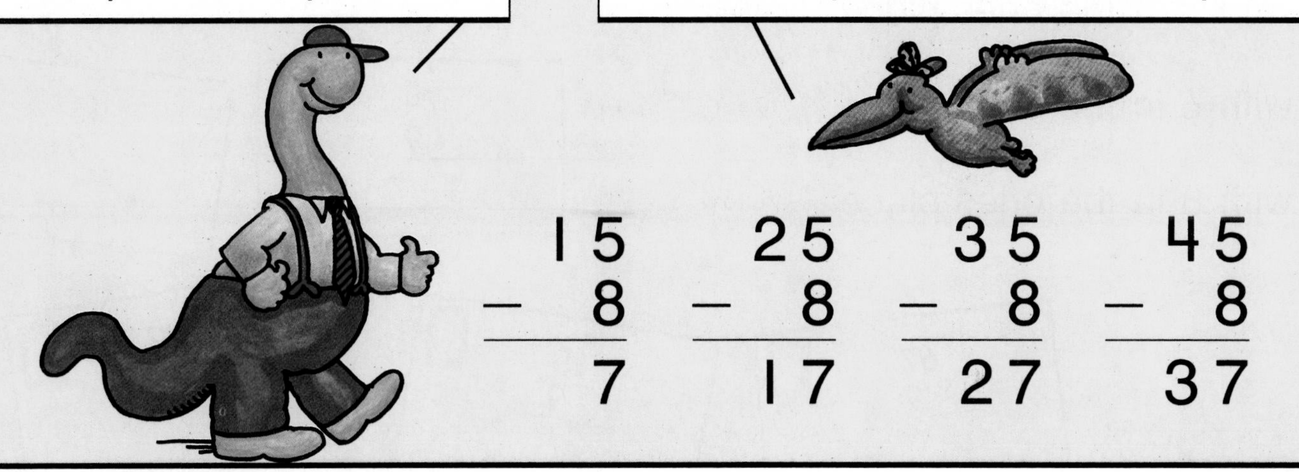

Write the difference.
Look for a pattern.

1.

8	18	28	38	48	58
− 6	− 6	− 6	− 6	− 6	− 6
2					

2.

12	22	32	42	52	62
− 10	− 10	− 10	− 10	− 10	− 10

3.

12	22	32	42	52	62
− 9	− 9	− 9	− 9	− 9	− 9

Notes for Home Children find differences of one- and two-digit numbers by looking for number patterns.

4. Color differences

with 5 in the ones place red.

with 3 in the ones place blue.

with 6 in the ones place green.

with 8 in the ones place yellow.

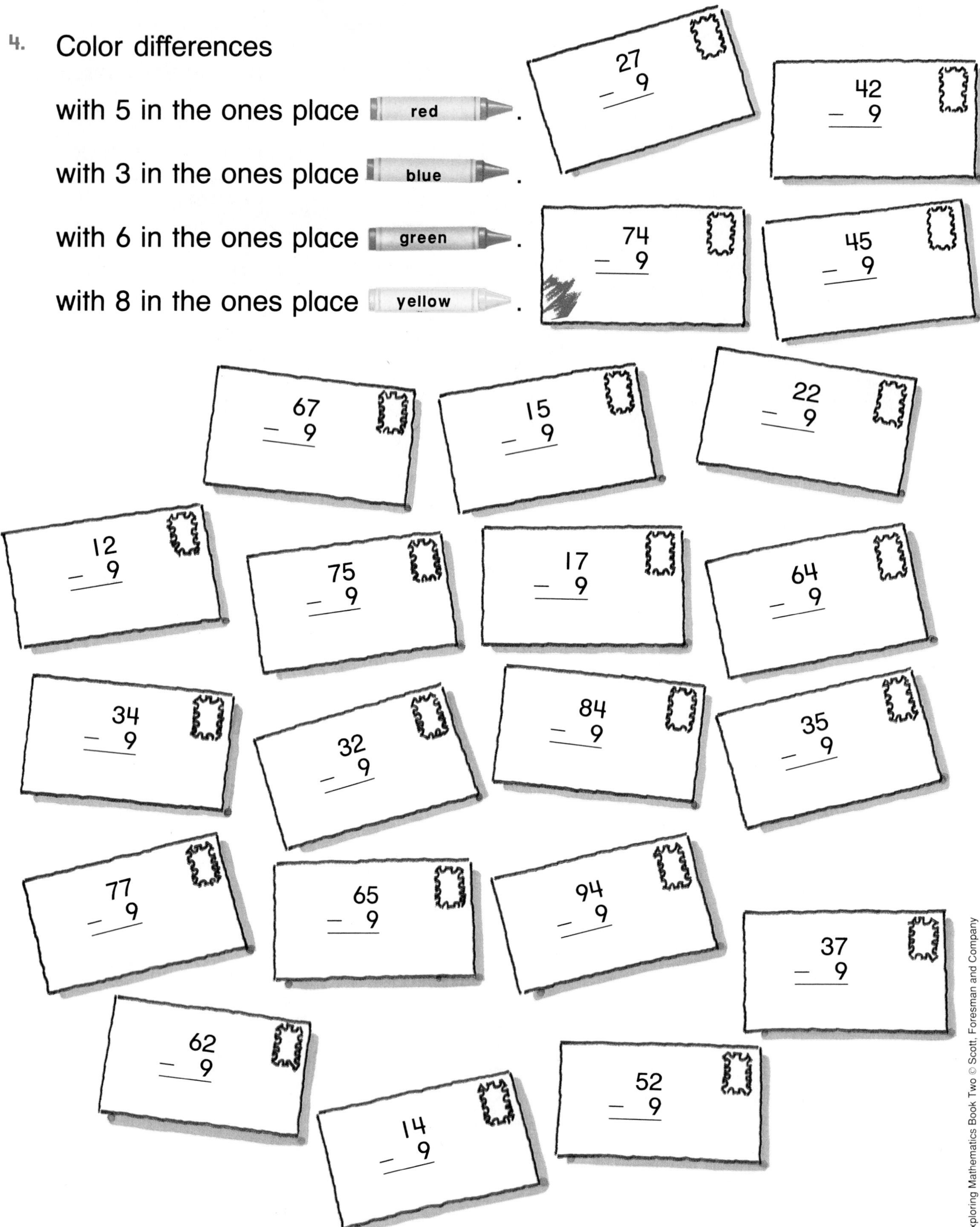

Exploring Mathematics Book Two © Scott, Foresman and Company

Notes for Home Children practice finding differences by looking for number patterns.

Name

Checking Subtraction by Adding

I can check my subtraction by adding.

$$\begin{array}{r} \overset{3}{\cancel{4}}\overset{15}{\cancel{5}} \\ -\ 29 \\ \hline 16 \end{array} \qquad \begin{array}{r} 16 \\ +\ 29 \\ \hline 45 \end{array}$$

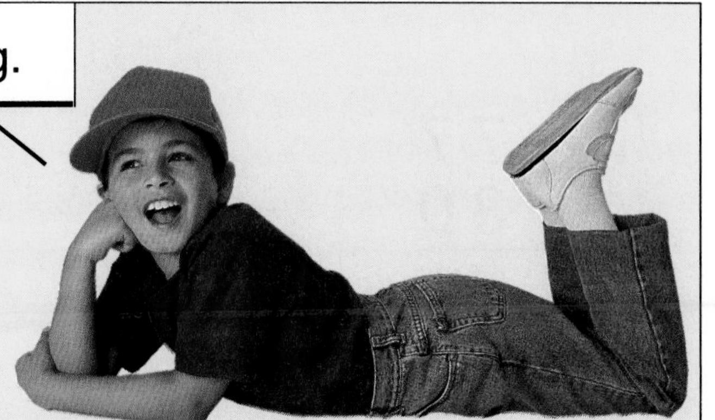

Subtract.
Then add to check.

1.
$$\begin{array}{r} 87 \\ -\ 39 \\ \hline 48 \end{array} \qquad \begin{array}{r} 48 \\ +\ 39 \\ \hline 87 \end{array}$$

2.
$$\begin{array}{r} 66 \\ -\ 45 \\ \hline \end{array} \qquad \begin{array}{r} \_\_\_ \\ +\ \_\_\_ \\ \hline \end{array}$$

3.
$$\begin{array}{r} 52 \\ -\ 24 \\ \hline \end{array} \qquad \begin{array}{r} \_\_\_ \\ +\ \_\_\_ \\ \hline \end{array}$$

4.
$$\begin{array}{r} 23 \\ -\ \ 7 \\ \hline \end{array} \qquad \begin{array}{r} \_\_\_ \\ +\ \_\_\_ \\ \hline \end{array}$$

5.
$$\begin{array}{r} 40 \\ -\ 15 \\ \hline \end{array} \qquad \begin{array}{r} \_\_\_ \\ +\ \_\_\_ \\ \hline \end{array}$$

6.
$$\begin{array}{r} 86 \\ -\ 25 \\ \hline \end{array} \qquad \begin{array}{r} \_\_\_ \\ +\ \_\_\_ \\ \hline \end{array}$$

Notes for Home Children subtract and then check their answers by adding.

Subtract.
Then add to check.

7.

$$\begin{array}{r} 77 \\ -\ 30 \\ \hline 47 \end{array} \qquad \begin{array}{r} 47 \\ \hline +\ 30 \\ \hline 77 \end{array}$$

8.

$$\begin{array}{r} 61 \\ -\ 22 \\ \hline \end{array} \qquad \begin{array}{r} \_\_ \\ +\ \_\_ \\ \hline \end{array}$$

9.

$$\begin{array}{r} 50 \\ -\ \ 4 \\ \hline \end{array} \qquad \begin{array}{r} \_\_ \\ +\ \_\_ \\ \hline \end{array}$$

10.

$$\begin{array}{r} 46 \\ -\ 29 \\ \hline \end{array} \qquad \begin{array}{r} \_\_ \\ +\ \_\_ \\ \hline \end{array}$$

Problem Solving

Solve.

11. Nancy had 35¢.
She loaned 17¢ to Benny.
How much money does she have left?

___ ¢

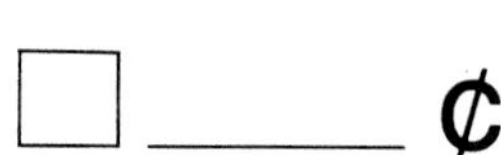

___ ¢

___ ¢

12. Nancy had 18¢.
Benny gave her 17¢.
Now how much money does Nancy have?

___ ¢

☐ ___ ¢

___ ¢

Notes for Home Children subtract and then check their answers by adding. Then they solve problems involving amounts of money.

Exploring Mathematics Book Two © Scott, Foresman and Company

Name

Multiple-Step Problems

Ernie earned 28¢ for cleaning his room and 35¢ for mowing the lawn. How much did he earn?

Ernie spent 47¢. How much does he have left?

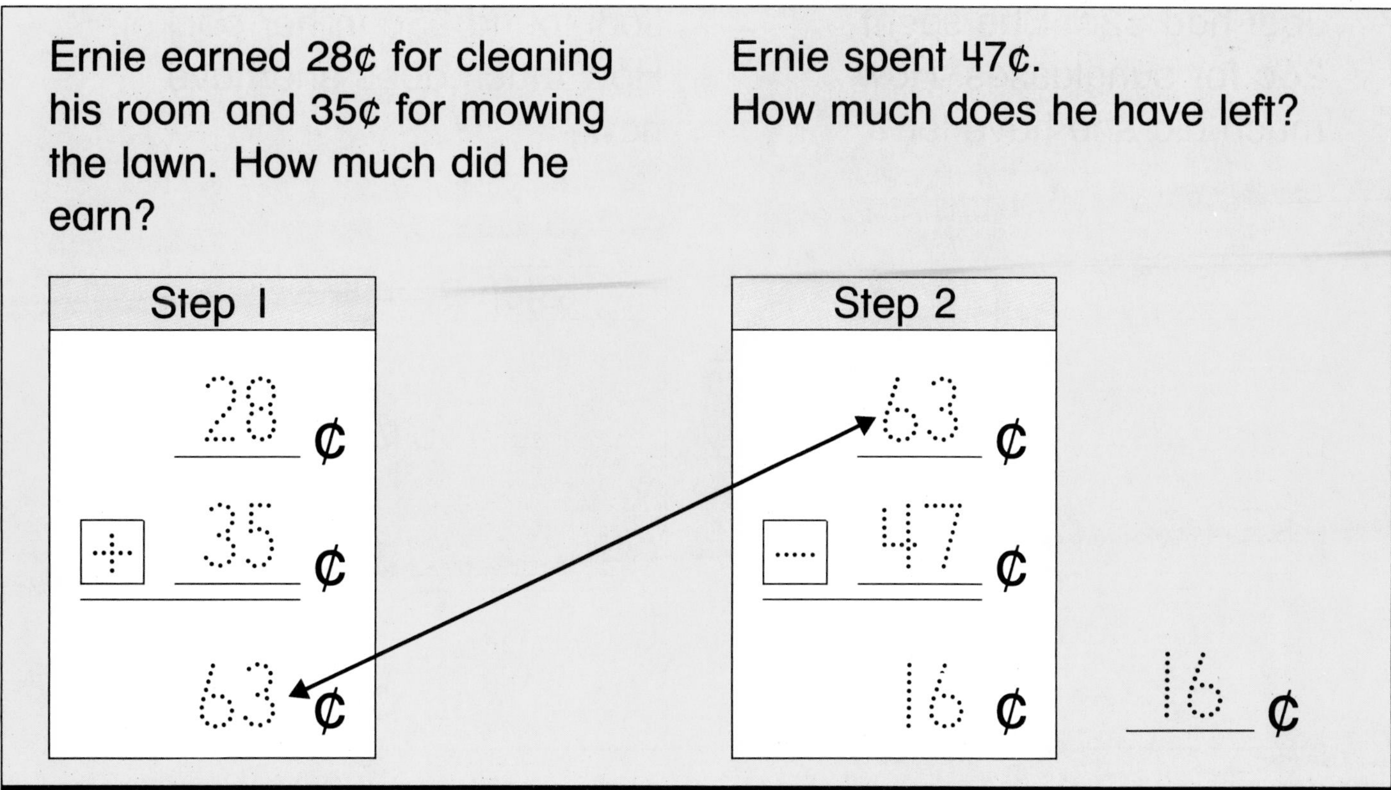

Show each step.
Then solve.

1. Juan bought a pencil for 18¢ and a notebook for 55¢. How much did he spend?

Then Juan bought a ruler. It cost 26¢. How much did he spend altogether?

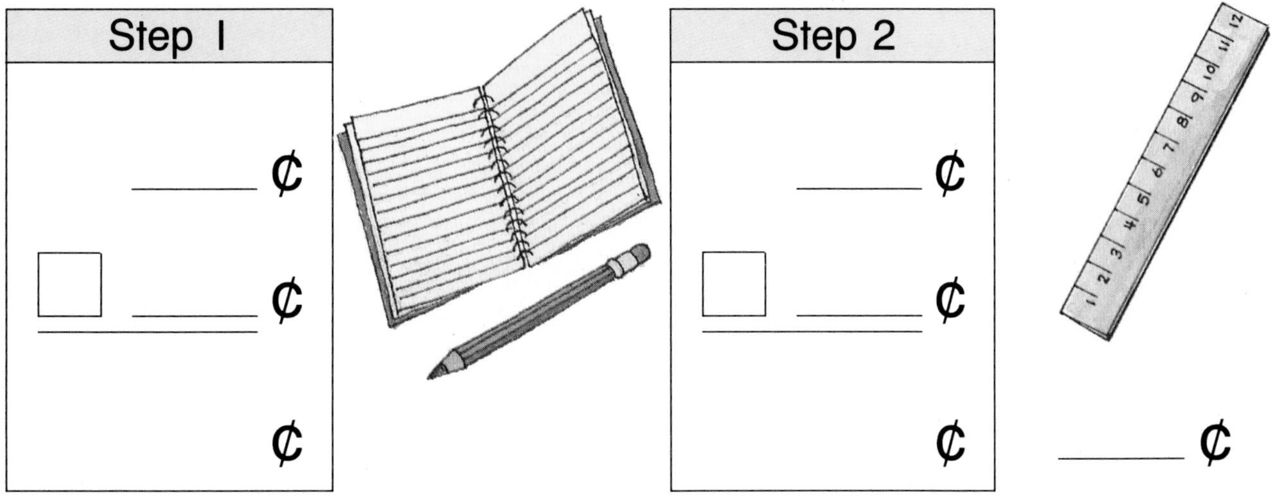

Notes for Home Children learn to solve multiple-step problems involving addition and subtraction.

Show each step.
Then solve.

2. Jodi had 52¢. She spent 26¢ for sunglasses. How much did she have left?

Jodi found 25¢ in her pocket. How much does she have now?

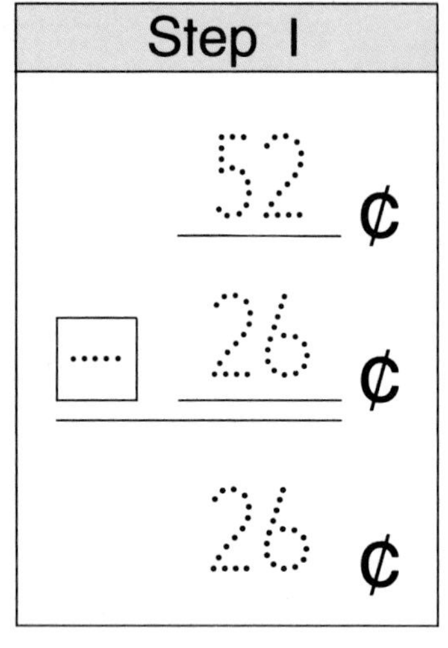

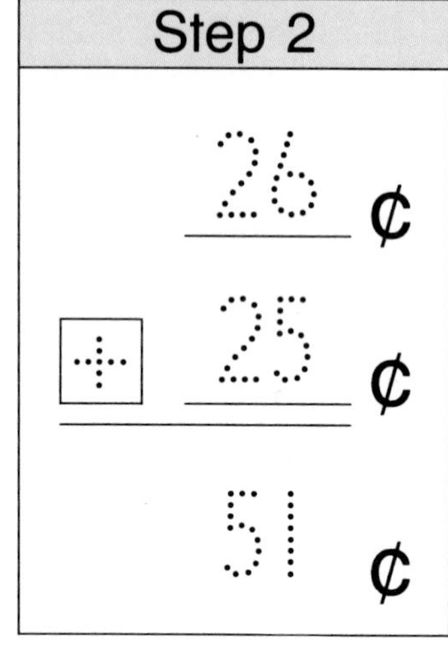

51 ¢

---

3. Lee took 65¢ to the swimming pool. He spent 33¢ for a waterslide ticket. How much did Lee have left?

Then Lee bought a water mask. It cost 25¢. How much money does Lee have left?

Step 1

_____ ¢

☐ _____ ¢

¢

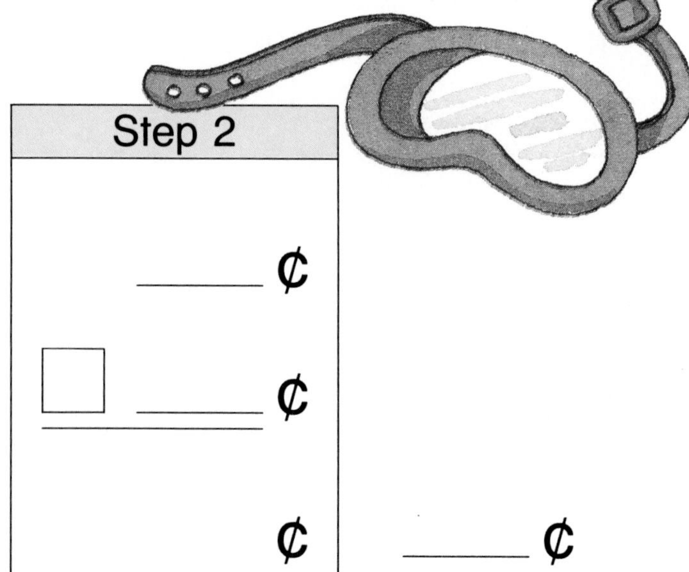

_____ ¢

Exploring Mathematics Book Two © Scott, Foresman and Company

Notes for Home Children solve multiple-step problems involving addition and subtraction.

Name

Problem-Solving Workshop

Explore as a Team

Work with a partner.

Write the missing number in each shape.

Look in the ones place first.

1.

	8	(7)
−	1	6
	(7)	1

2.

	9	8
−	☐	3
	4	5

3.

	⬭	◯
−	1	4
	2	⬭

4.

	4	⬭
−	2	7
	⬡	△

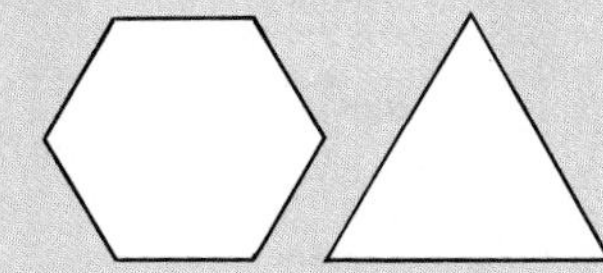

5.

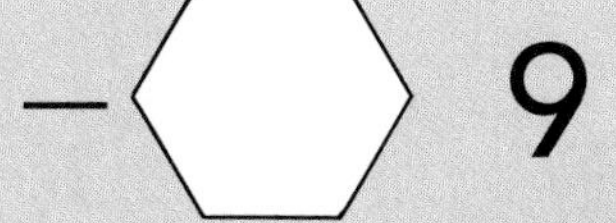

	△	⬭
−	⬡	9
	4	4

6.

	△	♡
−	2	9
	⬭	☐

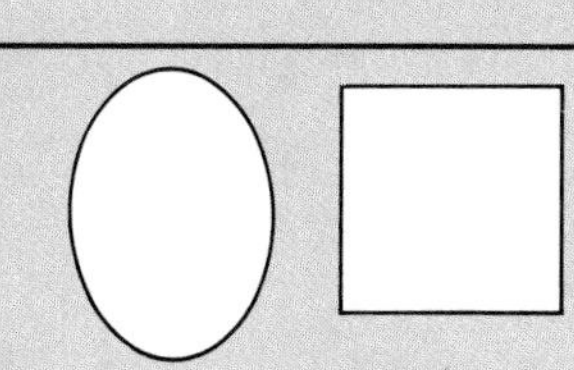

7. Write the number for each shape in the shape.

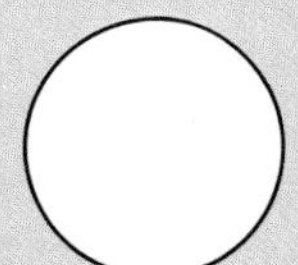    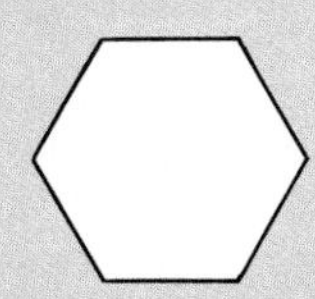 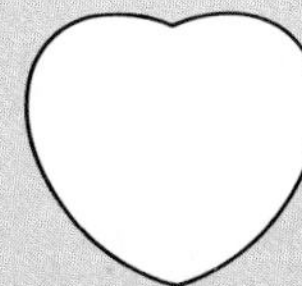

Notes for Home Children explore with a partner to find missing numerals.

Problem-Solving Workshop

Explore with a Calculator

Use a calculator to solve.

Enter the numbers.

Press [−] after each number but the last.

Press [=] after the last number.

Write what the calculator will show.

1. ninety-eight
seventy-five
seventeen

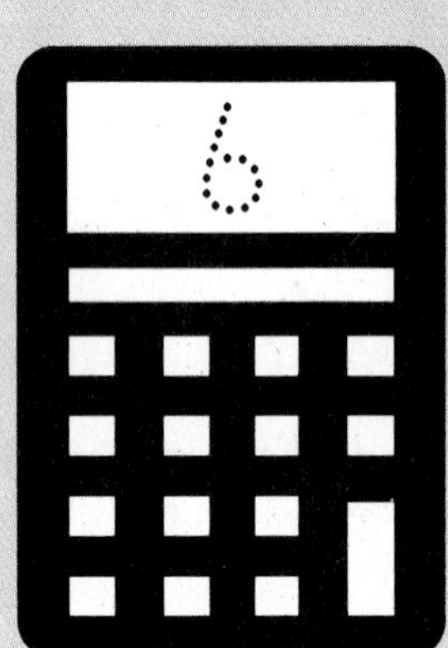

2. eighty-three
thirty-eight
forty-one

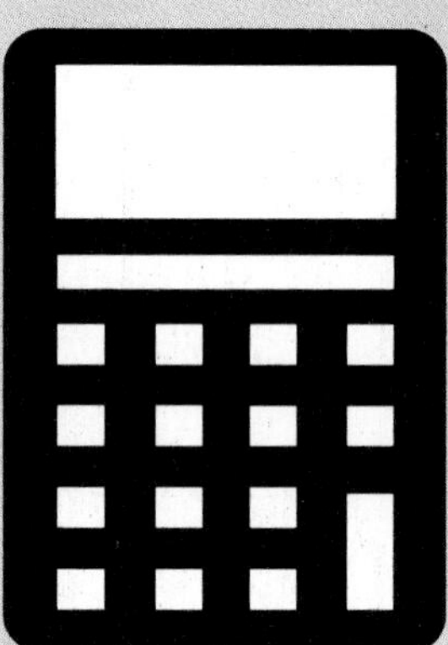

3. seventy
fifty-six
twelve

4. sixty-one
twenty-nine
thirty-one

Exploring Mathematics Book Two © Scott, Foresman and Company

Notes for Home Children explore with a calculator to solve two-digit subtaction problems.

Name

Set A Use after page 242.

Subtract. If you need to trade, color the space yellow.

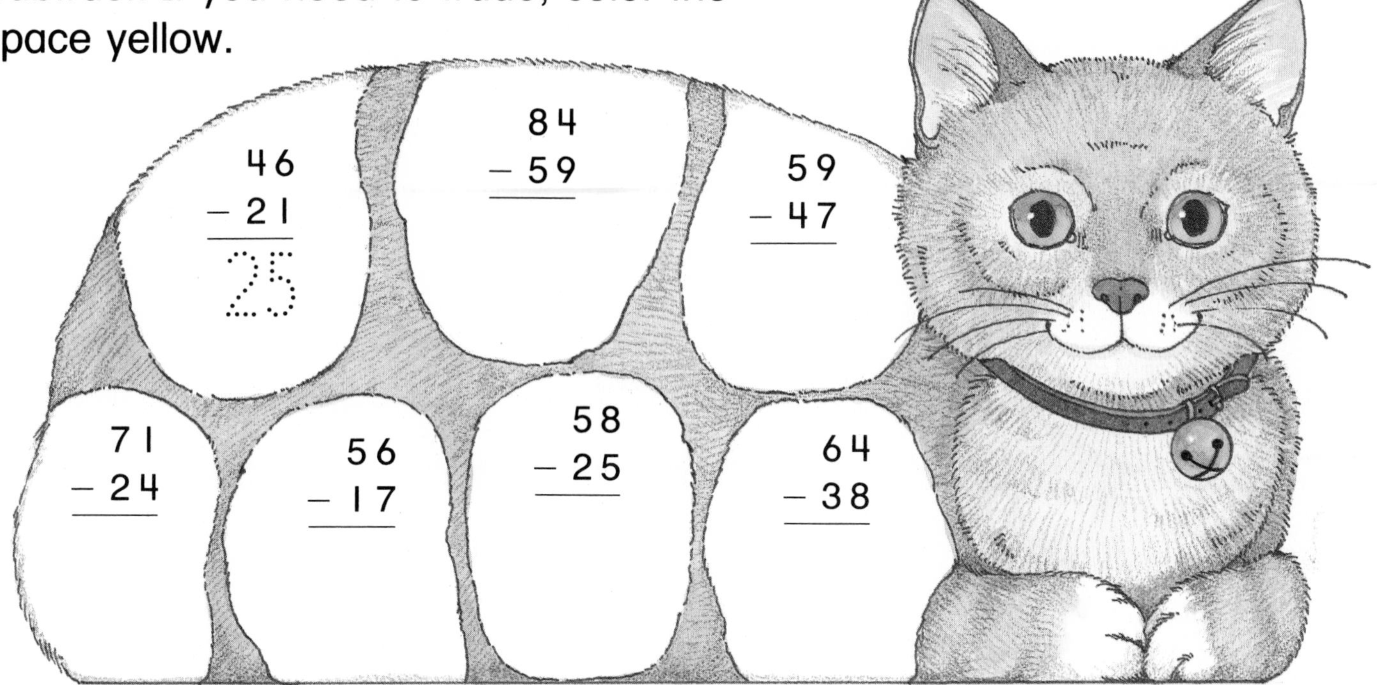

Set B Use after page 244.

Do you trade? Ring yes or no.
Then subtract.

1. $30 - 13 = 17$ yes no
2. $53 - 33 = 20$ yes no
3. $94 - 59 = 35$ yes no
4. $24 - 16 = 8$ yes no
5. $41 - 28 = 13$ yes no
6. $87 - 45 = 42$ yes no

Notes for Home Set A: Children practice finding differences of two-digit numbers.
Set B: Children decide if trading is necessary. Then they find differences of two-digit numbers.

Enrichment

There are 72 pages in my book.
I have read 38 pages.
About how many pages are left?

Think of the nearest 10, then subtract the tens.

72	70
− 38	− 40
About	30

Write the nearest 10.
Then subtract.

1.

53	50	28		47	
− 27	− 30	− 12	−	− 39	−
About	20	About		About	

  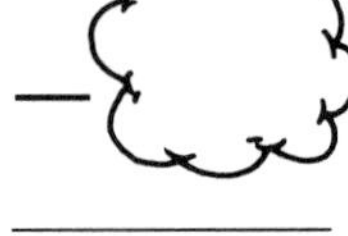
  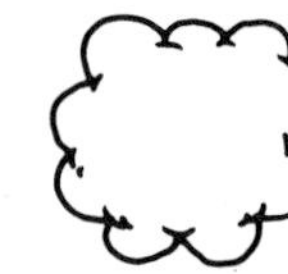

2.

87		53		88	
− 49	−	− 24	−	− 41	−
About		About		About	

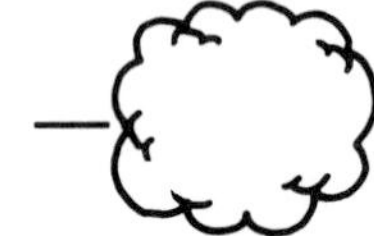 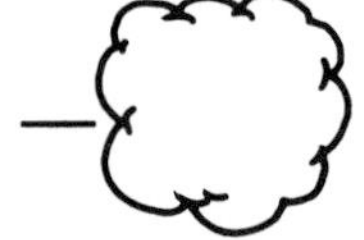 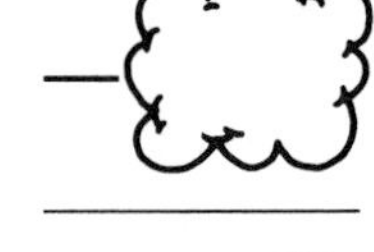

Exploring Mathematics Book Two © Scott, Foresman and Company

Notes for Home Children are challenged to estimate differences.

Name

Chapter 8 Review/Test

1. Cross out to subtract. Record.

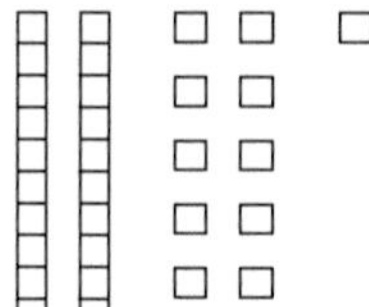

$$\begin{array}{r} 32 \\ -\ 17 \\ \hline \end{array}$$

2. Subtract and check.

$$\begin{array}{r} 37 \\ -\ 18 \\ \hline \end{array}$$

3. Subtract.

$$\begin{array}{r} 65 \\ -\ \ 8 \\ \hline \end{array} \quad \begin{array}{r} 73 \\ -\ 17 \\ \hline \end{array} \quad \begin{array}{r} 90 \\ -\ 36 \\ \hline \end{array} \quad \begin{array}{r} 67¢ \\ -\ 25¢ \\ \hline \end{array} \quad \begin{array}{r} 72¢ \\ -\ 35¢ \\ \hline \end{array}$$

4. How many? Ring.

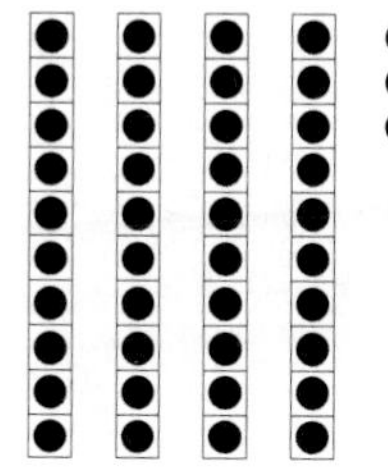

43 − 6

more than 40

less than 40

5. Subtract.

$$\begin{array}{r} 15 \\ -\ \ 7 \\ \hline \end{array} \quad \begin{array}{r} 25 \\ -\ \ 7 \\ \hline \end{array} \quad \begin{array}{r} 35 \\ -\ \ 7 \\ \hline \end{array}$$

6. Show each step. Solve.

Jodi's book has 75 pages. On Monday she read 32 pages. How many pages did she have left to read?

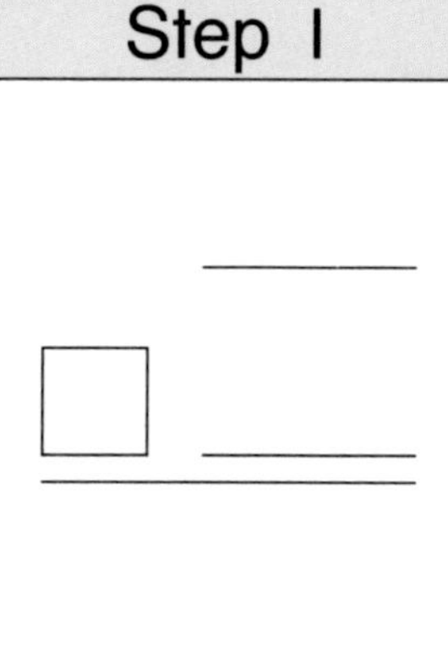

Step 1

On Tuesday Jodi read 17 more pages. Now how many pages does she have left to read?

Step 2

Notes for Home Children are assessed on Chapter 8 concepts, skills, and problem solving.

Exploring MATH AT HOME

Exploring Math at Home

Dear Family,

In this chapter I have learned two-digit subtraction and how to record a trade of 1 ten for 10 ones. I also learned to check my subtraction by adding. Please help me with the activities below.

Love, ______________________

1.

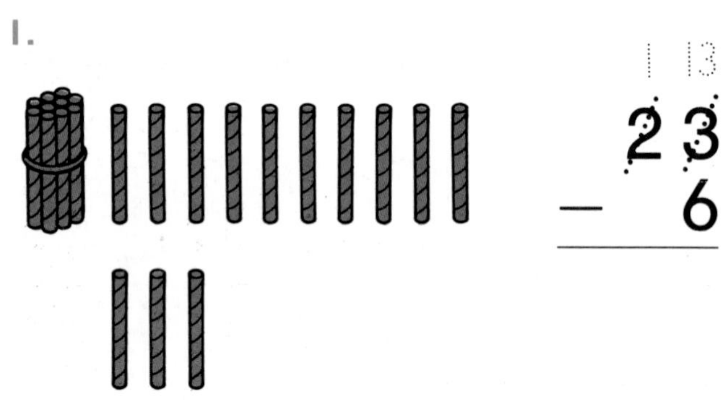

$$\begin{array}{r} \overset{1\ 13}{2\,3} \\ -\ \ 6 \\ \hline \end{array}$$

Use single straws and bundles of 10. Think up problems to practice subtracting one-digit numbers from two-digit numbers.

2.

Find two items in a newspaper that cost less than $1.00. Find the differences in cost. Tell if you need to trade when you subtract.

3.

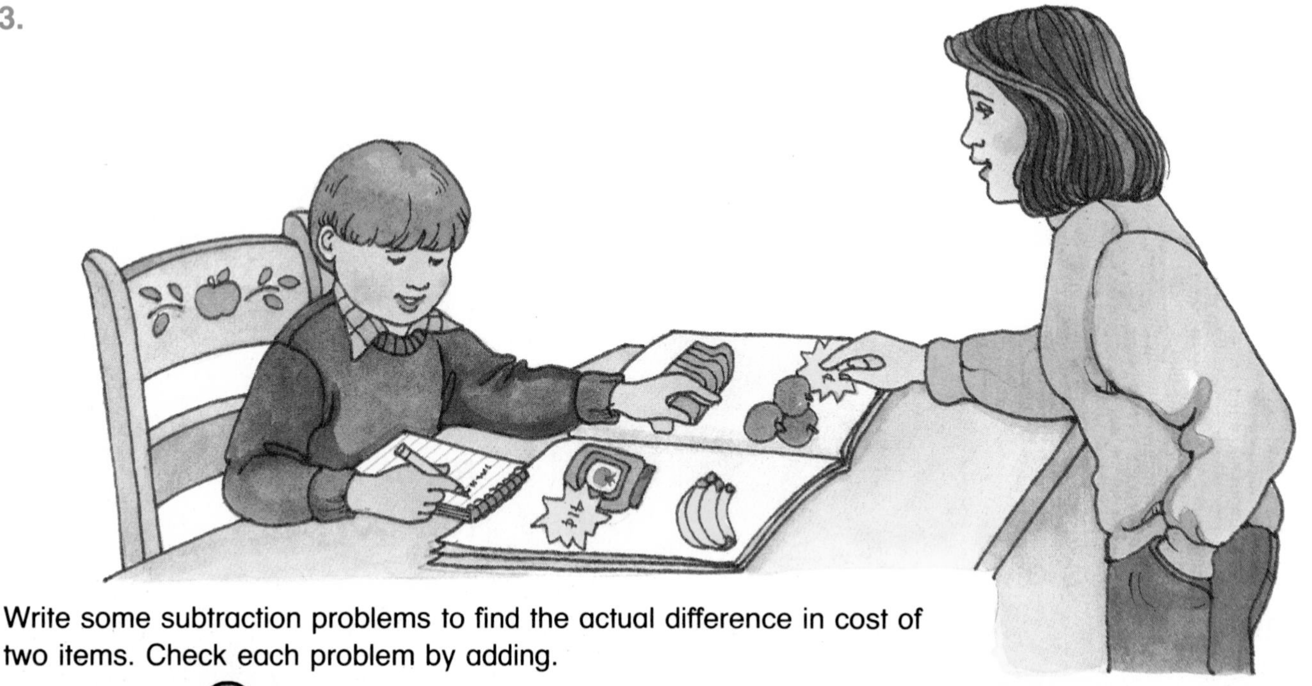

Write some subtraction problems to find the actual difference in cost of two items. Check each problem by adding.

Coming Attractions

In the next chapter I will learn about numbers through 999. I will also learn about number patterns.

Exploring Mathematics Book Two © Scott, Foresman and Company

Listen to the math story, "Balloonagrams."
Grandfather sent messages on 741 balloons.
Why did he send so many?

Notes for Home Children listen to a math story introducing chapter concepts and skills. Then they answer a question about the story.

Name

Counting Hundreds

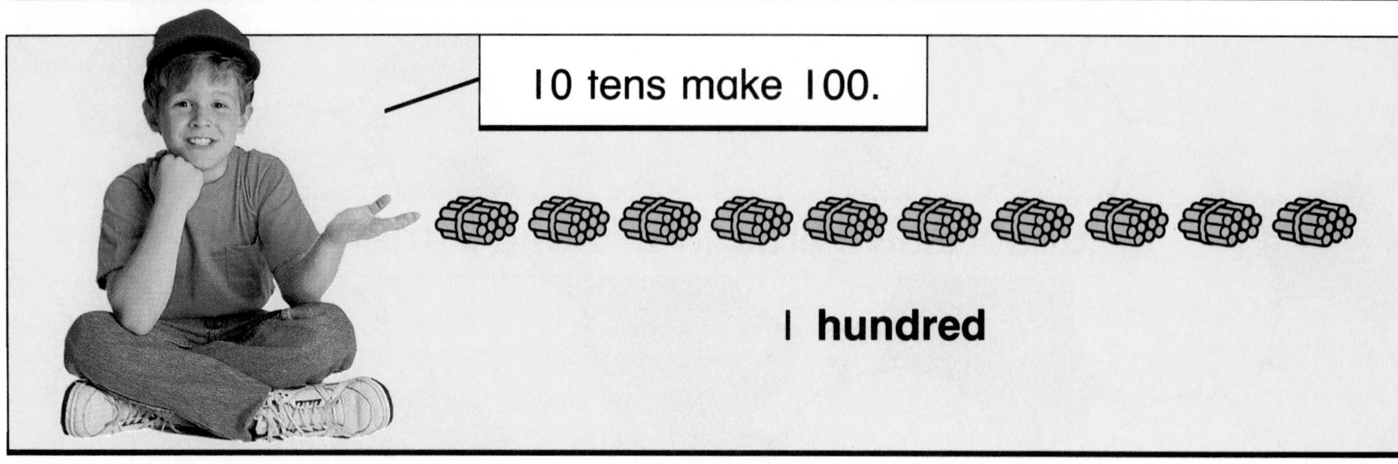

Ring groups of 100.
How many hundreds?

1. 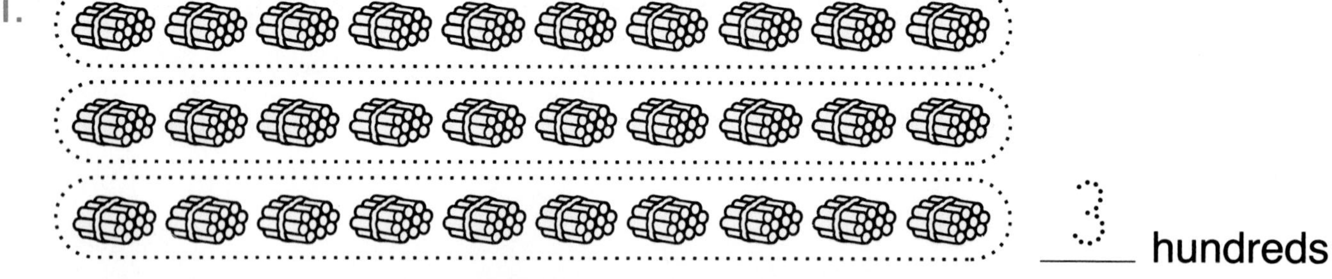

3 hundreds

2. 

_____ hundreds

3. 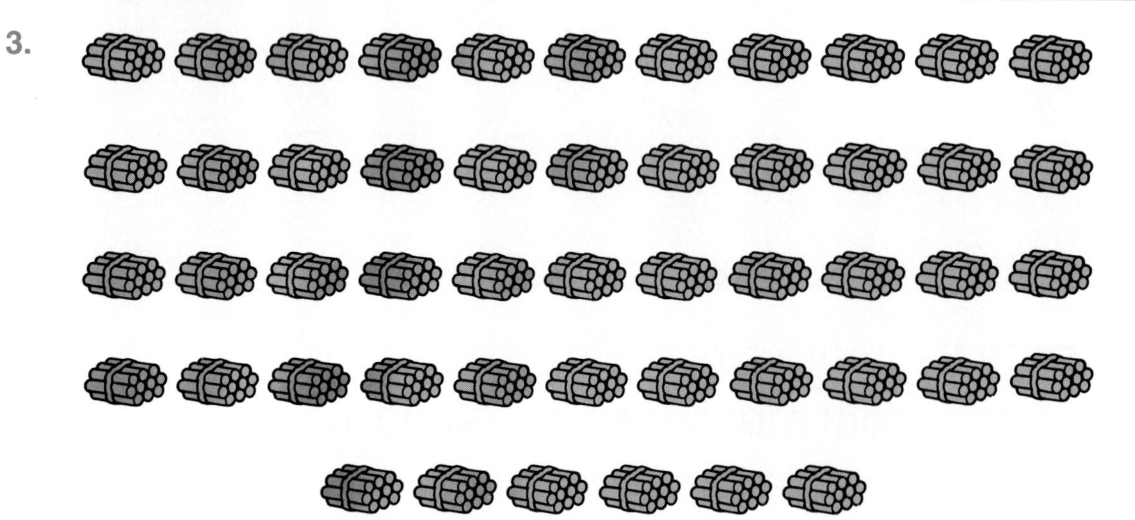

_____ hundreds

Exploring Mathematics Book Two © Scott, Foresman and Company

Notes for Home Children count tens to ring groups of 100.

Name

Understanding Hundreds

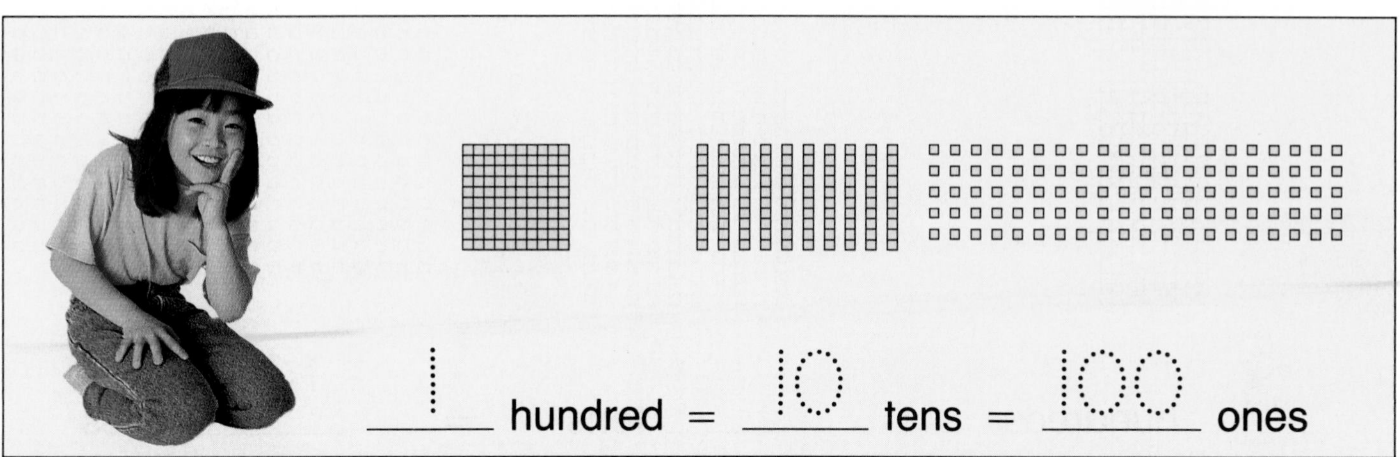

Write how many.

1.

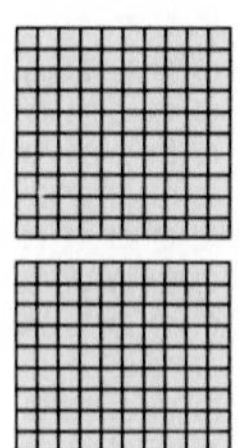

______ hundreds = ______ tens = ______ ones

2.

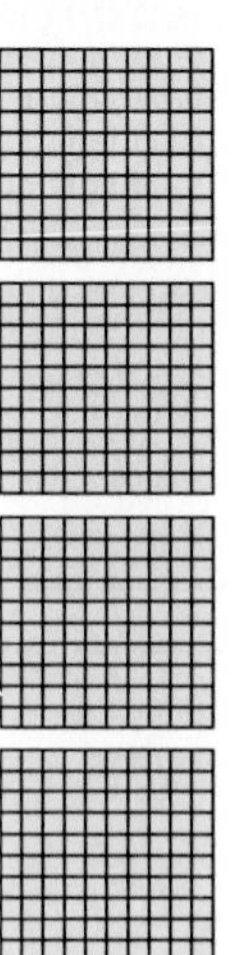

______ hundreds = ______ tens = ______ ones

Notes for Home Children count tens and ones to learn the meaning of hundreds.

Write how many.

3.

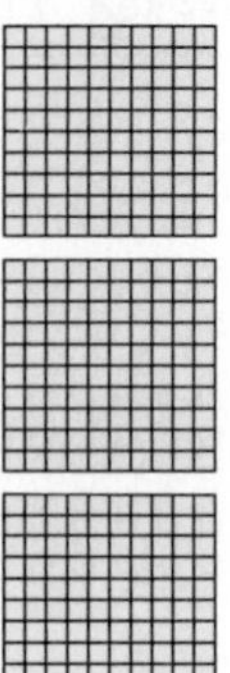

3 hundreds = 30 tens = 300 ones

4.

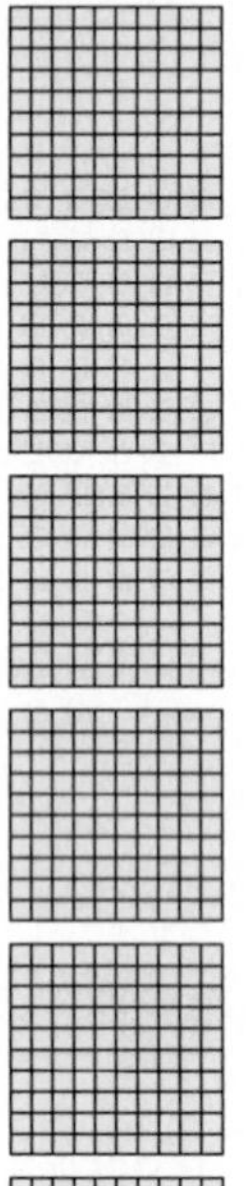

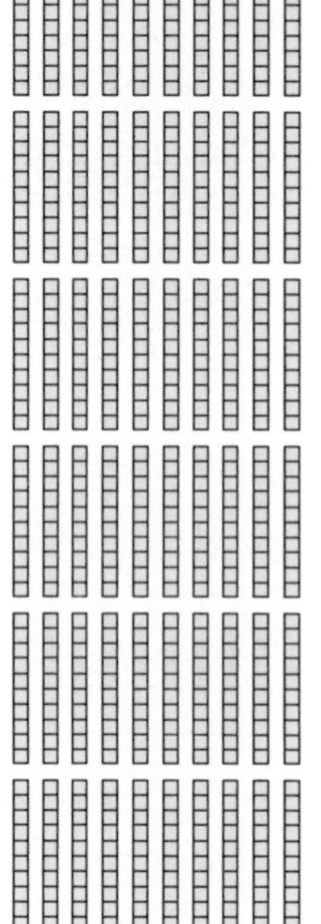

_____ hundreds = _____ tens = _____ ones

5. 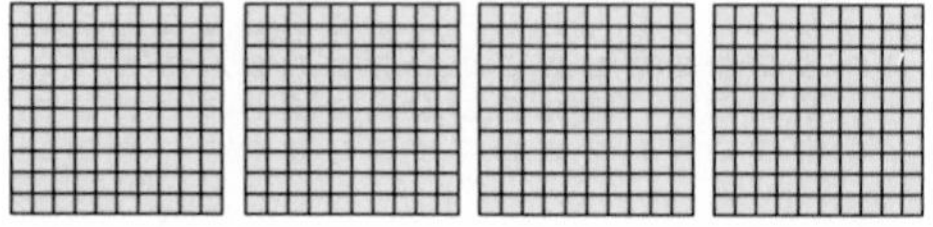 = _____

6. 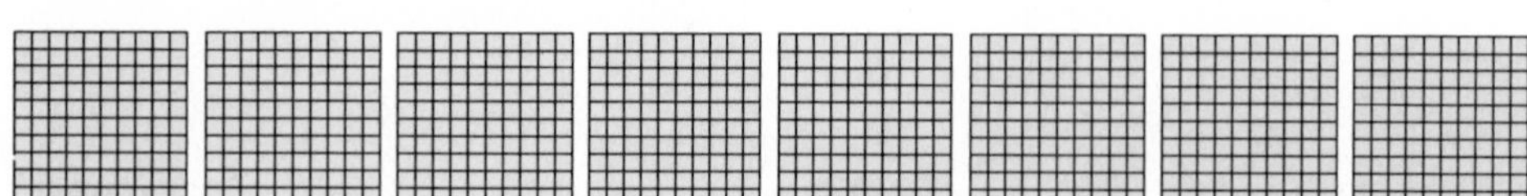 = _____

Notes for Home Children count tens and ones to learn the meaning of hundreds. Then they count hundreds.

Exploring Mathematics Book Two © Scott, Foresman and Company

Name

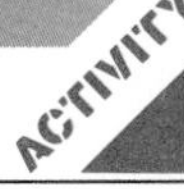

Identifying Hundreds, Tens, and Ones

hundreds	tens	ones
2	4	3

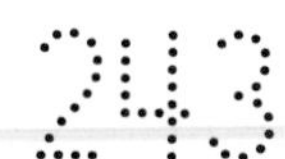

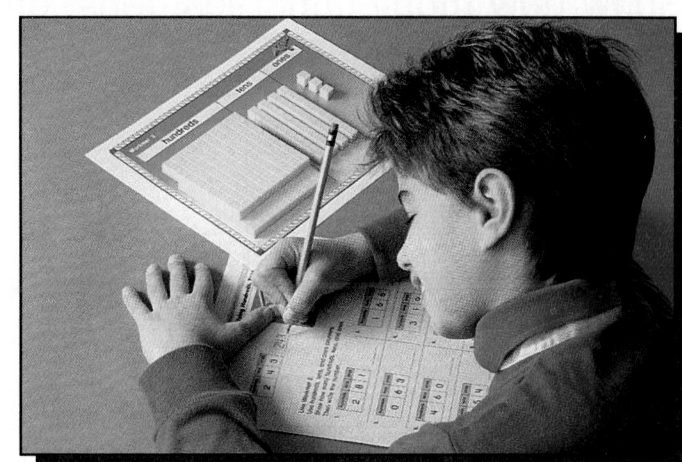

Use Workmat 2.
Use hundreds, tens, and ones counters.
Show how many hundreds, tens, and ones.
Then write the number.

1.

hundreds	tens	ones
2	8	1

______

2.

hundreds	tens	ones
1	6	6

______

3.

hundreds	tens	ones
0	6	3

______

4.

hundreds	tens	ones
3	1	9

______

5.

hundreds	tens	ones
4	6	0

______

6.

hundreds	tens	ones
2	0	7

______

7.

hundreds	tens	ones
1	5	4

______

8.

hundreds	tens	ones
4	1	5

______

Notes for Home Children explore at the CONCRETE level using hundreds, tens, and ones counters and a place-value workmat to identify and write numbers through 999.

Use Workmat 2.
Use hundreds, tens, and ones counters.
Show how many hundreds, tens, and ones.
Then write the number.

9.

hundreds	tens	ones
2	5	1

251

10.

hundreds	tens	ones
4	5	2

_____

11.

hundreds	tens	ones
2	4	7

_____

12.

hundreds	tens	ones
0	2	8

_____

13.

hundreds	tens	ones
4	2	0

_____

14.

hundreds	tens	ones
3	0	7

_____

15.

hundreds	tens	ones
3	7	5

_____

16.

hundreds	tens	ones
3	5	7

_____

17.

hundreds	tens	ones
2	1	7

_____

18.

hundreds	tens	ones
2	7	1

_____

Critical Thinking Which number below has the most hundreds?
Which number has the fewest hundreds?

305 176 548

Exploring Mathematics Book Two © Scott, Foresman and Company

Notes for Home Children explore at the CONCRETE level using hundreds, tens, and ones counters. They use a place-value workmat to identify and write numbers through 999. Then they discuss place value.

Name ______

Identifying Hundreds, Tens, and Ones

How many hundreds counters does Sandy have?
How many tens counters does she have?
How many ones counters does she have?
What number is Sandy showing?

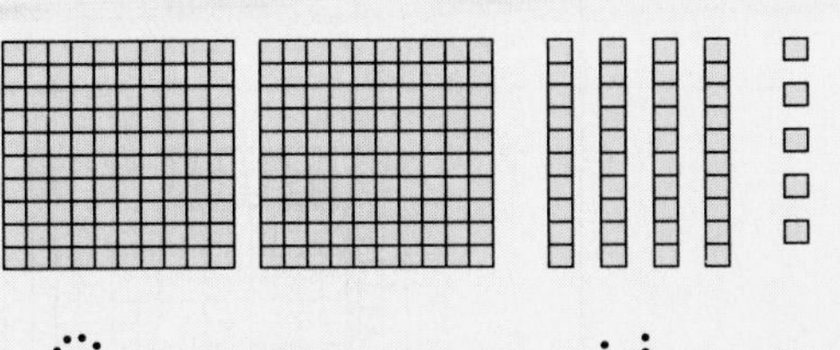

2 hundreds 4 tens 5 ones = 245

Write how many hundreds, tens, and ones.
Then write the number.

1. 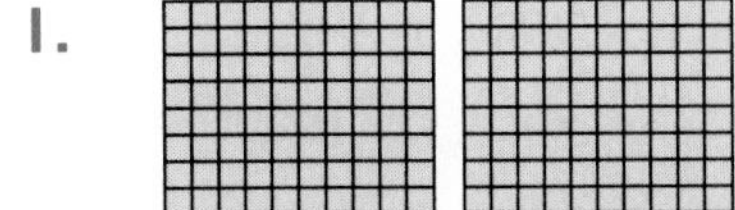 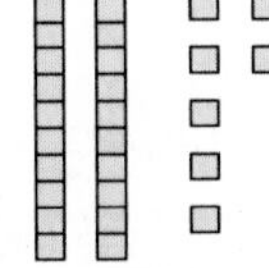

____ hundreds ____ tens ____ ones = ______

2. 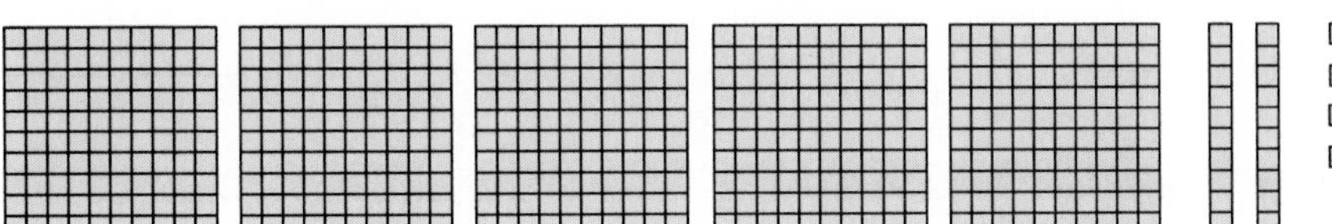

____ hundreds ____ tens ____ ones = ______

3. 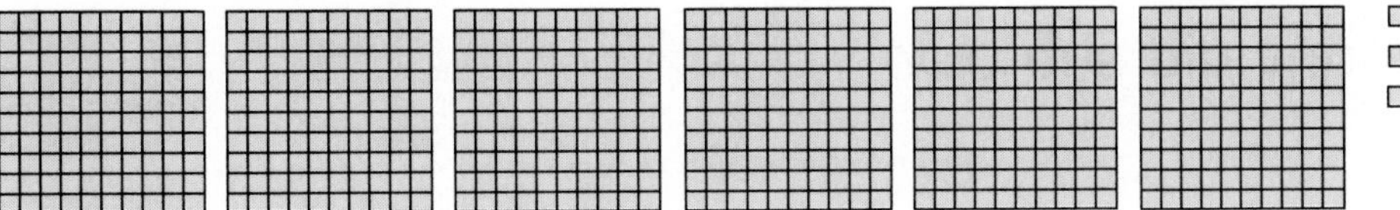

____ hundreds ____ tens ____ ones = ______

Notes for Home Children identify how many hundreds, tens, and ones. Then they write numbers through 999.

Write the number.

4.

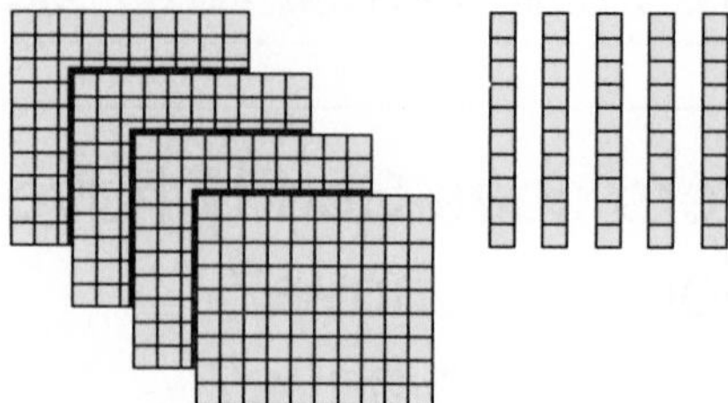

454

5.

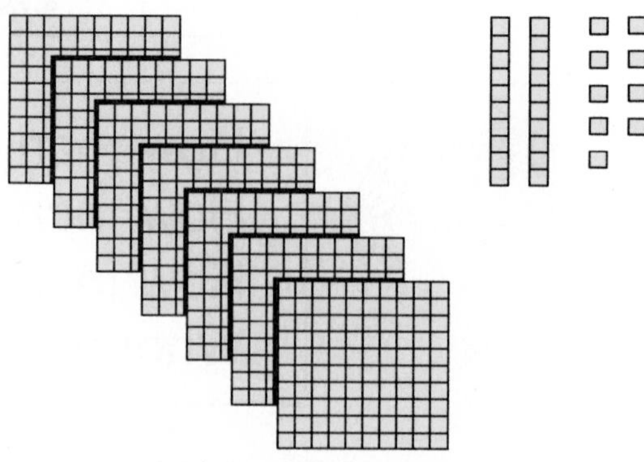

6.

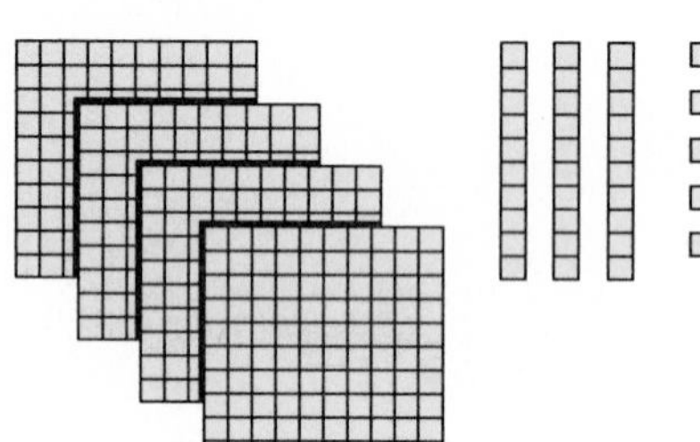

7.

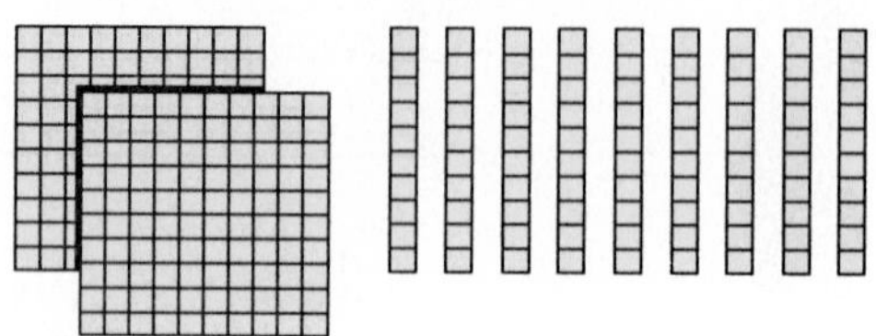

8.

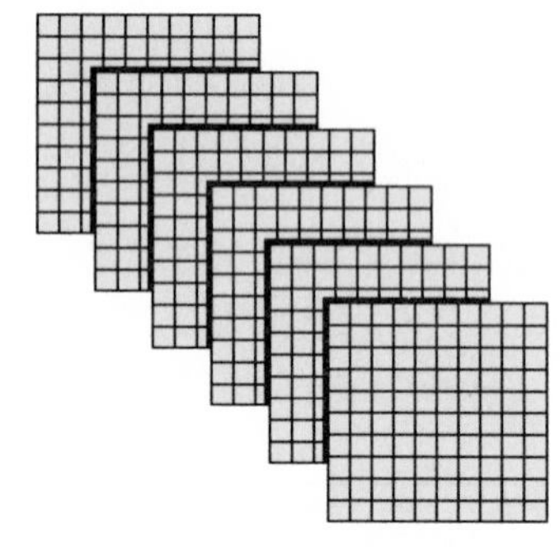

9.

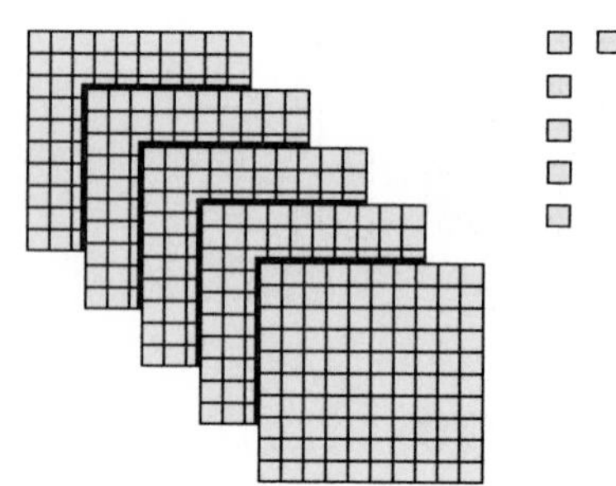

Problem Solving

Solve.

10. Mrs. Robinson bought these pencils. How many did she buy in all?

________ pencils

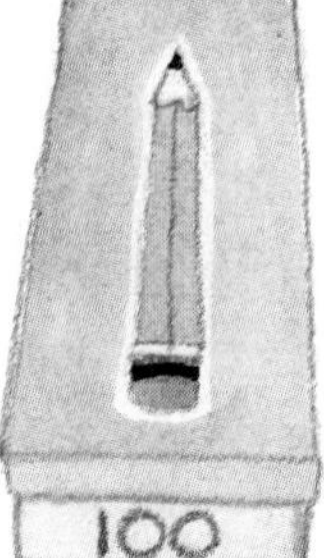

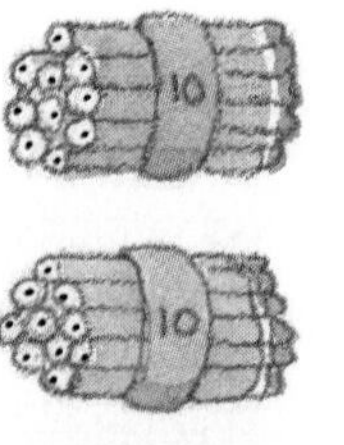

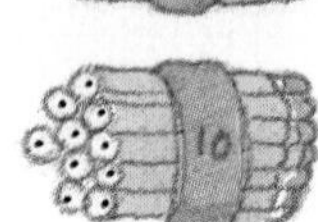

Exploring Mathematics Book Two © Scott, Foresman and Company

Notes for Home Children identify how many hundreds, tens, and ones in order to write numbers through 999. Then they solve a problem involving place value.

Name ______________________________

Place Value to 999 and Expanded Form

243 can be written in different ways.

2 hundreds 4 tens 3 ones

200 and 40 and 3

243

How many?

1. 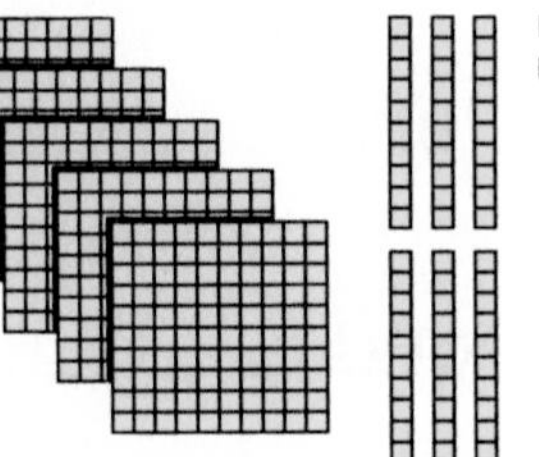

_____ hundreds _____ tens _____ ones

_____ and _____ and _____

_____

2. 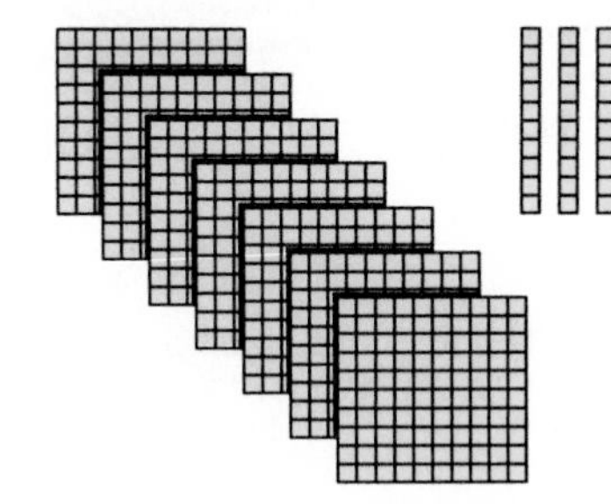

_____ hundreds _____ tens _____ ones

_____ and _____ and _____

_____

3. 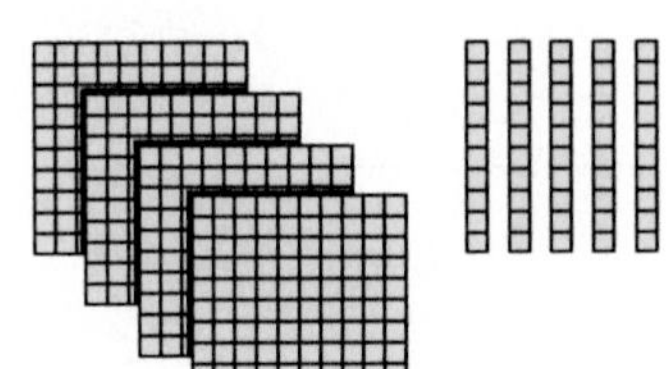

_____ hundreds _____ tens _____ ones

_____ and _____ and _____

_____

Notes for Home Children learn the value of each digit in numbers through 999.

How many?

4. 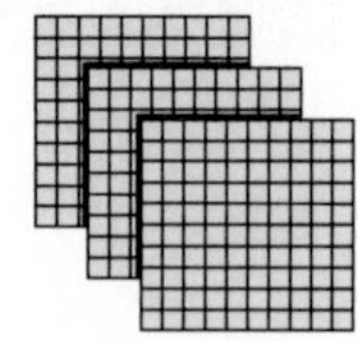

3 hundreds 6 tens 7 ones

300 and 60 and 7

367

5. 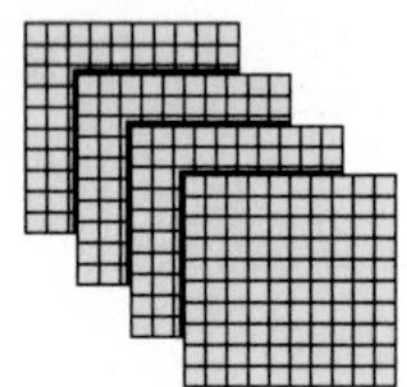

_____ hundreds _____ tens _____ ones

_____ and _____ and _____

_____

6. 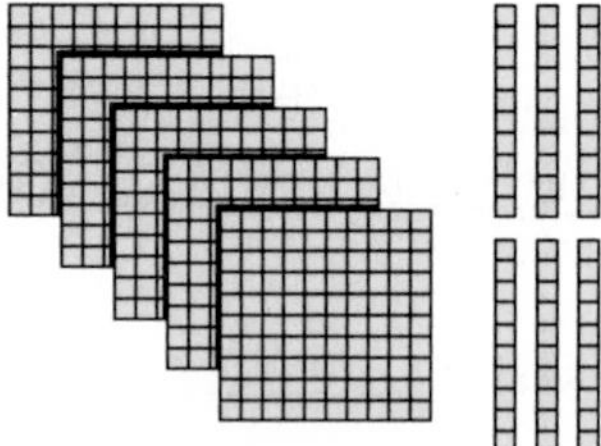

_____ hundreds _____ tens _____ ones

_____ and _____ and _____

_____

7. 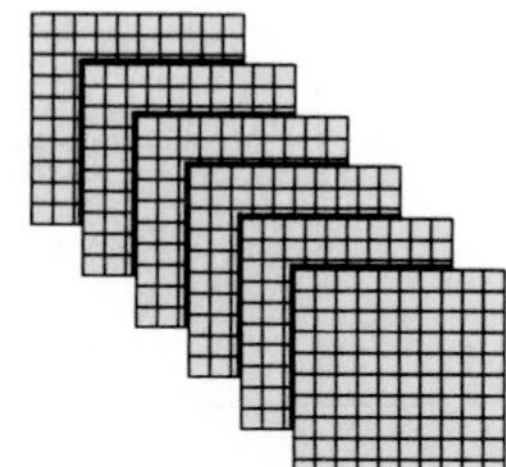

_____ hundreds _____ tens _____ ones

_____ and _____ and _____

_____

Write About Math

Write this number.
4 is in the tens place.
3 is in the hundreds place.
6 is in the ones place. _____

Notes for Home Children learn the value of each digit in numbers through 999. Then they write about place value.

Exploring Mathematics Book Two © Scott, Foresman and Company

Name

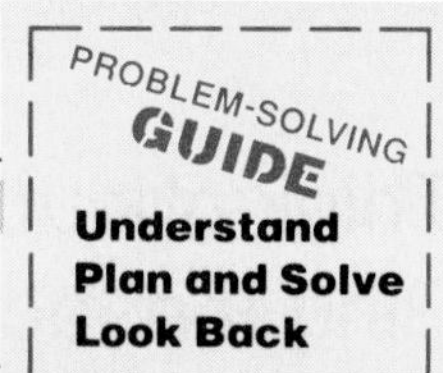

Using a Problem-Solving Guide

I use a 3-step guide to help me solve problems.

Eric has 42¢.
Steffi has 25¢.
How much more does Eric have?

PROBLEM-SOLVING GUIDE

Step 1: **Understand......**	**What is the question?**	How much more does Eric have?
	What are the facts?	Eric has 42¢. Steffi has 25¢.
Step 2: **Plan and Solve...**	**What can you do?** **How can you find the answer?**	Subtract. $42¢ - 25¢ = 17¢$ Eric has 17¢ more than Steffi.
Step 3: **Look Back.......**	**Does the answer make sense?**	42¢ is 17¢ more than 25¢. It makes sense that Eric has 17¢ more than Steffi.

Notes for Home Children learn to use a three-step problem-solving guide to solve problems.

Think about Step 1, **Understand.**
Ring the facts.
Underline the question.

1. Niki had 36¢.
She found 13¢ more.
How much does she have now?

2. Juan had 43¢.
He spent 13¢.
How much does he have now?

Think about Step 2, **Plan and Solve.**
Ring + or −.
Then solve.

3. Niki had 36¢.
She found 13¢ more.
How much does she have now?

+ −

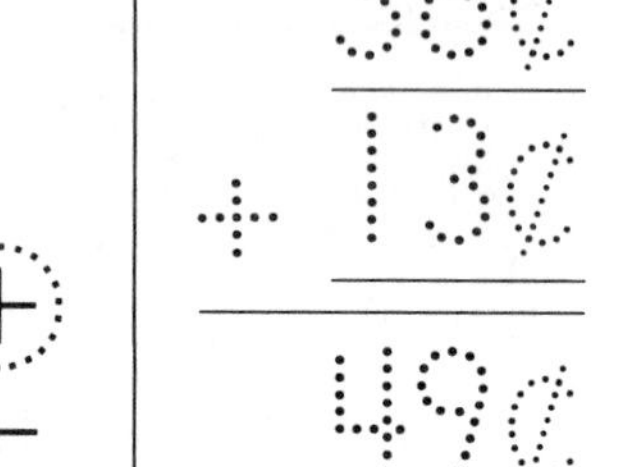

4. Juan had 43¢.
He spent 13¢.
How much does he have now?

+ −

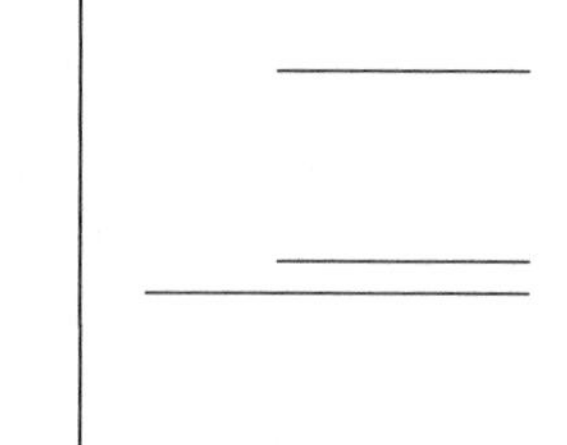

Think about Step 3, **Look Back.**
Write the answer in the sentence.
Decide if each answer makes sense. Ring yes or no.

5. Niki has 49¢ now.
yes no

6. Juan has ________ now.
yes no

Exploring Mathematics Book Two © Scott, Foresman and Company

Notes for Home Children use a three-step problem-solving guide to solve problems.

Name

Number Sense

About how many children are in your school? Tell different ways you could find the answer.

Let's do some more!

Write a story about how many children are in the second grade.

Notes for Home Children develop number understanding by describing numbers up to 999.

SKILLS REVIEW

Skills Review

Fill in the correct ◯.
Subtract.

1.	$\begin{array}{r} 58 \\ -43 \\ \hline \end{array}$	Ⓐ 13 Ⓑ 15 Ⓒ 18	
2.	$\begin{array}{r} 43 \\ -17 \\ \hline \end{array}$	Ⓐ 26 Ⓑ 36 Ⓒ 46	
3.	$\begin{array}{r} 76 \\ -22 \\ \hline \end{array}$	Ⓐ 52 Ⓑ 53 Ⓒ 54	
4.	$\begin{array}{r} 80 \\ -61 \\ \hline \end{array}$	Ⓐ 19 Ⓑ 20 Ⓒ 21	
5.	$\begin{array}{r} 68 \\ -38 \\ \hline \end{array}$	Ⓐ 30 Ⓑ 38 Ⓒ 40	
6.	$\begin{array}{r} 84 \\ -45 \\ \hline \end{array}$	Ⓐ 34 Ⓑ 39 Ⓒ 41	

Vocabulary

Write about yourself.

7. In what month is your birthday?

____

8. What is the date of your birthday?

____

9. In what year were you born?

____

Exploring Mathematics Book Two © Scott, Foresman and Company

Notes for Home Children practice finding differences of two-digit numbers. Then they review terms from the calendar.

Name

Order Through 999

1. Complete the chart.

900	901	902			905				
910									919
	921								
		932							
				944					
						956			
			963						
								978	
							987		
									999

Use the chart.
Write the numbers that come next.

2. 911, 912, 913, _____, _____, _____.

3. 934, 935, 936, _____, _____, _____.

4. 966, 967, 968, _____, _____, _____.

Notes for Home Children order numbers from 900 to 999 using a chart.

Write the missing numbers.

5.

After	
975	976
201	
349	
777	
521	
399	

6.

Before	
	157
	533
	299
	861
	401
	900

7.

Between		
341		343
724		726
110		112
507		509
298		300
499		501

Problem Solving

Solve.

8. Three pages fell out of David's book.
How would you put the pages back in order?

________, ________, ________

Exploring Mathematics Book Two © Scott, Foresman and Company

Notes for Home Children practice ordering numbers through 999 by writing numbers after, before, and between. Then they solve a problem involving number order.

See More Practice Set A on page 291.

Name

Comparing Numbers Through 999 Using < and >

To compare numbers, first look at the hundreds place. 3 hundreds are more than 2 hundreds.

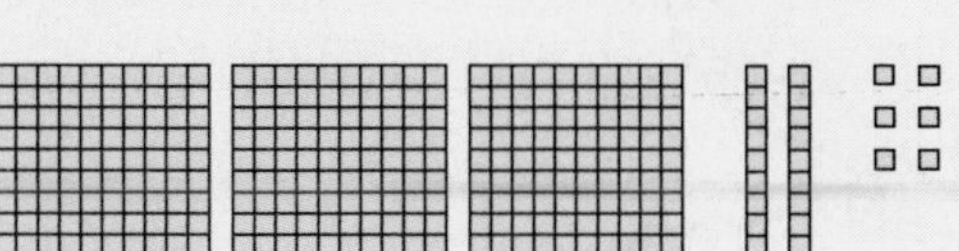 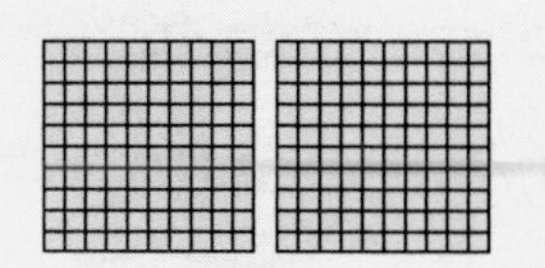 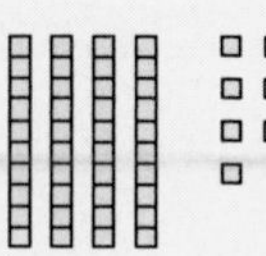

326 > 247

326 is **greater than** 247.

If the number of hundreds is the same, look at the tens place. 1 ten is less than 4 tens.

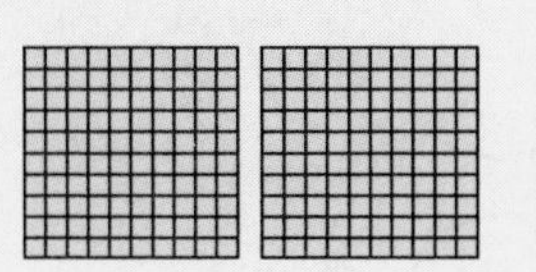 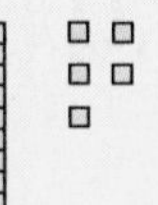 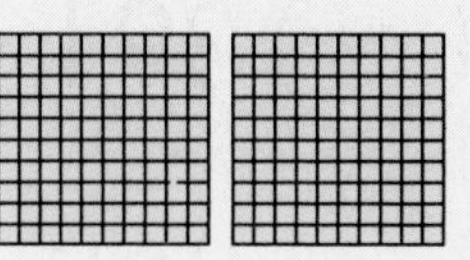 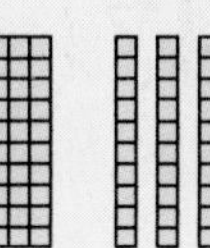   

215 < 243

215 is **less than** 243.

Write > or <.

1.	523 (>) 472	714 ( ) 612	428 ( ) 456
2.	293 ( ) 604	418 ( ) 431	657 ( ) 629
3.	235 ( ) 261	251 ( ) 153	530 ( ) 520
4.	529 ( ) 259	603 ( ) 630	912 ( ) 812

Notes for Home Children learn to compare the value of two three-digit numbers by comparing first the hundreds and then the tens, if necessary. Then they use the greater-than and less-than symbols.

Write > or <.

5.	300 ◯ 200	266 ◯ 251	318 ◯ 381
6.	215 ◯ 245	641 ◯ 289	407 ◯ 219
7.	347 ◯ 391	754 ◯ 672	327 ◯ 395
8.	581 ◯ 484	257 ◯ 314	108 ◯ 180
9.	237 ◯ 327	532 ◯ 353	333 ◯ 222
10.	303 ◯ 330	407 ◯ 470	642 ◯ 624

Write About Math

Put these numbers in order from least to greatest.

123 321 213

______, ______, ______

Exploring Mathematics Book Two © Scott, Foresman and Company

Notes for Home Children practice using the greater-than and less-than symbols when comparing numbers. Then they write about number order.

Name

Number Patterns

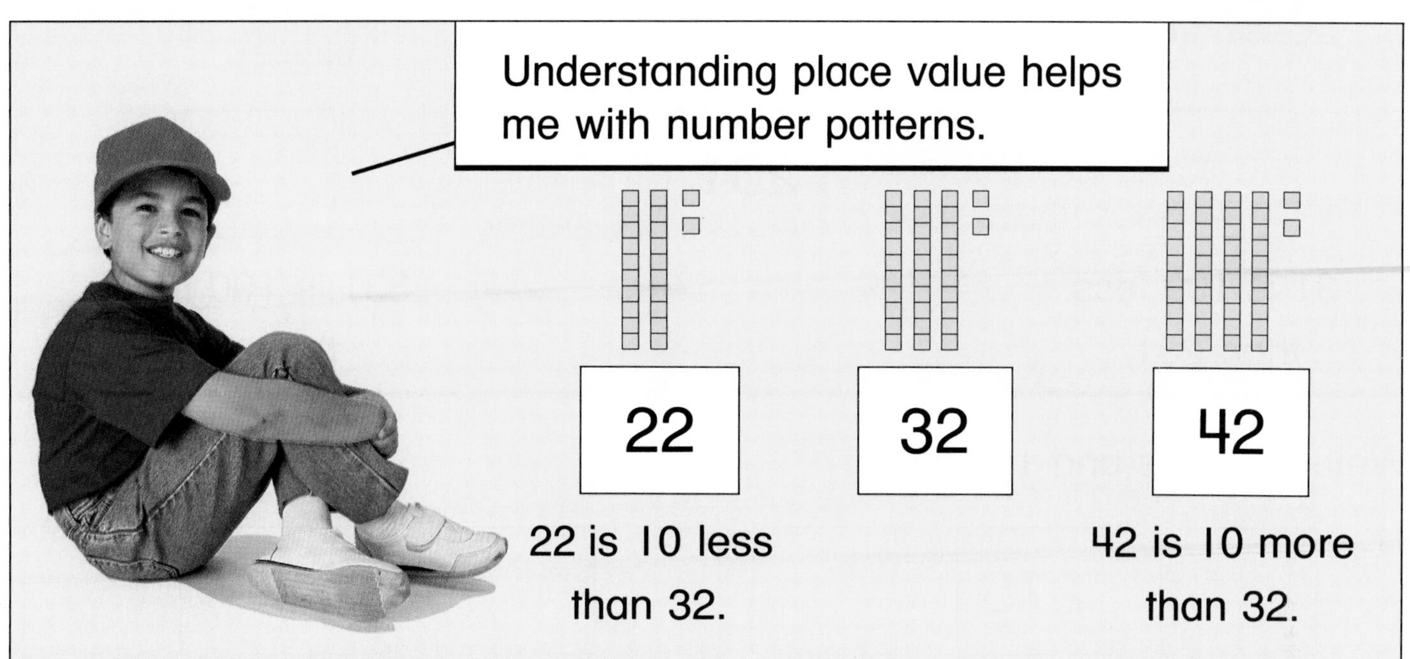

Write 10 less and 10 more.

	10 less	Number	10 more
1.	17	27	37
2.		15	
3.		84	
4.		63	
5.		56	
6.		90	
7.		268	
8.		355	
9.		313	
10.		200	

Notes for Home Children learn about number patterns by decreasing and increasing numbers by 10.

131 | 231 | 331

131 is 100 less than 231.

331 is 100 more than 231.

Write 100 less and 100 more.

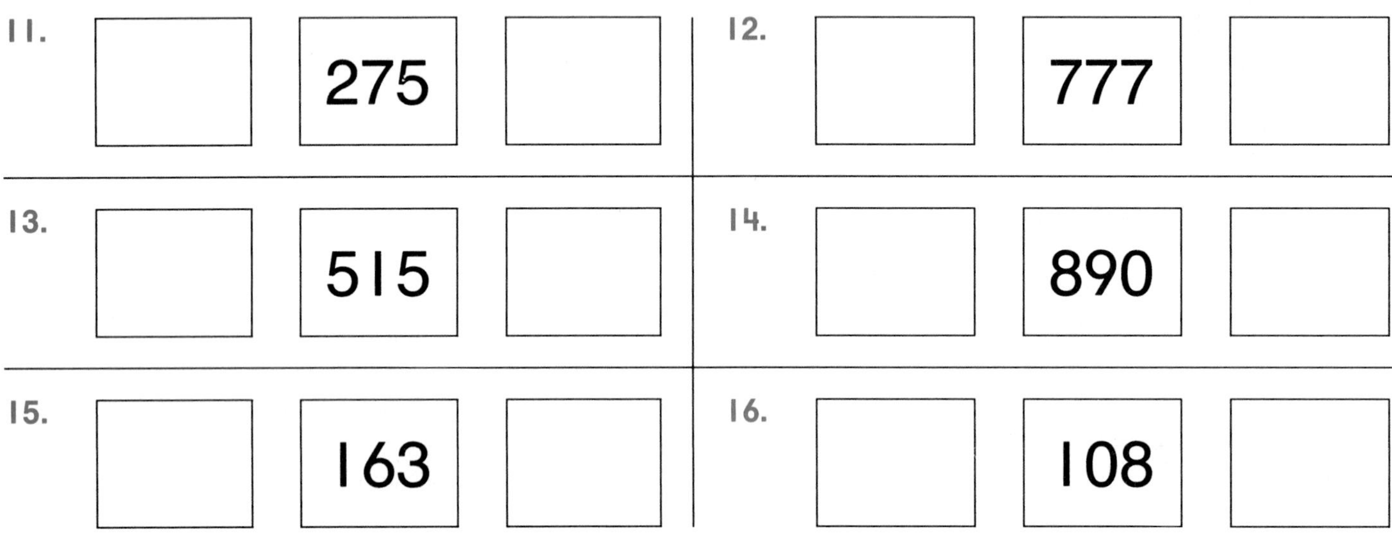

11. ___ 275 ___

12. ___ 777 ___

13. ___ 515 ___

14. ___ 890 ___

15. ___ 163 ___

16. ___ 108 ___

Problem Solving

Solve.
Ring the correct pattern.

17. The fastest boats in a race had these numbers. What pattern do you see?

236 | 246 | 256 | 266

10 more   100 more

Exploring Mathematics Book Two © Scott, Foresman and Company

Notes for Home Children learn about number patterns by decreasing and increasing numbers by 100. Then they solve a problem involving number patterns.

Name

Number Names

Room Numbers	
110	one hundred ten
	two hundred twenty
	three hundred thirty
	four hundred forty
	five hundred fifty
	six hundred sixty
	seven hundred seventy
	eight hundred eighty
	nine hundred ninety

Ring the number names.

1.

nine hundred forty-one

nine hundred fourteen

four hundred ninety-one

2.

three hundred seventeen

two hundred seventy-one

three hundred seventy-one

Notes for Home Children identify number names for three-digit numbers.

Write the numbers.

3. four hundred twenty-four 424

4. three hundred eighty-nine ______

5. five hundred seventeen ______

6. nine hundred fifty-one ______

7. six hundred twenty ______

8. one hundred nine ______

9. eight hundred thirty ______

10. eight hundred three ______

11. eight hundred thirteen ______

Problem Solving

Solve.

12. Jenny lives at four hundred seventy-three State Street. Write her house number.

______

13. The number on Lin's classroom door is two hundred six. Write his room number.

______

Notes for Home Children read number names and write the numerals. Then they solve problems which involve reading number names.

Exploring Mathematics Book Two © Scott, Foresman and Company

See More Practice Set B on page 291.

Name

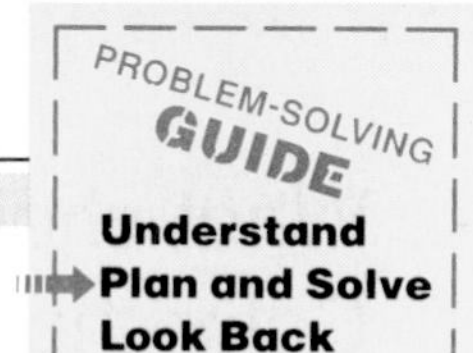

Find a Pattern

Which shoes should I wear?
Which strings should I put in my shoes?
These are my choices.

Choices	
Shoes	Strings
tan	yellow
tan	green
brown	yellow
brown	green

1. What choices does the boy have?
Complete the chart.

Choices	
Shirts	Pants
red	brown
red	black
orange	

Notes for Home Children solve problems by finding a pattern and listing all possible arrangements.

2. What choices does the girl have?
Color the chart.

Choices	
Dress	Shoes

3. What choices does the girl have?
Complete the chart.

Choices	
Dress	Shoes

Exploring Mathematics Book Two © Scott, Foresman and Company

Notes for Home Children solve problems by finding a pattern and listing all possible arrangements.

Name

Problem-Solving Workshop

Explore as a Team

Work with a partner.
Solve this riddle.
The address of this house has 3 digits.
All the digits are different.
The sum of the digits is 10.
The number is larger than 500.

Write all the numbers that could be the address.

9	1	0			

Let's do some more!

You and your partner make up one more clue to find the address of this house.

Notes for Home Children explore with a partner to solve a problem involving combinations.

Problem Solving WORKSHOP

Problem-Solving Workshop

Explore with a Calculator

Use your calculator to solve.

Add ones, tens, or hundreds.
Write what the calculator shows.

	Start	Add	Press	Total
1.	7 5	2 tens	=	95
2.	 1 3 6	3 ones	=	
3.	5 2 7	4 hundreds	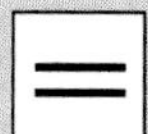 =	
4.	6 0 2	5 tens	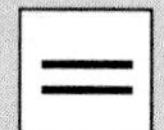 =	
5.	2 3 7	3 hundreds	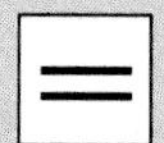 =	
6.	3 4 0	6 hundreds	 =	
7.	6 5 2	9 ones	=	
8.	4 9 5	1 ten	=	

Exploring Mathematics Book Two © Scott, Foresman and Company

Notes for Home Children explore with a calculator to solve place-value problems.

Name

Set A Use after page 280.

Write each missing number.

1.

After	
998	999
879	
190	
421	

2.

Before	
	431
	300
	584
	601

3.

Between		
189		191
870		872
508		510
791		793

Set B Use after page 286.

Write the number.

4. five hundred thirty-seven 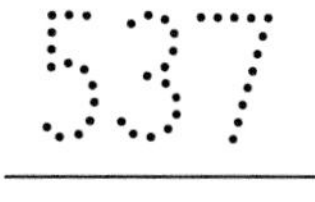 ________

5. eight hundred sixteen ________

6. one hundred ninety-nine ________

7. two hundred nine ________

8. seven hundred forty ________

Notes for Home Set A: Children practice ordering numbers through 999 by writing the number before, after, or between.
Set B: Children write the numbers for given number names.

Enrichment

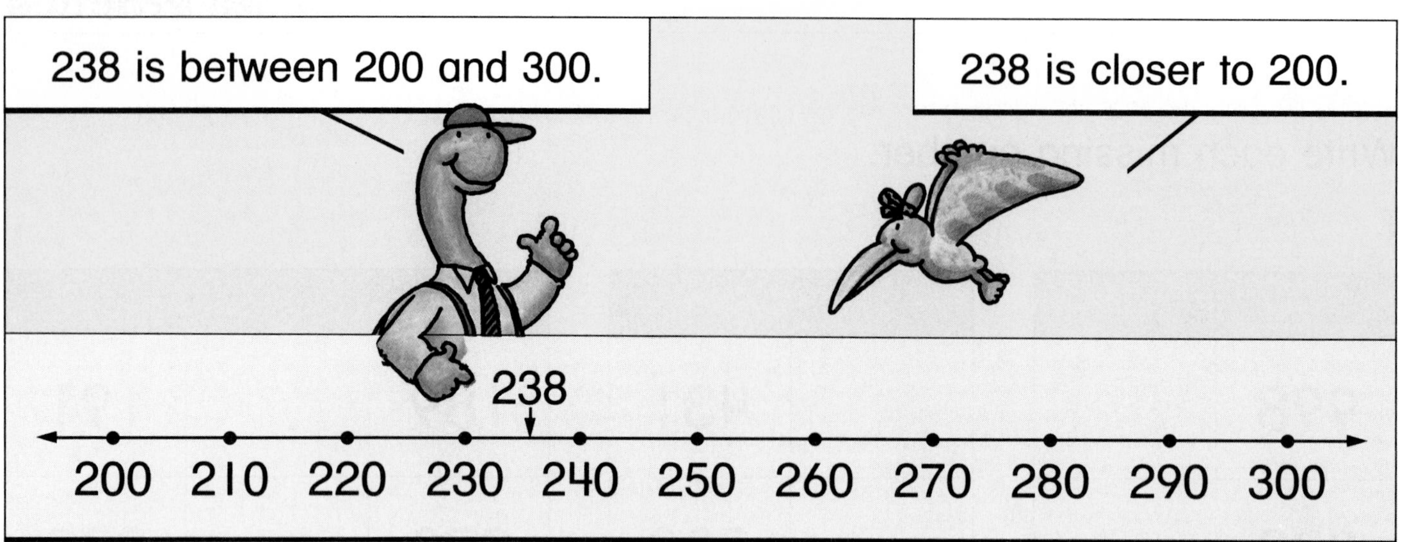

Use the number line.
Look for the nearer hundred. Complete.

600 610 620 630 640 650 660 670 680 690 700

1. 687 is between 600 and 700.

   687 is nearer to 700.

2. 614 is between ______ and ______.

   614 nearer to ______.

3. 673 is between ______ and ______.

   673 is nearer to ______.

4. 691 is nearer to ______.

5. 623 is nearer to ______.

Notes for Home Children are challenged to round numbers to the nearest hundred.

Exploring Mathematics Book Two © Scott, Foresman and Company

Name

Chapter 9 Review/Test

1. How many?

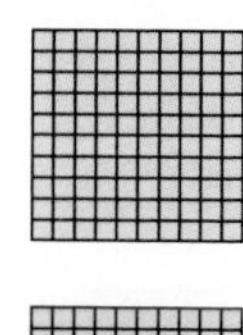

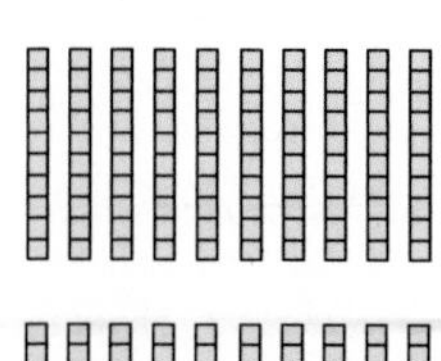

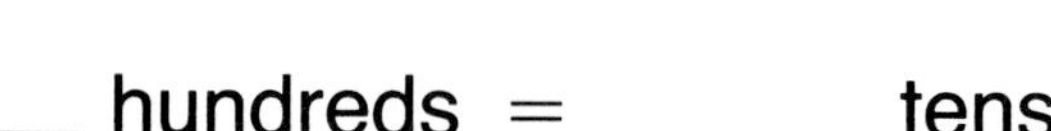

_____ hundreds = _____ tens

2. Write how many 3 ways.

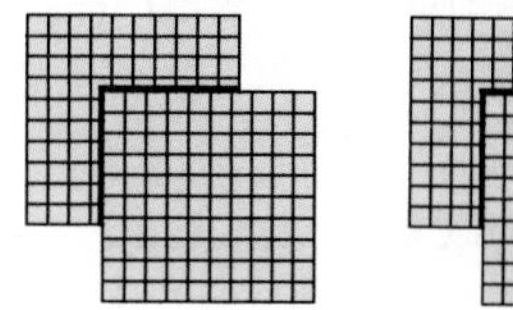

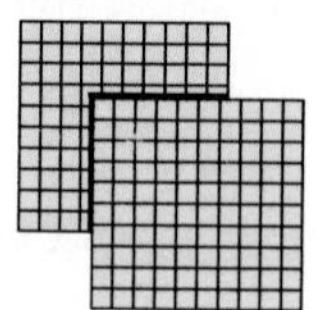

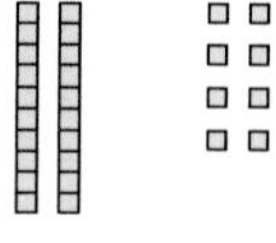

_____ hundreds _____ tens _____ ones

_____ and _____ and _____

_____

3. What numbers come next?

957, 958, ☐, ☐, ☐

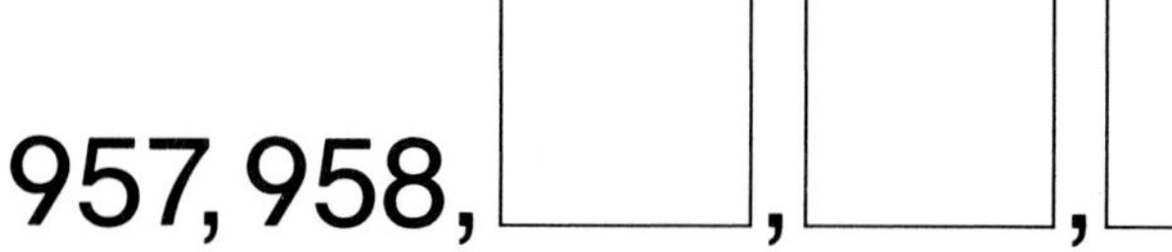

4. Write > or < in the ◯.

375 ◯ 357

5. Write 10 less and 10 more.

_____ 543 _____

6. Write the number.

six hundred twelve _____

7. Read the problem.
Ring the facts.
Underline the question.

Sally had 28¢.

Billy gave her 18¢ more.

Now how much does she have?

8. Draw your choices on the chart. You may have 1 fruit and 1 vegetable.

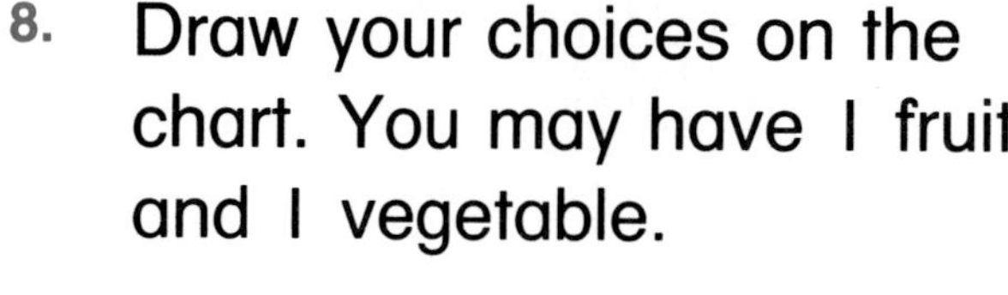

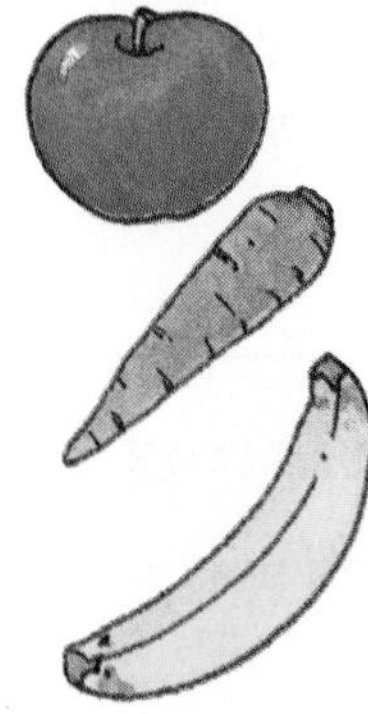

choice fruit	choice vegetable

Notes for Home Children are assessed on Chapter 9 concepts, skills, and problem solving.

Exploring Math at Home

Dear Family,

In this chapter I have learned about numbers through 999.
Please help me with the activities below.

Love, ______________________

1.

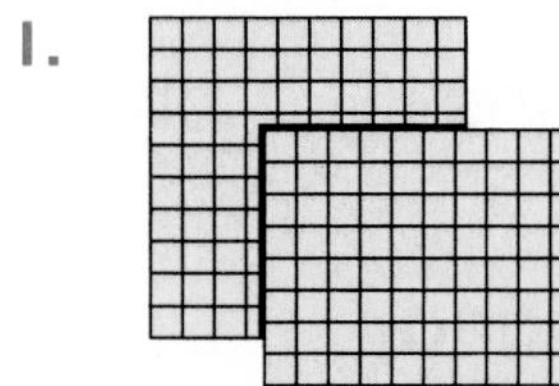

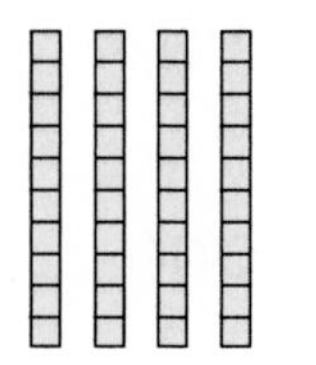

2 hundreds 4 tens 5 ones 245

Use heavy paper to make 9 (10 in. × 10 in.) squares for hundreds, 10 (10 in. × 1 in.) strips for tens, and 10 (1 in. × 1 in.) squares for ones. Make numbers by selecting various combinations of these cutouts. Say and write each number you make. (Save the cutouts to use again after Chapter 13.)

2.

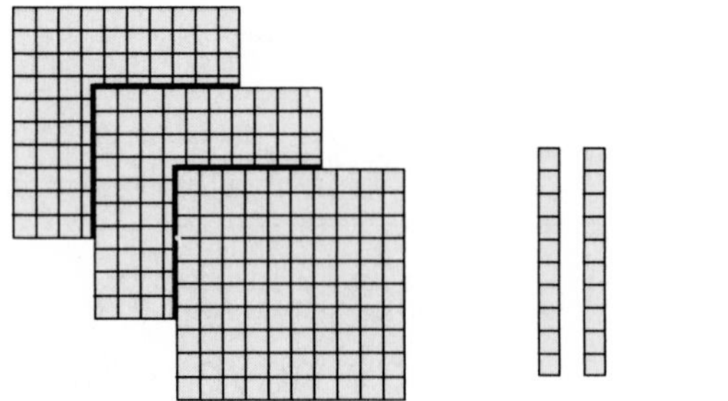

Have a family member write down a number through 999. Show the number with the squares and strips.

3.

Find books with pages through 999. Look at any page and read the number aloud. Tell how many hundreds, tens, and ones. Tell what number comes next.

Coming Attractions

In the next chapter I will learn to count and write amounts of money through $4.99.

Exploring Mathematics Book Two © Scott, Foresman and Company

Chapter 11

Fractions and Probability

Listen to the math story, "Equal Partners."
The brothers divided their land into 3 equal parts.
Why did this make Mario happy?

Notes for Home Children listen to a math story introducing chapter concepts and skills. Then they answer a question about the story.

Equal Parts

Is the pizza divided into 4 equal parts?
Is the bread divided into 4 equal parts?
How can you tell if the parts are **equal** or **not equal**?

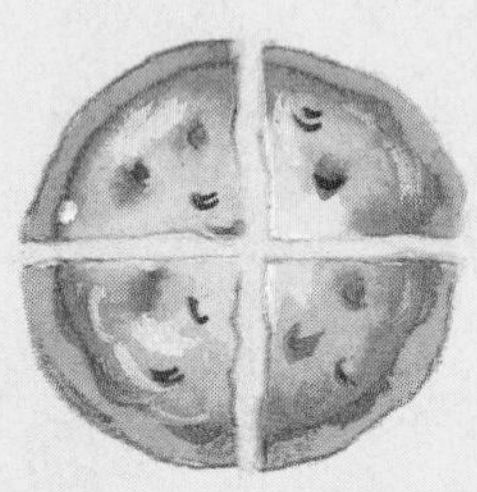

Write the number of parts.
Then ring equal or not equal.

1.

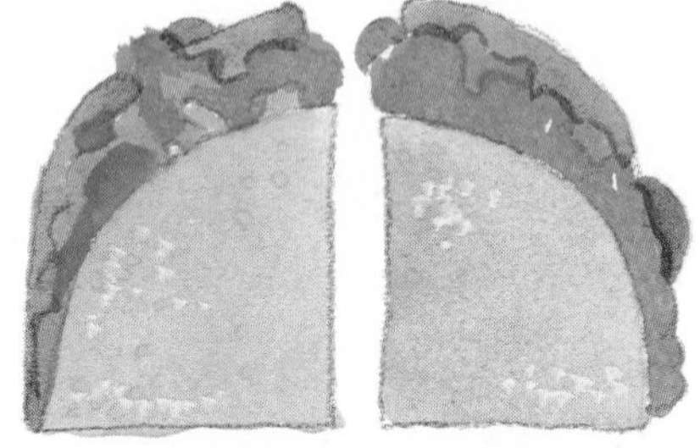

2 parts

equal

not equal

2.

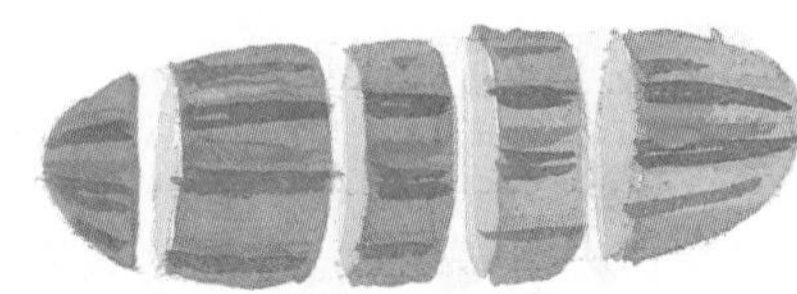

____ parts

equal

not equal

3.

____ parts

equal

not equal

4.

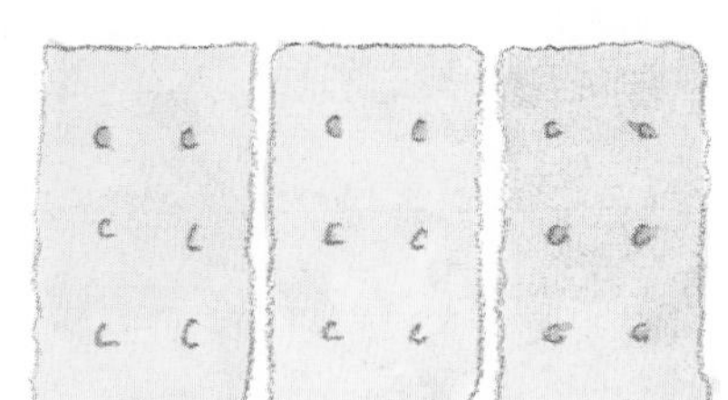

____ parts

equal

not equal

5.

____ parts

equal

not equal

6.

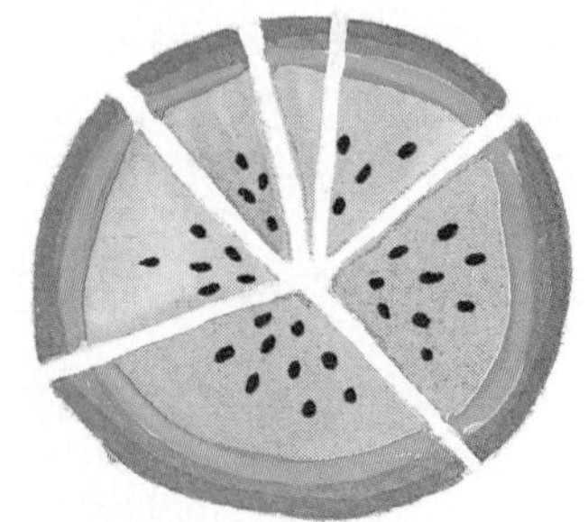

____ parts

equal

not equal

Exploring Mathematics Book Two © Scott, Foresman and Company

Notes for Home Children count the number of parts in a shape. Then they identify whether or not the parts are equal.

Name

Halves, Thirds, and Fourths

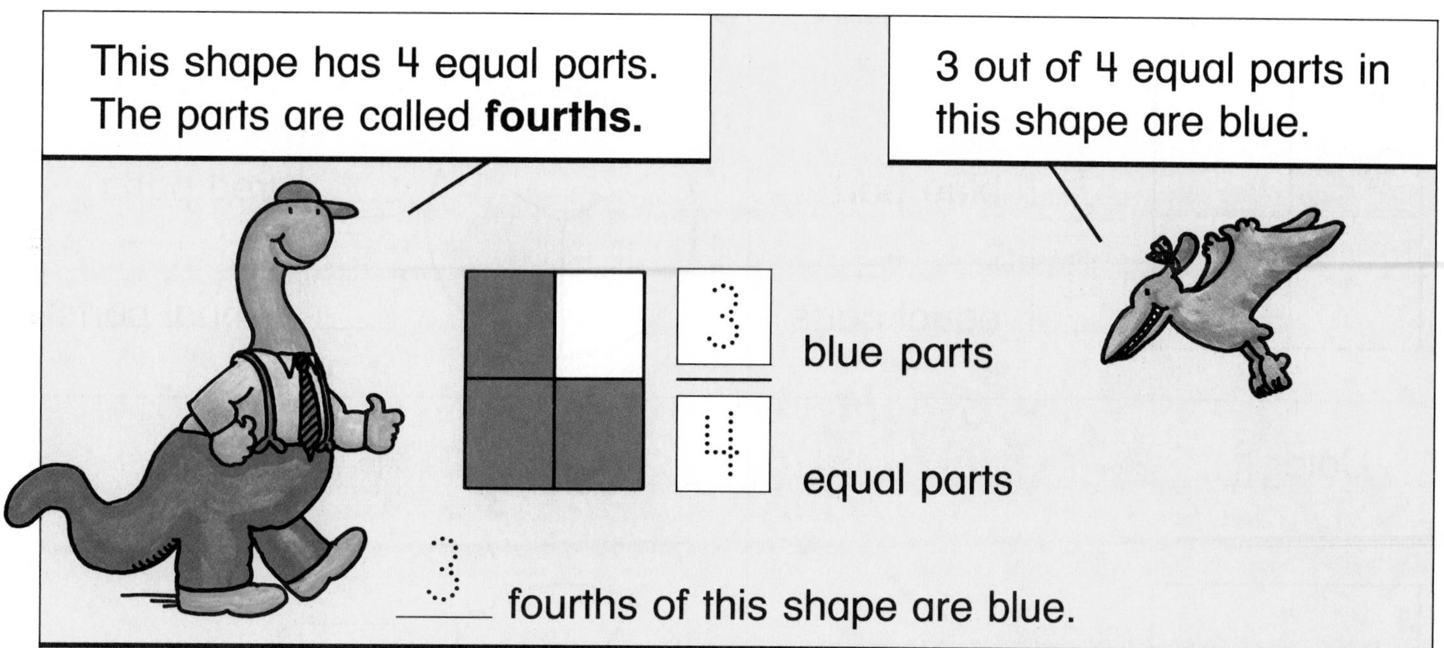

Complete.

1.

red part

equal parts

_____ half of this shape is red.

2.

yellow part

equal parts

_____ third of this shape is yellow.

3.

green parts

equal parts

_____ fourths of this shape are green.

4.

blue parts

equal parts

_____ thirds of this shape are blue.

Notes for Home Children identify halves, thirds, and fourths of shapes by determining the number of equal parts and the number of colored parts.

Complete.

5. Color $\frac{1}{4}$ .

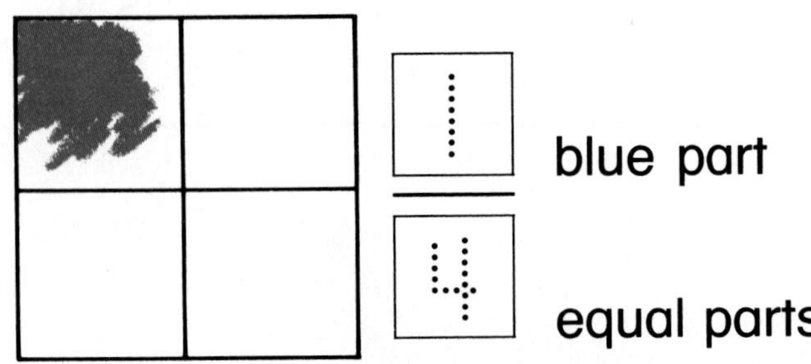

blue part

equal parts

6. Color $\frac{3}{3}$ 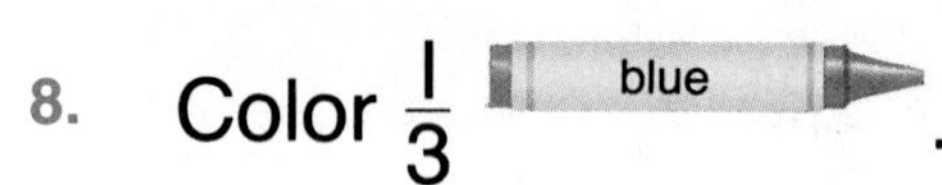.

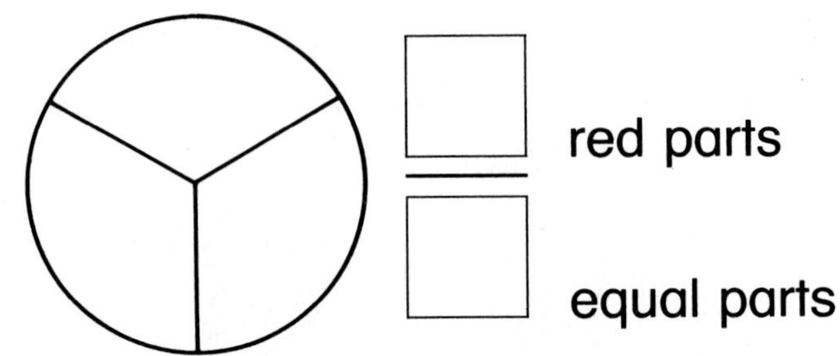

red parts

equal parts

7. Color $\frac{3}{4}$ .

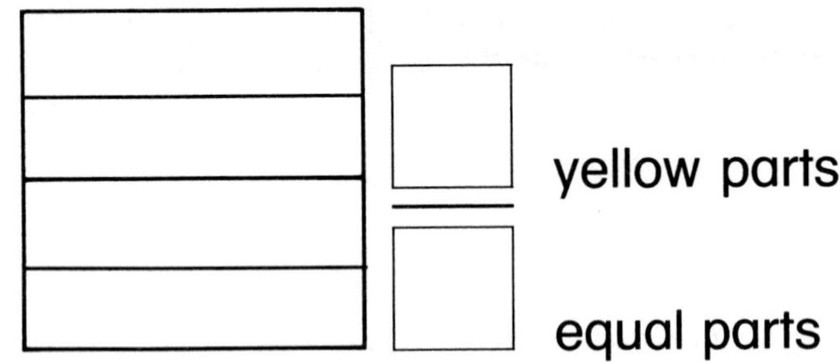

yellow parts

equal parts

8. Color $\frac{1}{3}$ 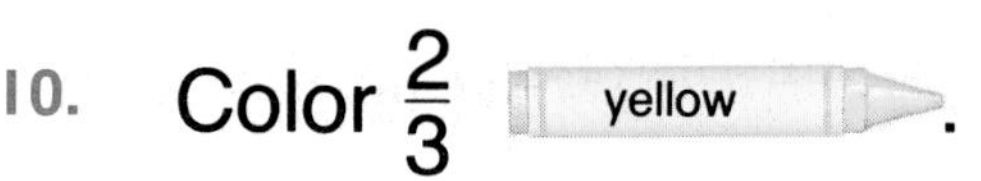.

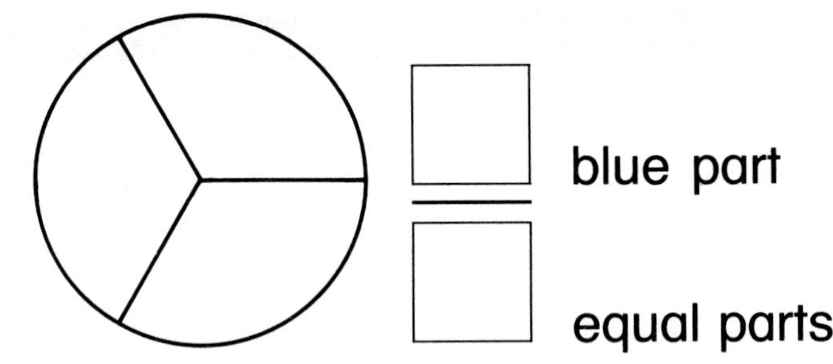

blue part

equal parts

9. Color $\frac{2}{2}$ red.

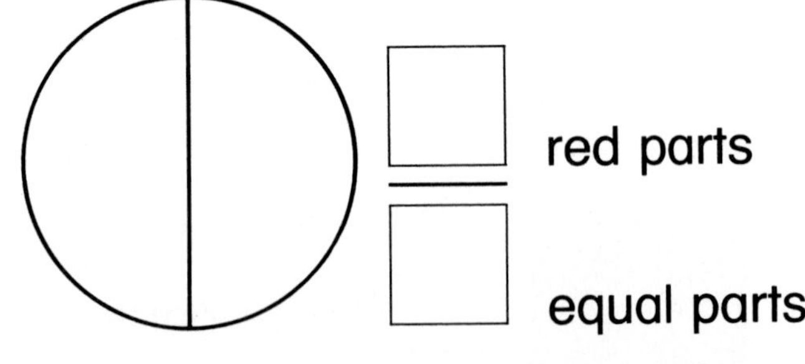

red parts

equal parts

10. Color $\frac{2}{3}$ yellow.

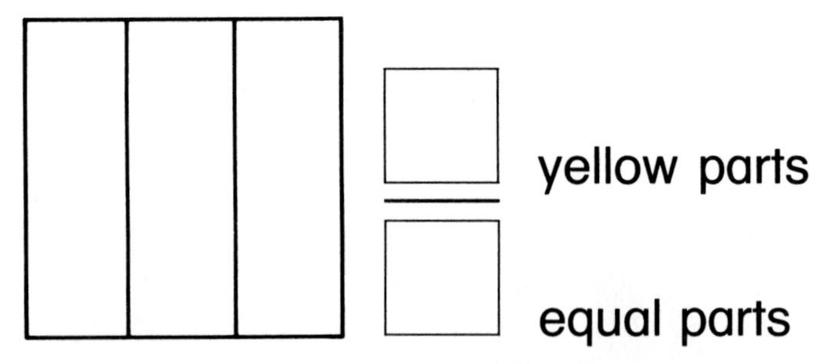

yellow parts

equal parts

Critical Thinking Tell why the clock shows half past 4.

Exploring Mathematics Book Two © Scott, Foresman and Company

Notes for Home Children identify and color halves, thirds, and fourths. Then they discuss dividing a clock face into halves.

Name

Fifths and Sixths

This shape has 5 equal parts.
The parts are called **fifths.**

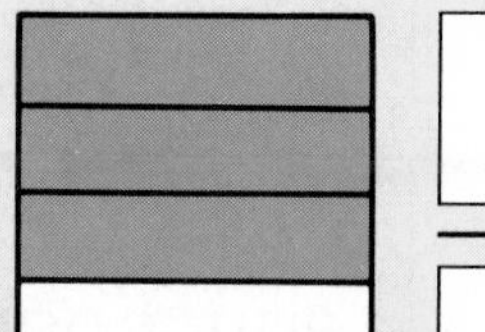

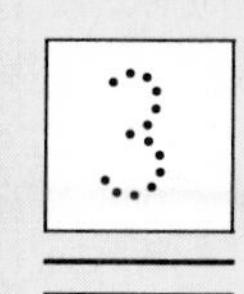 green parts

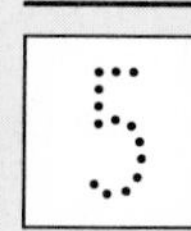 equal parts

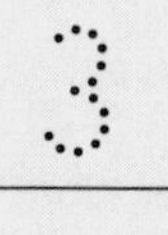 fifths of this shape are green.

This shape has 6 equal parts.
The parts are called **sixths.**

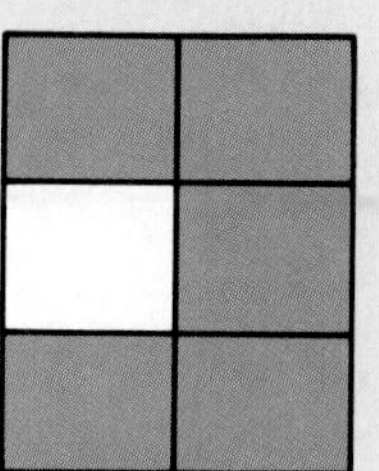

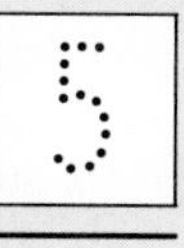 blue parts

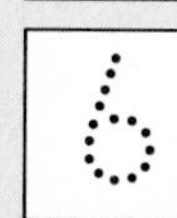 equal parts

5 ____ sixths of this shape are blue.

Complete.

1\. 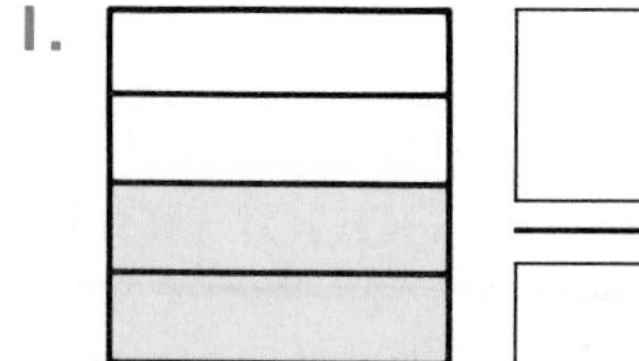

☐ yellow parts

☐ equal parts

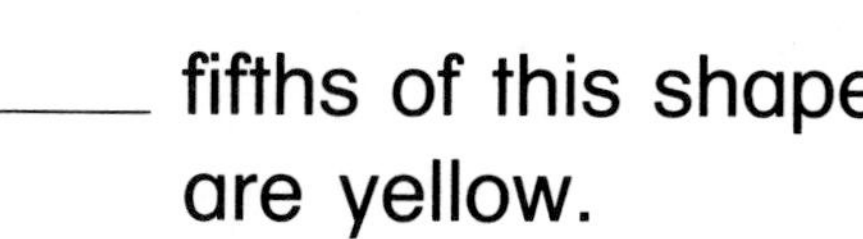

____ fifths of this shape are yellow.

2\. 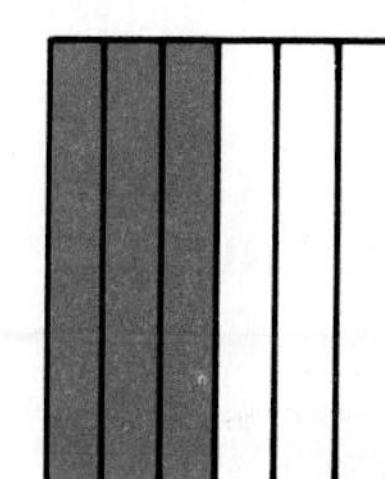

☐ red parts

☐ equal parts

____ sixths of this shape are red.

3\. 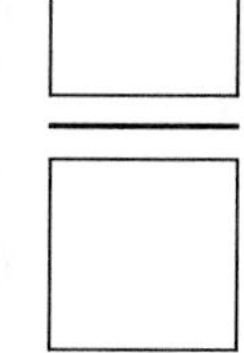

☐ blue parts

☐ equal parts

____ sixths of this shape are blue.

4\. 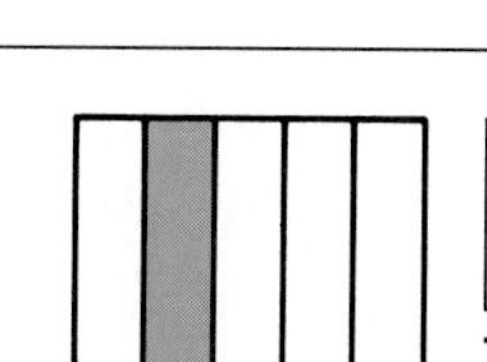

☐ green part

☐ equal parts

____ fifth of this shape is green.

Notes for Home Children identify fifths and sixths of shapes by determining the number of equal parts and the number of colored parts.

Complete.

5. Color $\frac{3}{6}$ red.

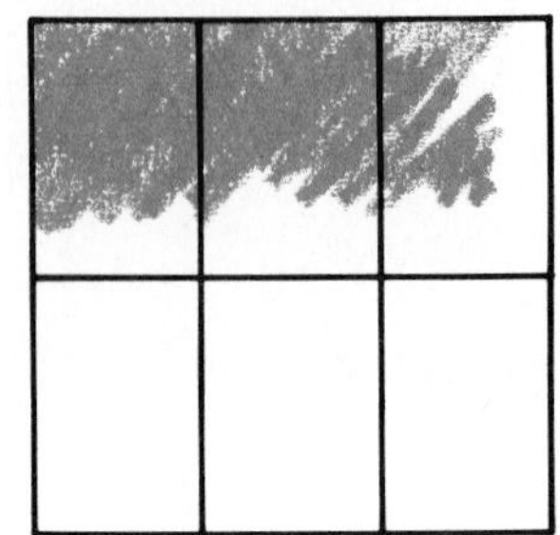

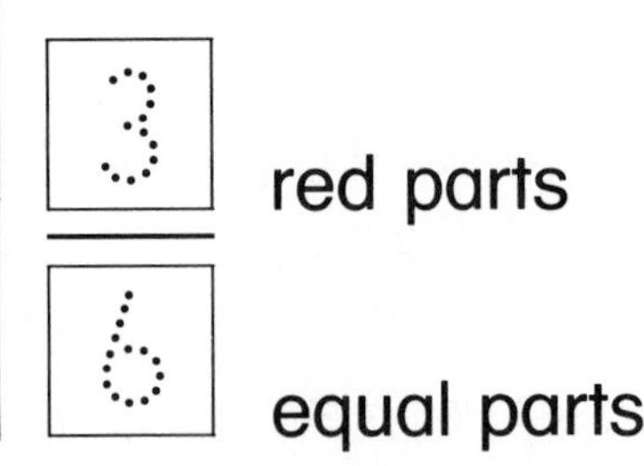

red parts

equal parts

6. Color $\frac{4}{5}$ blue.

blue parts

equal parts

7. Color $\frac{2}{3}$ yellow.

yellow parts

equal parts

8. Color $\frac{1}{6}$ blue.

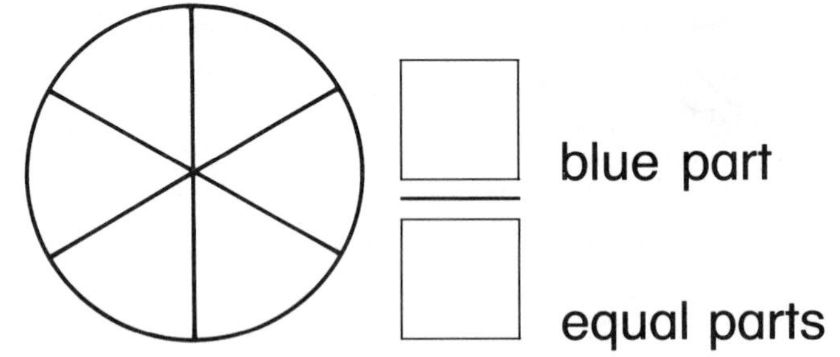

blue part

equal parts

Estimation

9. Color $\frac{1}{4}$ green.

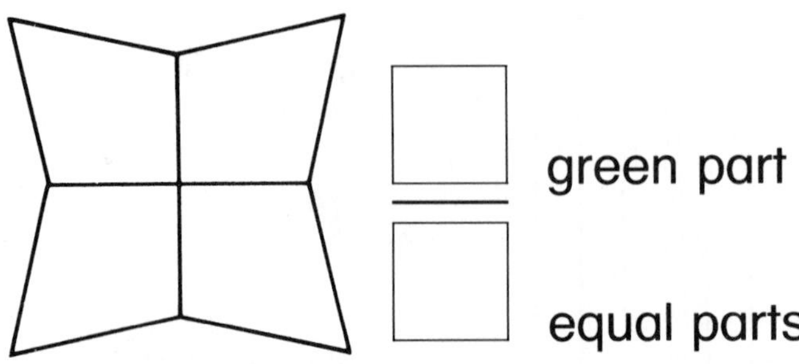

green part

equal parts

10. Color $\frac{3}{4}$ red.

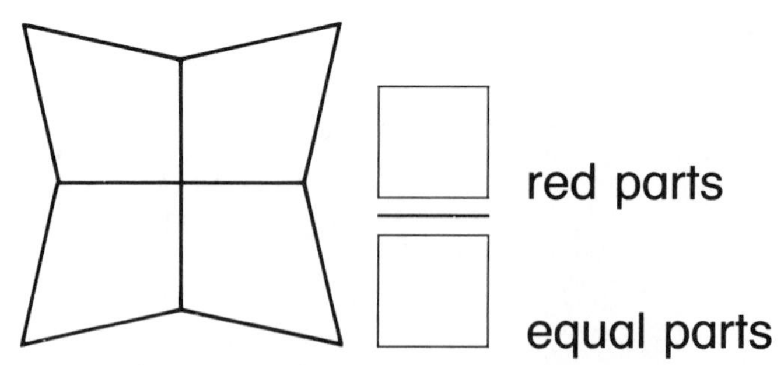

red parts

equal parts

11. Which fraction is almost a whole, $\frac{1}{4}$ or $\frac{3}{4}$?

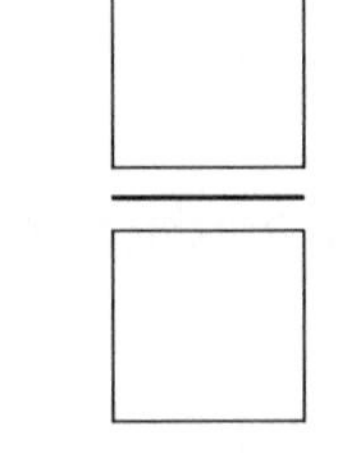

Exploring Mathematics Book Two © Scott, Foresman and Company

Notes for Home Children identify and color fractional parts through sixths. Then they discuss the relative size of fractions.

Name

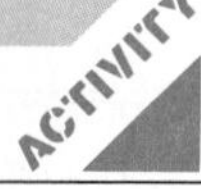

Identifying Fractions of a Set

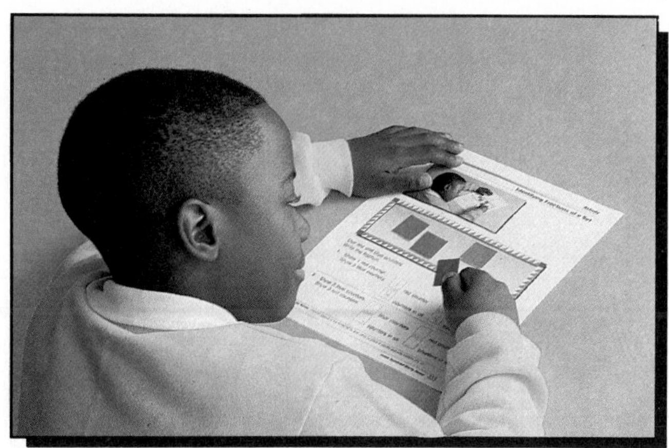

Use red and blue counters.
Write the fraction.

1. Show 1 red counter.
Show 3 blue counters.

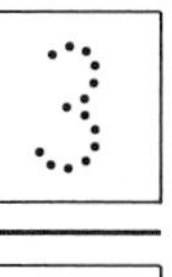 red counter / 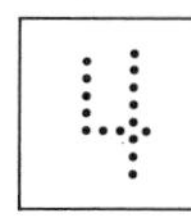 counters in all

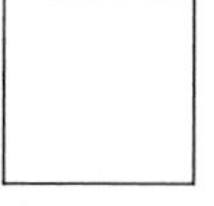 blue counters / counters in all

2. Show 2 blue counters.
Show 3 red counters.

blue counters / counters in all

red counters / counters in all

Notes for Home Children explore at the CONCRETE level using counters to identify and write fractions of a set.

Use red and blue counters.
Write the fraction.

3. Show 4 red counters.
Show 1 blue counter.

$\frac{4}{5}$ red counters / counters in all

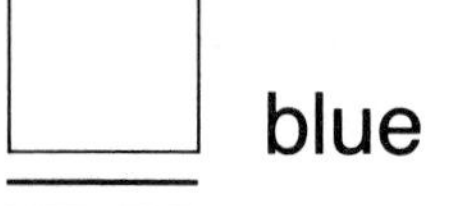

[ ] blue counter / [ ] counters in all

4. Show 4 red counters.
Show 2 blue counters.

[ ] red counters / [ ] counters in all

[ ] blue counters / [ ] counters in all

5. Show 1 red counter.
Show 2 blue counters.

[ ] red counter / [ ] counters in all

[ ] blue counters / [ ] counters in all

6. Show 3 red counters.
Show 3 blue counters.

[ ] red counters / [ ] counters in all

[ ] blue counters / [ ] counters in all

Notes for Home Children explore at the CONCRETE level using counters to identify and write fractions of a set.

Exploring Mathematics Book Two © Scott, Foresman and Company

Name

Fractions of a Set

Write the fraction for each group.

1. 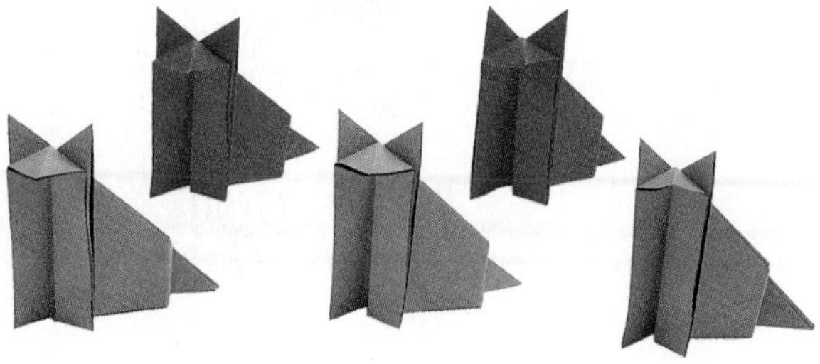 2 red foxes
5 foxes in all
$\frac{2}{5}$ are red.

2. 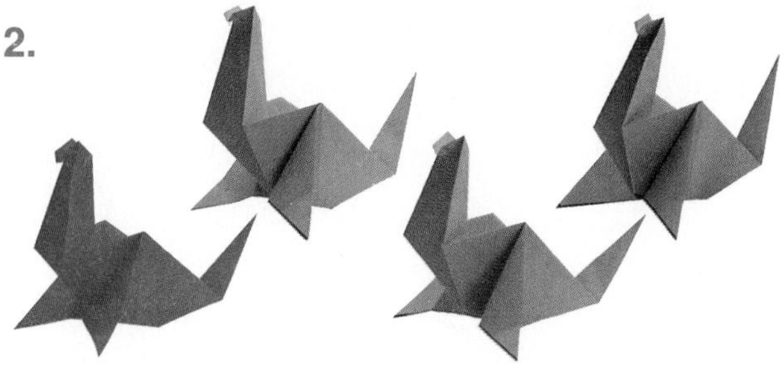 ____ orange seal
____ seals in all
$\frac{\square}{\square}$ is orange.

3. 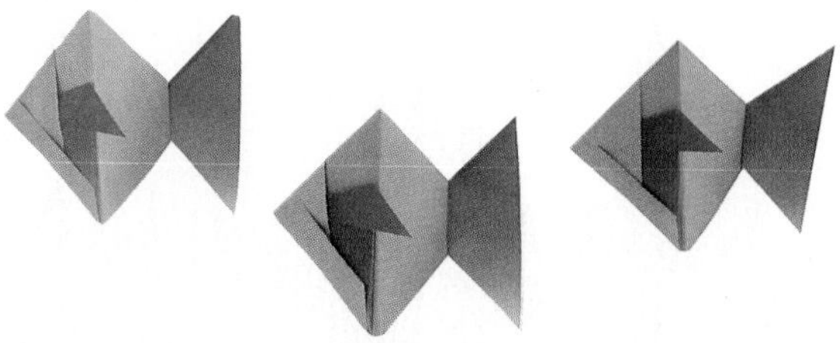 ____ green fish
____ fish in all
$\frac{\square}{\square}$ are green.

Notes for Home Children use pictures to identify fractions of a set.

Write the fraction.

4. What fraction is green?

3 green turtles
—
4 turtles in all

What fraction is brown?

☐ brown turtle
—
☐ turtles in all

5. What fraction is yellow?

☐ yellow flowers
—
☐ flowers in all

What fraction is purple?

☐ purple flower
—
☐ flowers in all

6. What fraction is blue?

☐ blue birds
—
☐ birds in all

What fraction is red?

☐ red birds
—
☐ birds in all

Problem Solving

Solve.

7. Draw 5 flowers. Color $\frac{2}{5}$ blue.
Color the rest yellow.
What fraction is yellow?

☐
—
☐ of the flowers are yellow.

Exploring Mathematics Book Two © Scott, Foresman and Company

Notes for Home Children use pictures to practice writing fractions of a set. Then they solve a problem involving fractions of a set by drawing a picture.

See More Practice Set A on page 351.

Name

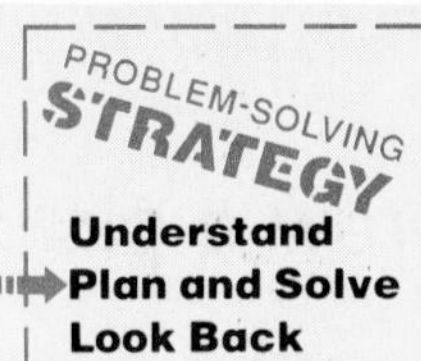

Draw a Picture

Draw a picture. Then solve.

1. There are 1 tall rocket and 2 short rockets. What fraction of the group is tall?

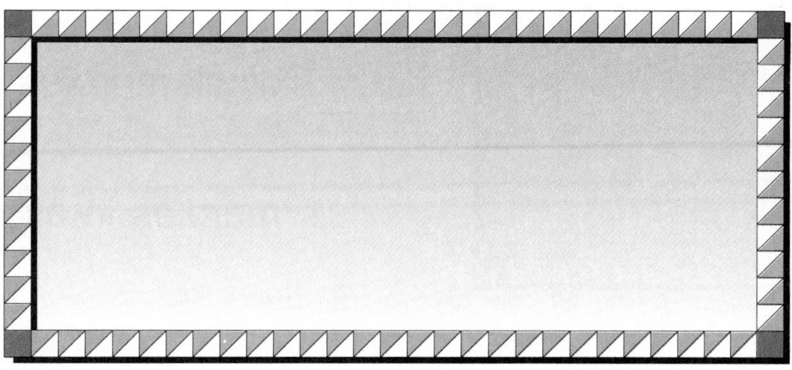

1 tall rockets
3 rockets in all

2. There are 3 goldfish and 2 angelfish. What fraction of the group is angelfish?

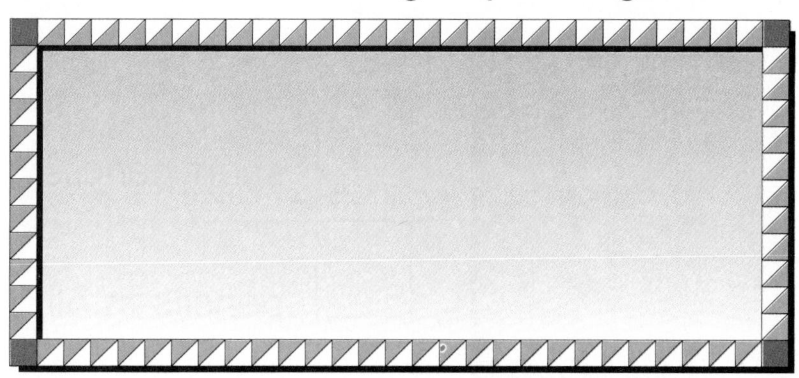

☐ angelfish
☐ fish in all

Notes for Home Children solve problems by drawing pictures to identify fractions of a set.

Draw a picture. Then solve.

3. There are 1 doll with brown hair and 3 dolls with yellow hair. What fraction of the group has brown hair?

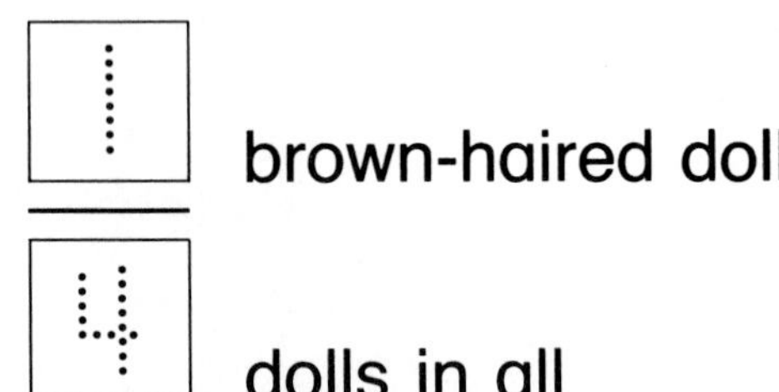

4. There are 4 marbles. All 4 are black. What fraction of the group is black?

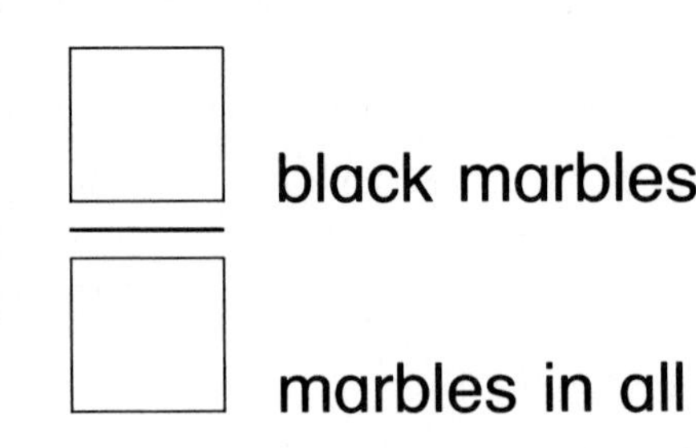

5. There are 2 short pencils and 1 long pencil. What fraction of the group is short?

short pencils

pencils in all

Exploring Mathematics Book Two © Scott, Foresman and Company

Notes for Home Children solve problems by drawing pictures to identify fractions of a set.

Name ____________________

Number Sense

Color $\frac{1}{3}$ of the stars red.

Color $\frac{1}{3}$ of the stars blue.

Color $\frac{1}{3}$ of the stars green.

Color the stars so that each color appears only once in each row and only once in each column.

Let's do some more!

On another sheet of paper draw 4 rows of stars and 4 columns of stars. Color them 4 different colors. Color them so that each color appears only once in each row and each column.

Notes for Home Children develop number understanding by solving a problem involving logical reasoning.

SKILLS REVIEW

Skills Review

Fill in the correct ◯.
How much?

1.     

Ⓐ $3.22
Ⓑ $3.32
Ⓒ $3.42

2.  

Ⓐ $4.71
Ⓑ $4.76
Ⓒ $4.86

3.     

Ⓐ $2.16
Ⓑ $2.31
Ⓒ $2.41

Vocabulary

Choose the correct letter.

a e i o u

4. m __o__ ney
5. nick ____ l
6. d ____ me
7. p ____ nny
8. doll ____ r
9. co ____ nt

Exploring Mathematics Book Two © Scott, Foresman and Company

Notes for Home Children review counting amounts of money through $4.99. Then they complete the spelling of math money terms.

Name

Probability

Fran is serving frozen yogurt at a summer picnic. It is hot outside. Will the yogurt melt?

sure to happen

may happen

impossible

What do you think could happen at a summer picnic? Ring your guess.

1. Will there be bugs at the picnic?

   sure to happen

   may happen

   impossible

2. Will the children build a snowman?

   sure to happen

   may happen

   impossible

3. Will the children play games?

   sure to happen

   may happen

   impossible

Notes for Home Children identify whether an event is sure to happen, may happen, or is impossible.

What do you think could happen at a summer picnic?
Ring your guess.

4. Will the juice on the table get warm if no one drinks it?

   sure to happen

   may happen

   impossible

5. Will Fran's watch show 25 o'clock when the picnic is over?

   sure to happen

   may happen

   impossible

6. Will everyone have a good time?

   sure to happen

   may happen

   impossible

Talk About Math

Will everyone ring the same answers to the questions on this page?

Exploring Mathematics Book Two © Scott, Foresman and Company

Notes for Home Children identify whether an event is sure to happen, may happen, or is impossible. Then they talk about the meaning of probability.

See More Practice Set B on page 351.

Name

ACTIVITY

Investigating Probability

The bag has 4 blue counters and 1 red counter. If you pick a counter without looking, what color do you think you will pick?

I'm not sure. Let's experiment and find out.

Use a bag.
Use 4 blue counters and 1 red counter.

1. Put the counters in the bag.
Pick a counter without looking.
Record your pick on the chart.
Put the counter back in the bag after each pick.
Do this 8 times in all.

	Number of Picks							
	1	2	3	4	5	6	7	8
Red counter								
Blue counter								

2. Read the chart.

How many times did you pick a red counter? _____

How many times did you pick a blue counter? _____

Which color did you pick more often? ___________

Notes for Home Children explore at the CONCRETE level using counters to record outcomes of events that are not equally likely.

Use a bag.
Use 4 red counters and 2 blue counters.

3. Put the counters in the bag.
Pick a counter without looking.
Record your pick on the chart.
Put the counter back in the bag after each pick.
Do this 8 times in all.

	Number of Picks							
	1	2	3	4	5	6	7	8
Red counter								
Blue counter								

4. Read the chart.

How many times did you pick a red counter? _____

How many times did you pick a blue counter? _____

Which color did you pick more often? ____________

Problem Solving

Solve. Then ring the correct answer.

5. Carly is putting 8 green marbles and 2 orange marbles in a bag. If she picks 1 marble without looking, what color is she more likely to pick?

green orange

Exploring Mathematics Book Two © Scott, Foresman and Company

Notes for Home Children explore at the CONCRETE level using counters to predict and record outcomes of events that are not equally likely. Then they solve a problem about probability.

Name

Investigating Probability

Use a red and blue card.

1. Flip the card.
   Record on the chart if the card lands red side up or if it lands blue side up.
   Do this 10 times in all.

	Number of Picks									
	1	2	3	4	5	6	7	8	9	10
Blue side										
Red side										

2. Read the chart.

   How many times did the card land blue side up? ____

   How many times did the card land red side up? ____

Notes for Home Children explore at the CONCRETE level using a red and blue card to record outcomes of events that are equally likely.

Use a penny.

3. Drop the penny on your paper.
Record on the chart if it lands heads up or tails up.
Do this 10 times in all.

	Number of Picks									
	1	2	3	4	5	6	7	8	9	10
Heads										
Tails										

4. Read the chart.

How many times did the penny land heads up? ____

How many times did the penny land tails up? ____

5. If you drop the penny one more time, on which side is it more likely to land?

Ring your guess.

Heads is more likely.

Tails is more likely.

They are equally likely.

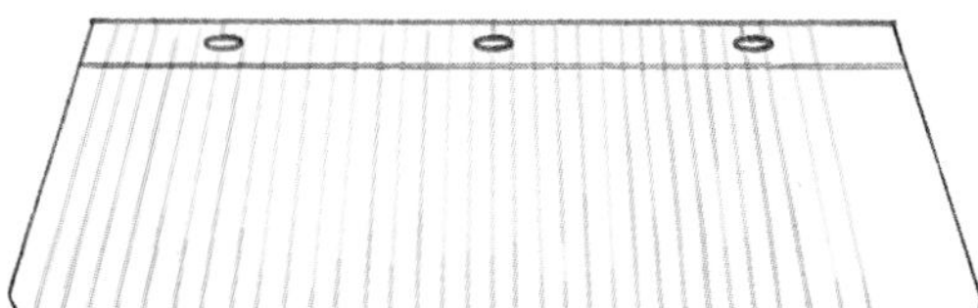

Talk About Math

If you drop a quarter, which side will be face up when it lands?

Heads is more likely.

Tails is more likely.

They are equally likely.

Exploring Mathematics Book Two © Scott, Foresman and Company

Notes for Home Children explore at the CONCRETE level using a penny to predict and record outcomes of events that are equally likely. Then they talk about predicting outcomes.

Name

PROBLEM-SOLVING GUIDE
Understand
Plan and Solve
Look Back

Collecting Data

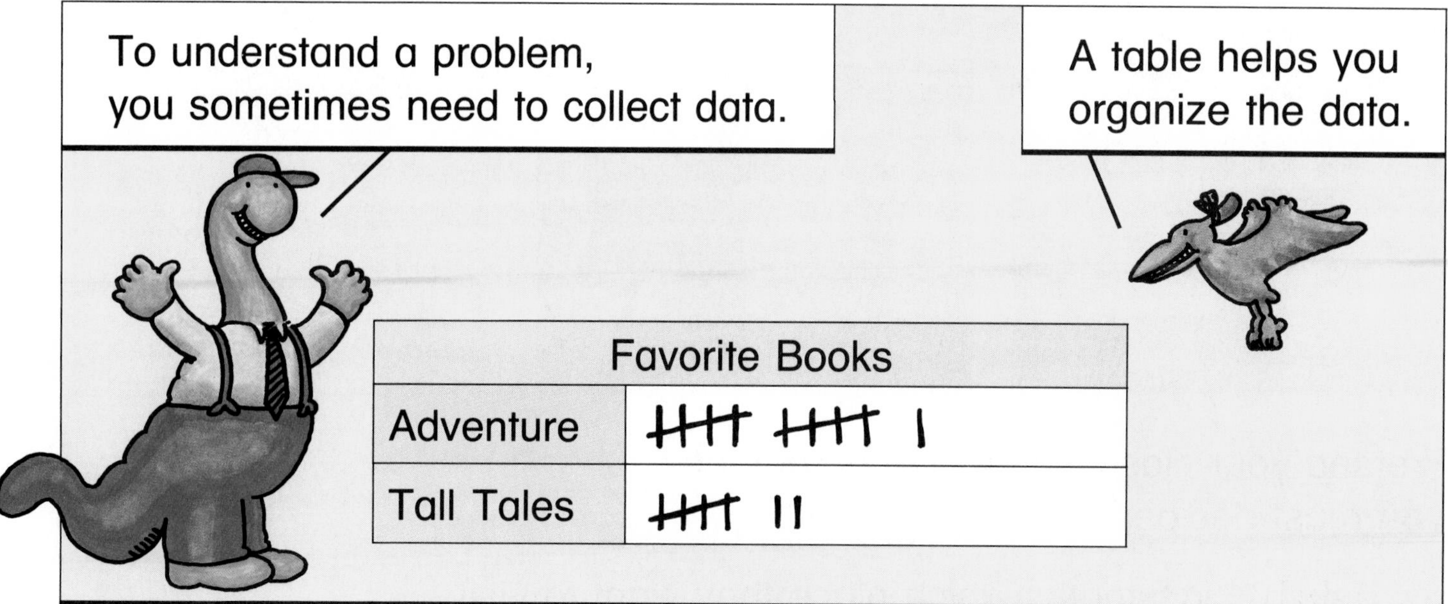

Pretend you must choose a story to read to your class. Collect data from your classmates to help you decide which kind of story to read.

1. Ask 10 classmates which kind of story they like best. Make tallies on the table to organize the data.

Favorite Kind of Story	
Animal	
Sports	
Make-believe	

2. What kind of story did your classmates like best?

____

3. What kind of story would you read to your class? Why?

____

Notes for Home Children solve problems by collecting data and organizing it on a table. Then they answer questions about the data.

Pretend your class is planning a field trip.
You must decide where you want to go.

4. Ask 10 classmates which place they want to visit.
Make tallies on the table to organize the data.

Field Trip Choices	
Art Museum	
Aquarium	
Zoo	

5. Which place do most of your classmates want to visit?

____

6. Which place do you think the second grade class should visit? Why?

____

____

____

Notes for Home Children solve problems by collecting data and organizing it on a table. Then they answer questions about the data.

Exploring Mathematics Book Two © Scott, Foresman and Company

Name

Problem-Solving Workshop

Explore as a Team

Work with a partner to help Pedro find his pets.

There are 5 boxes.
Boxes A, B, and E are empty.
C has a gerbil inside.
D has a hamster inside.

Pedro may choose 2 boxes.
He does not know which boxes have pets inside.
Write the ways Pedro can choose.

Pedro's Choices

A									
B									

Use the chart to complete.

1. Pedro can choose ______ ways altogether.
2. Pedro gets both pets ______ way.
3. Pedro can choose ______ ways to get only the gerbil.
4. Pedro can choose ______ ways to get only the hamster.
5. Pedro can choose ______ ways to get a pet.
6. Does Pedro have a very good chance to choose both pets? ______

Notes for Home Children explore with a partner to find how many ways pets can be chosen.

Problem Solving WORKSHOP

Problem-Solving Workshop

Explore with a Computer

Primary Graphing and Probability Project

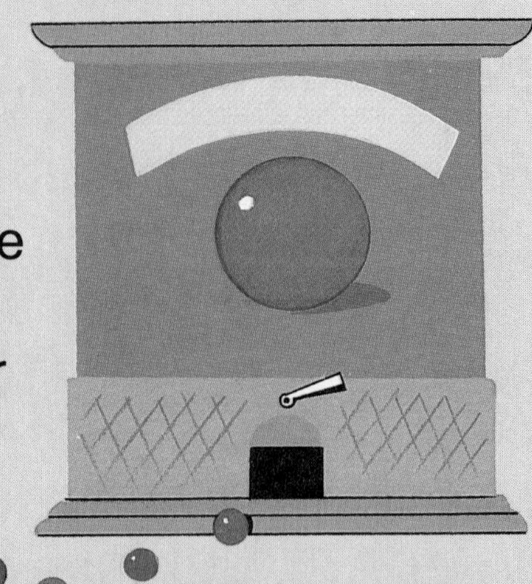

1. Pretend you have a vending machine with 100 blue and red marbles. Think about how many of each color may be in the machine

2. At the computer, choose a bag of colored marbles. Use the chart to record if a red or a blue marble comes out. Do this 10 times in all.

	Number of Picks									
Color	1	2	3	4	5	6	7	8	9	10
Red										
Blue										

3. How many times did a blue marble come out? ______

How many times did a red marble come out? ______

4. Tell how many of each marble you think is in the vending machine. Have the computer show you the marbles in the machine.

Red: ______ tens ______ ones Blue: ______ tens ______ ones

Exploring Mathematics Book Two © Scott, Foresman and Company

Notes for Home Children use computer to determine the outcome of a random selection of red and blue marbles. They then record their findings in a chart and estimate the probable distribution of red and blue marbles.

Name

More Practice

Set A Use after page 336.

What fraction of each group is green?

1. 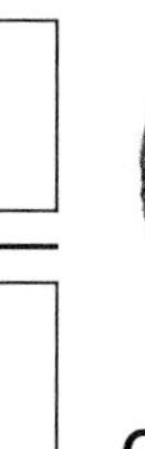 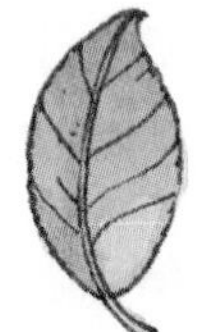 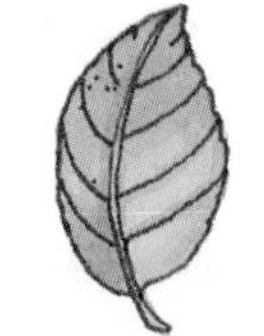 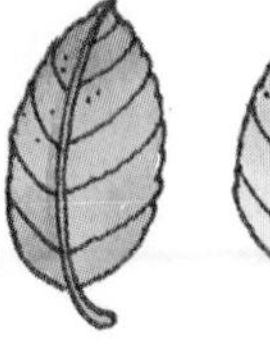 

of the leaves are green.

2. 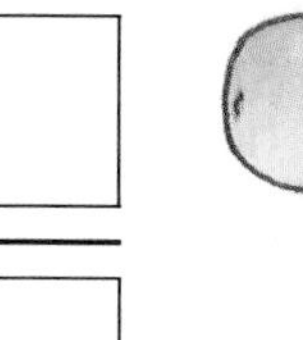 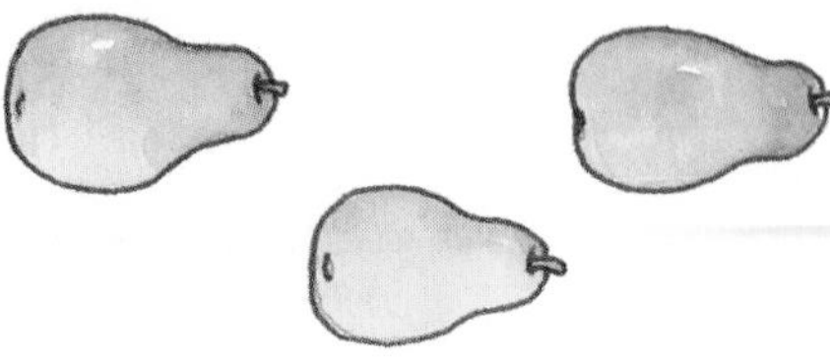

of the pears are green.

3.  

of the apples are green.

4.   

of the plants are green.

Set B Use after page 342.

Ring your guess.

1. If you drop a glass bowl, will it break?

   sure to happen

   may happen

   impossible

2. Will the tadpole change into a butterfly?

   sure to happen

   may happen

   impossible

Notes for Home Set A: Children practice using pictures to identify fractions of a group.
Set B: Children identify whether an event is sure to happen, may happen, or is impossible.

Independent Study ENRICHMENT

Enrichment

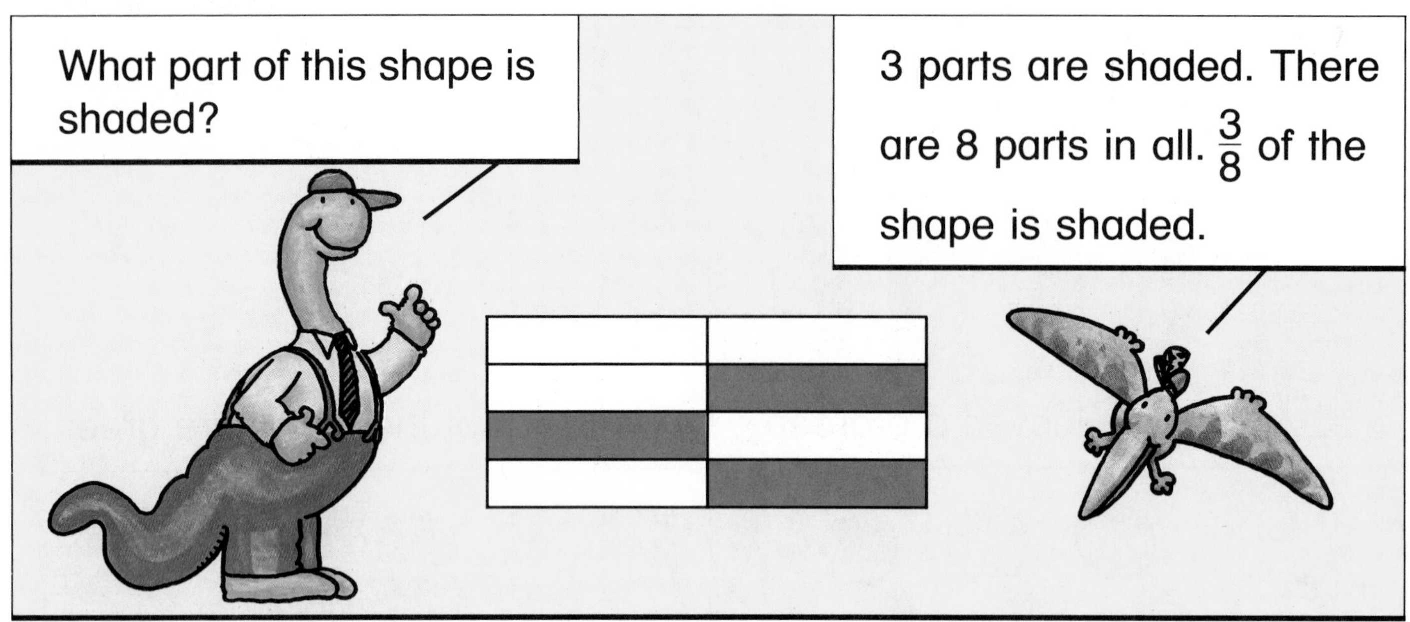

What part of each shape is shaded?

1. 

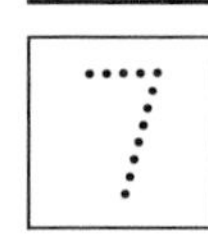

4 parts shaded

7 parts in the shape

2. 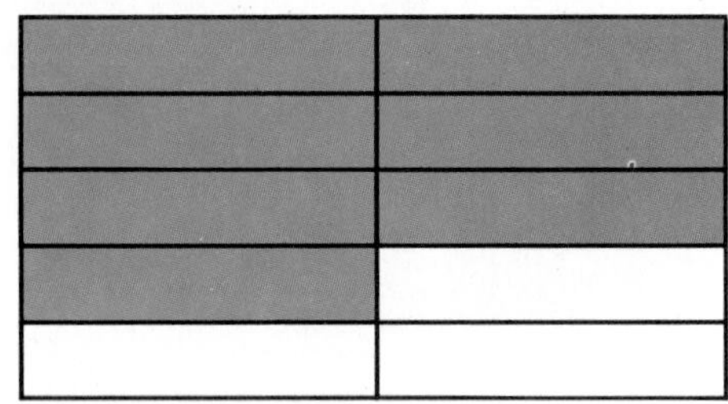

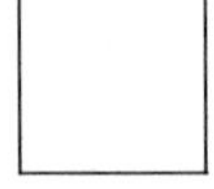

parts shaded

parts in the shape

3. 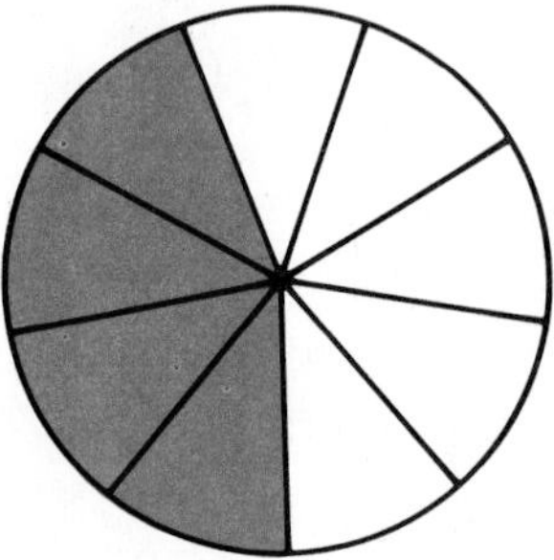

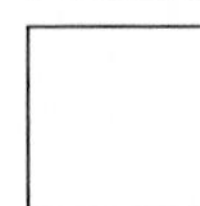

parts shaded

parts in the shape

Exploring Mathematics Book Two © Scott, Foresman and Company

Notes for Home Children are challenged to find fractional parts of sevenths, eighths, ninths, and tenths.

Name

1. What part of the shape is shaded?

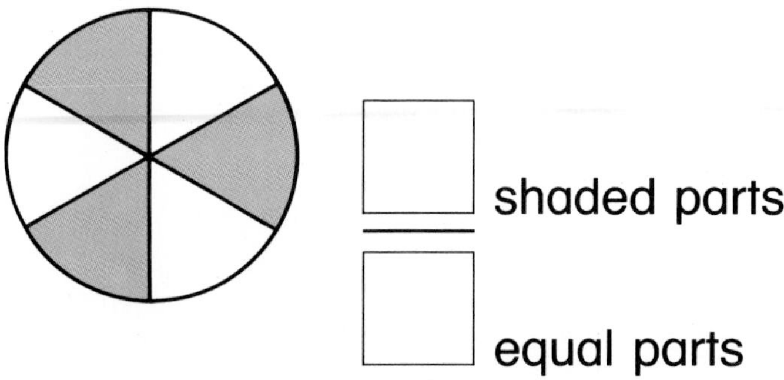

☐ shaded parts
☐ equal parts

2. What part of the group is red?

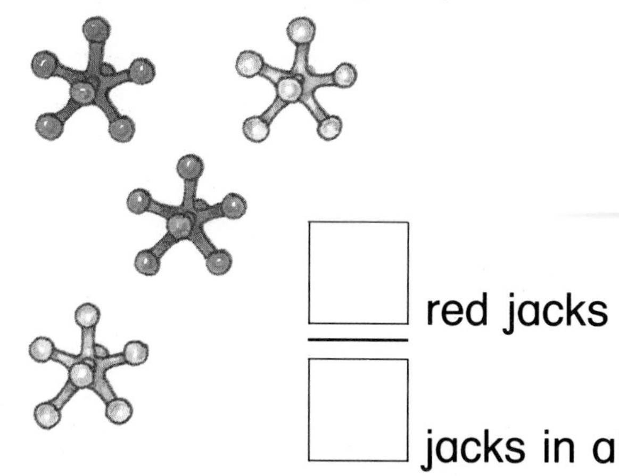

☐ red jacks
☐ jacks in all

3. Will you see stars tonight? Ring.

sure to happen

may happen

impossible

4. There is 1 red pencil and 1 blue pencil in a bag. If you take 1 pencil out without looking, what color is it more likely to be? Ring.

Red is more likely.

Blue is more likely.

They are equally likely.

5. Draw a picture to solve. There are 3 red flowers and 2 blue flowers in a pot. What part of the flowers are blue?

☐ blue flowers
☐ flowers in all

6. Put the data on the table. Mark 1 space for the fruit each person likes.

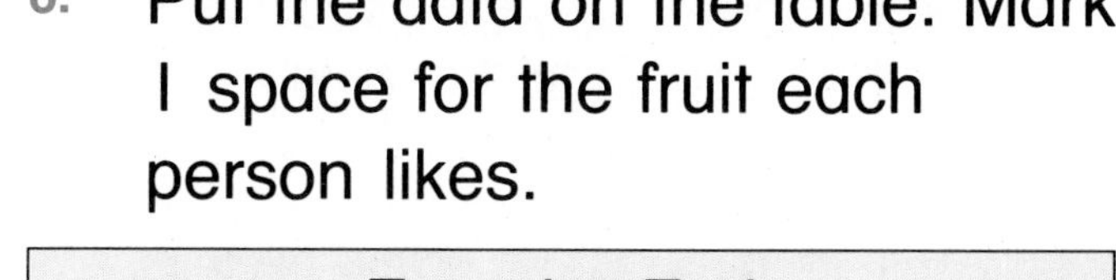

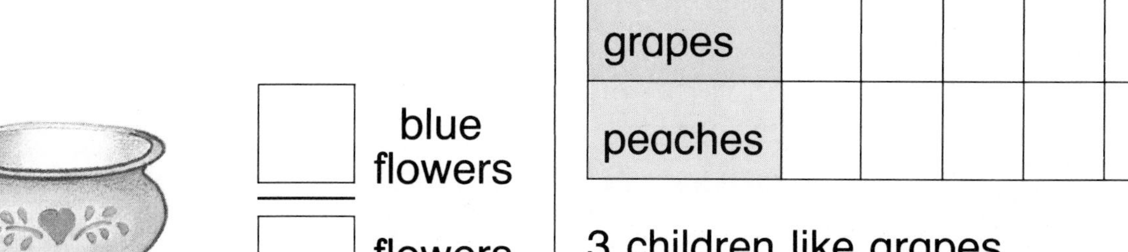

Favorite Fruit						
grapes						
peaches						

3 children like grapes.
4 children like peaches.

Notes for Home Children are assessed on Chapter 11 concepts, skills, and problem solving.

Exploring Math at Home

Dear Family,

In this chapter I have learned about halves, thirds, fourths, fifths, and sixths. I have also worked with probability problems. Please help me with the activities below.

Love, ______________________________

1.

Cut paper plates into equal parts. Tell what each part is called.

2.

Look at 6 buildings in your neighborhood. Think of the fraction that shows how many of the buildings have chimneys. How many have fences?

3.

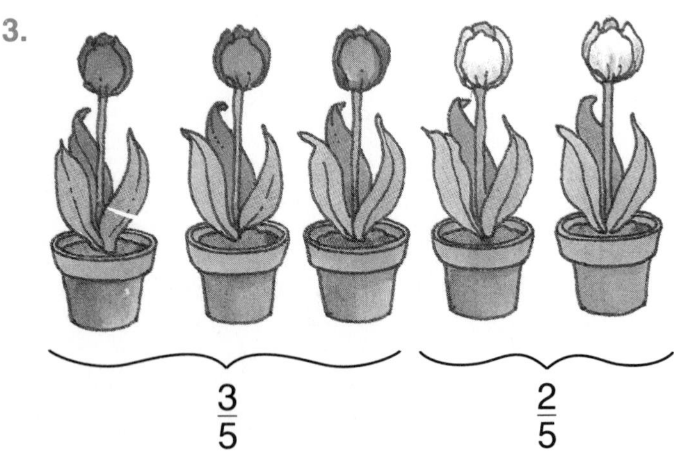

Use up to 6 objects of two different colors to identify fractions of a set.

4.

Guess how many times something will happen. Record on a chart the times it does occur.

Coming Attractions

In the next chapter I will learn more about shapes and how to measure them. I will also learn to measure liquids and read a thermometer.

Exploring Mathematics Book Two © Scott, Foresman and Company

Name

Cumulative Review/Test

Fill in the correct ⬭.
Add.

1. 6 + 7
Ⓐ 13 Ⓑ 14 Ⓒ 15

2. 58 + 26
Ⓐ 74 Ⓑ 84 Ⓒ 72

3. 37 + 23
Ⓐ 50 Ⓑ 60 Ⓒ 54

Subtract.

4. 17 − 8
Ⓐ 8 Ⓑ 9 Ⓒ 11

5. 27 − 5
Ⓐ 18 Ⓑ 12 Ⓒ 22

6. 31 − 8
Ⓐ 23 Ⓑ 37 Ⓒ 27

Subtract.

7. 66 − 35
Ⓐ 31 Ⓑ 29 Ⓒ 21

8. 82 − 45
Ⓐ 43 Ⓑ 47 Ⓒ 37

9. 40 − 18
Ⓐ 38 Ⓑ 28 Ⓒ 22

10. What time is it?

6:45 Ⓐ 7:45 Ⓑ

11. About how long is the comb?

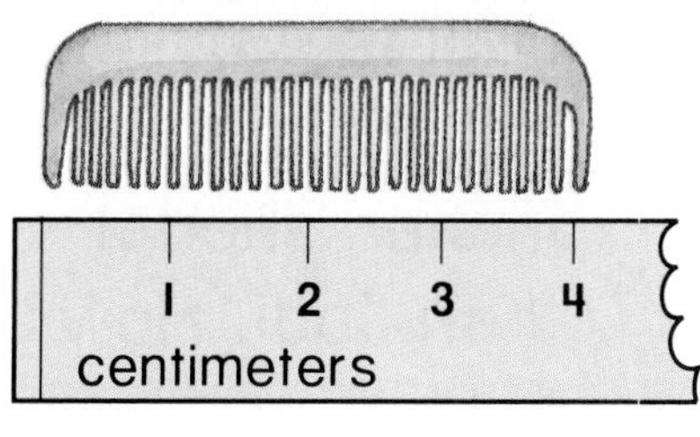

4 cm Ⓐ 3 cm Ⓑ

12. How much?

$1.80 Ⓐ $1.85 Ⓑ

Notes for Home Children are assessed on Chapters 1–11 concepts, skills, and problem solving using a multiple-choice format.

Fill in the correct ◯.

13. How much?

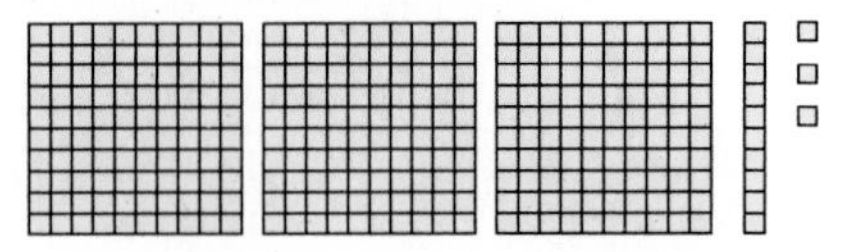

313 (A) 331 (B)

14. How much?

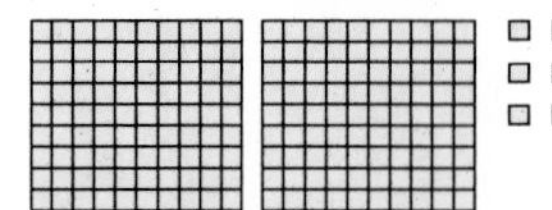

260 (A) 206 (B)

15. How much?

500 and 60 and 2

562 (A) 265 (B)

16. How many?

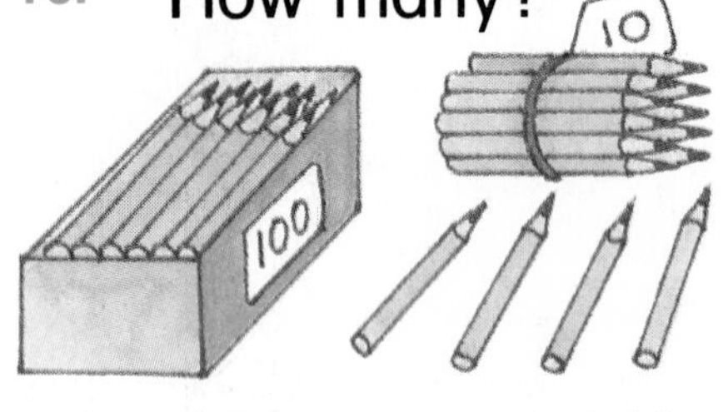

141 (A) 114 (B)

17. How much?
I have 3 dollars, 2 quarters, and 1 nickel.

\$3.55 (A) \$3.30 (B)

18. What part of the circle is shaded?

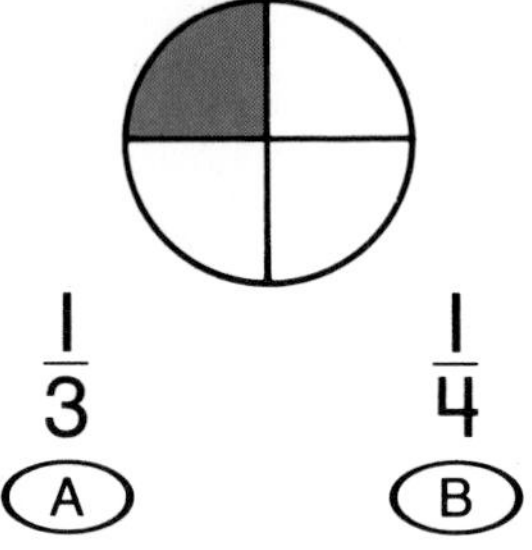

$\frac{1}{3}$ (A) $\frac{1}{4}$ (B)

19. Which number is next?

298, 299, ____

300 (A) 210 (B)

20. Which number is 10 greater than 372?

472 (A) 382 (B)

21. Find the number.

six hundred thirteen

613 (A) 630 (B)

22. Which is the more sensible answer?

How many hours do most people sleep each night?

10 hours (A) 25 hours (B)

23. Solve.

Jodi is 43 inches tall. Fred is 5 inches shorter than Jodi. How tall is Fred?

48 inches (A) 38 inches (B)

24. What part of the group of circles is blue?

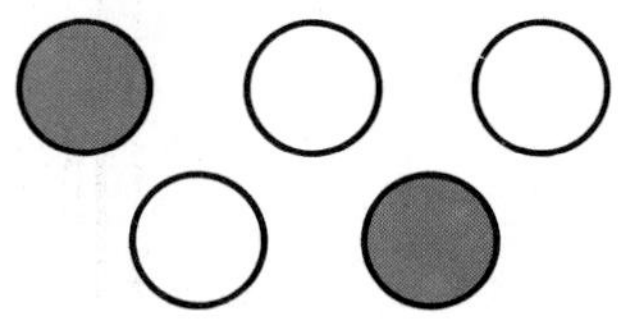

$\frac{2}{3}$ (A) $\frac{2}{5}$ (B)

Exploring Mathematics Book Two © Scott, Foresman and Company

Notes for Home Children are assessed on Chapters 1–11 concepts, skills, and problem solving using a multiple-choice format.

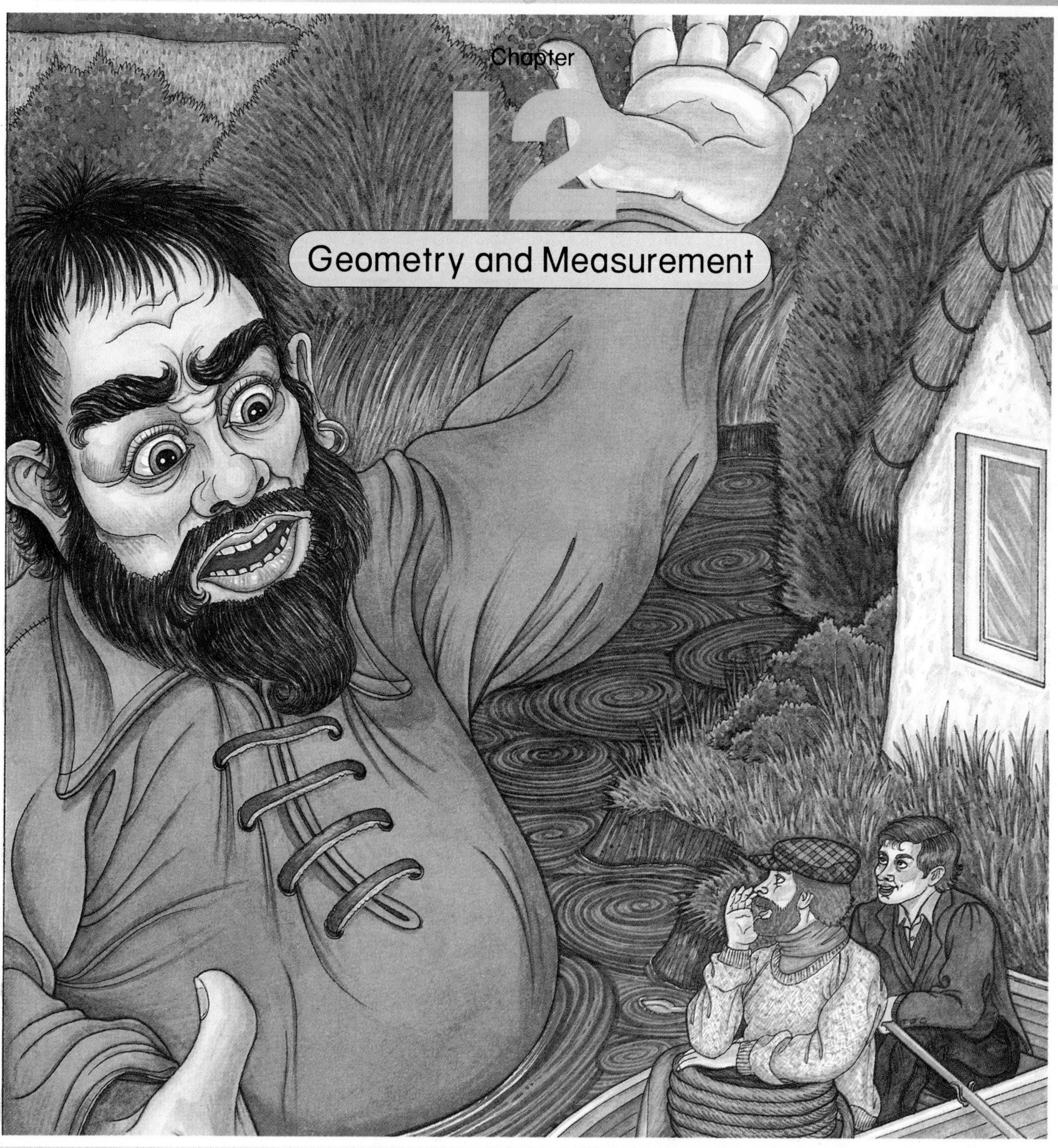

Listen to the math story, "A Giant Problem."
Patrick Finn's window had 4 sides.
Why did he change it to have 6 sides?

Notes for Home Children listen to a math story introducing chapter concepts and skills. Then they answer a question about the story.

Name

Plane Shapes

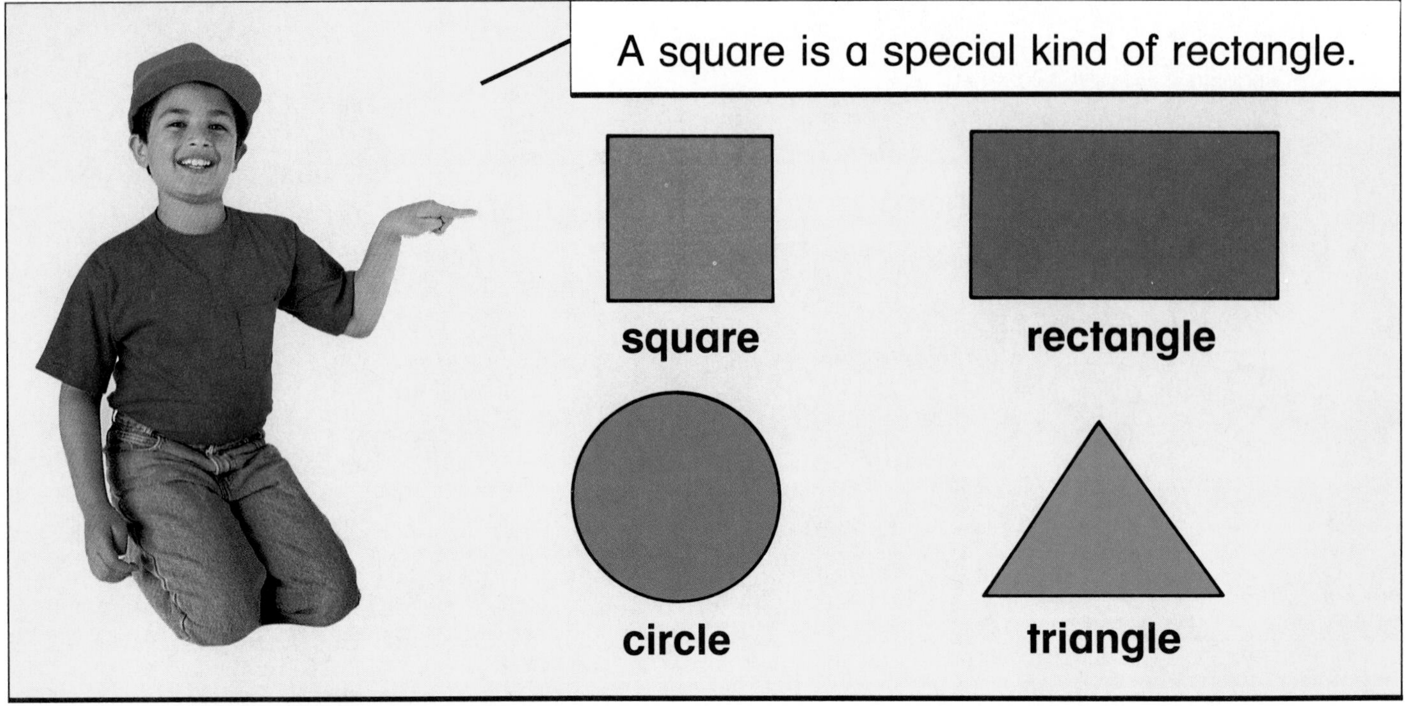

Ring the name for the shape.

1. 
triangle
circle
square

2. 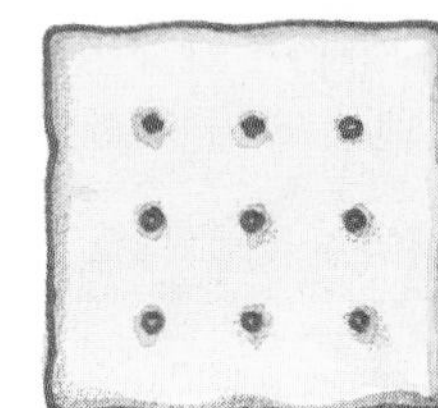
triangle
circle
square

3. 
triangle
circle
rectangle

4. 

triangle
circle
rectangle

5. 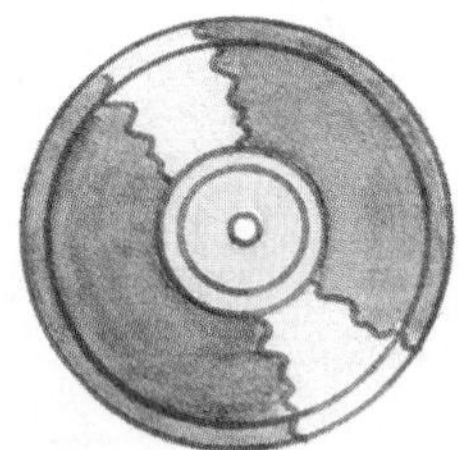
triangle
circle
rectangle

6. 

triangle
circle
square

Exploring Mathematics Book Two © Scott, Foresman and Company

Notes for Home Children review plane shapes.

Name

Sides and Corners

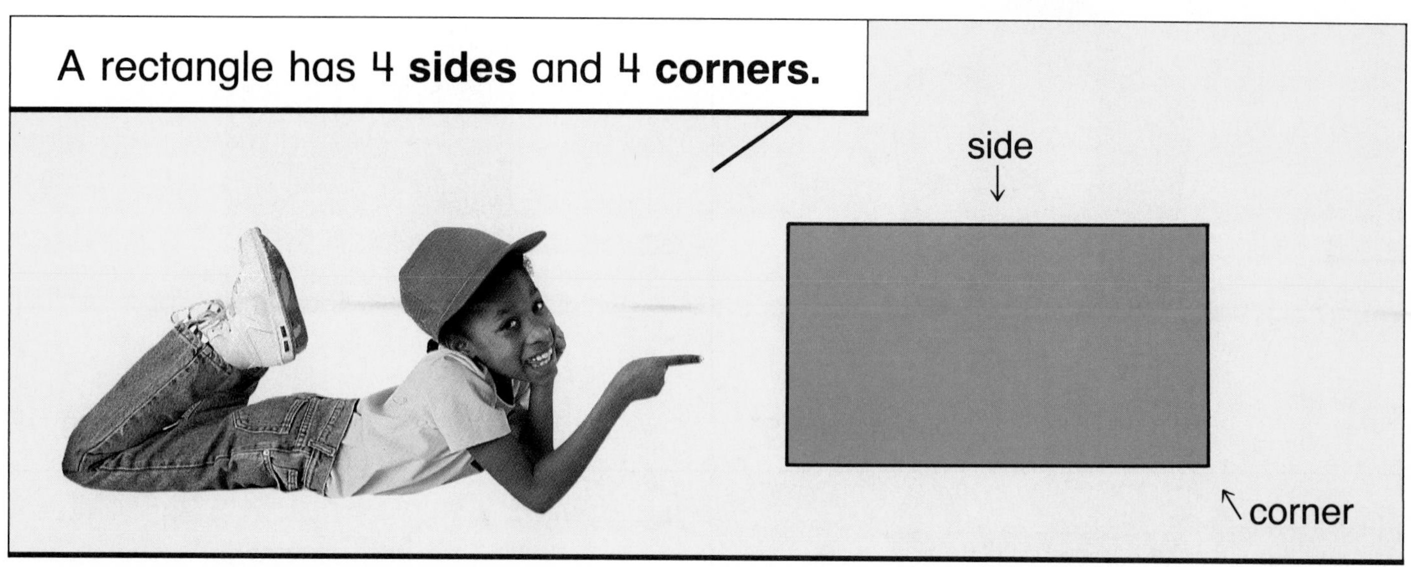

How many sides and corners?

1\. 3 sides 3 corners

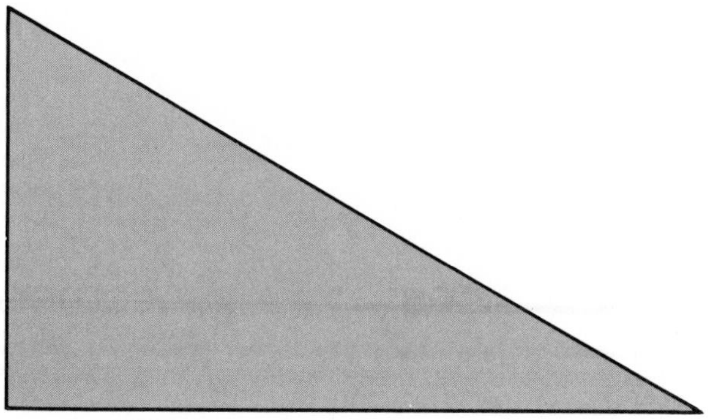

2\. ____ sides ____ corners

3\. ____ sides ____ corners

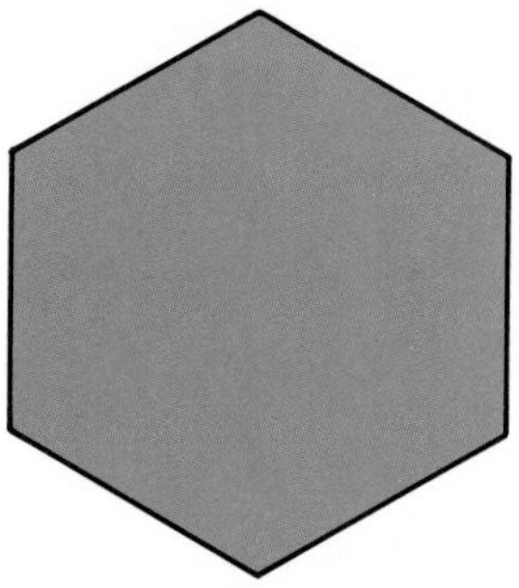

4\. ____ sides ____ corners

Notes for Home Children learn to identify the sides and corners of plane shapes.

How many sides and corners?

5.

5 sides 5 corners

6.

_____ sides _____ corners

7.

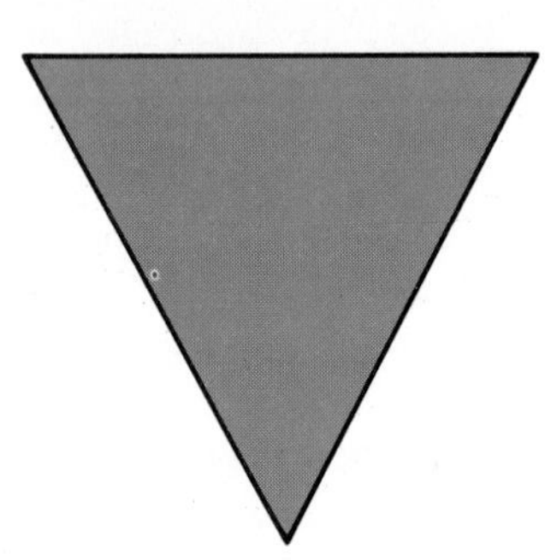

_____ sides _____ corners

8.

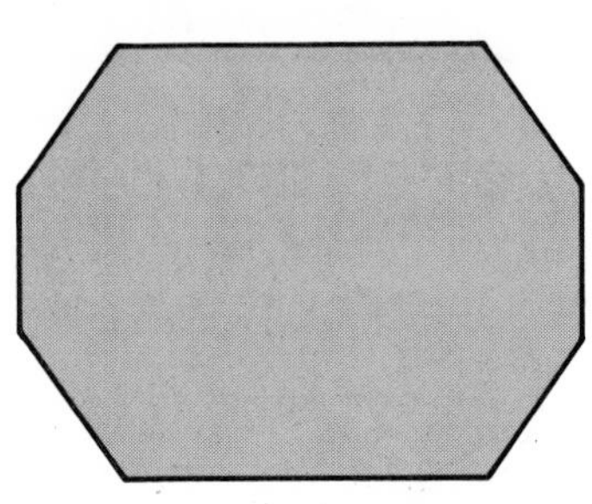

_____ sides _____ corners

Problem Solving

Solve.

circle

square

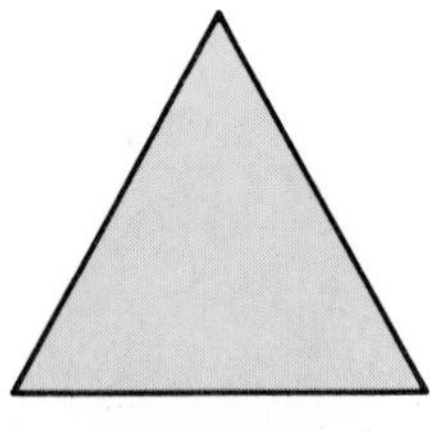

triangle

Which shape has four sides the same length? _______________

Which shape has no corners? _______________

Exploring Mathematics Book Two © Scott, Foresman and Company

Notes for Home Children practice identifying sides and corners of plane shapes. Then they solve problems involving plane shapes.

Name

Congruence

Color the one that is the same shape and size.

1.

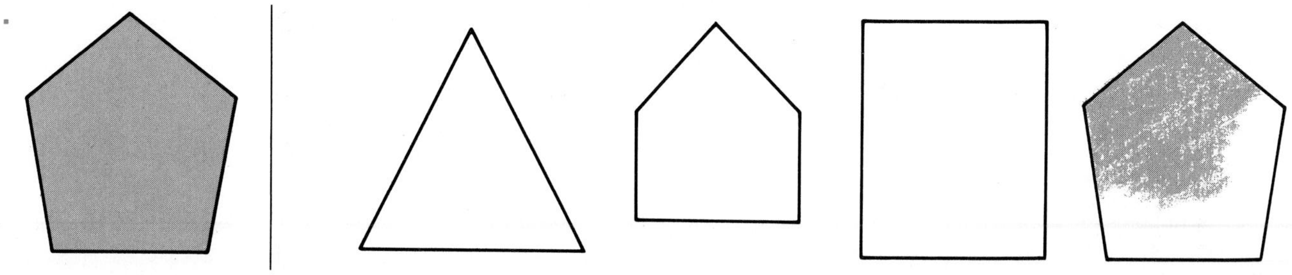

2.

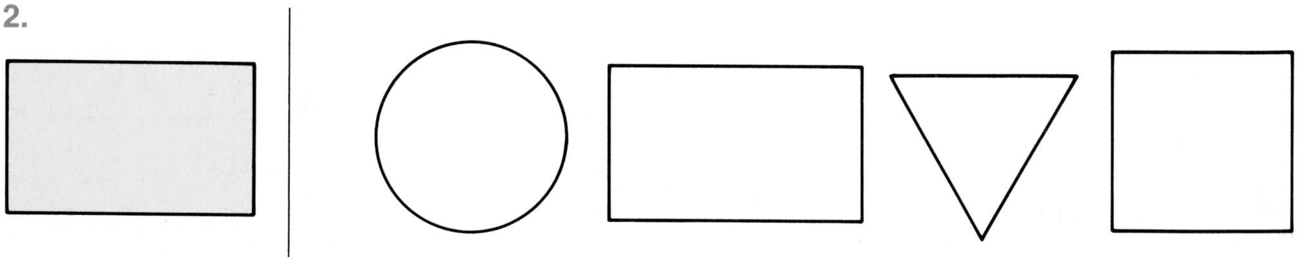

3.

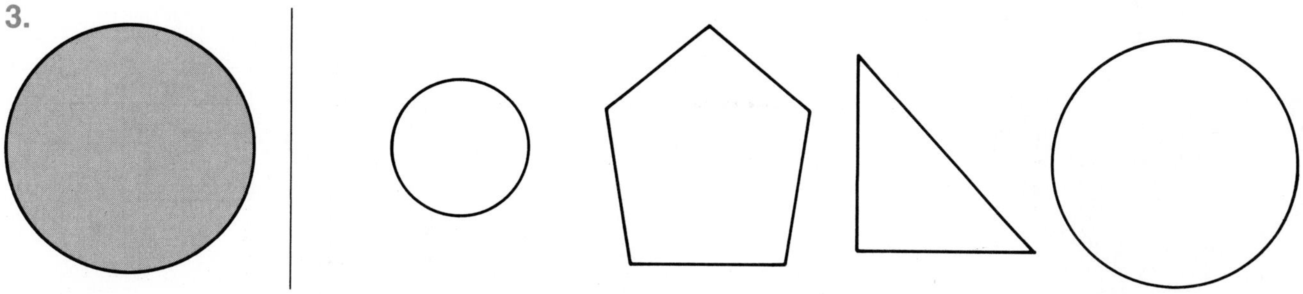

Notes for Home Children identify shapes that have the same shape and size.

Copy the shape.
Write how many sides and corners.

4. 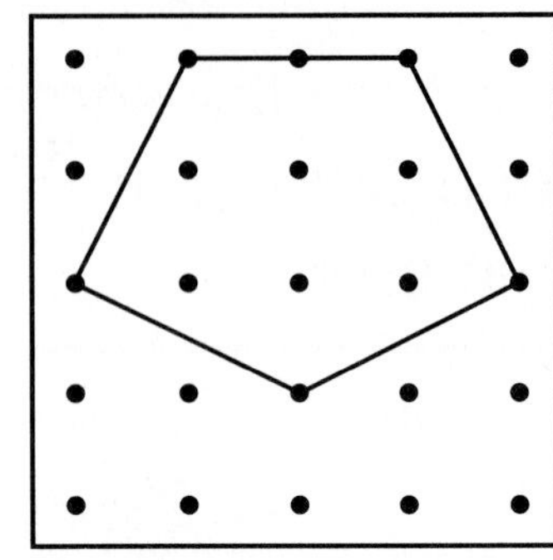 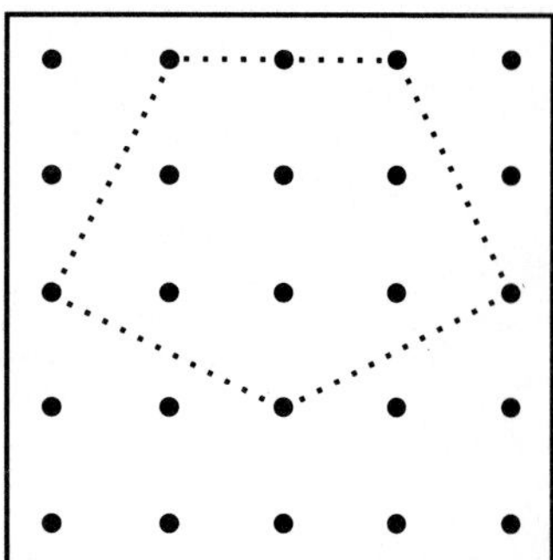

5 sides

_____ corners

5. 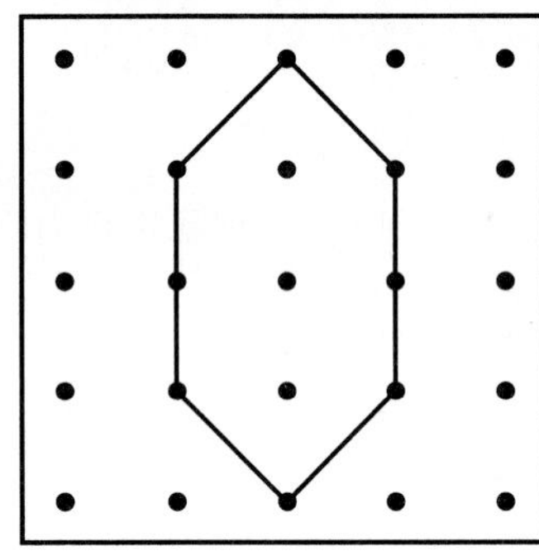 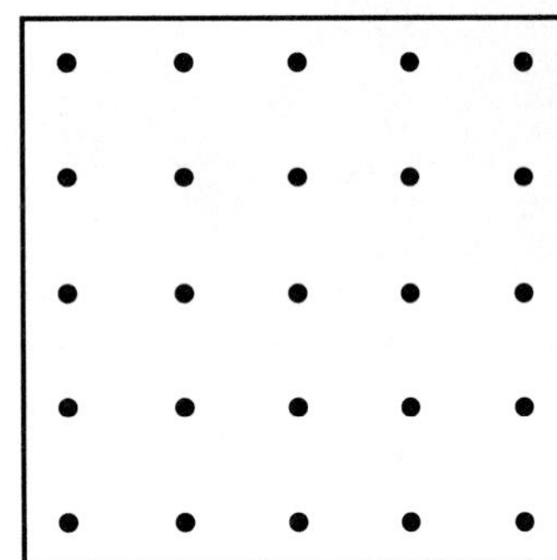

_____ sides

_____ corners

6. 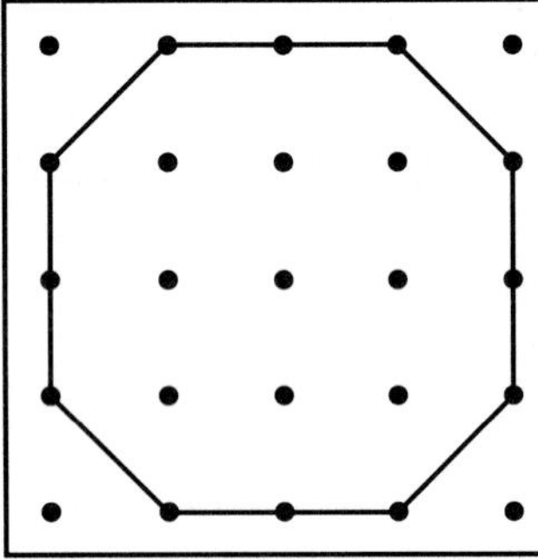 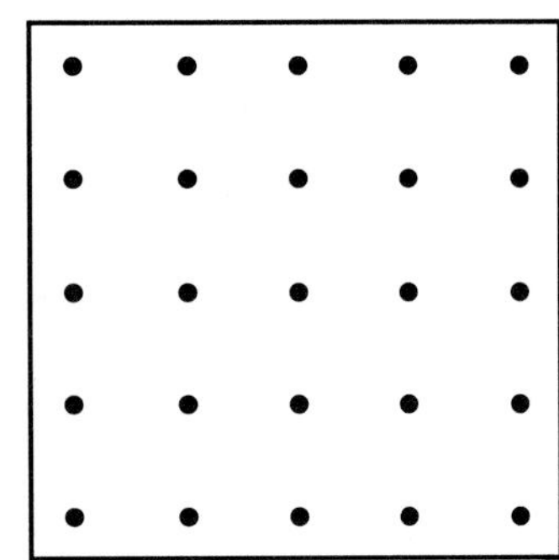

_____ sides

_____ corners

Talk About Math

How are the shapes alike?
How are they different?

 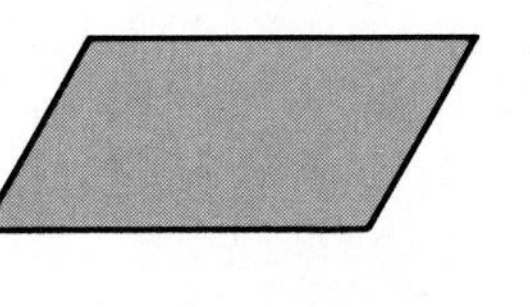

Exploring Mathematics Book Two © Scott, Foresman and Company

Notes for Home Children copy plane shapes and write the number of sides and corners. Then they talk about characteristics of shapes.

Name

Readiness for Perimeter

To find the distance around, measure the length of each side. Then add the lengths.

inches 1 2 3

inches 1 2

inches 1 2 3 4

3

2

4

3
2
+ 4

9 inches

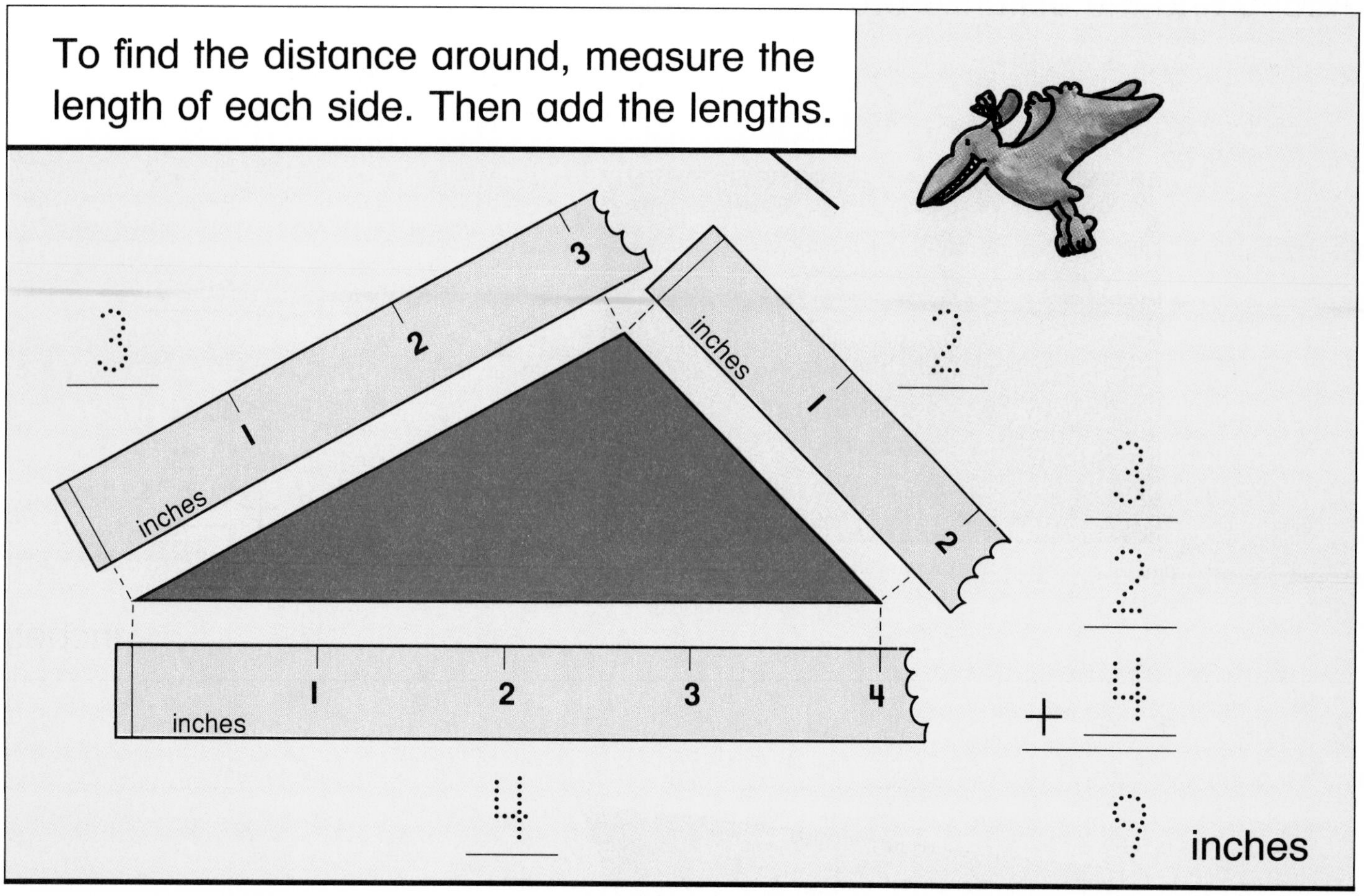

Use an inch ruler.
Measure to find the length of each side.
Add to find the distance around the shape.

1.

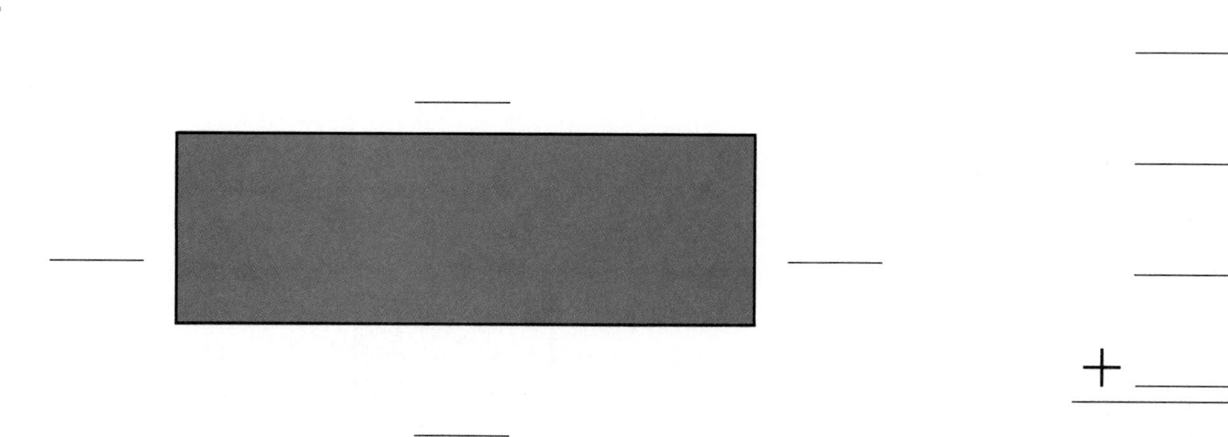

\+

inches

Notes for Home Children develop readiness for perimeter by measuring the length of each side of plane shapes and then adding the lengths.

Use an inch ruler.
Measure to find the length of each side.
Add to find the distance around the shape.

2.

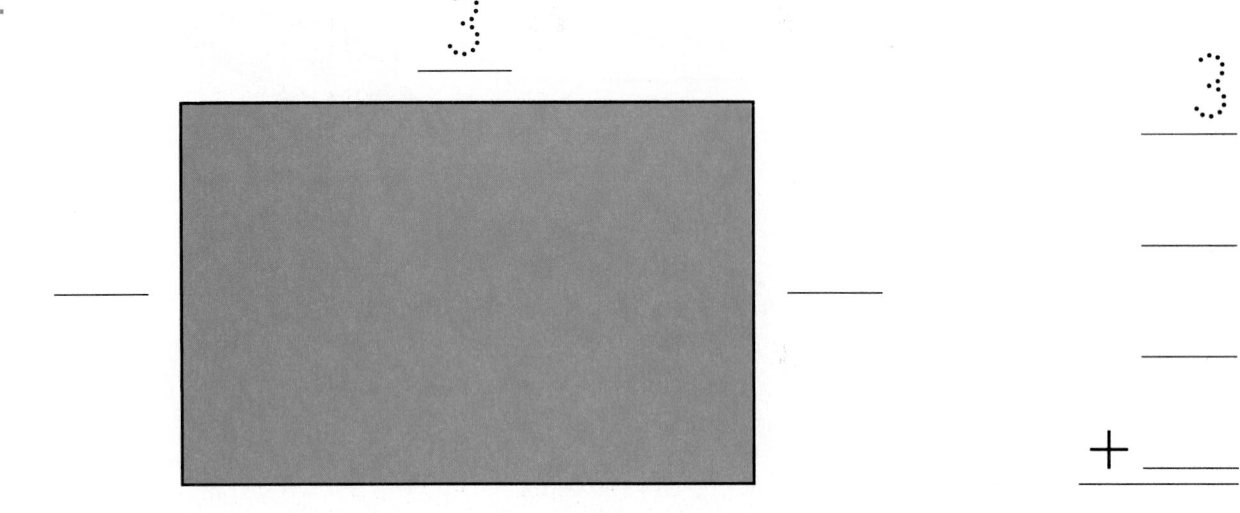

____ inches

3.

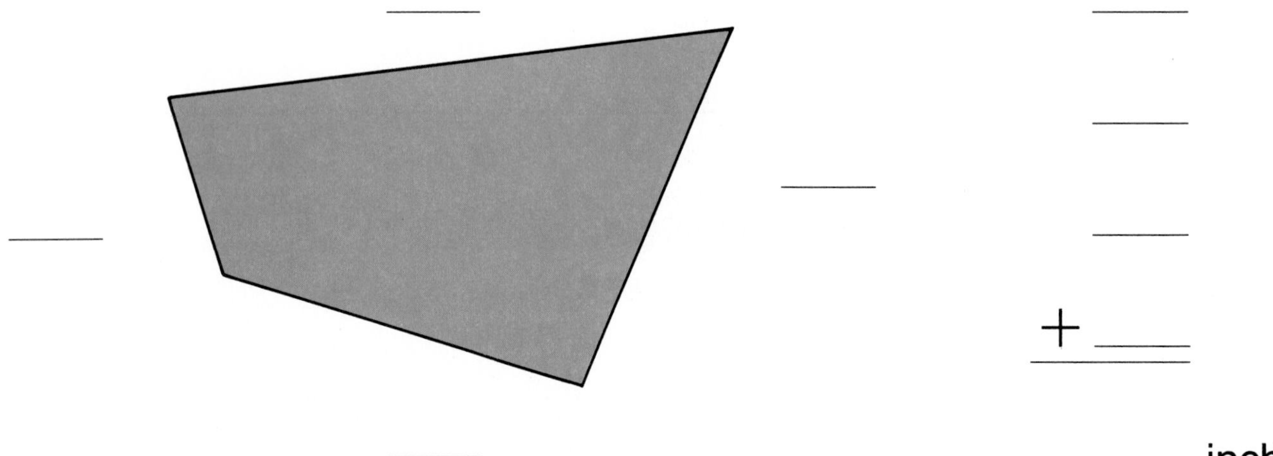

____ inches

Problem Solving

Solve.

4. One side of a square measures 1 inch. What is the distance around the square?

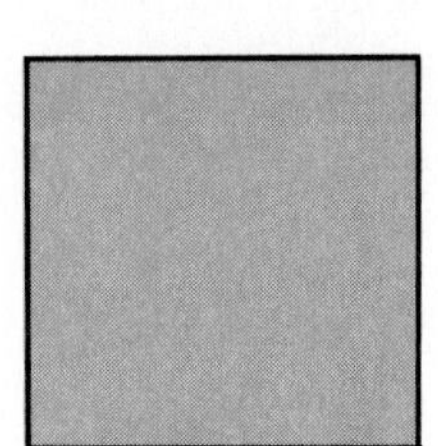

____ inches

Exploring Mathematics Book Two © Scott, Foresman and Company

Notes for Home Children find perimeter by measuring the length of each side of plane shapes and then adding the lengths. Then they solve a problem involving perimeter.

Name

ACTIVITY

Finding Symmetrical Shapes

1. Do the parts match when folded on the line?
Use shapes on page 367.
Cut and paste.

Parts Match	Parts Do Not Match

Notes for Home Children cut each shape on page 367 and decide whether or not it is symmetrical by folding it on the dotted line. They paste the shapes on the page accordingly.

Will the parts match when folded on the line?
Ring yes or no.

2. yes no

3. yes no

4. yes no

5. yes no

6. yes no

7. yes no

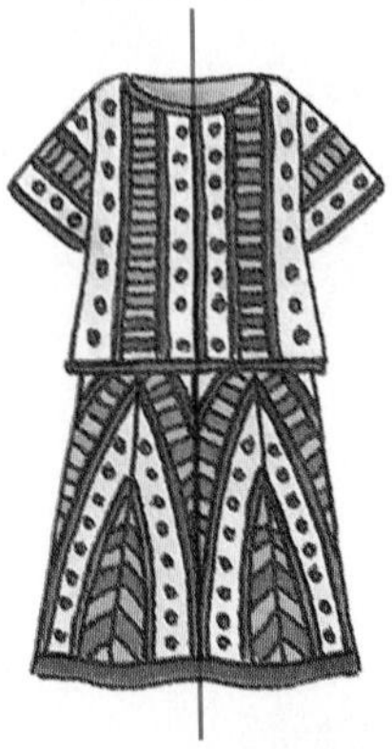

8. yes no

9. yes no

Exploring Mathematics Book Two © Scott, Foresman and Company

Notes for Home Children decide whether or not the two parts of a given shape match.

Use with page 365.

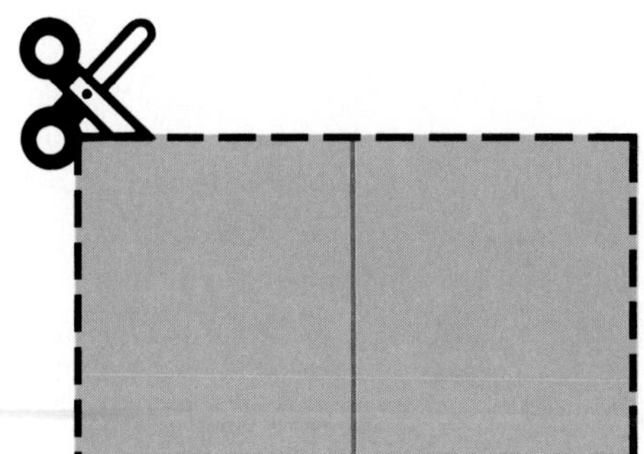

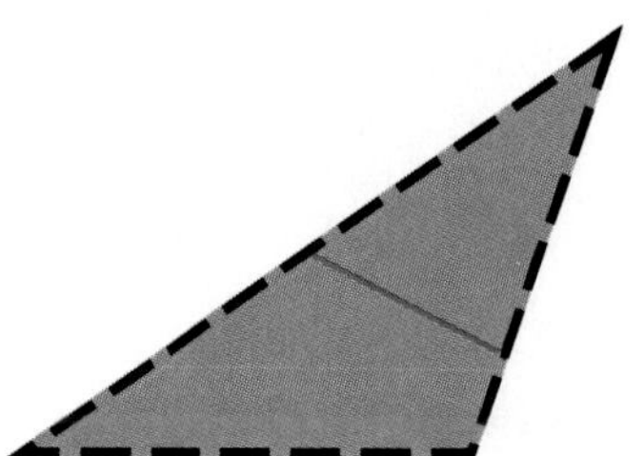

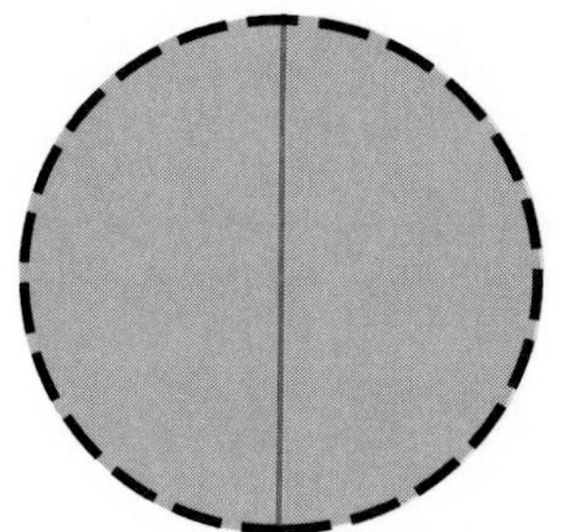

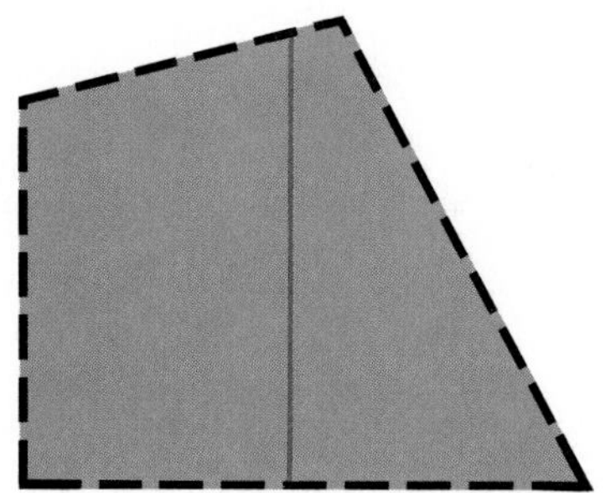

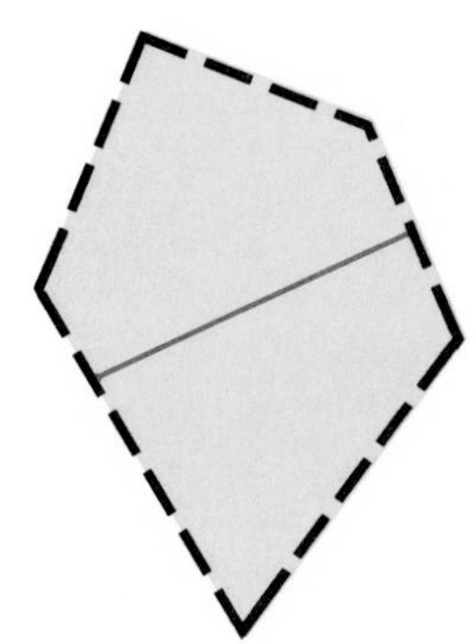

Use with page 365.

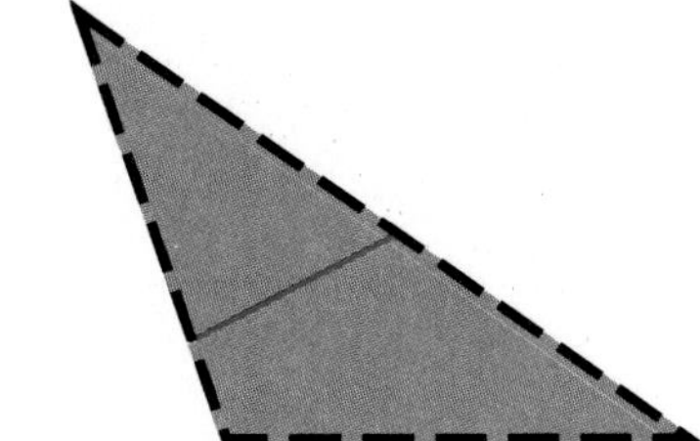

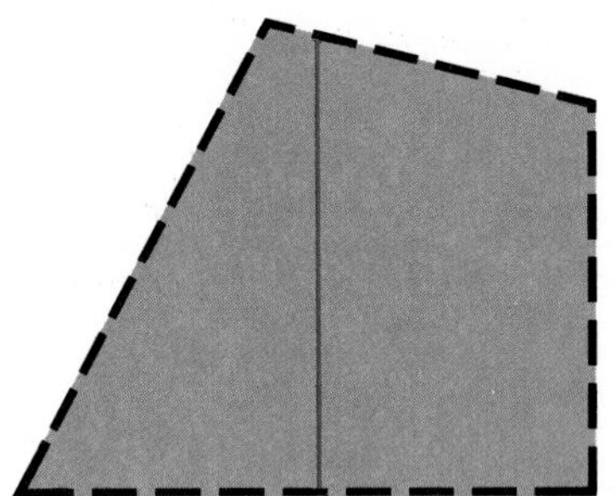

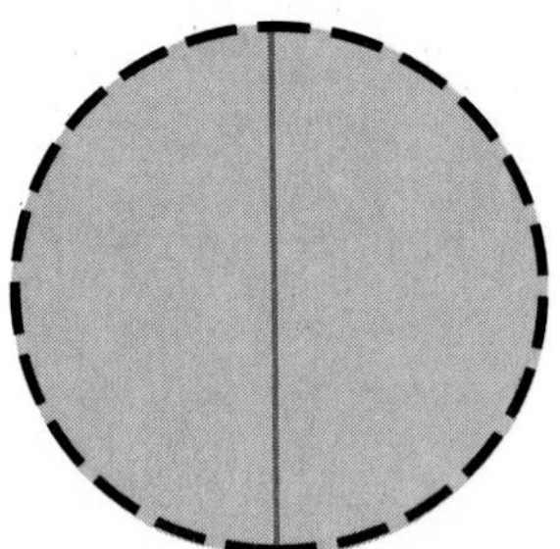

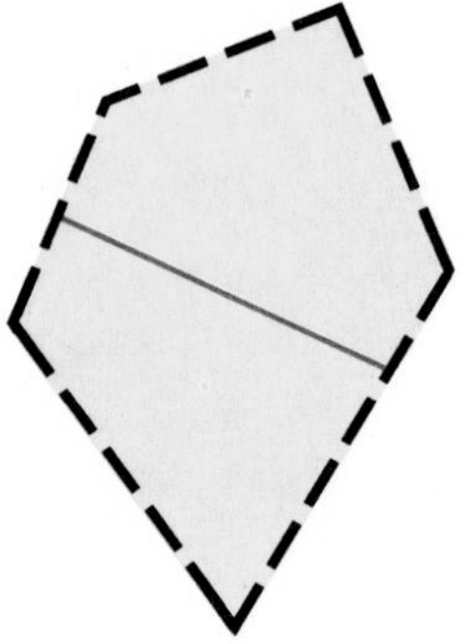

Exploring Mathematics Book Two © Scott, Foresman and Company

Name ______________________

Solids

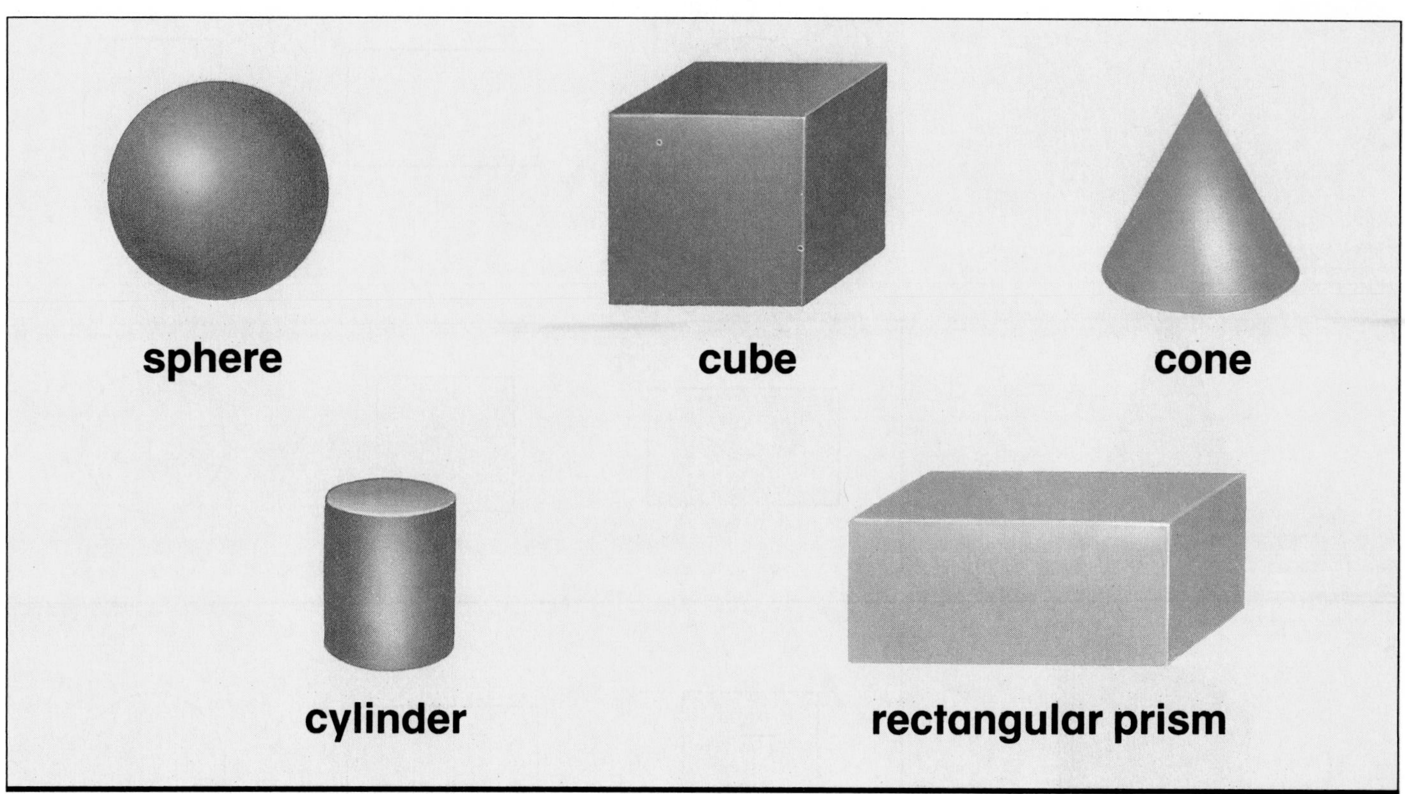

Write the name for the solid.

1. 

cylinder

2. 

____

3. 

____

4. 

____

5. 

____

Notes for Home Children learn to identify solids by name.

What will you see if you trace the shape?

6.

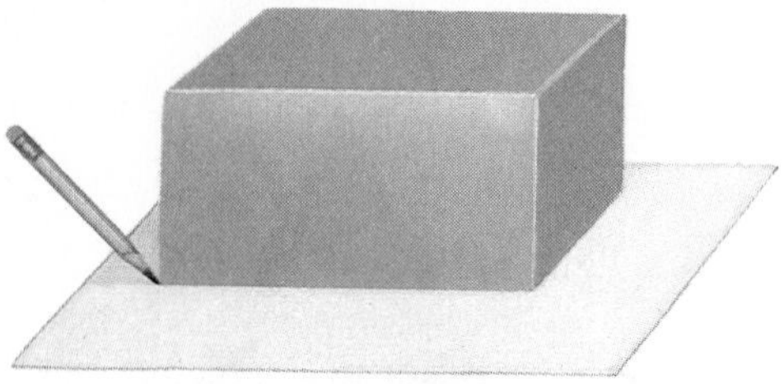

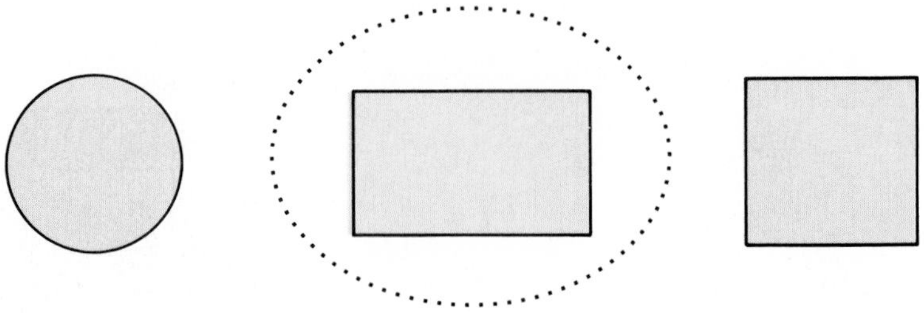

7.

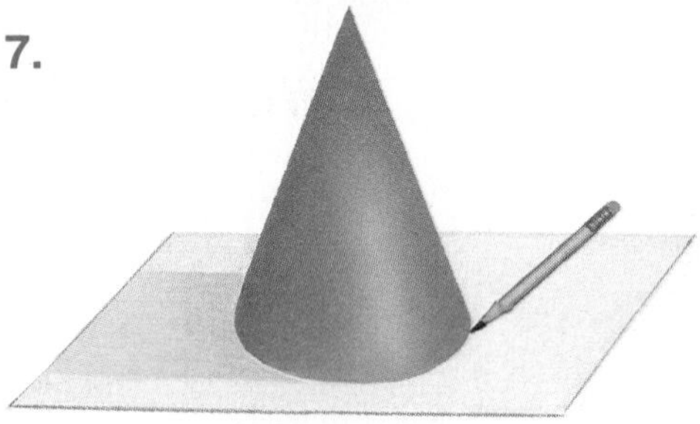

8.

9.

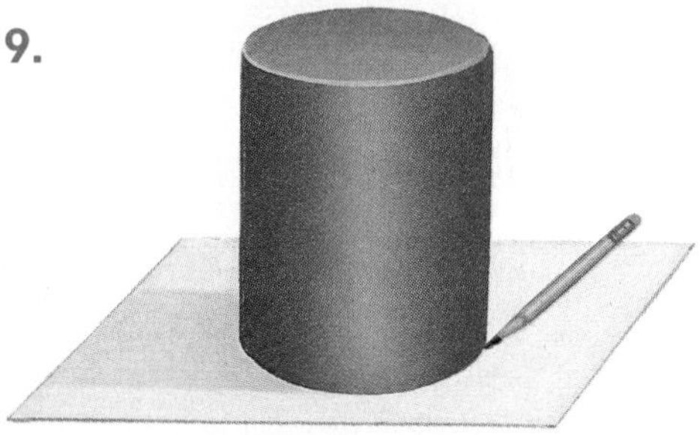

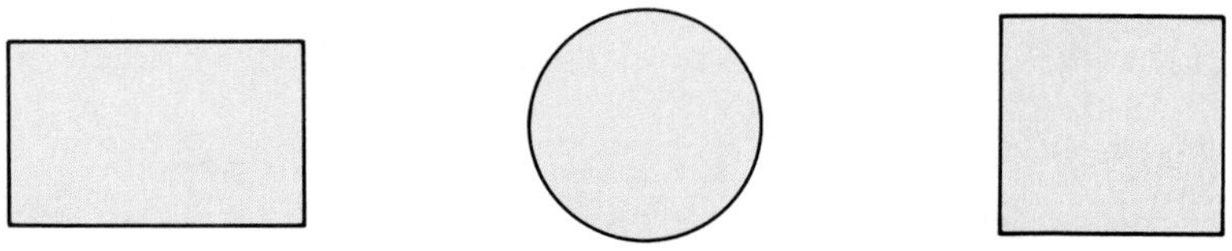

Talk About Math

Which shapes will slide down a board?
Which shapes will roll down a board?

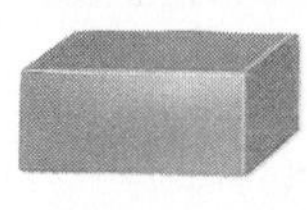

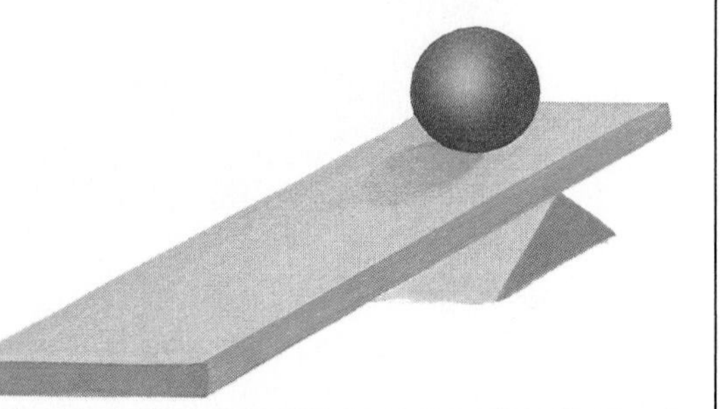

Exploring Mathematics Book Two © Scott, Foresman and Company

Notes for Home Children learn the relationship between solids and plane shapes. Then they talk about some attributes of solids.

Name

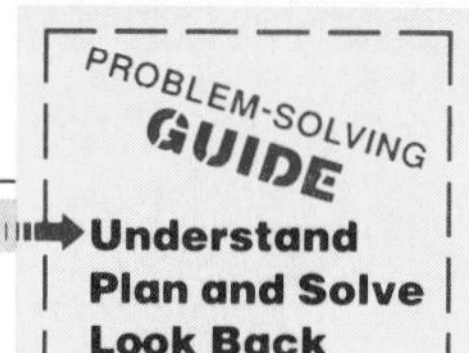

Use Data from a Graph

How do you find the moon on the graph?

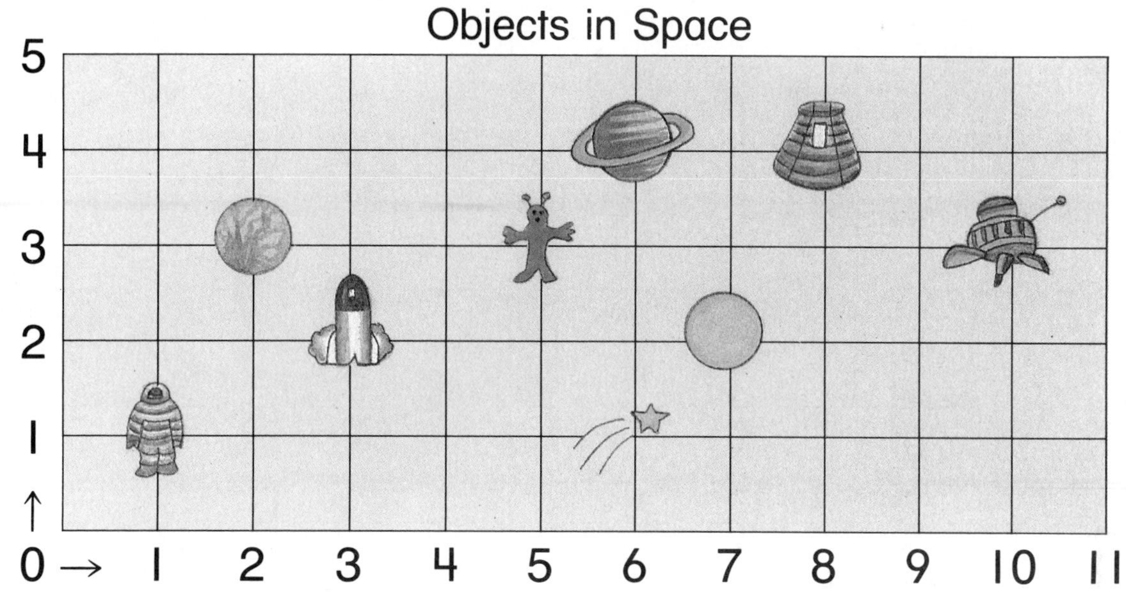

Start at 0. Go across 2. Go up 3.

The moon is at | 2 | 3 | on the graph.

Find each object on the graph above.
Ring the object.

1.

across	up	object
6	4	
7	2	
8	4	
5	3	

2.

across	up	object
3	2	
2	3	
10	3	
1	1	

Notes for Home Children solve problems by locating data on a graph.

At the Campground

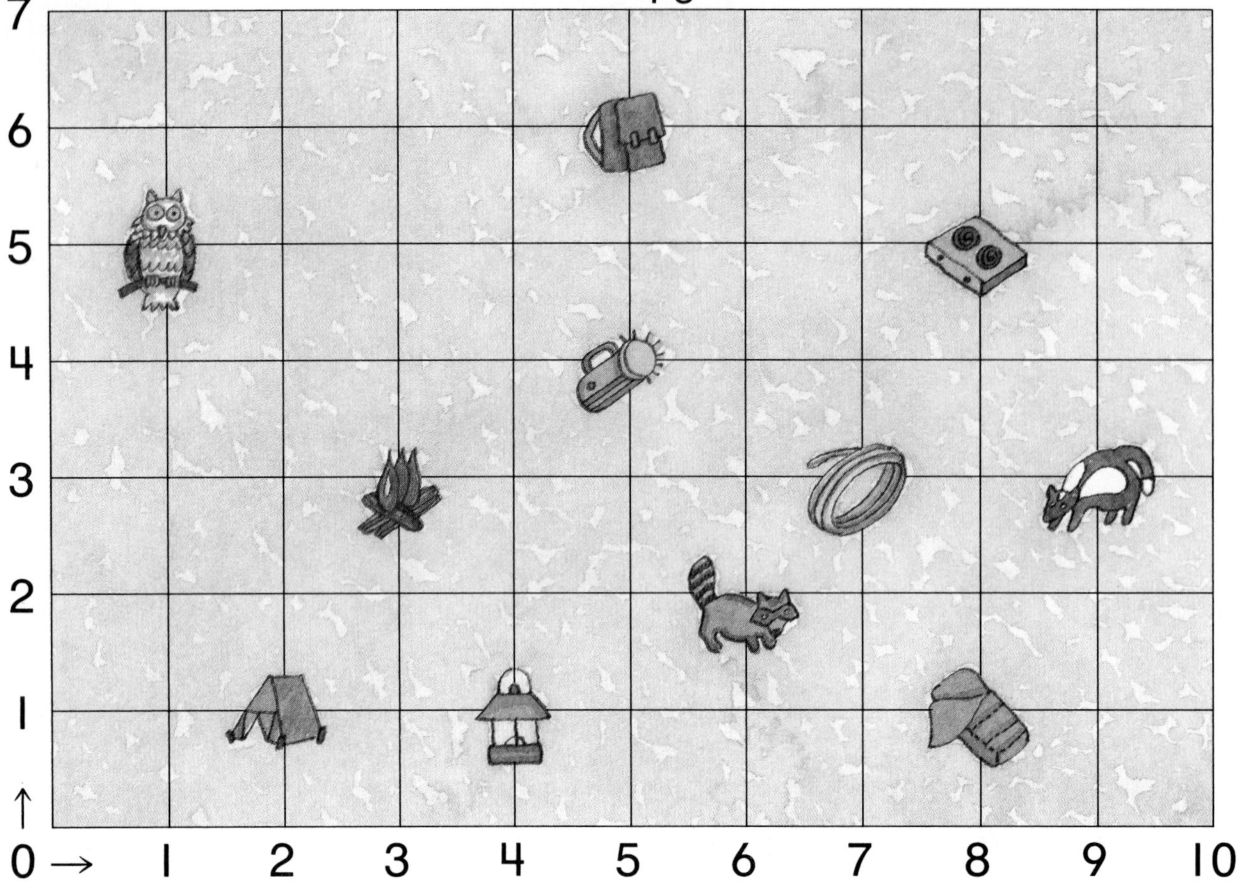

Where is each item on the graph?
Start at 0. Go across and then up.

3.

object	across	up
	1	5

4.

object	across	up
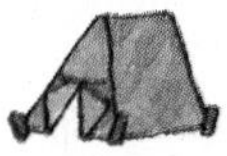		

Exploring Mathematics Book Two © Scott, Foresman and Company

Notes for Home Children solve problems by using data from a graph to locate points on the graph.

Number Sense

About how many centimeters long is each path?
First guess. Then measure with a string.

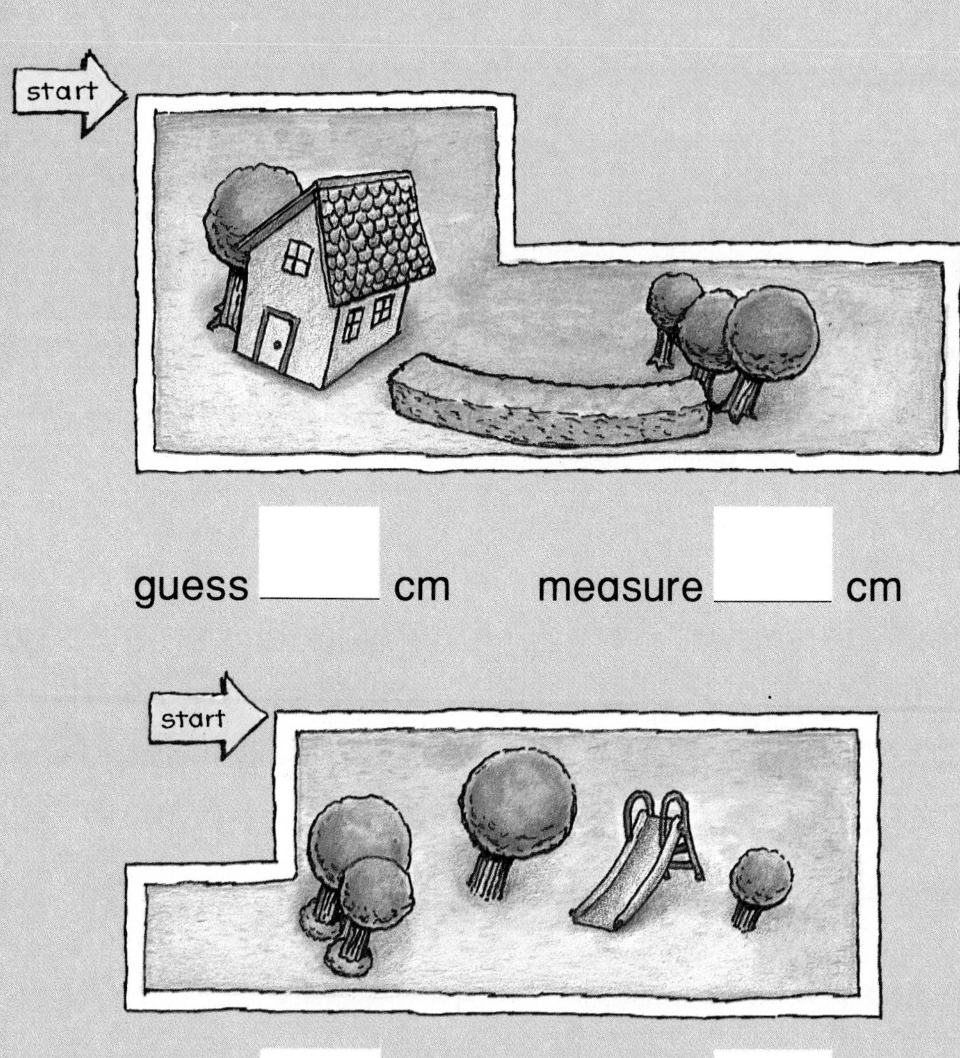

guess ____ cm measure ____ cm

guess ____ cm measure ____ cm

Let's do some more!

Draw a path about 16 cm around.
Then measure your path to see how close you are.

Notes for Home Children develop number understanding by estimating and measuring perimeters.

SKILLS REVIEW

Skills Review

Fill in the correct ◯.
What fraction of the shape is colored?

1. 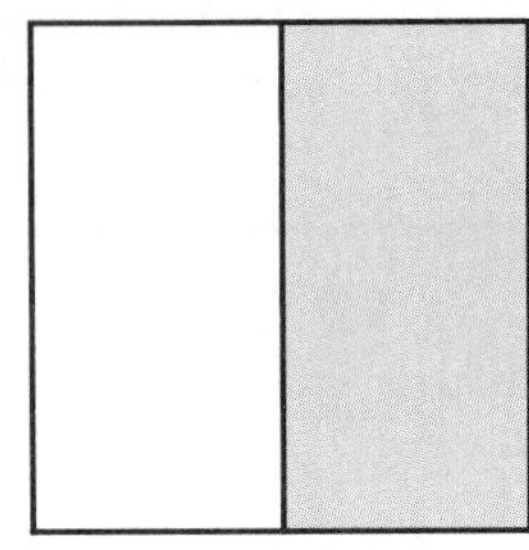

(A) $\frac{1}{2}$
(B) $\frac{1}{3}$
(C) $\frac{1}{4}$

2. 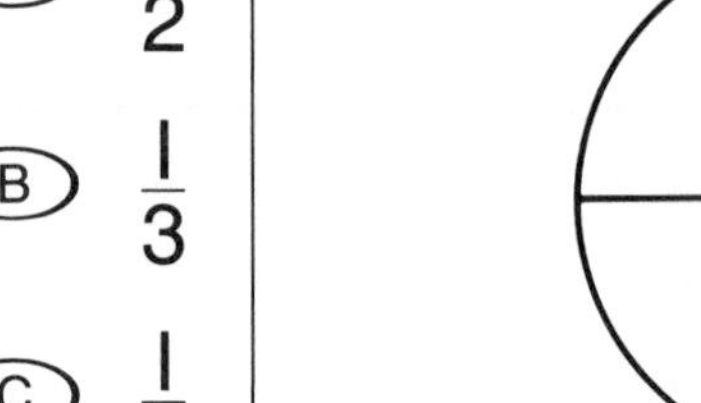

(A) $\frac{2}{3}$
(B) $\frac{2}{4}$
(C) $\frac{1}{4}$

3. 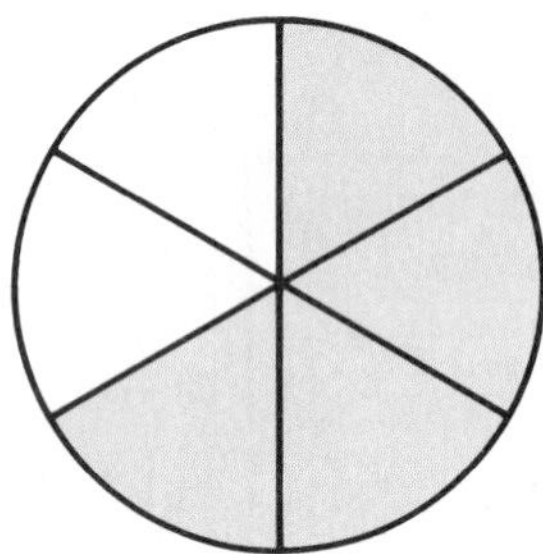

(A) $\frac{2}{6}$
(B) $\frac{1}{2}$
(C) $\frac{4}{6}$

4. 

(A) $\frac{3}{6}$
(B) $\frac{2}{5}$
(C) $\frac{4}{5}$

What is your guess?

5. If you walk in the snow, will you leave footprints?
   (A) sure to happen
   (B) may happen
   (C) impossible

6. If you fall in a mud puddle, will you stay clean?
   (A) sure to happen
   (B) may happen
   (C) impossible

Vocabulary

7. Match.

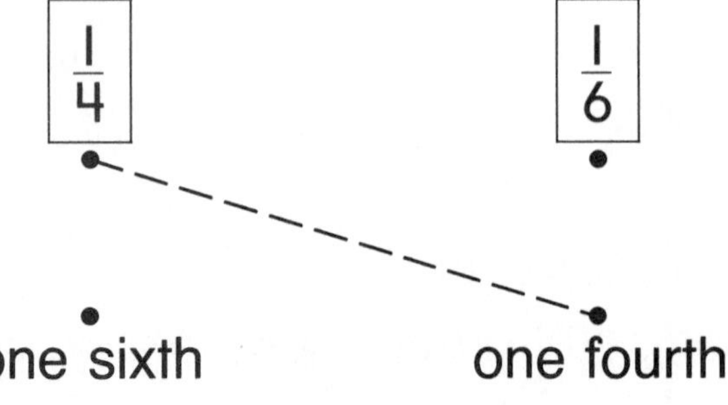

Notes for Home Children review fractional parts of shapes and probability. Then they review fraction terms.

Exploring Mathematics Book Two © Scott, Foresman and Company

Name

Cups, Pints, Quarts, Gallons

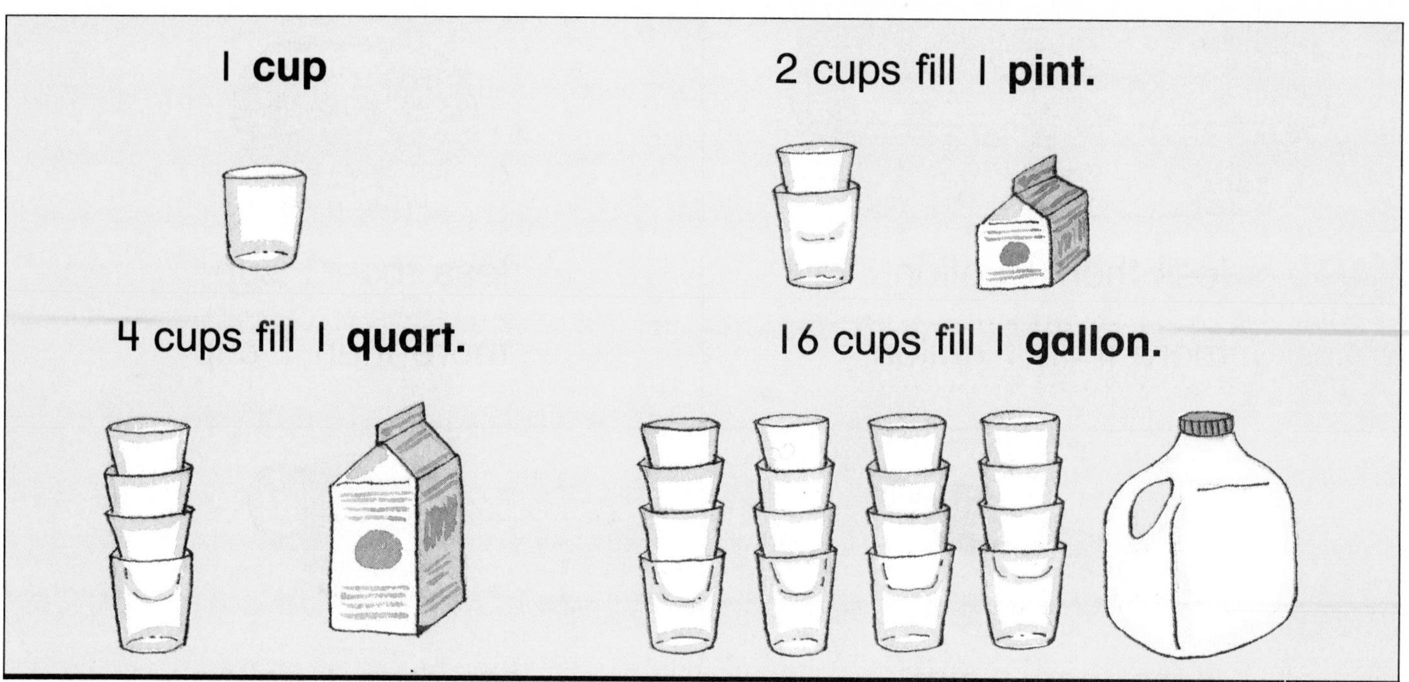

About how much does each container hold?
Ring the better estimate.

1. 

less than 1 quart

more than 1 quart

2. 

less than 1 pint

more than 1 pint

3. 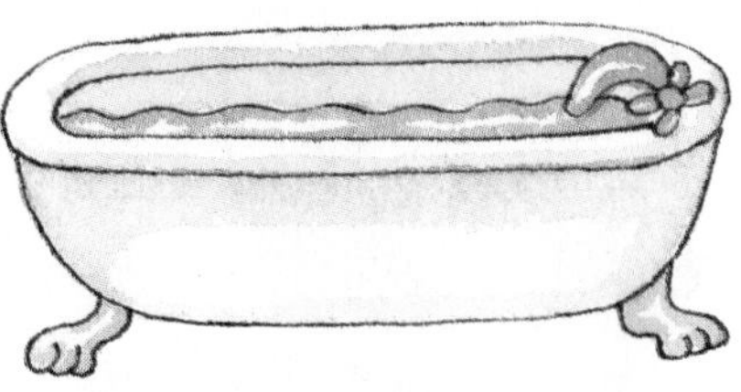

less than 1 gallon

more than 1 gallon

4. 

less than 1 cup

more than 1 cup

Notes for Home Children learn to estimate whether a container holds more or less than 1 pint, 1 quart, or 1 gallon.

About how much does each container hold?
Ring the better estimate.

5.

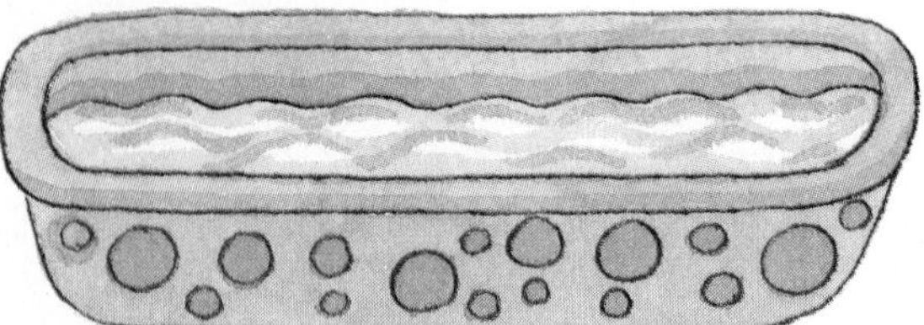

less than 1 gallon

more than 1 gallon

6.

less than 1 cup

more than 1 cup

7.

less than 1 pint

more than 1 pint

8.

less than 1 gallon

more than 1 gallon

9.

less than 1 pint

more than 1 pint

10.

less than 1 quart

more than 1 quart

Talk About Math

How many quarts fill 1 gallon?
How would you find out?

Exploring Mathematics Book Two © Scott, Foresman and Company

Notes for Home Children practice estimating whether a container holds more or less than 1 cup, 1 pint, 1 quart, or 1 gallon. Then they talk about relative capacity.

See More Practice Set A on page 389.

Name

Liters

Each container holds about 1 **liter.**

About how much does each container hold?
Ring the better estimate.

1.

less than 1 liter

more than 1 liter

2.

less than 1 liter

more than 1 liter

3.

less than 1 liter

more than 1 liter

4.

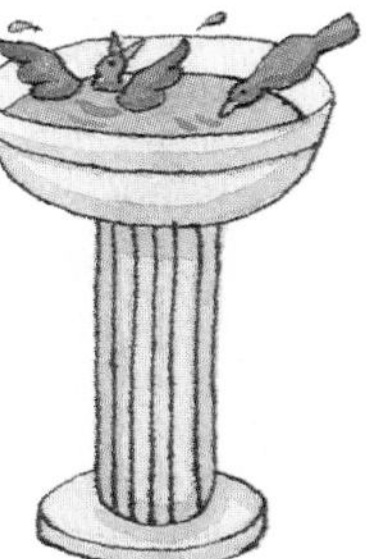

less than 1 liter

more than 1 liter

5.

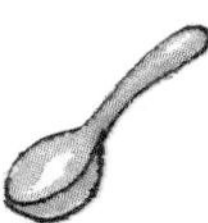

less than 1 liter

more than 1 liter

6.

less than 1 liter

more than 1 liter

Notes for Home Children learn to estimate whether a container holds more than or less than 1 liter.

About how much does each hold?
Ring the better estimate.

7.

less than 1 liter

more than 1 liter

8.

less than 1 liter

more than 1 liter

9.

less than 1 liter

more than 1 liter

10.

less than 1 liter

more than 1 liter

11.

less than 1 liter

more than 1 liter

12.

less than 1 liter

more than 1 liter

Problem Solving

Solve.

13. Mr. Salvo had 32 liters of juice in his store. At the end of the week he had 15 liters left. How many liters of juice did Mr. Salvo sell?

____

− ____

____ liters

Exploring Mathematics Book Two © Scott, Foresman and Company

Notes for Home Children practice estimating the capacity of containers that hold more than or less than 1 liter. Then they solve a problem about liters.

Name

Pounds

This weighs less than 1 **pound.**

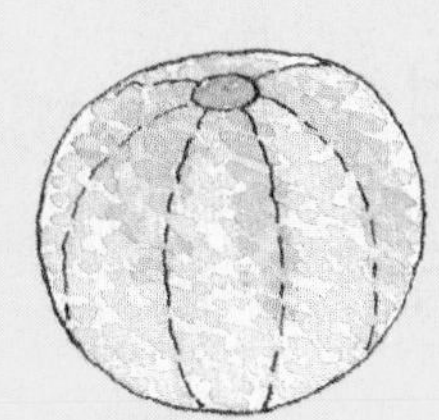

This weighs about 1 **pound.**

This weighs more than 1 **pound.**

1. Draw pictures of objects in your classroom that weigh about 1 pound.

2. Draw pictures of objects in your classroom that weigh less than 1 pound.

3. Draw pictures of objects in your classroom that weigh more than 1 pound.

Notes for Home Children identify and draw objects that weigh 1 pound, less than 1 pound, and more than 1 pound.

About how much does each weigh?
Ring the better estimate.

4.

less than I pound

more than I pound

5.

less than I pound

more than I pound

6.

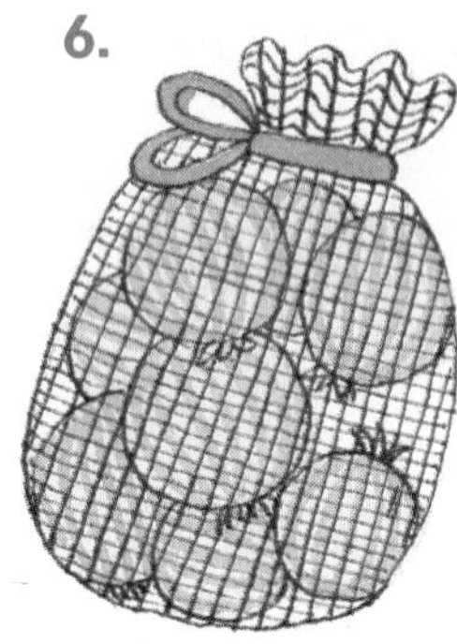

less than I pound

more than I pound

7.

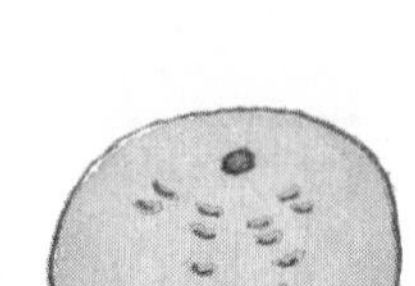

less than I pound

more than I pound

8.

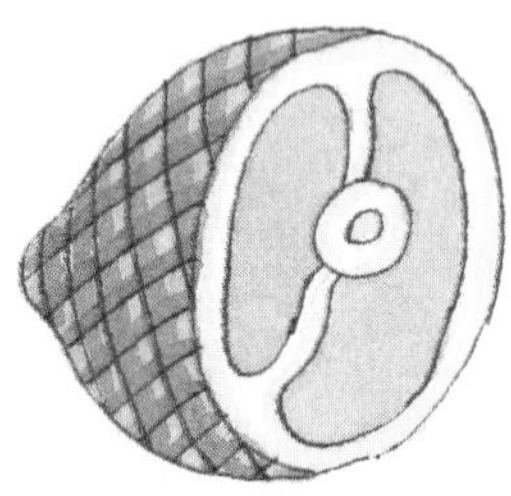

less than I pound

more than I pound

9.

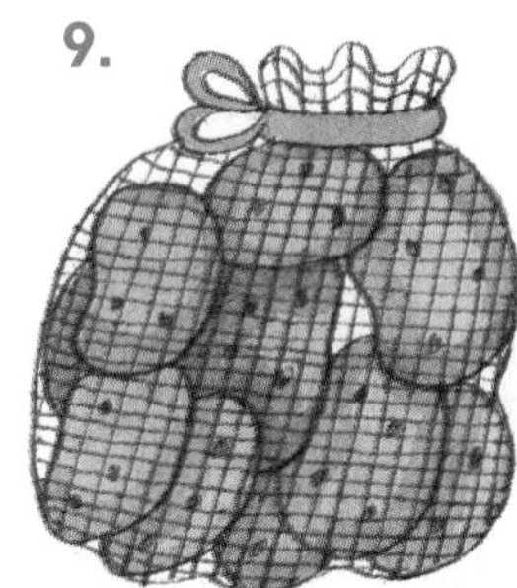

less than I pound

more than I pound

10. **Estimation** How many of each weigh about I pound?

_____ apples weigh about I pound.

_____ tennis balls weigh about I pound.

_____ green peppers weigh about I pound.

Exploring Mathematics Book Two © Scott, Foresman and Company

Notes for Home Children practice estimating whether objects weigh more than or less than I pound. Then they estimate how many of an item weigh about I pound.

See More Practice Set B on page 389.

Name

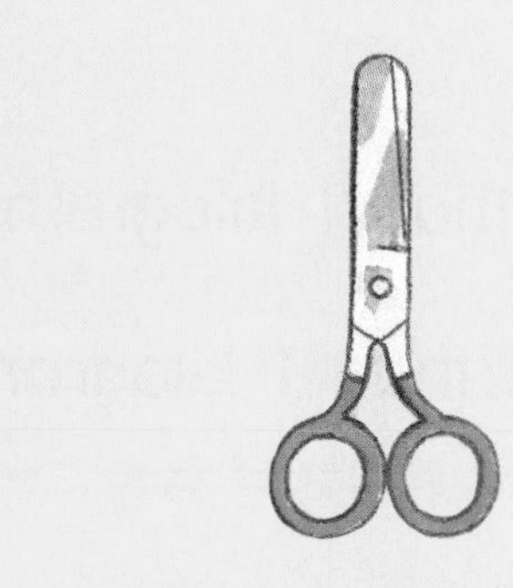

This is lighter than 1 **kilogram.**

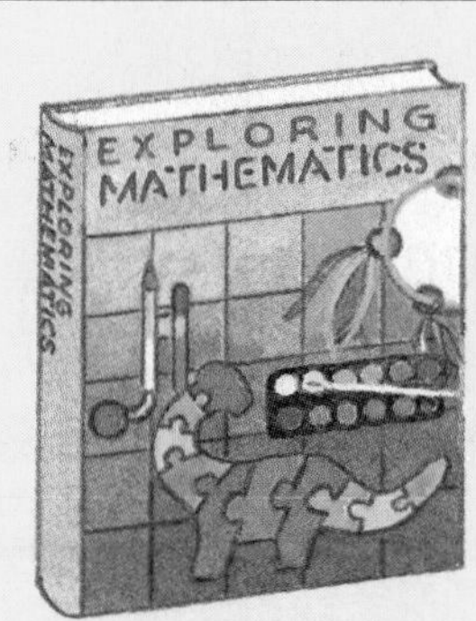

This is about as heavy as 1 **kilogram.**

This is heavier than 1 **kilogram.**

1. Draw pictures of objects in your classroom that weigh about 1 kilogram.

2. Draw pictures of objects in your classroom that weigh less than 1 kilogram.

3. Draw pictures of objects in your classroom that weigh more than 1 kilogram.

Notes for Home Children identify and draw objects that weigh 1 kilogram, less than 1 kilogram, and more than 1 kilogram.

About how heavy is each one?
Ring the better estimate.

4.

lighter than 1 kilogram

heavier than 1 kilogram

5.

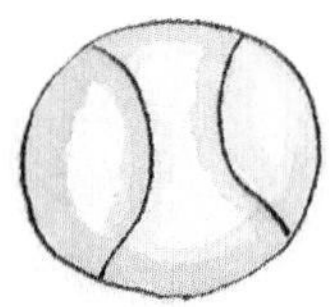

lighter than 1 kilogram

heavier than 1 kilogram

6.

lighter than 1 kilogram

heavier than 1 kilogram

7.

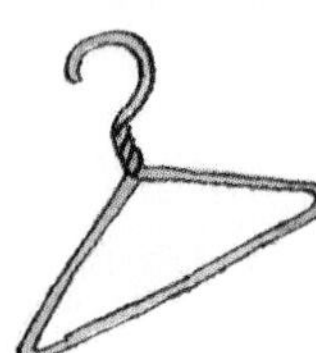

lighter than 1 kilogram

heavier than 1 kilogram

8.

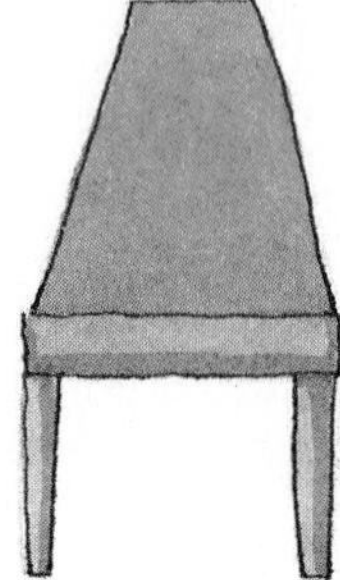

lighter than 1 kilogram

heavier than 1 kilogram

9.

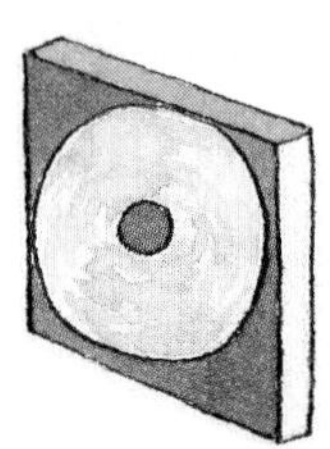

lighter than 1 kilogram

heavier than 1 kilogram

10.

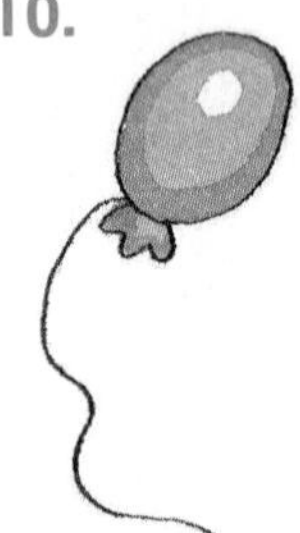

lighter than 1 kilogram

heavier than 1 kilogram

11.

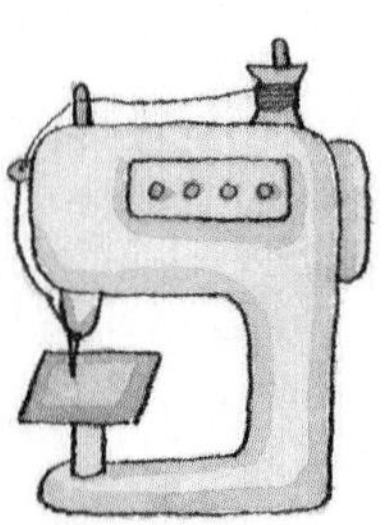

lighter than 1 kilogram

heavier than 1 kilogram

Exploring Mathematics Book Two © Scott, Foresman and Company

Notes for Home Children practice estimating whether objects are lighter than or heavier than 1 kilogram.

Name

Temperature

Write how many degrees.

1. ____° F

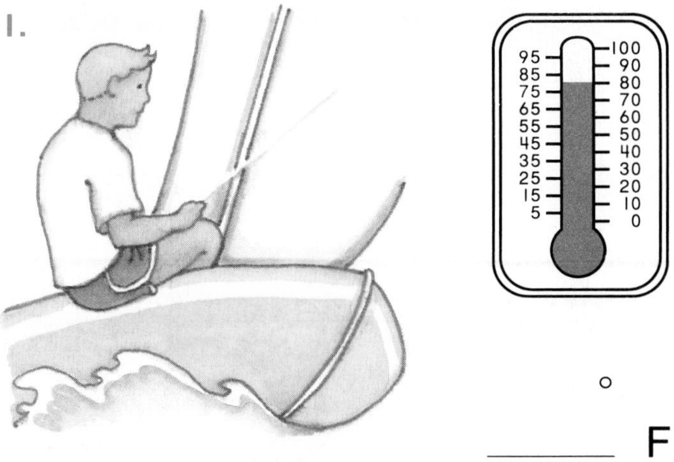

2. ____° F

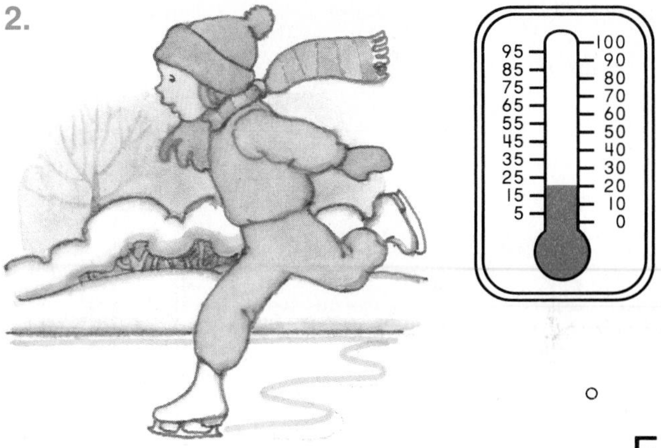

3. ____° F

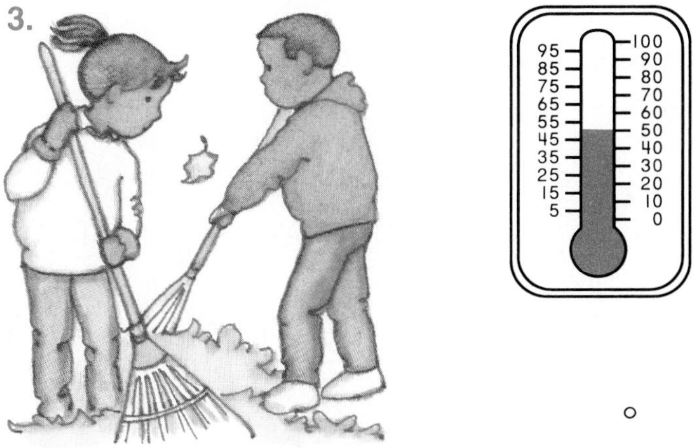

4. ____° F

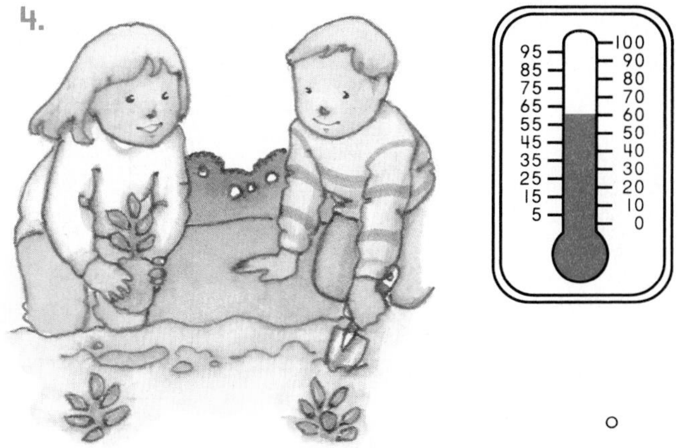

Notes for Home Children learn to read a thermometer.

Write how many degrees.

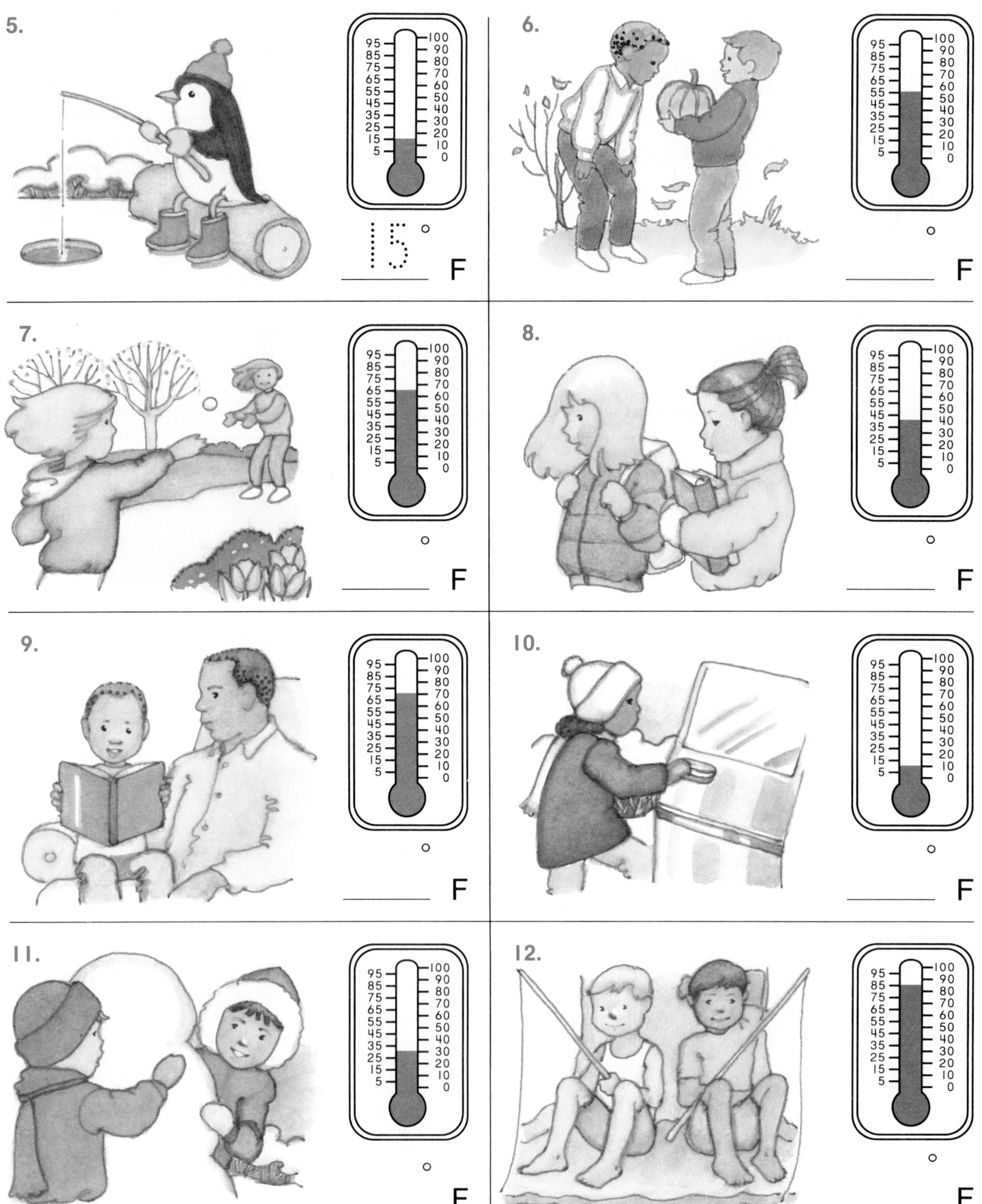

Exploring Mathematics Book Two © Scott, Foresman and Company

Notes for Home Children practice reading a thermometer.

Name

Use Logical Reasoning

Ring the better estimate.

1. What weighs about the same as a lamp?

3 books 20 books

2. What weighs about the same as a shoe?

2 cups 15 cups

3. What weighs about the same as a puppy?

1 orange 8 oranges

4. What weighs about the same as a dime?

5 paperclips 100 paperclips

Notes for Home Children use logical reasoning when using non-standard units to compare weights.

Ring the better estimate.

5. What weighs about the same as a telephone?

1 apple 12 apples

6. What weighs about the same as a pen?

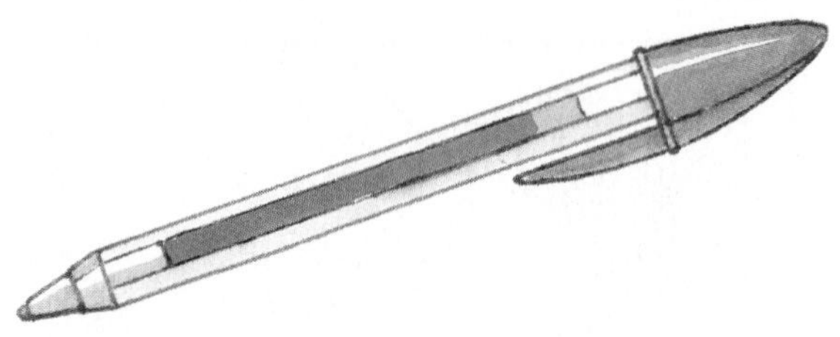

2 pencils 15 pencils

7. What weighs about the same as a bicycle?

1 television 20 televisions

8. What weighs about the same as a sofa?

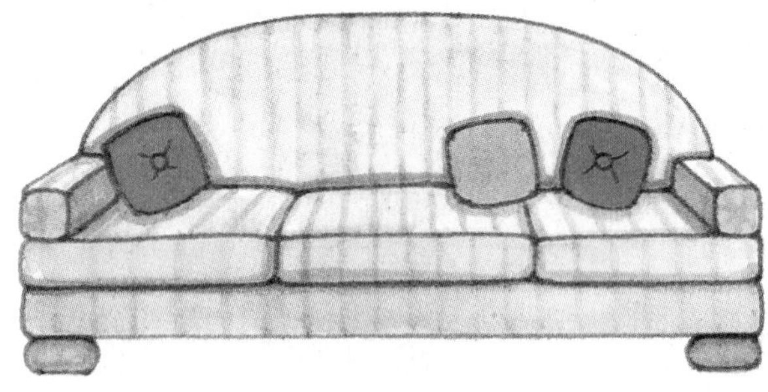

1 turkey 21 turkeys

9. What weighs about the same as a baby?

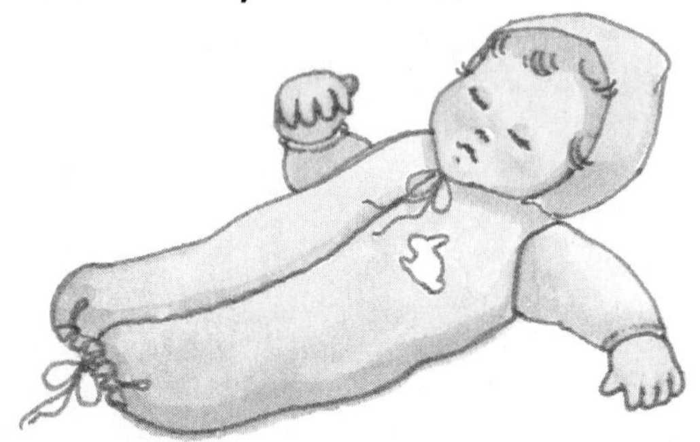

3 puppies 20 puppies

10. What weighs about the same as a horse?

5 second graders 20 second graders

Exploring Mathematics Book Two © Scott, Foresman and Company

Notes for Home Children use logical reasoning when using non-standard units to compare weights.

Name

Problem-Solving Workshop

Explore as a Team

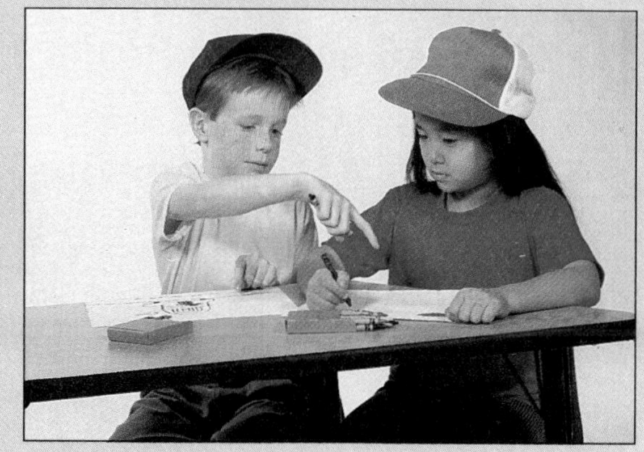

Work with a partner.
Find as many triangles as you can.
Use a different color crayon
to draw around each triangle.
Be sure to find different size triangles.

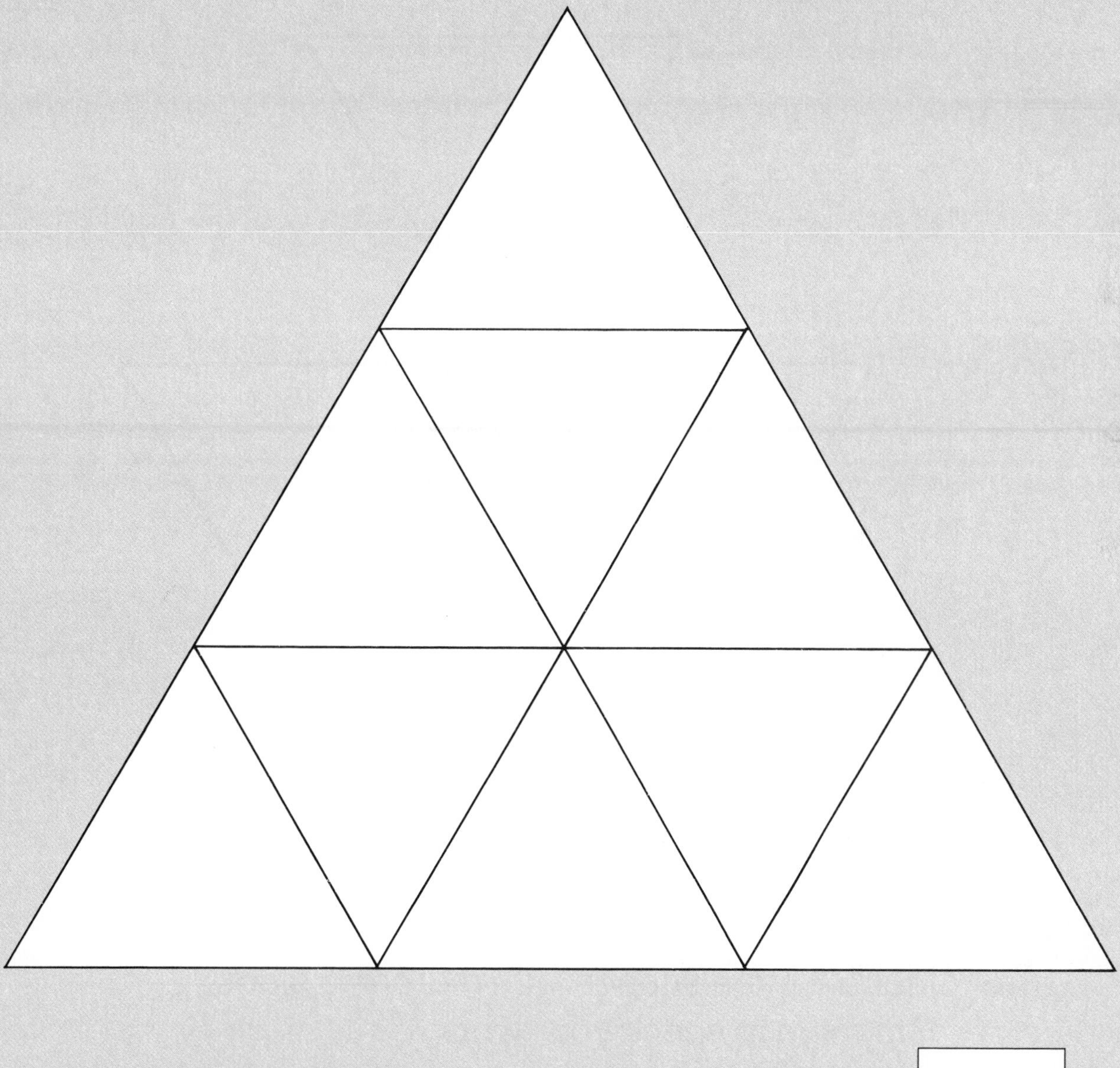

How many triangles did you find altogether? 

Notes for Home Children explore with a partner to find how many triangles there are in a given shape.

Problem-Solving Workshop

Explore with a Computer

Primary Geometry Project

1. At the computer, flip the shape to see if the sides match.
Ring yes if the sides match. Ring no if they do not match.

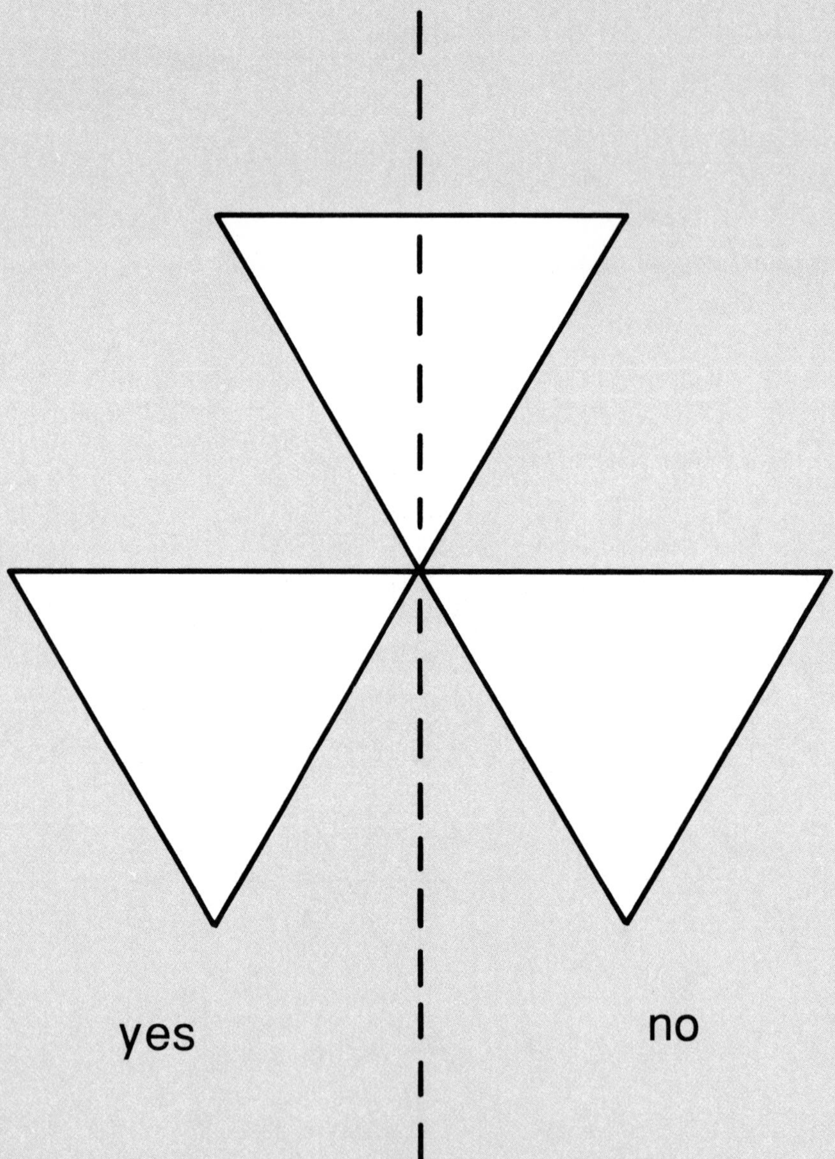

yes no

2. Make 3 more shapes with matching sides.
Flip them to check your work.
Draw one of the shapes you made that has matching sides.

Exploring Mathematics Book Two © Scott, Foresman and Company

Notes for Home Children determine whether the shapes are symmetrical by using the computer to flip them. Then they create additional symmetrical shapes and flip them to check their symmetry.

Name

More Practice

Set A Use after page 376.

I quart fills 2 pints.

2 quarts fill 4 pints.

How many?

quarts	I	2		4	
pints	2		6		I0

Set B Use after page 380.

About how much does each weigh?
Ring the better estimate.

I. 

less than I pound

more than I pound

2. 

less than I pound

more than I pound

3. 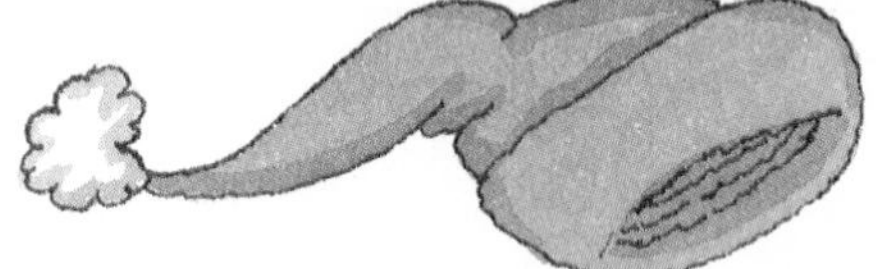

less than I pound

more than I pound

4. 

less than I pound

more than I pound

Notes for Home Set A: Children practice using the relationship of pint to quart.
Set B: Children practice estimating weight.

Enrichment

How many squares cover each shape?

1. 10 squares

2. 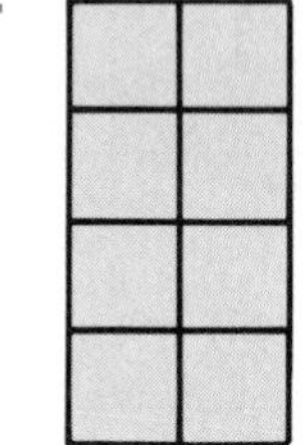
____ squares

3. 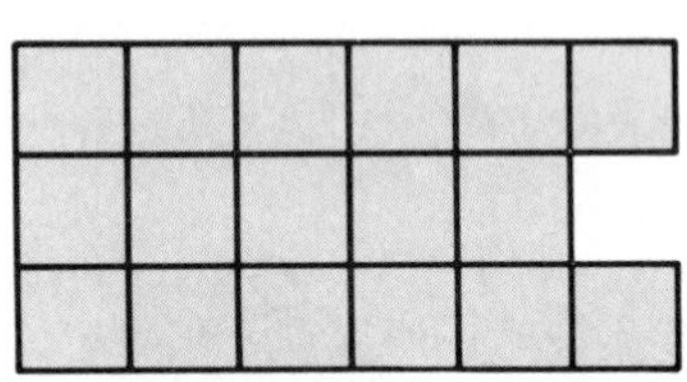
____ squares

4. 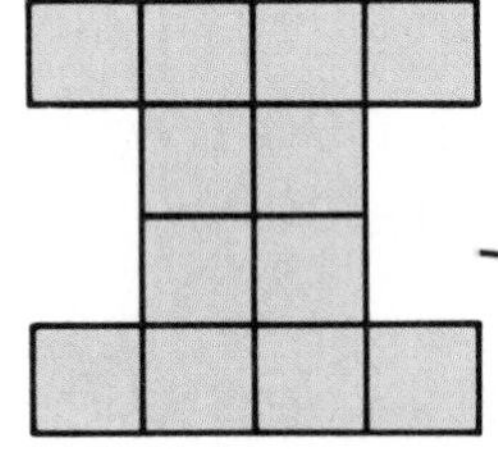
____ squares

5. 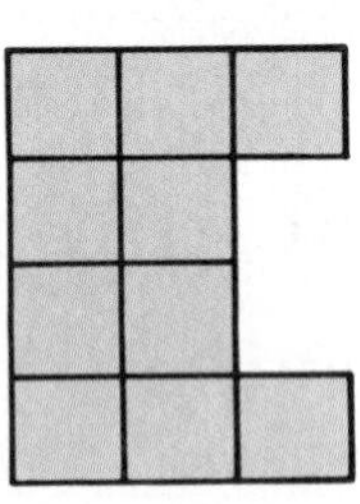
____ squares

6. 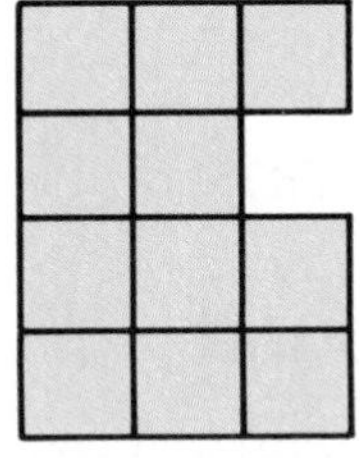
____ squares

7. 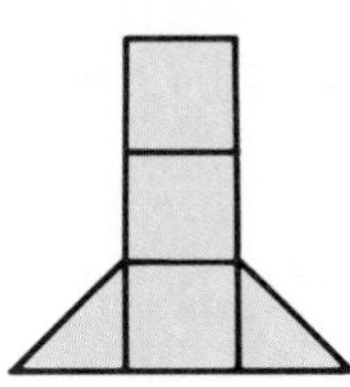
____ squares

8. 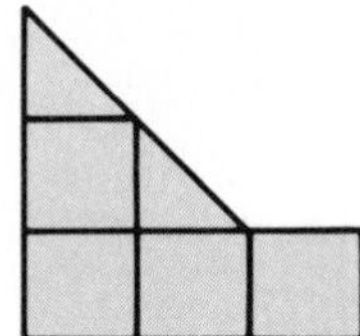
____ squares

Exploring Mathematics Book Two © Scott, Foresman and Company

Notes for Home Children are challenged to find the number of square units in each shape.

Name

Chapter 12 Review/Test

1. How many sides and corners?

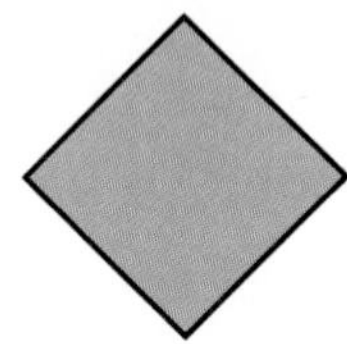

_____ sides _____ corners

2. Circle the one that is the same size and shape.

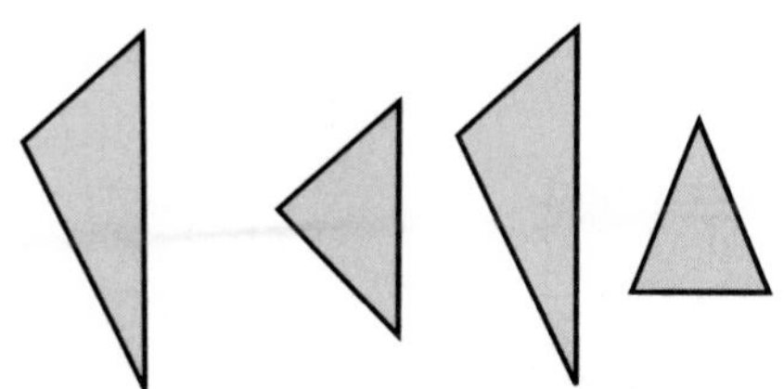

3. Measure the distance around the shape.

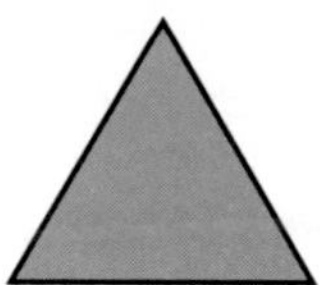

_____ centimeters

4. Do the parts match when folded? Ring yes or no.

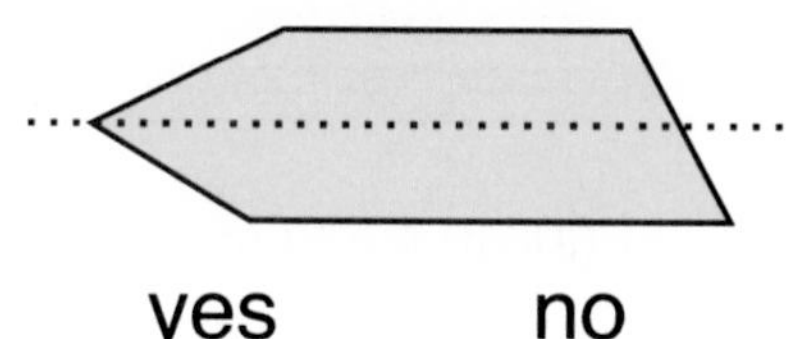

yes no

5. Ring the name of this solid.

sphere

cone

cylinder

6. How many degrees?

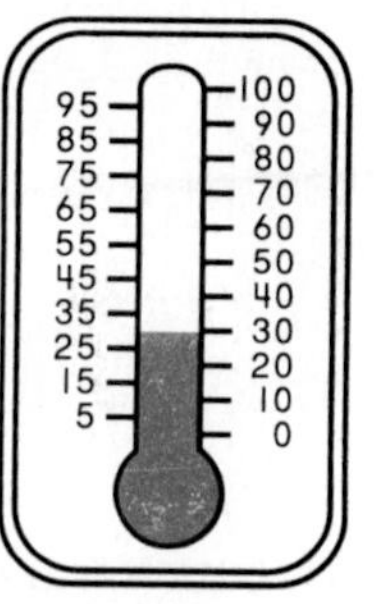

_____ degrees

7. Ring about how much each holds.

less than 1 gallon

more than 1 gallon

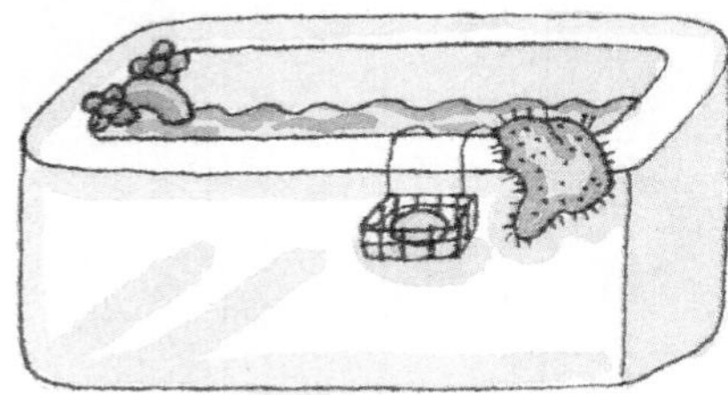

less than 1 liter

more than 1 liter

8. Where is the ● on the graph?

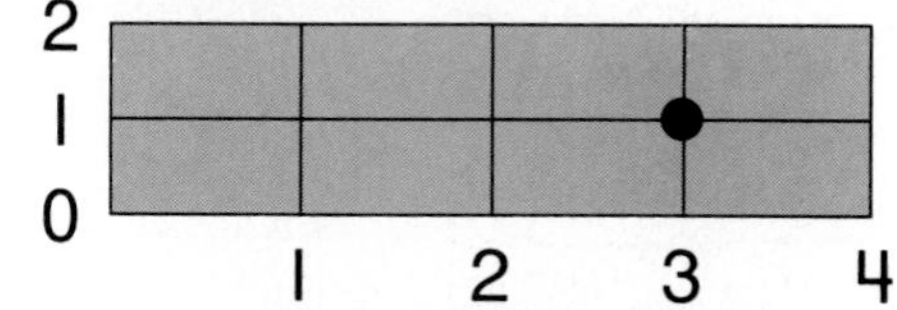

across	up

9. Ring about how much each weighs.

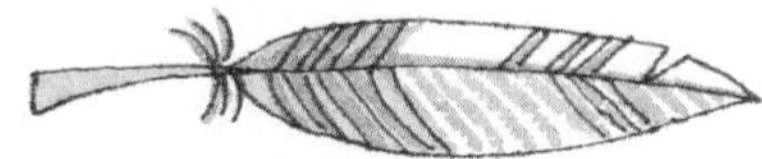

less than 1 kilogram

more than 1 kilogram

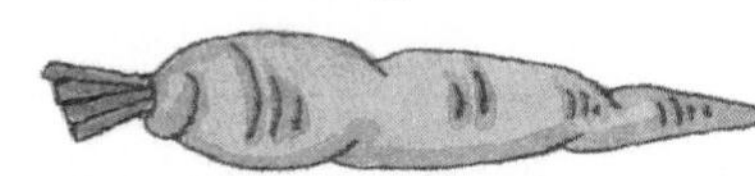

less than 1 pound

more than 1 pound

10. About how much does a kitten weigh? Ring the better measure.

3 pounds 50 pounds

Notes for Home Children are assessed on Chapter 12 concepts, skills, and problem solving.

Exploring Math at Home

Dear Family,

In this chapter I have learned more about shapes and how to measure them. I have also learned about estimating capacity and reading a thermometer. Please help me with the activities below.

Love, ______________________________

1.

Measure the distance around objects. Then add the inches along each side.

2.

Use cup, pint, quart, and gallon containers to compare capacities.

3.

Estimate if something is heavier or lighter than 1 pound or heavier or lighter than 1 kilogram. Use a scale to check.

4.

Compare thermometer readings taken at different times of the day. Compare indoor and outdoor temperatures.

Coming Attractions

In the next chapter I will learn to add and subtract three-digit numbers.

Exploring Mathematics Book Two © Scott, Foresman and Company

Chapter

13 Three-Digit Addition and Subtraction

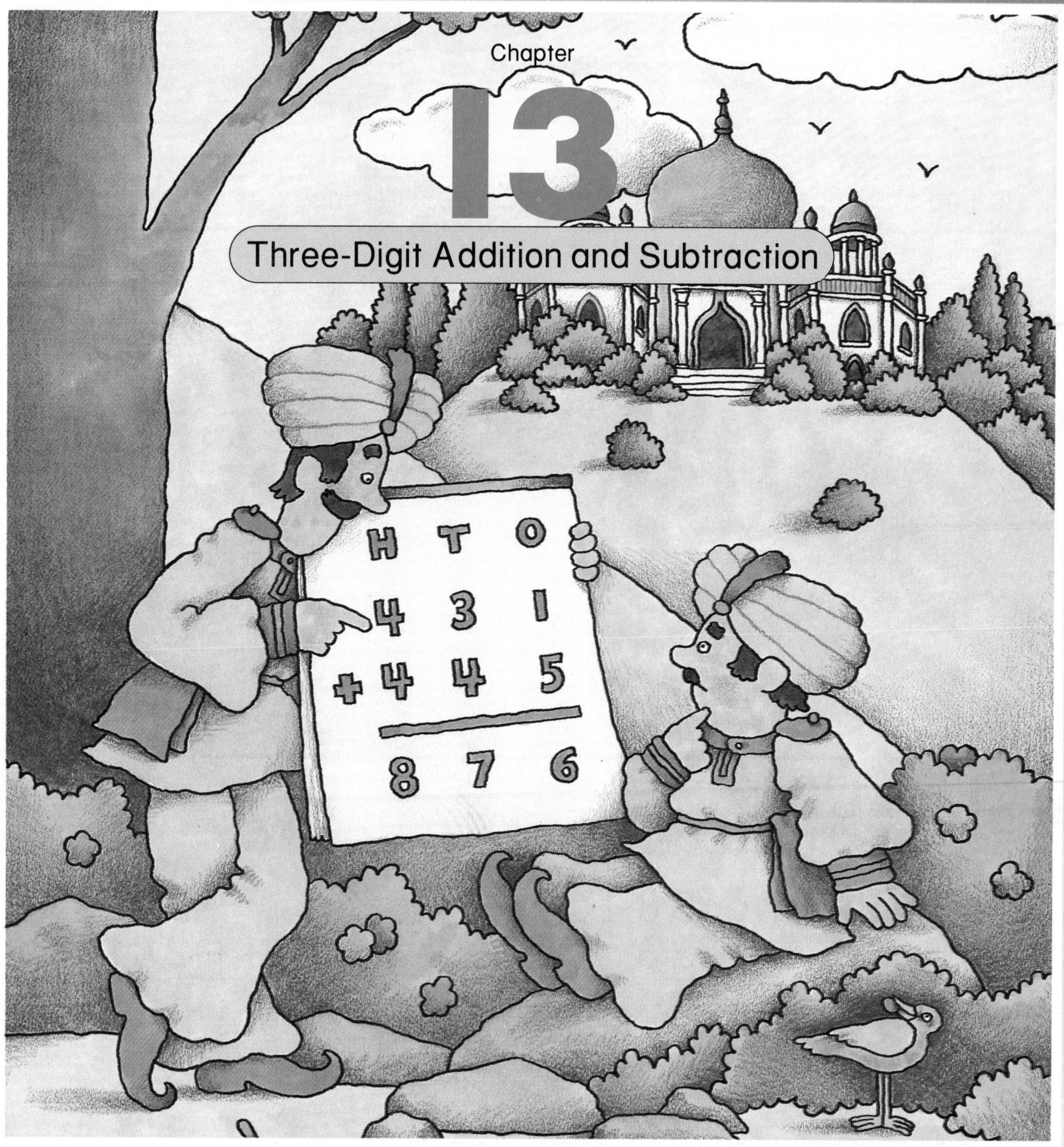

Listen to the math story, "The Lost Marbles."
Ali and Baba found 876 of the marbles.
How did they find how many were still missing?

Notes for Home Children listen to a math story introducing chapter concepts and skills. Then they answer a question about the story.

Reviewing Two-Digit Computation

I do not need to trade to find this sum.

I need to trade to find this difference.

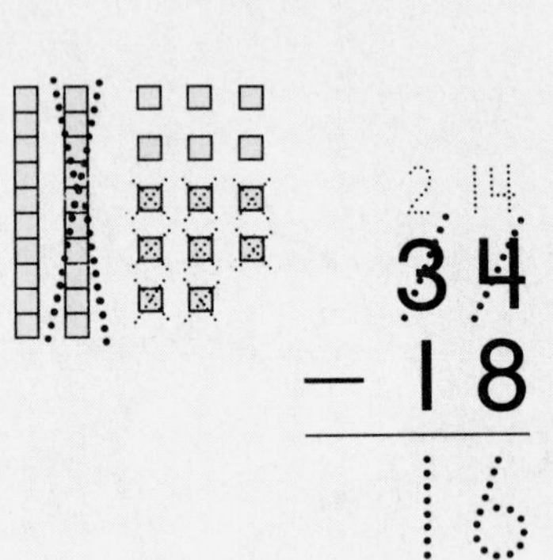

Do you need to trade?
Ring yes or no. Then add or subtract.

1. $\begin{array}{r} 52 \\ +\ 15 \\ \hline \end{array}$ yes no $\begin{array}{r} 38 \\ +\ 26 \\ \hline \end{array}$ yes no $\begin{array}{r} 65 \\ +\ 18 \\ \hline \end{array}$ yes no $\begin{array}{r} 33 \\ +\ 24 \\ \hline \end{array}$ yes no

2. $\begin{array}{r} 62 \\ -\ 18 \\ \hline \end{array}$ yes no $\begin{array}{r} 53 \\ -\ 27 \\ \hline \end{array}$ yes no $\begin{array}{r} 47 \\ -\ 25 \\ \hline \end{array}$ yes no $\begin{array}{r} 80 \\ -\ 26 \\ \hline \end{array}$ yes no

Exploring Mathematics Book Two © Scott, Foresman and Company

Notes for Home Children prepare for three-digit computation by reviewing two-digit computation.

Name

Trading 10 Ones for 1 Ten

Add the ones.
Trade 10 ones for 1 ten.
Add the tens.

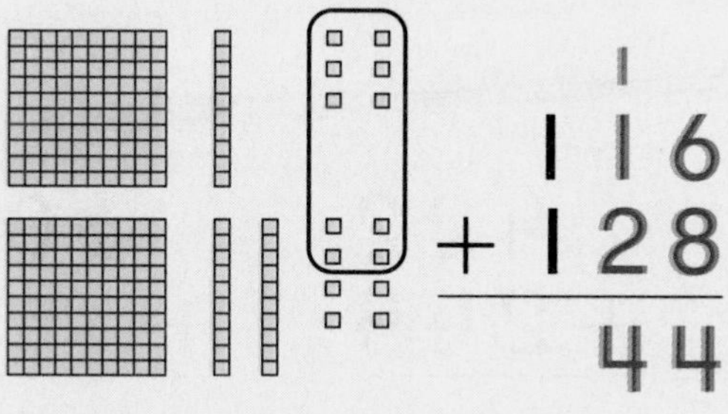

Now add the hundreds.

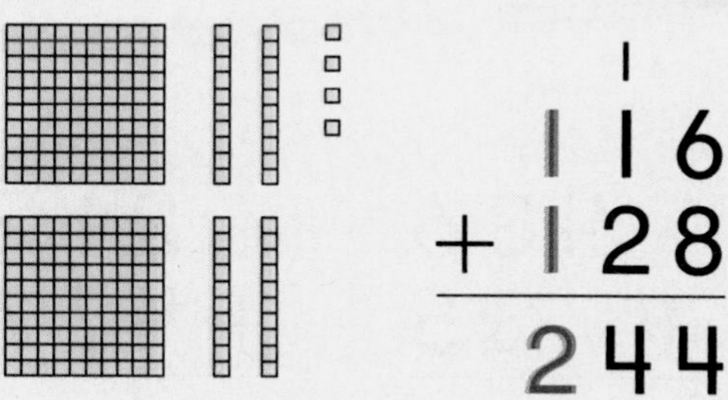

Do you need to trade? Ring yes or no.
Ring the trade. Then add.

hundreds	tens	ones

1.

$$\begin{array}{r} 327 \\ +\ 135 \\ \hline 462 \end{array}$$

yes (ringed)
no

hundreds	tens	ones

2.

$$\begin{array}{r} 234 \\ +\ 23 \\ \hline \end{array}$$

yes
no

Notes for Home Children find three-digit sums using pictures of place-value materials.

Ring if you need to trade.
Then add.

3.

223	328	123	429	164
+ 528	+ 37	+ 344	+ 5	+ 527
751				

4.

436	212	305	422	606
+ 35	+ 477	+ 239	+ 244	+ 6

5.

718	326	619
+ 8	+ 454	+ 38

Problem Solving

Solve.

6. Mr. and Mrs. Lu went shopping.
Mr. Lu spent $228. Mrs. Lu
spent $55 more than Mr. Lu.
How much money did Mrs. Lu spend?

Exploring Mathematics Book Two © Scott, Foresman and Company

Notes for Home Children practice adding one-, two-, and three-digit numbers to find three-digit sums.
Then they solve a problem that has a three-digit sum.

Name

Trading 10 Tens for 1 Hundred

1. Add the ones. Add the tens. Trade 10 tens for 1 hundred.

	hundreds	tens	ones
	[1]		
	1	4	3
+	2	9	2
		3	5

2. Then add the hundreds.

	hundreds	tens	ones
	[1]		
	1	4	3
+	2	9	2
	4	3	5

Use Workmat 2.
Use hundreds, tens, and ones counters.
Add.

1.

	hundreds	tens	ones
	[1]		
	2	3	4
+	1	8	2
	4	1	6

	hundreds	tens	ones
	[ ]		
	1	7	3
+		6	4

	hundreds	tens	ones
	[ ]		
	2	3	7
+	1	2	2

Notes for Home Children explore at the CONCRETE level using hundreds, tens, and ones counters and a place-value workmat to find three-digit sums.

Use Workmat 2.

Use hundreds, tens, and ones counters.

Add.

2.

	hundreds	tens	ones
	☐		
	1	3	2
+	2	8	1
	4	1	3

	hundreds	tens	ones
	☐		
	3	1	5
+	1	7	2

	hundreds	tens	ones
	☐		
	2	2	3
+	1	9	4

3.

	hundreds	tens	ones
	☐		
	2	3	6
+			3

	hundreds	tens	ones
	☐		
	1	8	5
+	1	4	3

	hundreds	tens	ones
	☐		
	2	2	7
+	1	0	2

4.

	hundreds	tens	ones
	☐		
	2	3	6
+	1	9	2

	hundreds	tens	ones
	☐		
	1	6	4
+		8	2

	hundreds	tens	ones
	☐		
	2	7	4
+	1	7	4

Exploring Mathematics Book Two © Scott, Foresman and Company

Notes for Home Children explore at the CONCRETE level using hundreds, tens, and ones counters and a place-value workmat to find three-digit sums.

Name

Adding Three-Digit Numbers

Alma is pasting stamps of musical instruments in her stampbook. How many stamps will she paste in her stampbook?

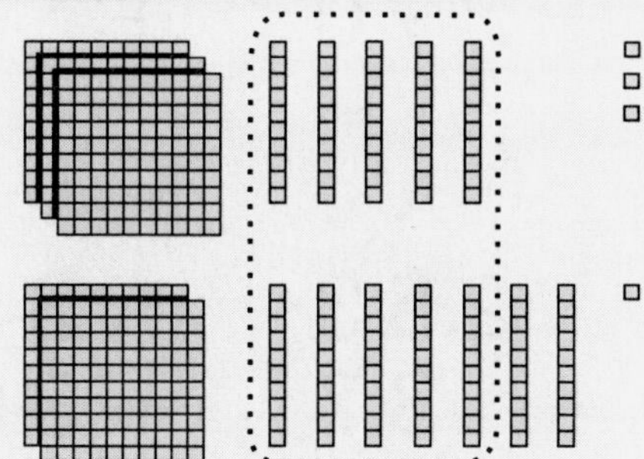

```
  356
+ 271
  627 stamps
```

Add. Ring if you need to trade.

1. 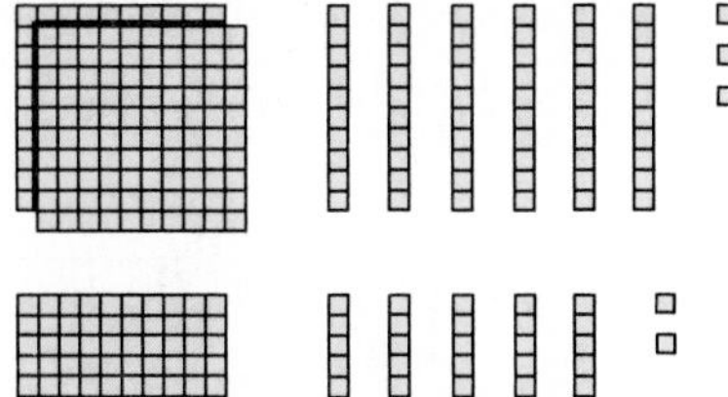

```
  263
+ 152
```

2. 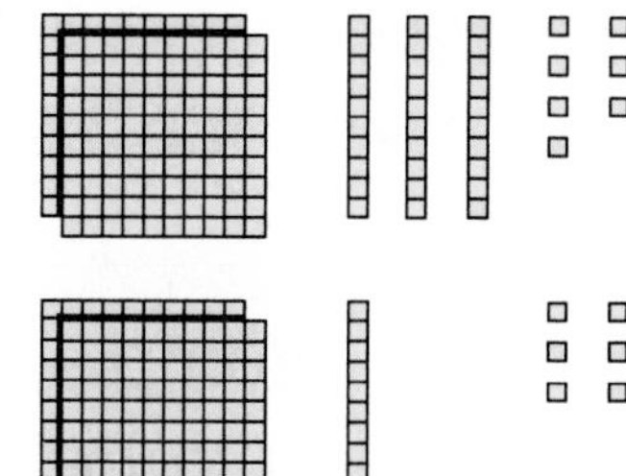

```
  237
+ 216
```

3. 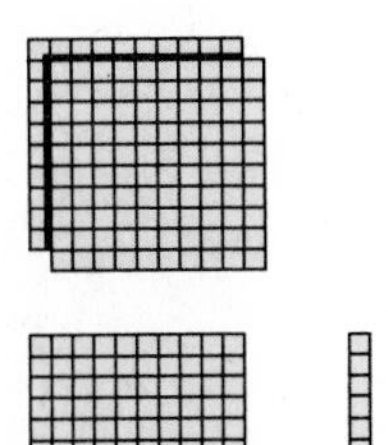

```
  204
+ 121
```

4. 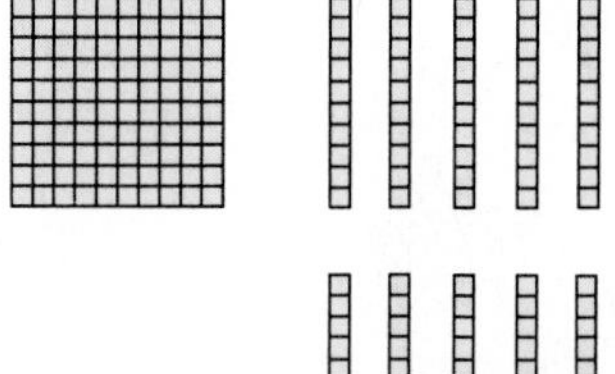

```
  152
+  56
```

Notes for Home Children find three-digit sums using pictures of place-value materials.

Add. Trade if necessary.

5.	338 + 70 408	247 + 135	309 + 88	371 + 291	128 + 62
6.	467 + 125	232 + 151	163 + 9	330 + 290	316 + 39
7.	256 + 183	526 + 82	463 + 475	253 + 37	333 + 303
8.	372 + 594	629 + 8	301 + 89	282 + 435	393 + 393

Write About Math

Make up an addition example in which you must make a trade.

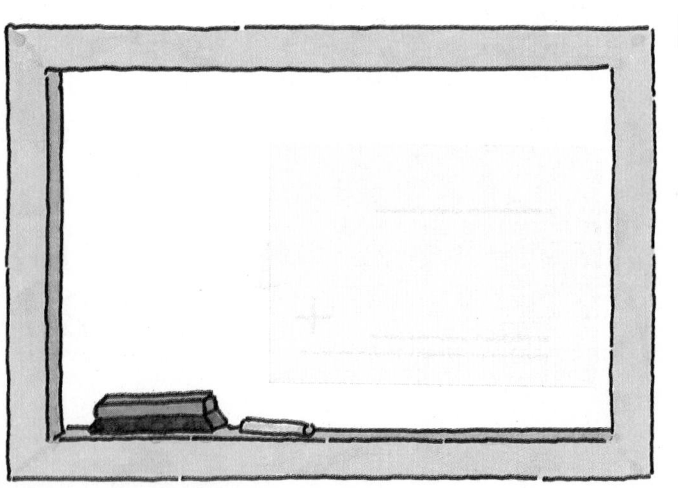

Exploring Mathematics Book Two © Scott, Foresman and Company

Notes for Home Children practice finding three-digit sums. Then they write a problem involving a trade.

See More Practice Set A on page 419.

Name

PROBLEM-SOLVING GUIDE
Understand
Plan and Solve
Look Back

Use Logical Reasoning

Tom is thinking of one of these numbers.
It is greater than 300.
There is an 8 in the tens place.
Which number is he thinking of?

307 261 485

Use the clues to solve.
Ring the number.

1. Erik is between 100 and 128 centimeters tall. You say the number in the ones place when you count by fives. How tall is Erik?

188 cm 125 cm 116 cm

2. There is a number on Jane's car.
It is less than 700.
There is a 3 in the ones place.
What is the number?

631 863 563

3. The number on Sheila's shirt has a 4 in the ones place and a 6 in the tens place. The number in the hundreds place is 3 greater than the number in the ones place. What number is on Sheila's shirt?

764 463 364

Notes for Home Children solve problems involving number relationships and place value by using logical reasoning.

Use the clues to solve.

4. The baby weighs less than 11 pounds. and more than 8 pounds. You say the number when you count by twos. How much does the baby weigh?

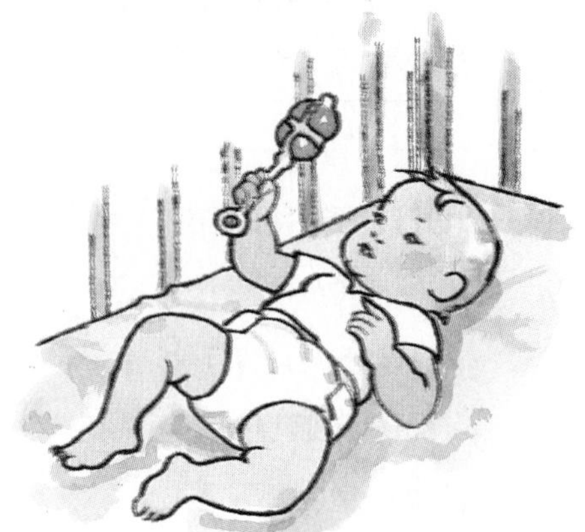

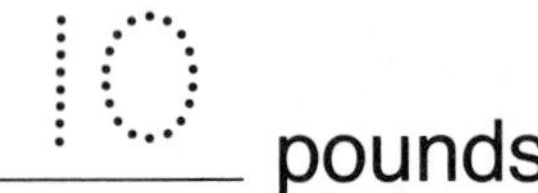

_____ pounds

5. It is hot outside. The temperature is between 85 degrees and 95 degrees. There is a 7 in the number. What is the temperature?

_____ degrees

6. Jon's father is between 30 and 40 years old. The number in the tens place is the same as the number in the ones place. How old is Jon's father?

_____ years old

7. Bill has a new book. It has fewer than 100 pages and more than 50 pages. There is a 7 in the number. You say this number when you count by tens.

_____ pages

Exploring Mathematics Book Two © Scott, Foresman and Company

Notes for Home Children solve problems involving number relationships and place value by using logical reasoning.

Name

Number Sense

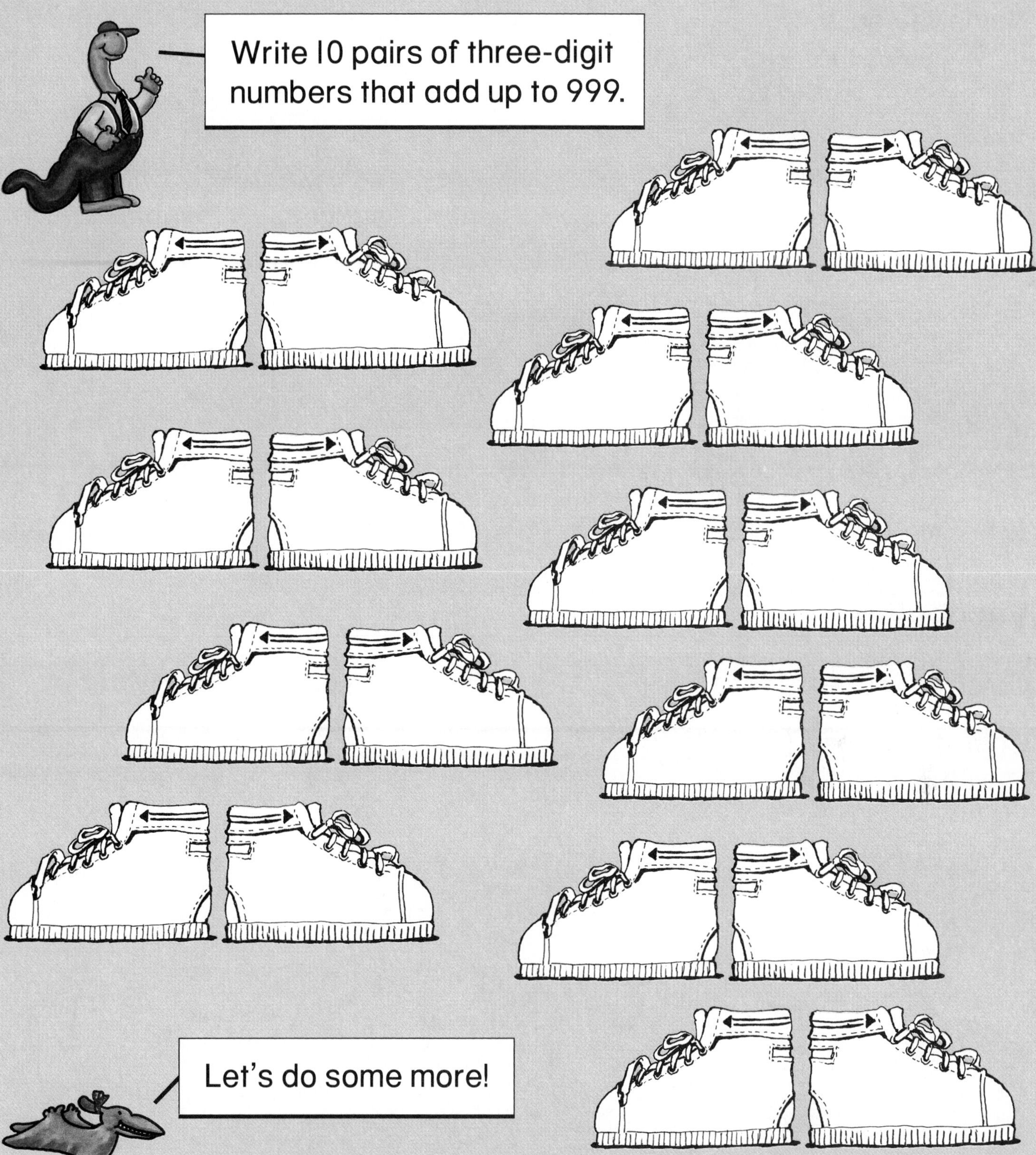

Write 3 three-digit numbers that add up to 999.
Do this two more times.

Notes for Home Children develop number understanding by making up problems that have sums of 999.

SKILLS REVIEW

Skills Review

Fill in the correct ◯.
Name the solid.

1\.

cone (A) cylinder (B)

2\.

square (A) cube (B)

3\.

cube (A) cylinder (B)

4\.

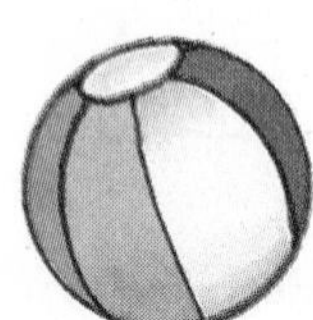

circle (A) sphere (B)

Vocabulary

Color the cubes red.

Color the spheres green.

Color the cones blue.

Color the cylinders yellow.

Exploring Mathematics Book Two © Scott, Foresman and Company

Notes for Home Children review identifying solids. Then they color solids in a picture.

Name

Trading 1 Ten for 10 Ones

Trade 1 ten for 10 ones before subtracting the ones and tens.

Now subtract the hundreds.

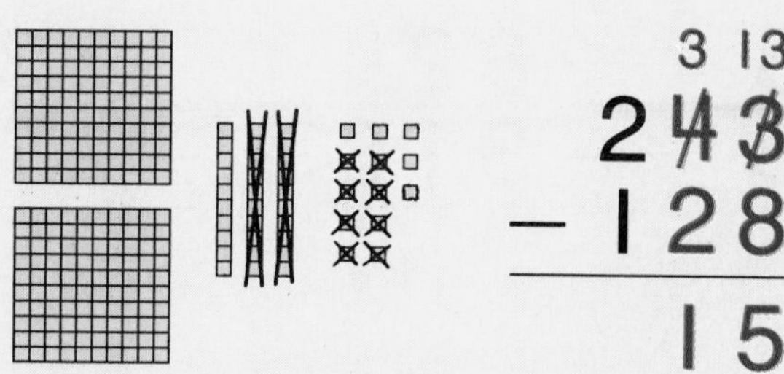

```
  3 13
  2 4 3
- 1 2 8
    1 5
```

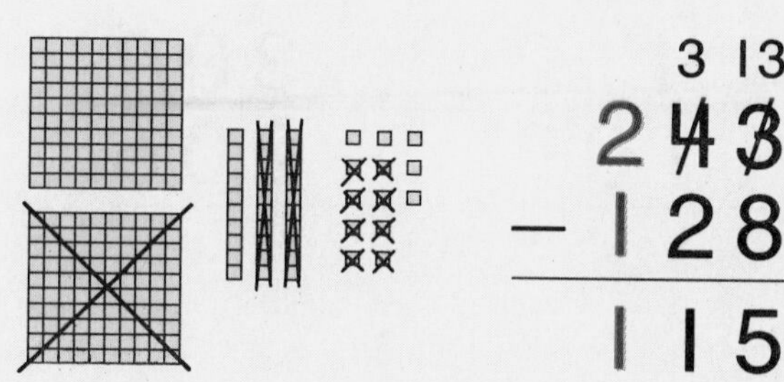

```
  3 13
  2 4 3
- 1 2 8
  1 1 5
```

Cross out to subtract. Then record.

1.

hundreds	tens	ones

```
  4 16
  3 5 6
- 1 3 9
  2 1 7
```

2.

hundreds	tens	ones

```
  4 3 6
- 2 1 4
```

Notes for Home Children subtract from three-digit numbers using pictures of place-value materials.

Ring if you need to trade. Then subtract.

3.	$\begin{array}{r} {\scriptstyle 4\ 12} \\ 452 \\ -\ 137 \\ \hline 315 \end{array}$	$\begin{array}{r} 366 \\ -\ 38 \\ \hline \end{array}$	$\begin{array}{r} 423 \\ -\ 412 \\ \hline \end{array}$	$\begin{array}{r} 352 \\ -\ 128 \\ \hline \end{array}$	$\begin{array}{r} 943 \\ -\ 716 \\ \hline \end{array}$
4.	$\begin{array}{r} 412 \\ -\ 109 \\ \hline \end{array}$	$\begin{array}{r} 309 \\ -\ 206 \\ \hline \end{array}$	$\begin{array}{r} 423 \\ -\ 5 \\ \hline \end{array}$	$\begin{array}{r} 824 \\ -\ 318 \\ \hline \end{array}$	$\begin{array}{r} 532 \\ -\ 215 \\ \hline \end{array}$
5.	$\begin{array}{r} 323 \\ -\ 219 \\ \hline \end{array}$	$\begin{array}{r} 435 \\ -\ 418 \\ \hline \end{array}$	$\begin{array}{r} 631 \\ -\ 20 \\ \hline \end{array}$	$\begin{array}{r} 768 \\ -\ 325 \\ \hline \end{array}$	$\begin{array}{r} 437 \\ -\ 419 \\ \hline \end{array}$
6.	$\begin{array}{r} 607 \\ -\ 305 \\ \hline \end{array}$	$\begin{array}{r} 751 \\ -\ 234 \\ \hline \end{array}$	$\begin{array}{r} 541 \\ -\ 327 \\ \hline \end{array}$	$\begin{array}{r} 973 \\ -\ 458 \\ \hline \end{array}$	$\begin{array}{r} 862 \\ -\ 554 \\ \hline \end{array}$

Problem Solving

Solve.

7. Mr. Little weighs 182 pounds. Mrs. Little weighs 135 pounds. How much more does Mr. Little weigh than Mrs. Little?

$\begin{array}{r} \underline{\qquad} \\ \square\ \underline{\qquad} \\ \hline \end{array}$

_______ pounds more

Exploring Mathematics Book Two © Scott, Foresman and Company

Notes for Home Children practice subtracting from three-digit numbers. Then they solve a problem involving three-digit subtraction.

Name

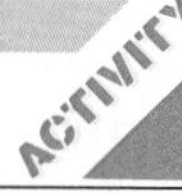

Trading 1 Hundred for 10 Tens

1. Subtract the ones. Trade 1 hundred for 10 tens.

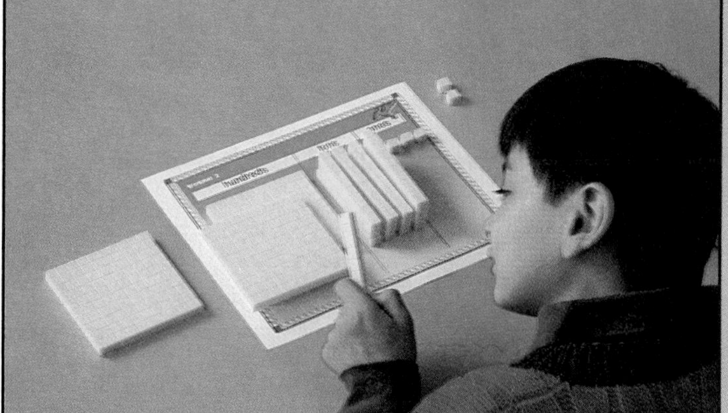

	hundreds	tens	ones
	2	14	
	~~3~~	~~4~~	5
−	1	6	2
			3

2. Then subtract the tens and the hundreds.

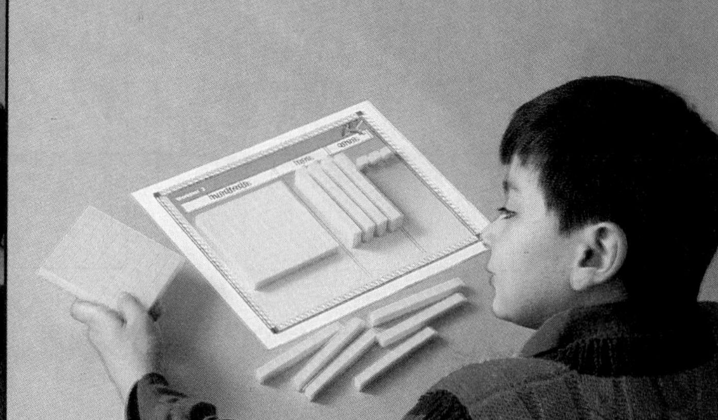

	hundreds	tens	ones
	2	14	
	~~3~~	~~4~~	5
−	1	6	2
	1	8	3

Use Workmat 2.
Use hundreds, tens, and ones counters.
Subtract.

1.

	hundreds	tens	ones
	3	13	
	~~4~~	~~3~~	6
−	1	9	2
	2	4	4

	hundreds	tens	ones
	5	8	7
−	3	2	4

	hundreds	tens	ones
	2	3	8
−		5	6

Notes for Home Children explore at the CONCRETE level using hundreds, tens, and ones counters and a place-value workmat to find three-digit differences.

Use Workmat 2.
Use hundreds, tens, and ones counters.
Then subtract.

2.

	hundreds	tens	ones
	3	15	
	4	5	3
−	1	7	2
	2	8	1

	hundreds	tens	ones
	3	1	5
−		3	2

	hundreds	tens	ones
	4	8	8
−	2	2	2

3.

	hundreds	tens	ones
	4	3	6
−		5	6

	hundreds	tens	ones
	4	2	4
−	2	8	1

	hundreds	tens	ones
	3	1	8
−	2	7	6

4.

	hundreds	tens	ones
	3	1	5
−	2	1	2

	hundreds	tens	ones
	4	2	8
−		7	3

	hundreds	tens	ones
	4	3	5
−	1	5	0

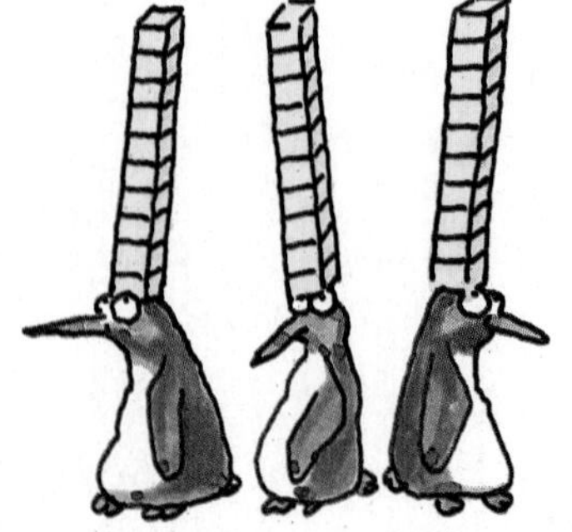

Exploring Mathematics Book Two © Scott, Foresman and Company

Notes for Home Children explore at the CONCRETE level using hundreds, tens, and ones counters and a place-value workmat to find three-digit differences.

Name

Subtracting Three-Digit Numbers

Mr. Ricks had 404 letters to deliver. He delivered 132. How many letters does he have left?

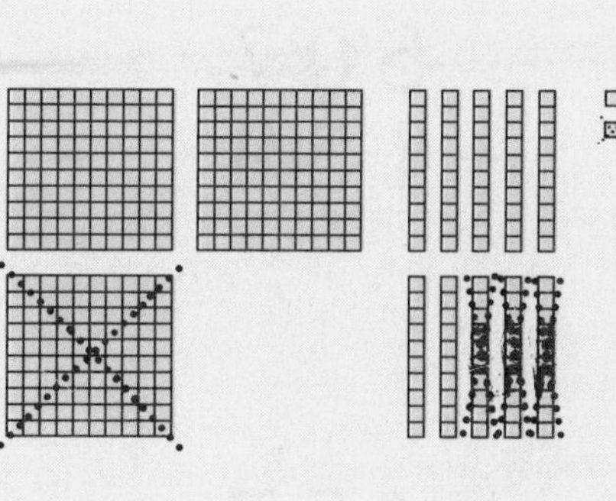

$$\begin{array}{r} \overset{3}{\cancel{4}}\overset{10}{\cancel{0}}4 \\ -\ 132 \\ \hline 272 \end{array}$$

Cross out to subtract. Record.

1.

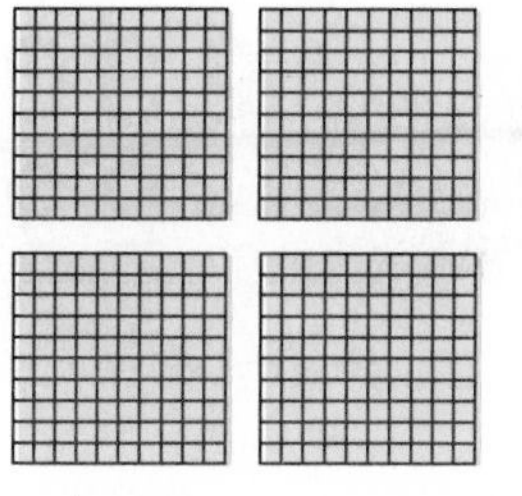

$$\begin{array}{r} 430 \\ -\ 123 \\ \hline \end{array}$$

2.

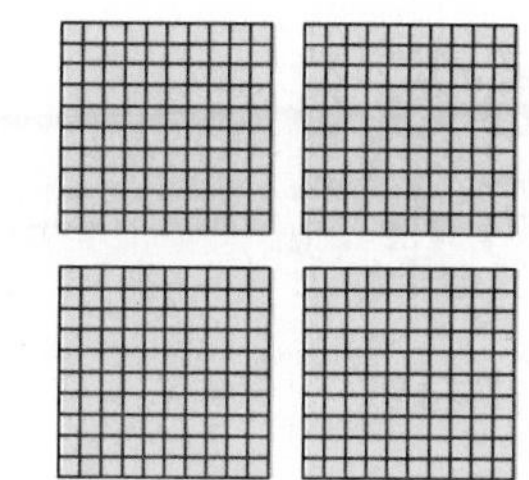

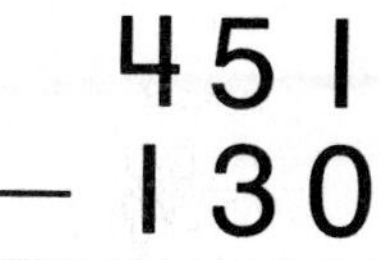

$$\begin{array}{r} 451 \\ -\ 130 \\ \hline \end{array}$$

3.

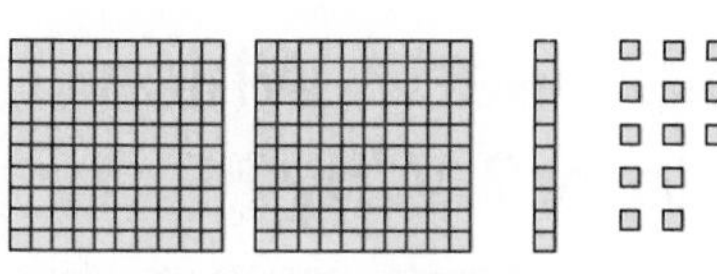

$$\begin{array}{r} 223 \\ -\ 14 \\ \hline \end{array}$$

4.

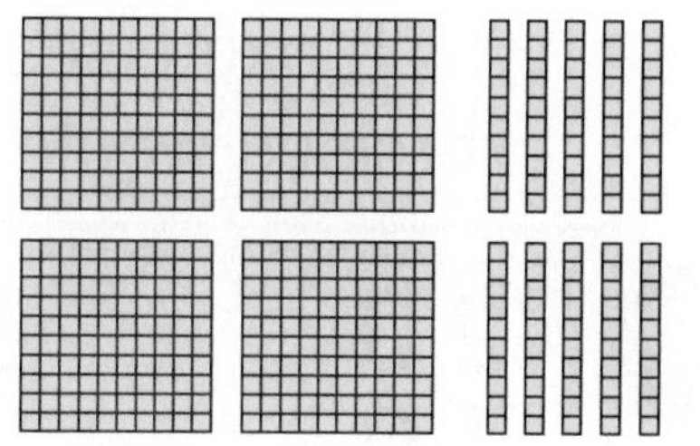

$$\begin{array}{r} 502 \\ -\ 341 \\ \hline \end{array}$$

Notes for Home Children subtract from three-digit numbers with emphasis on 0, using pictures of place-value materials.

Subtract.
Trade if necessary.

5.

3 11 3~~41~~	424	603	223	800
− 105	− 19	− 191	− 218	− 170
236				

6.

454	433	606	507	980
− 32	− 8	− 123	− 134	− 850

7.

374	716	509	657	930
− 127	− 382	− 247	− 248	− 726

8.

427	658	716	845	230
− 115	− 563	− 107	− 161	− 29

Talk About Math

Which exercises would you do in your head? Which exercises would you do with a calculator? Why?

20	642	30	256
− 10	− 238	+ 50	+ 439

Notes for Home Children practice subtracting from three-digit numbers. Then they talk about using different methods when adding or subtracting.

See More Practice Set B on page 419.

Exploring Mathematics Book Two © Scott, Foresman and Company

Name ______________________________

Adding and Subtracting Money

Add to find how much they cost in all.

Subtract to find how much change you will get from $5.00.

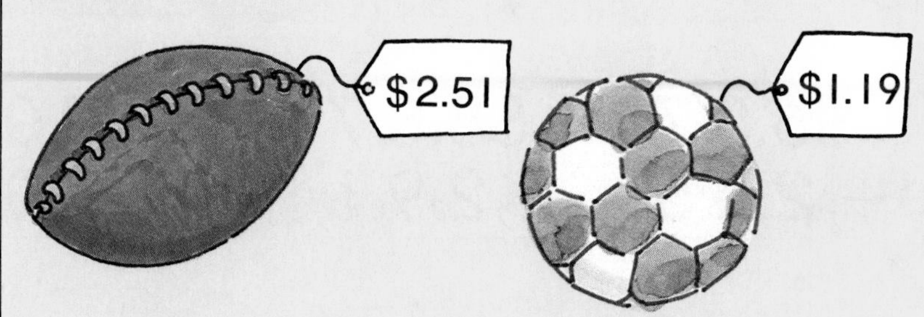

$\begin{array}{r} \scriptstyle 1 \\ \$2.51 \\ +\ 1.19 \\ \hline \$3.70 \end{array}$	$\begin{array}{r} \scriptstyle 4\ 10 \\ \$5.00 \\ -\ 3.70 \\ \hline \$1.30 \end{array}$

Add or subtract.

1.

$\begin{array}{r} \$1.68 \\ +\ 4.51 \\ \hline \end{array}$	$\begin{array}{r} \$3.62 \\ +\ 0.53 \\ \hline \end{array}$	$\begin{array}{r} \$4.28 \\ +\ 1.55 \\ \hline \end{array}$	$\begin{array}{r} \$3.29 \\ +\ 0.19 \\ \hline \end{array}$	$\begin{array}{r} \$2.84 \\ +\ 1.02 \\ \hline \end{array}$

2.

$\begin{array}{r} \$3.52 \\ -\ 1.18 \\ \hline \end{array}$	$\begin{array}{r} \$2.13 \\ -\ 1.61 \\ \hline \end{array}$	$\begin{array}{r} \$2.56 \\ -\ 1.83 \\ \hline \end{array}$	$\begin{array}{r} \$2.84 \\ -\ 0.65 \\ \hline \end{array}$	$\begin{array}{r} \$6.65 \\ -\ 3.25 \\ \hline \end{array}$

3.

$\begin{array}{r} \$6.30 \\ -\ 1.15 \\ \hline \end{array}$	$\begin{array}{r} \$3.21 \\ +\ 2.92 \\ \hline \end{array}$	$\begin{array}{r} \$2.28 \\ +\ 1.28 \\ \hline \end{array}$	$\begin{array}{r} \$4.23 \\ -\ 1.61 \\ \hline \end{array}$	$\begin{array}{r} \$8.20 \\ -\ 2.15 \\ \hline \end{array}$

Notes for Home Children add and subtract amounts of money.

Add or subtract.

4.	$3.25 − 2.92 $0.33	$8.00 − 2.40	$3.86 + 1.32	$3.50 − 1.31	$7.66 − 0.49
5.	$2.86 + 1.08	$9.42 − 0.28	$6.37 + 2.45	$8.87 − 2.91	$9.00 − 4.30
6.	$5.76 − 0.32	$8.42 − 7.90	$9.23 − 4.81	$7.60 − 2.46	$8.50 − 3.44

Problem Solving

Solve.

7. Peter bought a comb for $1.12. He bought a brush for $1.48. How much money did he spend?

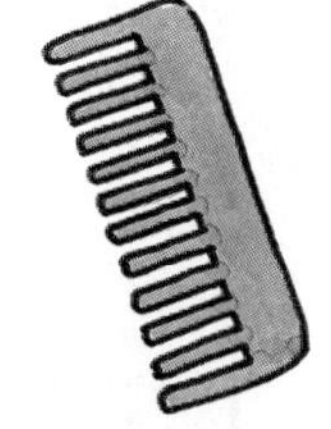

8. Peter gave the clerk $5.00 for both items. How much change did he get?

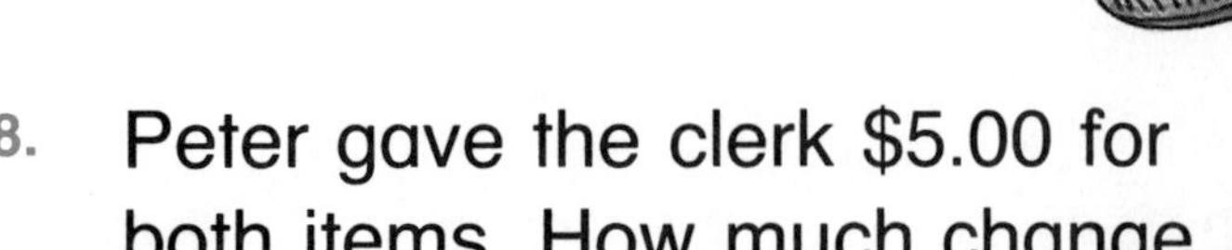

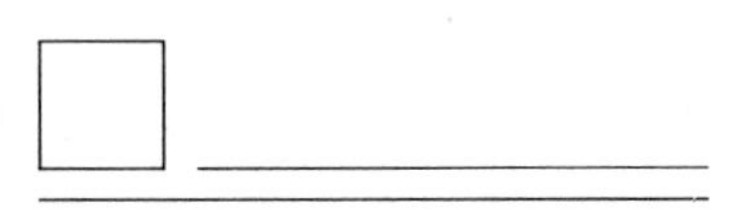

Exploring Mathematics Book Two © Scott, Foresman and Company

Notes for Home Children add and subtract amounts of money. Then they solve problems involving money.

Name

Finding Patterns with Money

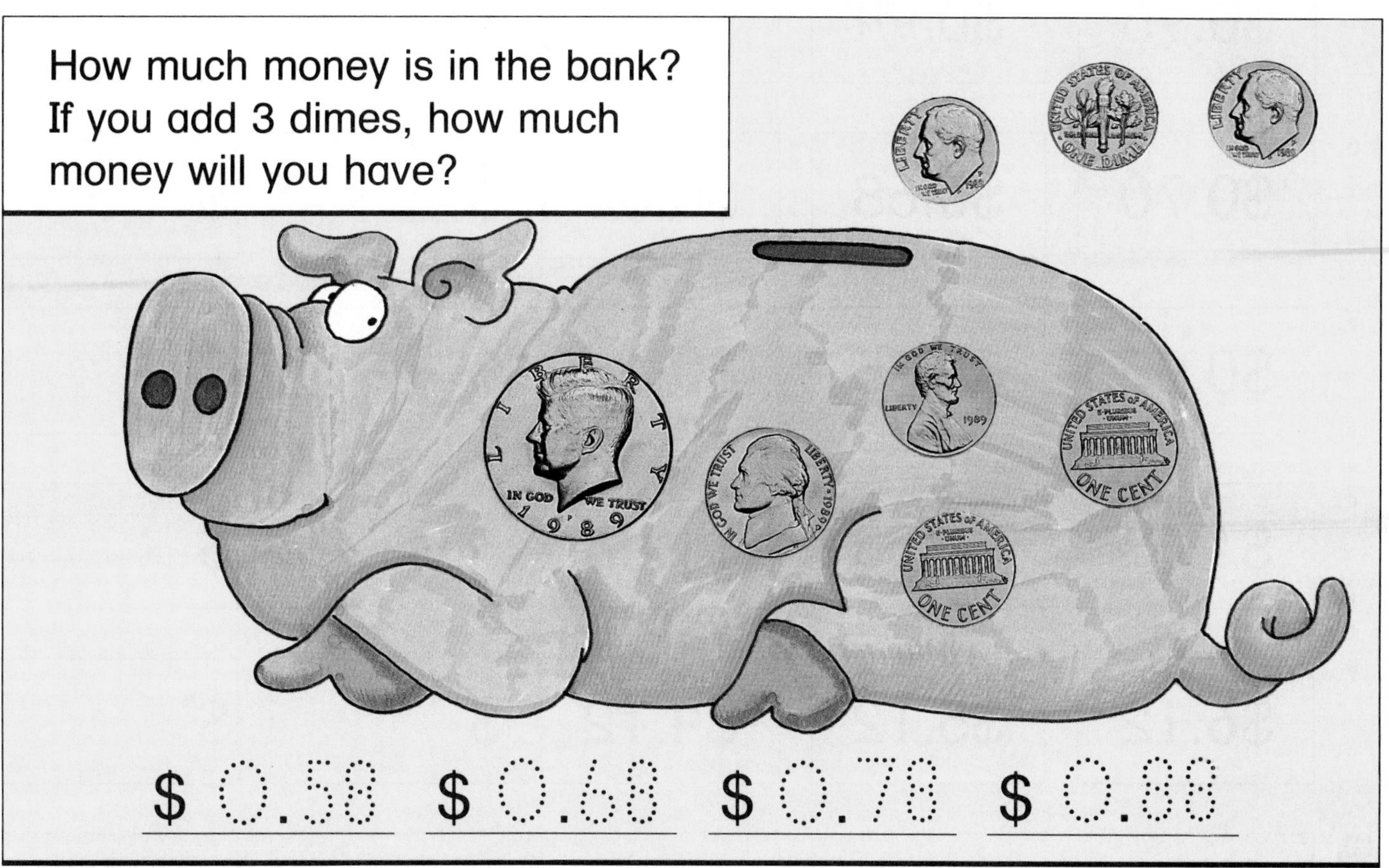

Continue each pattern.
Add pennies, dimes, or dollars.

1. $0.43 | $0.45 | $0.47 | $ | $

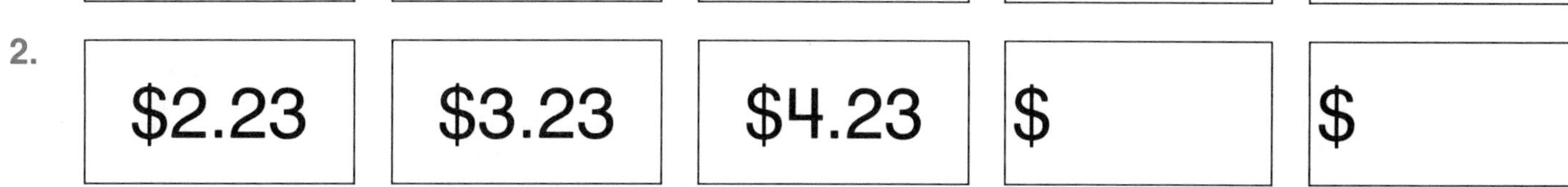

2. $2.23 | $3.23 | $4.23 | $ | $

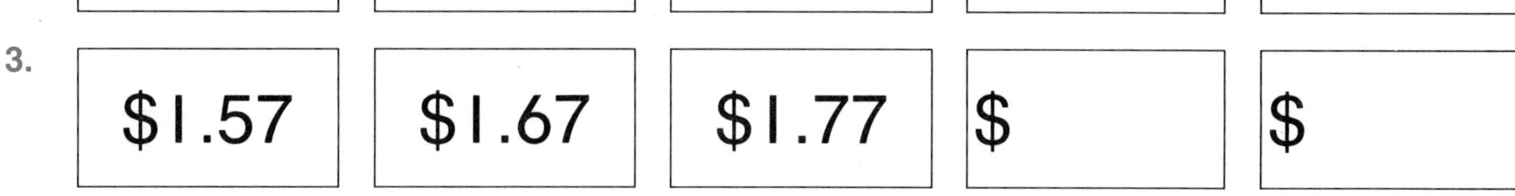

3. $1.57 | $1.67 | $1.77 | $ | $

4. $0.44 | $2.44 | $4.44 | $ | $

Notes for Home Children find and then continue number patterns by adding amounts of money.

Continue each pattern.

5.	$0.95	$0.94	$0.93	$	$
6.	$0.70	$0.68	$0.66	$	$
7.	$0.85	$0.75	$0.65	$	$
8.	$1.63	$1.53	$1.43	$	$
9.	$6.12	$5.12	$4.12	$	$
10.	$9.98	$7.98	$5.98	$	$

Problem Solving

Solve.

11. Tony had $6.84 in his bank. Each day he took out 1 dime. At the end of 5 days, how much money did Tony have left?

____

12. Sal had $2.12 in her bank. Each day she put 3 pennies in it. At the end of 5 days, how much money did Sal have?

____

Exploring Mathematics Book Two © Scott, Foresman and Company

Notes for Home Children find and then continue number patterns by subtracting amounts of money. Then they solve problems involving patterns.

Name

Choose an Operation

Many children in Ghana play a game with a small bag of stones tied to a rope. One class collected 364 stones for the game. Another class collected 129 stones. How many stones did the two classes collect altogether?

493 stones

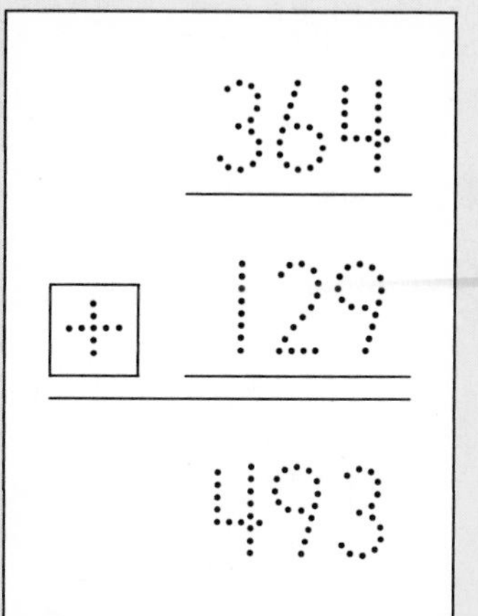

Add or subtract.

1. Ron celebrates his birthday on May 22. Many Korean children celebrate Children's Day 17 days earlier. On which day in May is Children's Day celebrated?

May ______

2. Some people have American Indian totem poles in their community. A totem pole near Eva's house is 52 feet tall. The totem pole near Mark's house is 17 feet shorter. How tall is the totem pole near Mark's house?

______ feet tall

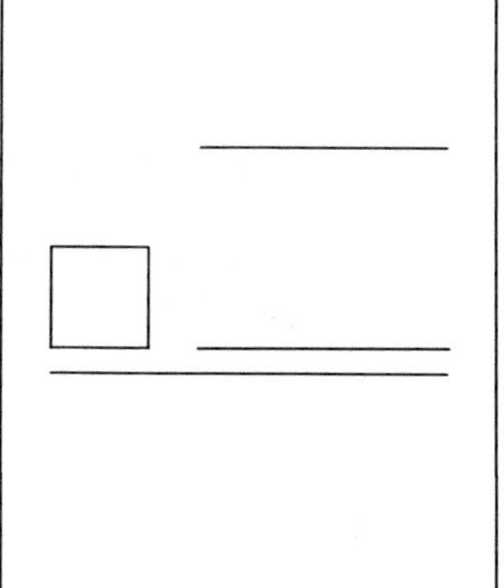

Notes for Home Children solve problems by choosing the operation.

Add or subtract.

3. Second graders learned that pandas live in the thick bamboo forests of China. A grown male panda weighs about 310 pounds. The female usually weighs about 50 pounds less. How much does a female panda weigh?

260 pounds

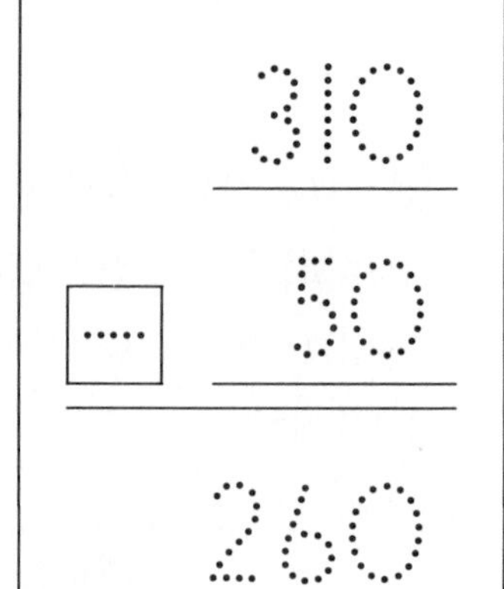

4. Written Japanese characters stand for whole words or ideas. In kindergarten children learn to read about 50 characters. By third grade they can read 885 characters. How many more characters can Japanese children read in third grade than kindergarten?

_______ more

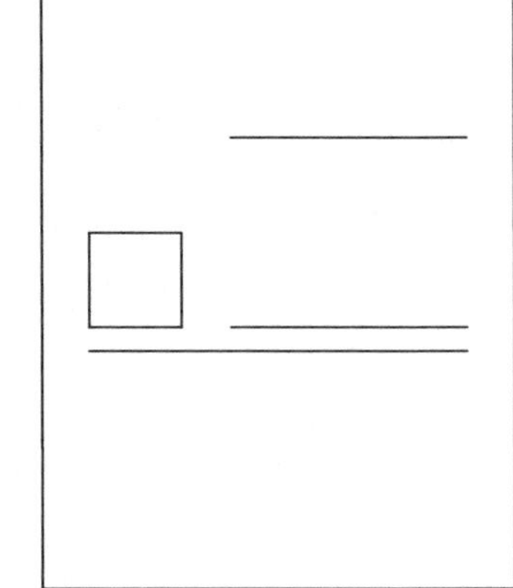

5. People hang piñatas filled with candy and small toys at many Hispanic parties. Rosi's piñata held 167 pieces of candy. Leon's piñata had 82 more pieces than Rosi's. How many pieces of candy did Leon's piñata have?

_______ pieces

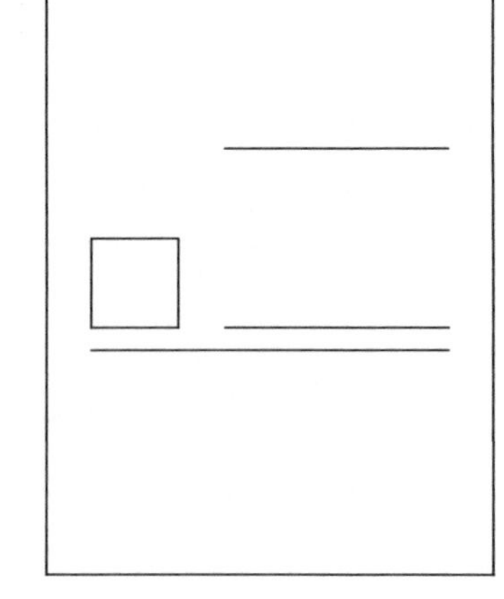

Exploring Mathematics Book Two © Scott, Foresman and Company

Notes for Home Children solve problems by choosing the operation.

Name

Problem-Solving Workshop

Explore as a Team

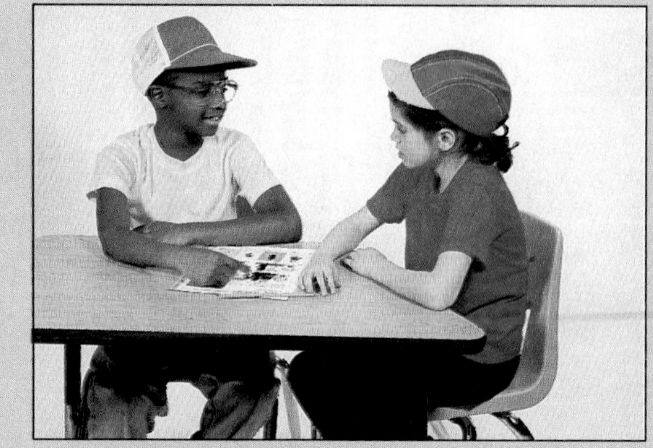

Work with a partner.
How many pounds does each weigh?
Look at the clues.
First find the weight of the man.

Write the weight of each.

Notes for Home Children explore with a partner to solve a problem involving logic and subtraction.

Problem-Solving Workshop

Explore with a Computer

Money and Time Project

1. Ring 3 animals you would like to buy.

2. How much will the three animals cost? ______

3. At the computer, there is $4.75 in the sack.

4. Buy each animal.

How much do you have left? ______

5. Have the computer count the coins to check your work.

Exploring Mathematics Book Two © Scott, Foresman and Company

Notes for Home Children add three-digit prices. At the computer, they subtract from $4.75 to determine their change and have the computer check their work.

Name

Set A Use after page 400.

Add.

Ring if you need to trade.

1. 436 + 127 = 563

2. 394 + 253

3. 506 + 342

4. 637 + 281

5. 265 + 427

6. 723 + 230

7. 478 + 341

8. 548 + 234

Set B Use after page 410.

Subtract.

Connect the answers in order.

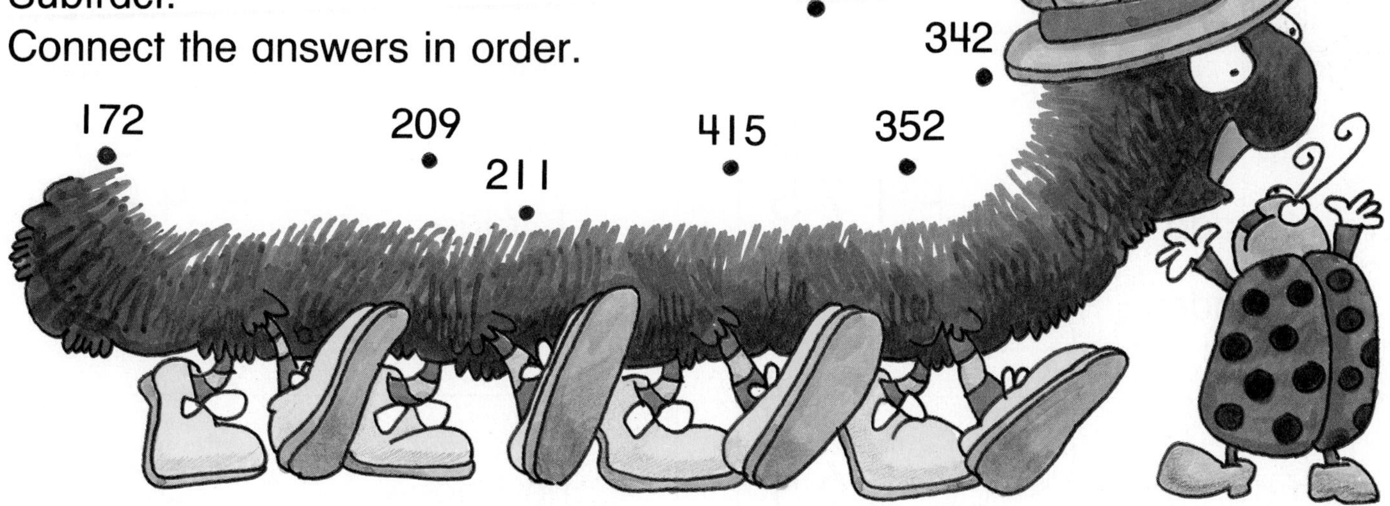

1. 604 − 262 = 342

2. 422 − 7

3. 357 − 148

4. 519 − 347

Notes for Home Set A: Children practice finding sums for three-digit numbers.
Set B: Children practice subtracting from three-digit numbers.

Enrichment

Ring how many trades are needed.

Add		Subtract	
1. no trades 1 trade 2 trades	642 + 183 = 825	4. no trades 1 trade 2 trades	435 − 268 = 167
2. no trades 1 trade 2 trades	448 + 175	5. no trades 1 trade 2 trades	781 − 423
3. no trades 1 trade 2 trades	464 + 103	6. no trades 1 trade 2 trades	523 − 276

Exploring Mathematics Book Two © Scott, Foresman and Company

Notes for Home Children are challenged to determine the number of trades needed when finding three-digit sums and differences.

Name

Chapter 13 Review/Test

1. Ring if you make a trade.
Then add.

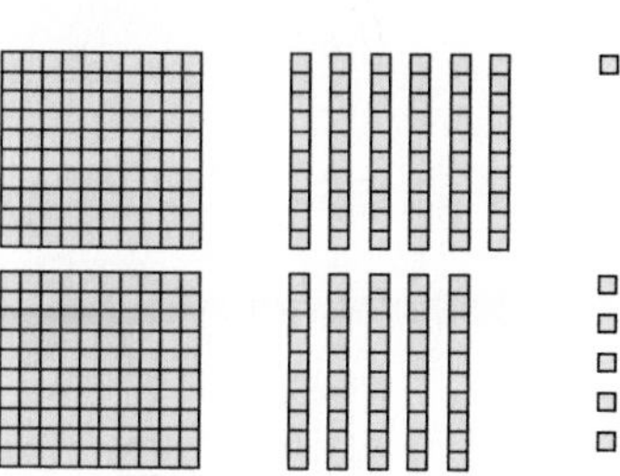

$$\begin{array}{r} 161 \\ +\ 155 \\ \hline \end{array}$$

2. Cross out to subtract.
Then record.

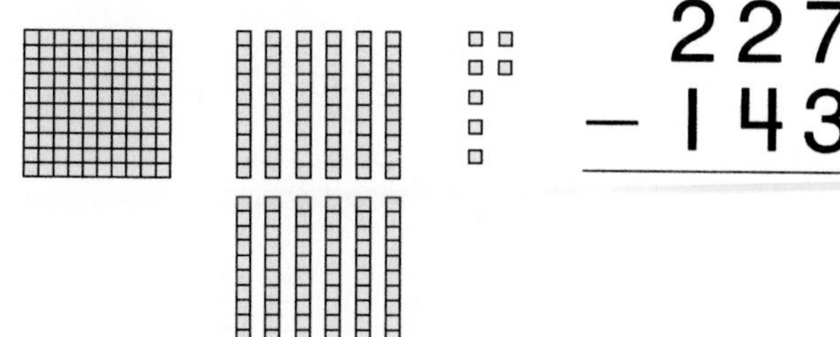

$$\begin{array}{r} 227 \\ -\ 143 \\ \hline \end{array}$$

3. Add.

$$\begin{array}{r} 646 \\ +\ 217 \\ \hline \end{array} \qquad \begin{array}{r} \$\,5.62 \\ +\ 1.42 \\ \hline \end{array}$$

4. Subtract.

$$\begin{array}{r} 621 \\ -\ 108 \\ \hline \end{array} \qquad \begin{array}{r} \$\,3.40 \\ -\ 1.27 \\ \hline \end{array}$$

5. Continue the pattern.

$1.44	$1.54	$1.64	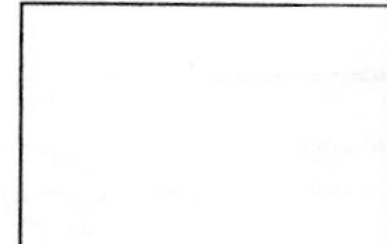	

Solve.

6. Amy's book has 124 pages.
Steve's book has 133 pages.
How many more pages are in
Steve's book than Amy's?

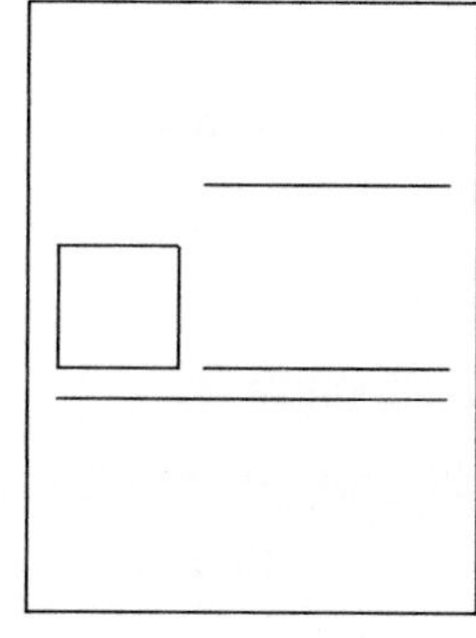

_____ pages

Solve.

7. How long did it take Carla to do her homework? It took more than 25 minutes. It took fewer than 35 minutes. There is a zero in the number.

_____ minutes

Notes for Home Children are assessed on Chapter 13 concepts, skills, and problem solving.

Exploring Math at Home

Dear Family,

In this chapter I have learned about three-digit addition and subtraction. I have also learned about money. Please help me with the activities below.

Love, ______________________________

1.

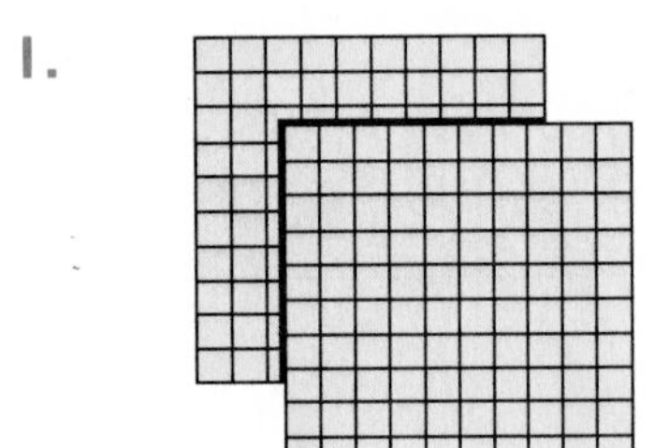

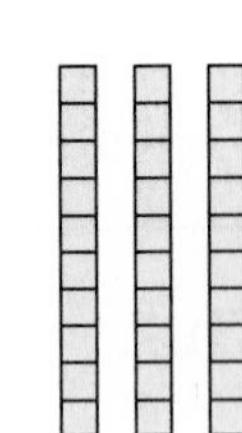

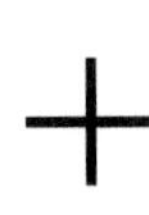

+

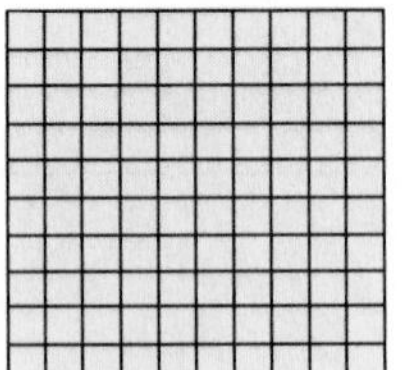

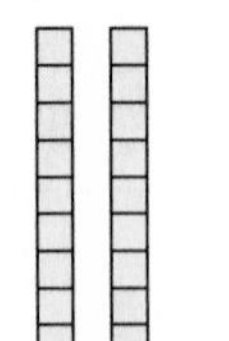

Use the squares and strips you used with Chapter 9. Show three-digit numbers. Add or subtract. Tell if you need to trade. Write the answer. Have a family member show the answer with your squares and strips.

2.

Use newspaper ads to find two objects with a combined cost of less than $10.00. Then find the difference between the costs of the same items. Your child should trade only once when adding or subtracting.

Coming Attractions

In the next chapter I will use counters and pictures to learn the meaning of multiplication and division.

Exploring Mathematics Book Two © Scott, Foresman and Company

Name

Cumulative Review/Test

Fill in the correct .
Add.

1. 6 + 8
   - Ⓐ 12
   - Ⓑ 13
   - Ⓒ 14

2. 45 + 31
   - Ⓐ 76
   - Ⓑ 86
   - Ⓒ 66

3. 61 + 29
   - Ⓐ 88
   - Ⓑ 90
   - Ⓒ 80

4. 427 + 57
   - Ⓐ 474
   - Ⓑ 484
   - Ⓒ 481

5. 266 + 418
   - Ⓐ 674
   - Ⓑ 784
   - Ⓒ 684

6. $3.45 + 2.92
   - Ⓐ $6.37
   - Ⓑ $6.47
   - Ⓒ $5.37

7. What is the name of this solid?

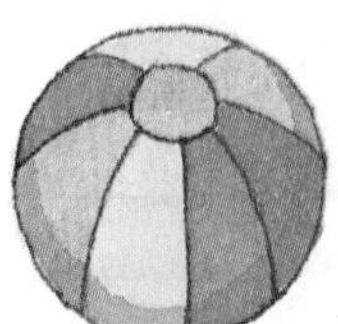

   - Ⓐ sphere
   - Ⓑ cylinder
   - Ⓒ cone

8. About how much does the dog weigh?

   - Ⓐ less than a pound
   - Ⓑ more than a pound

9. How many in all?

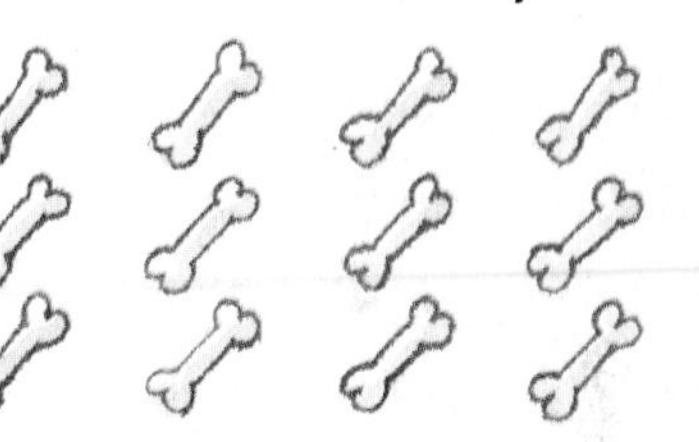

   15 Ⓐ 5 Ⓑ

10. What time is it?

   3:00 Ⓐ 3:30 Ⓑ

11. How much?

   $2.35 Ⓐ $2.40 Ⓑ

12. How much is shaded?

   $\frac{3}{4}$ Ⓐ $\frac{3}{5}$ Ⓑ

Notes for Home Children are assessed on Chapters 1–14 concepts, skills, and problem solving using a multiple-choice format.

Fill in the correct ◯.
Subtract.

13.
$$\begin{array}{r} 13 \\ -\ 6 \\ \hline \end{array}$$
Ⓐ 6
Ⓑ 7
Ⓒ 8

14.
$$\begin{array}{r} 86 \\ -\ 15 \\ \hline \end{array}$$
Ⓐ 74
Ⓑ 71
Ⓒ 61

15.
$$\begin{array}{r} 40 \\ -\ 27 \\ \hline \end{array}$$
Ⓐ 13
Ⓑ 17
Ⓒ 23

16.
$$\begin{array}{r} 515 \\ -\ 62 \\ \hline \end{array}$$
Ⓐ 557
Ⓑ 553
Ⓒ 453

17.
$$\begin{array}{r} 405 \\ -\ 131 \\ \hline \end{array}$$
Ⓐ 274
Ⓑ 234
Ⓒ 334

18.
$$\begin{array}{r} \$\ 7.32 \\ -\ 1.08 \\ \hline \end{array}$$
Ⓐ \$6.36
Ⓑ \$6.24
Ⓒ \$6.34

Solve.

19.

The pet store has 38 more goldfish than angelfish. It has 143 goldfish. How many angelfish does the pet store have?

181 Ⓐ 105 Ⓑ

20.

How much money do I have?

I have 2 one-dollar bills, 3 quarters, and 4 pennies.

\$2.79 Ⓐ \$2.34 Ⓑ

21.

Each red box is filled with 100 crayons. Each blue box is filled with 10 crayons. Ellie has 4 red boxes and 3 blue boxes. How many crayons does Ellie have?

430 Ⓐ 403 Ⓑ

Exploring Mathematics Book Two © Scott, Foresman and Company

Notes for Home Children are assessed on Chapters 1–14 concepts, skills, and problem solving using a multiple-choice format.

centimeter (cm)

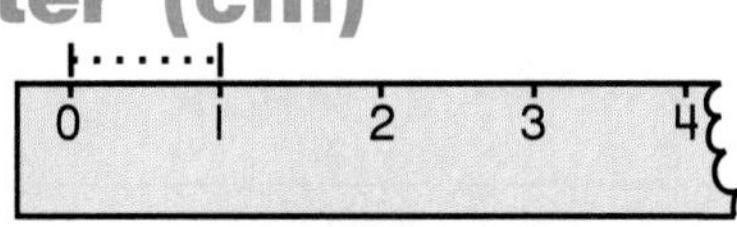

circle

cone

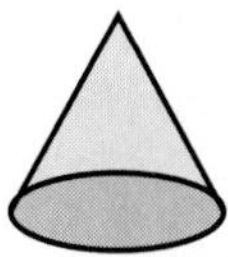

corner

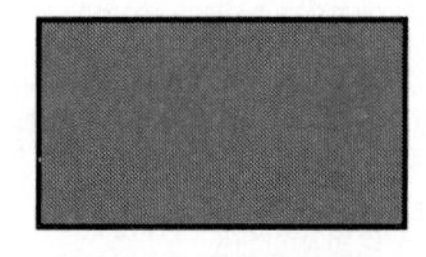

← **corner**

cube

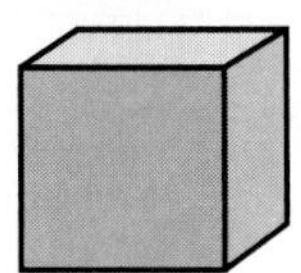

cup

cylinder

degrees

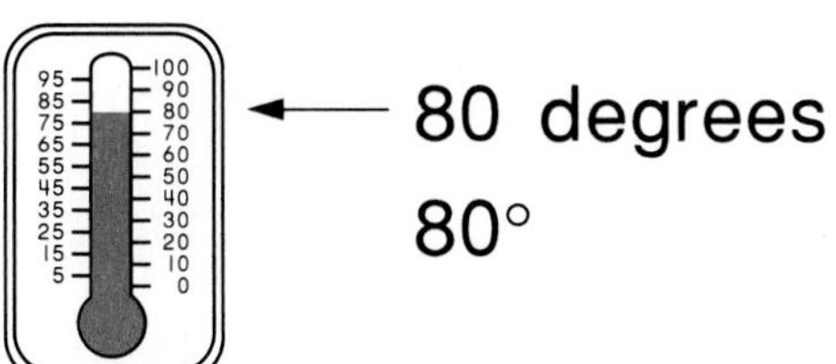

← 80 degrees

80°

difference

13 − 6 = 7

↑

difference

dollar

$1.00

equal parts

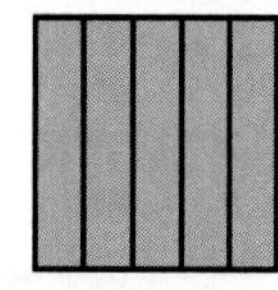

fifths

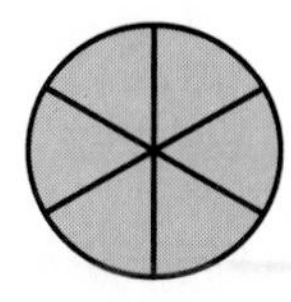

sixths

equal sign =

2 + 3 **=** 5

foot

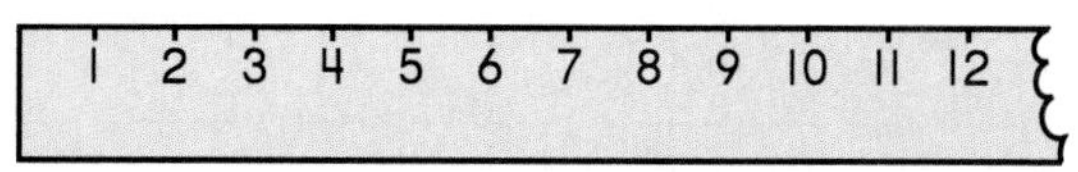

gallon

=

greater than >

99 > 32

half dollar

50¢

half hour

Notes for Home Children use a picture glossary for Grade Two math vocabulary development.

hour

inch

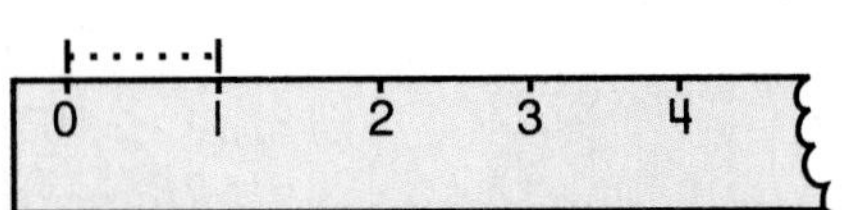

kilogram

less than <

$23 < 56$

liter

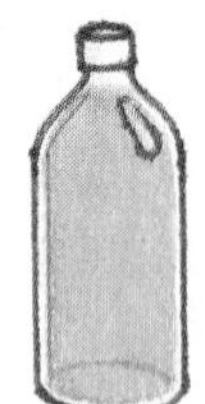

meter (100 cm)

minute

pint

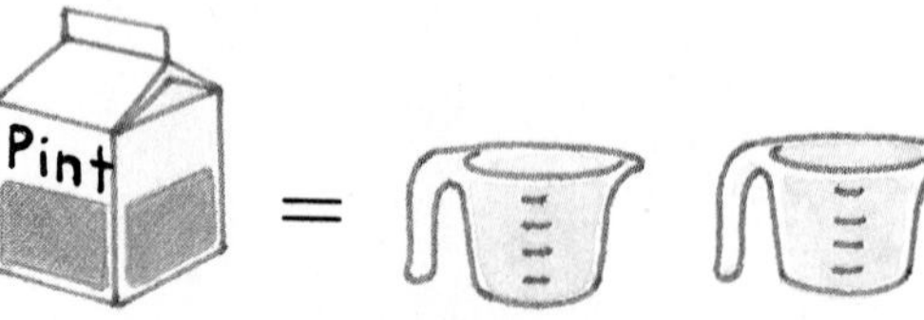

pound

product

$3 \times 4 = 12$ ← **product**

quart

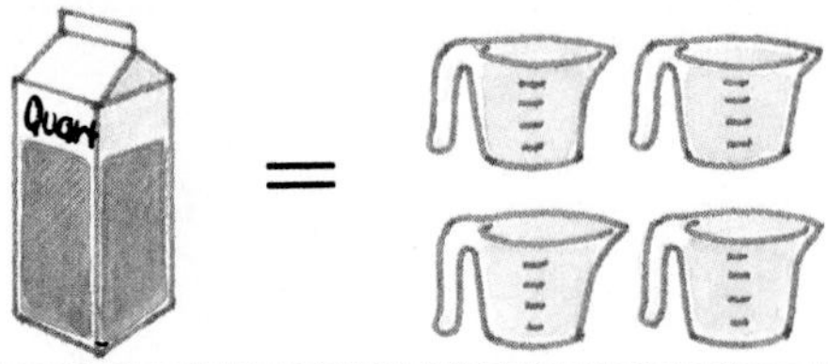

quarter

25¢

rectangle

rectangular prism

side

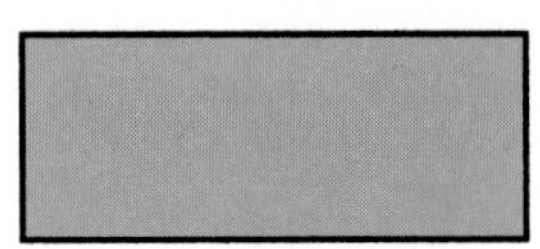

← **side**

sphere

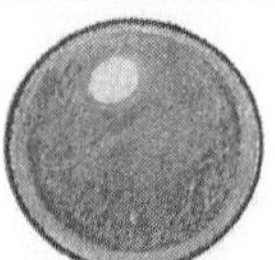

square

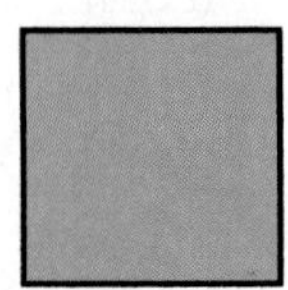

sum

$7 + 9 = 16$ ← **sum**

triangle

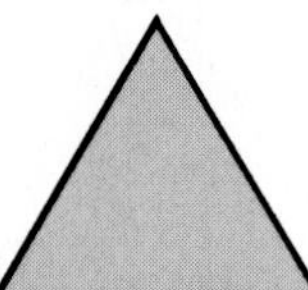

Notes for Home Children use a picture glossary for Grade Two math vocabulary development.

Exploring Mathematics Book Two © Scott, Foresman and Company

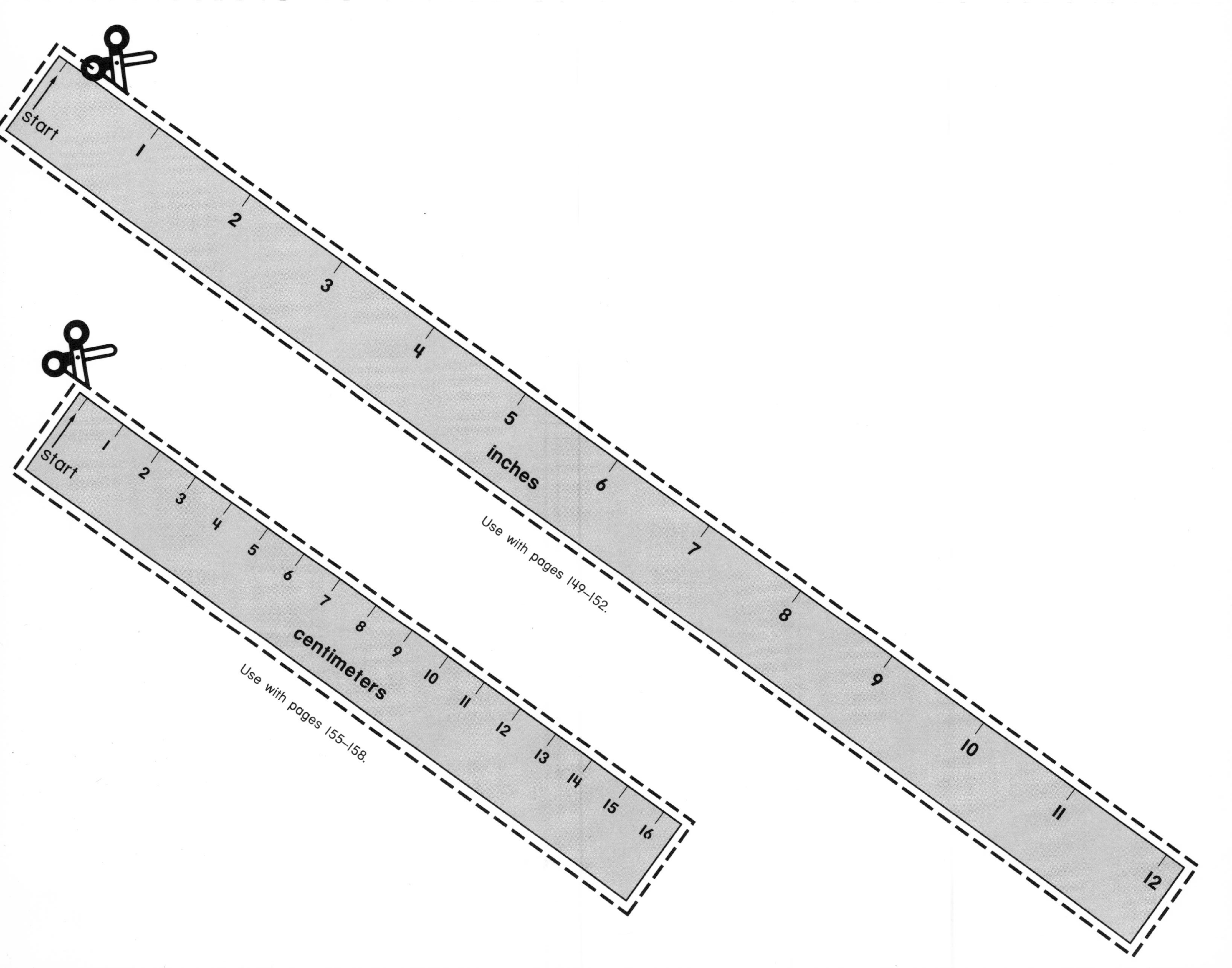

start
1
2
3
4
5
inches
6
7
8
9
10
11
12
Use with pages 149–152.
start
1
2
3
4
5
6
7
8
9
centimeters
10
11
12
13
14
15
16
Use with pages 155–158.

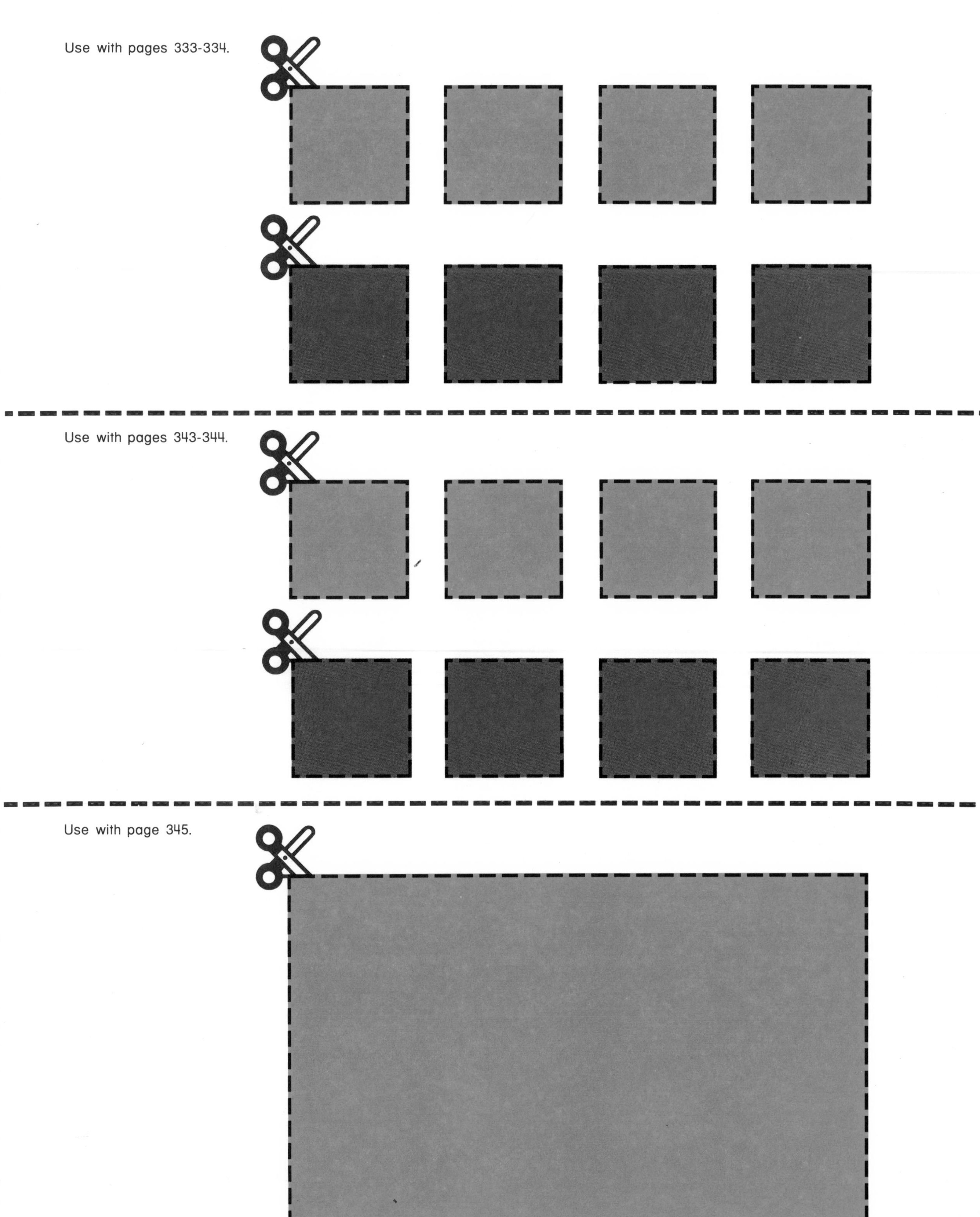
Use with pages 333-334.
Use with pages 343-344.
Use with page 345.

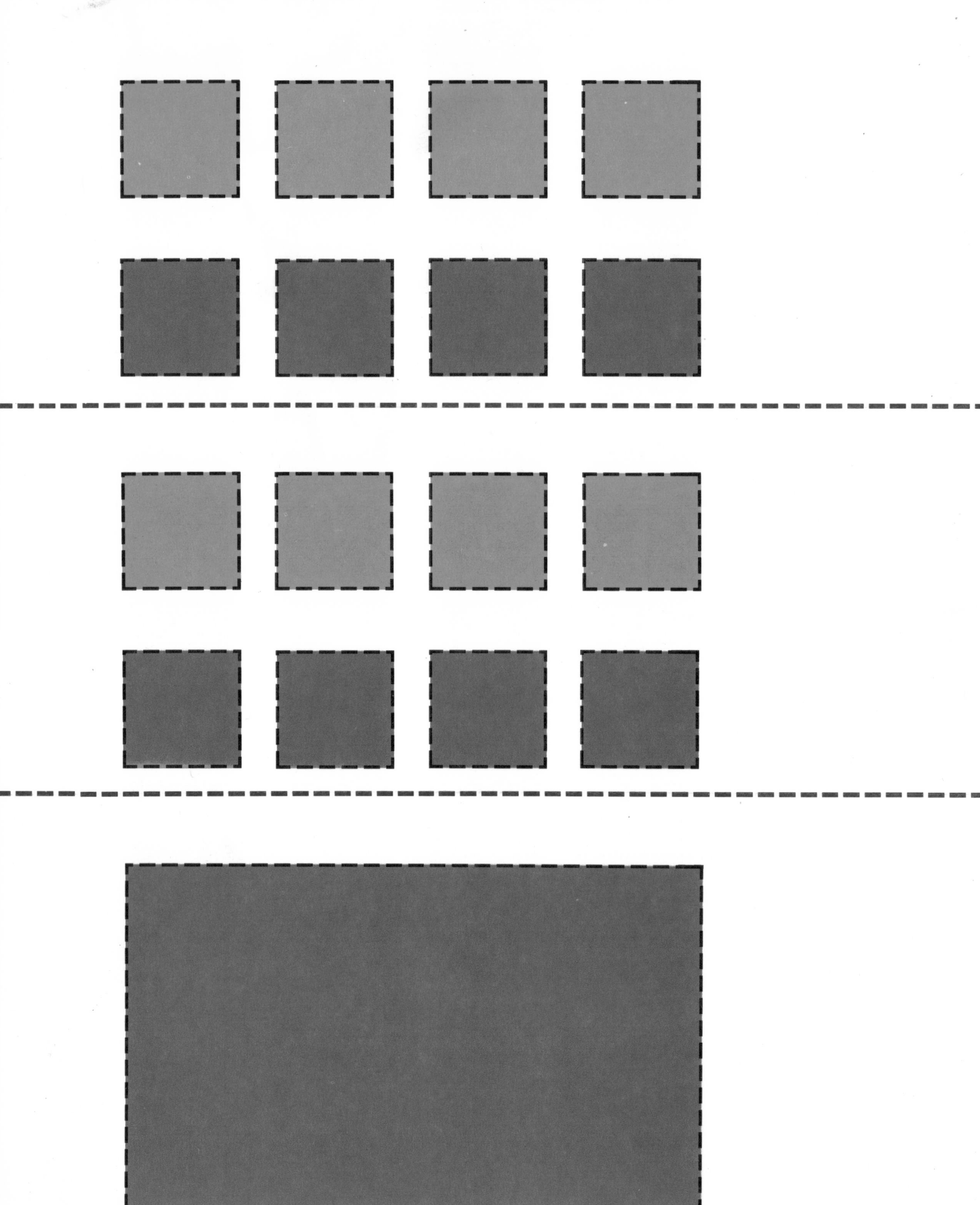